INTRODUCTION TO
ASTRONAUTICS

VOLUME 2

INTRODUCTION TO
ASTRONAUTICS

HARRY O. RUPPE

TECHNISCHE HOCHSCHULE MÜNCHEN
LEHRSTUHL FÜR RAUMFAHRTTECHNIK
MUNICH, GERMANY

VOLUME 2

1967

ACADEMIC PRESS   New York and London

ACADEMIC PRESS INC.
111 Fifth Avenue, New York, New York 10003

United Kingdom Edition published by
ACADEMIC PRESS INC. (LONDON) LTD
Berkeley Square House, London W.1

Library of Congress Catalog Card Number: 66-14469

PRINTED IN THE UNITED STATES OF AMERICA

TO PROFESSOR DR. WERNHER VON BRAUN
FATHER OF ROCKETRY

PREFACE

The field of astronautics is quite young: many of the essential concepts were formulated in the 1920's, followed by decades of pioneering rocket development, and, finally, the explosive growth of space achievements since the beginning of the 1960's.

The student of astronautics will find an overwhelming amount of literature on the subject, as must be expected from an activity which so profoundly influences our daily lives and our foreseeable future. Nevertheless, he may not see what he is looking for, because many of these publications are either of a popular nature or so specialized that they constitute communications among experts. So there is room and need for a textbook that emphasizes the theoretical and scientific fundamentals of astronautics.

Of course, there is no sharp boundary between engineering and science; but this book concentrates on basic physical understanding rather than hardware. It is directed toward several groups of readers:

(1) Students, both undergraduate and graduate; for class work, or as parallel reading to a relevant subject.

(2) Those interested in serious self-study; therefore, problems and solutions have been included, and much material is actually presented in this form. Furthermore, the overall development follows a pace commensurate with self-study; prior knowledge of the subject is not assumed. On the other hand, a working knowledge of calculus is required, and vector notation is often used.

(3) Professionals considering a career in astronautics but working at present in another area.

(4) Astronautics specialists who desire a view of the whole field in order to better understand their own activity.

This book has a fairly long history. About the summer of 1940, I became interested in astronautics. A semipopular book by O. W. Gail (*Mit Raketenkraft ins Weltall, By Rocketpower into Space*, 1928) started me on this subject. During an interval 3 to 4 years later, I accumulated astronomical data and wrote a few pages on "How to Reach the Stars." In 1948 I began lecturing on astronautics, and a few portions of this book stem from these lecture notes. The major stimulus, though, came from a paper prepared originally for the First Institute on Missile Technology, University of Connecticut, September 21 to October 3, 1958. Concentrated work started toward the end of the same year.

This book appears in two volumes: an elementary part (Volume 1) and an advanced part (Volume 2). In the sense I use these words, the advanced part is not necessarily more difficult, nor is the elementary part necessarily simple. Rather, Volume 1 contains information that constitutes the routine working tools in the area of conceptual design and fundamental understanding of astronautics; whereas Volume 2 contains information that will be helpful for a deeper understanding of present activities or that constitutes the basic knowledge for future activities.

Volume 1. The first two chapters describe rocket theory in its most elementary shape, being developed around the so-called "fundamental equation," sometimes referred to as "Ziolkovsky's equation." In order to understand the derivation of this simple yet important relationship, rocket motor fundamentals are discussed: how a rocket motor generates thrust and how the most widely used thermodynamic types work, with special emphasis on the chemical subgroup, since practically all engines operational today fall into this category. Unconventional rocket motors (by today's standards) are listed, and, for completeness, nonrocket space propulsion systems are discussed very briefly.

Chapter 2 considers the fundamental theory of rocket propelled vehicles. The basic equation is derived, and increasingly difficult applications to vehicle optimization are given. To point out the importance of the structure ratio, the particularly simple case of a propellant tank is discussed.

Sufficient groundwork is now completed to follow an astronautical mission all the way through from launch via free-flight to landing. This comprises the next three chapters.

In Chapter 3 the equations of motion are derived, and useful simple approximations of these equations are considered. The special case of near-horizontal flight, which for upper stages is quite important, is also treated. A discussion of the neglected factors completes the picture, justifying the approximations and showing the limits of validity.

After the basic discussion of computation of the powered flight trajectory, its optimization must be considered. Therefore, energy management of rocket vehicles is described; for the special case of constant flight acceleration, closed solutions are derived. During this discussion, the importance of initial acceleration becomes clear, leading to a description of staging possibilities. If a vehicle is to be forced to fly a particular trajectory, the vehicle has to be sufficiently controllable. What are the main difficulties?

The problems of optimization of the ascent trajectory can now be understood. Since one of the general results is to keep the cutoff altitude low, a remark is made concerning its minimum value.

After cutoff, the free-flight trajectory in space begins. The first part of Chapter 4 concentrates on the astronomical tools but presents them in a manner most applicable for astronautical usage: the two-body problem, the restricted three-body problem, including its treatment as two separate two-body problems, and some important approximate concepts are discussed. For completeness, a glance is given to the multibody problem.

The second part of this chapter concentrates on the direct problems of astronautics and shows how more realistic considerations modify results valid for idealized astronomical models. At first it is shown why these idealized models are good approximations. This is by no means obvious, considering, for example, the treatment of Earth as a mass point in connection with an artificial Earth satellite. Thereafter, Earth satellite mechanics and motion in Earth-Moon space are discussed, and the perturbations of a satellite are discussed in considerable detail. For lunar trajectories, more basic information is presented, and details are indicated under the heading "Neglected Influences."

Interplanetary trajectories are not considered here, because a detailed treament is given in Chapter 6 and in Chapter 1 of Volume 2, in order to develop some important guidance criteria.

The landing on a celestial body follows the free-flight phase and is treated in Chapter 5. Again there are two parts: landing on a body which has no atmosphere, such as the Moon, and landing with the help of an atmosphere. The simplest atmospheric braking maneuver is the straight-line descent. Variable drag is a refinement. These solutions are not usable to describe the entry following the drag-decay of a circular orbit; therefore, this case warrants special treatment.

So far, only the case of zero lift has been considered. "Entry Using Lift" remedies this situation. This concludes the aerodynamic flight mechanics discussion. But flight mechanics is not the only problem of aerodynamic entry; a discussion of aerodynamic heating during entry, a topic of equal importance, completes this chapter.

If, for preliminary estimates, the payload-carrying capabilities of a group of vehicles for many missions are to be computed, Chapters 3, 4, and 5 would be applicable; but much computation is involved. Therefore, a simplified method is generally utilized, based upon one characteristic figure of "required speed" for each mission. This figure permits the application of the simple theory of Chapter 2 for performance estimates and optimum staging estimates. For proper results corrections must be applied, as treated for aerodynamic landings in Chapter 5 and for midcourse propulsion maneuvers in Chapter 1 of Volume 2.

Chapter 6 is devoted to the computation of the required speed for many important missions, leading farther and farther away from Earth. This chapter also considers the minimization of required speed, which is a simple optimization criterion.

If the required speed gets too large for a vehicle, mission staging must be introduced. This very important concept for mission planning is discussed in some detail, concluding the chapter.

Volume 2. Volume 2 assumes that the basic material from Volume 1 is known, especially the conceptual definitions and preliminary computations of various mission profiles.

Chapter 1 treats the problem of making a vehicle fly its desired trajectory. Communication and navigation are considered together, because many methods of navigation rely traditionally upon communication. A discussion of communication systems leads logically to radar, and some typical reliability considerations are developed, starting from considerations of reliability in electronic systems.

Turning to navigation, the typical concepts are described and their capabilities shown in the example of the ICBM. Proceeding further, two general astronautical problems of importance are discussed: midcourse guidance and attitude control systems. Thereafter, attention is focused on the main astronautical missions: satellite, lunar, and planetary flights. The close connection between guidance considerations and flight mechanics is demonstrated.

From the previous discussion, it is obvious that propulsion is the major bottleneck for astronautical missions. Therefore, Chapter 2 discusses the promise of the use of nonchemical energy for propulsion. Some advanced high-thrust systems are treated first; this leads to consideration of nuclear energy and the radiation problems connected with it.

Low-acceleration propulsion systems require electric energy, with only a few exceptions. After a general survey, therefore, solar and nuclear electric power supply systems are discussed in detail, and the more promising propulsion systems are described. For one typical and very promising case—the ion propulsion system—a vehicle optimization procedure is developed, in scope similar to the procedure of Chapter 2 of Volume 1.

The flight mechanics of low-acceleration vehicles are not described by the methods in Volume 1. Therefore, the corresponding procedures are repeated for the low-acceleration case in condensed form, because only the variations from the high-acceleration case have to be pointed out.

Chapter 3 describes effects and protection against extraterrestrial environments. It is organized around a list of the major environmental factors, taking a broad view. For example, the many problems of storage of liquids in space are discussed under "Temperature in Space." "Generation of Nonpropulsion Energy" is treated after the radiation environment is described, and "Man in Space" is included in this chapter because of the many man-environment interactions. This completes the technical discussion.

Beyond the scientific and technical fundamentals, another question must be asked of an endeavor as large and expensive as astronautics: Is it worth all these efforts? To answer this question in depth is not possible at present: We are too close yet to the beginnings. Nevertheless, an attempt at an answer should be formulated;but this does not belong to a scientific-technical introduction proper. The interested reader will find this author's thoughts on the subject in Volume 10 of *Advances in Space Science and Technology*.

Let me point out again that this book contains few actual hardware data, and no projects are described in great detail. Statements and opinions are to be understood as individual expressions of the author and do not necessarily reflect the views and opinions of the Army Ballistic Missile Agency (ABMA) or the National Aeronautics and Space Administration (NASA).

Finally, I would like to express my appreciation to all those who made this book possible: my teachers who passed their knowledge on to me and the many scientists and engineers, especially the pioneers and developers of space flight, who provided us with the means to reach for the stars.

In a more direct way, my friends and co-workers who so often helped to clarify problems, or who actually solved them, must be mentioned. The ABMA as well as NASA provided the space-minded atmosphere which is necessary for this type of work. Without the help generously given by Mr.

J. Smith and Mr. F. I. Ordway III, this book could never have been completed. The patience shown and aid rendered by the publisher deserves praise. Lastly, I would like to thank my wife, who typed the first draft of the manuscript.

November, 1967   HARRY O. RUPPE
Munich, Germany

CONTENTS

CONTENTS OF VOLUME 1

CHAPTER 1   COMMUNICATION AND NAVIGATION

1.1 Space Communication (Pierce and Cutler, 1959)

Line-of-sight radio communication appears to be of primary importance in this field.

If we have an omnidirectional transmitter radiating power P_T and a receiver at a distance r from it, then the energy density at the receiver, assuming no energy loss along the way, is given by

$$P_R' = \frac{P_T}{4\pi r^2} \, .$$

$$(1.1)$$

What is the gain for a directional antenna? Let us first consider the case for the beam width φ of a circular parabolic antenna of diameter D and wavelength λ.

From Fig. 1.1 we have, directly,

$$D \sin(\varphi/2) = \lambda/2 \quad \text{or} \quad \sin \varphi \approx \lambda/D.$$

For parabolic antennas of circular cross section, the beam width, from a more exact theory, is given by

$$\sin \varphi = 1.26\lambda/D.$$

$$(1.2)$$

(This is not true within the near zone. Therefore, we must demand that the condition $r \geq 2D^2/\lambda$ be fulfilled.)

For isotropic radiation, the energy is spread over the area $A' = 4\pi r^2$. With the antenna, it is spread only over $A = 4\pi r^2 \sin^2(\varphi/4)$, instead. So,

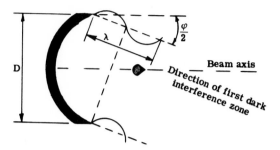

FIG. 1.1. Circular parabolic antenna.

for a beam width φ, we expect a transmitter antenna gain of

$$G = \frac{A'}{A} = \frac{1}{\sin^2(\varphi/4)} .$$

Assuming that φ is small, we can write

$$G \approx \frac{16}{\varphi^2} = 10.1 \frac{D^2}{\lambda^2} . \tag{1.3}$$

Of course, the real gain is smaller, as part of the energy is radiated outside the beam width given in Eq. (1.2). Thus, the gain[1] for the transmitter may be given by

$$G_T = \eta_i \frac{10 D_T^2}{\lambda^2} , \tag{1.4}$$

where η_i stands for an efficiency. For the receiver, from simple geometry we know that

$$G_R \approx \eta_2 (\pi/4) D_R^2 .$$

Hence, for the received energy, we have

$$P_R = P_R' G_t G_R = \frac{P_T}{4\pi r^2} \eta_1 \frac{10 D_T^2}{\lambda^2} \eta_2 \frac{\pi}{4} D_R^2$$

$$= \frac{P_T}{160} \left(\frac{\lambda}{r}\right)^2 \eta_1 \cdot 10 \left(\frac{D_T}{\lambda}\right)^2 \eta_2 \cdot 10 \left(\frac{D_R}{\lambda}\right)^2 .$$

[1] We have to demand that beam width φ be larger than the pointing accuracy α. Let us assume that $\varphi \geq 2\alpha$, or $0.63\lambda/D \geq \alpha$, or $D \leq (0.63/\alpha)\lambda$. For $\alpha = 0.1$ sec of arc $= 0.485 \times 10^{-6}$ rad we have $D \leq 1.3 \times 10^6 \lambda$ or $G \leq 17 \times 10^{12}$. If $D \leq 13$ m, then in order to approach the limit we need $\lambda \leq 10^{-5}$ m, corresponding to the infrared region.

Finally, assuming $\eta_1 = \eta_2 = \frac{1}{2}$ it follows that

$$P_R = \frac{P_T}{6.4}\left(\frac{\lambda}{r}\right)^2\left(\frac{D_T}{\lambda}\right)^2\left(\frac{D_R}{\lambda}\right)^2. \tag{1.5}$$

[With $D_T = D_R$ and $r > 2D_T{}^2/\lambda$ we get $P_R \leq P_T/(25.6)$.]

If we have an omnidirectional transmitter, then

$$P_R = \frac{P_T}{32}\left(\frac{D_R}{r}\right)^2 = \frac{P_T}{6.4}\left(\frac{\lambda}{r}\right)^2\left(\frac{0.447\lambda}{\lambda}\right)^2\left(\frac{D_R}{\lambda}\right)^2. \tag{1.6}$$

An onmidirectional transmitter (dipole) has, therefore, an "effective cross section" $D_t' = 0.447\lambda$.

If the receiver is also omnidirectional, we have

$$P_R = \frac{P_T}{4\pi r^2}A,$$

where A is the "effective area."

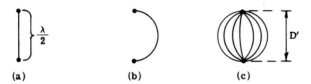

(a)   **(b)**   **(c)**

FIG. 1.2. Dipole configurations: (a) dipole; (b) bent dipole; (c) omnidirectional transmitter, $\pi D' = \lambda$ or $D' = \lambda/\pi$ and $A = \frac{1}{4}\pi D'^2 = \frac{1}{4}\lambda^2/\pi$.

How big is A? Figure 1.2 gives an approximation. Hence,

$$P_R = P_T\left(\frac{\lambda}{4\pi r}\right)^2 = \frac{P_T}{6.4}\left(\frac{\lambda}{r}\right)^2\left(\frac{0.449\lambda}{\lambda}\right)^2\left(\frac{0.449\lambda}{\lambda}\right)^2. \tag{1.7}$$

We see that Eqs. (1.6) and (1.7) follow from Eq. (1.5), if we put $D = 0.448\lambda$ for omnidirectional (approximate dipole) antennas.[1] With $\eta_i = \frac{1}{2}$, using Eq. (1.4), we get $G \approx 1$ for dipoles.

For receiver noise, we can write (regarding internal noise only, since

---

[1] Adaptive antenna: omnidirectional antenna array, which goes to a beamed operation if phasing of antenna elements is introduced, e.g., by echo from a satellite. Furthermore, by proper phasing the beam is kept at the satellite, without mechanical motion of the antenna.

external noise is usually negligible at frequencies above 200 Mc/sec, and generally decreasing with increasing frequency)

$$N = FLkTB, \tag{1.8}$$

where k is the Boltzmann constant, 1.38×10^{-23} W sec/°K, F the noise figure, B the band width (cycles per second), T the reference temperature, degrees Kelvin (°K), and L is the loss factor for the transmission line.

With a sensitive receiver input (Unger, 1959), we can get $F = 0.2$, $L = 2$, and $T = 290$°K, which yields

$$N = 1.6 \times 10^{-21}B \quad \text{[W]}. \tag{1.9}$$

A further reduction of N by perhaps two orders of magnitude may be possible using latest techniques and developments (maser; parametric amplifier). Here we will go along with the more conservative value given by Eq. (1.9). The bandwidth B determines the information rate. With $B = 1$ cps, an information rate of one bit per second (which is equivalent to 86,400 bits per day) may be handled.[1] Printed English text contains an amount of information of about 25 bits/word, with 12 words/line and 30 lines/page. So about 9 pages of printed English text could be transmitted in one day over a 1-cps channel.

Because of oscillator stability, a value of $B = 5$ cps appears at present to be a practical lower limit. Therefore, we will assume from here on a minimum of $B \approx 5$ cps.

Table 1.1 gives the required information rate R for bandwidth B and several typical tasks. The factor

$$K = \frac{3(P_R/N)R(T/290)}{\log_2(1 + P_R/N)}$$

will be utilized later.

Color-TV: For same picture quality, at least double the bandwidth as that of black and white transmission is required (*Fortune Magazine*, 1959).

Assuming the minimum bandwidth of $B = 5$ cps, we have $N \approx 0.8 \times 10^{-20}$ W. If the signal-to-noise ratio P_R/N is about 1, we will just be able to find the existence of the transmitter by time-consuming corre-

---

[1] Under certain conditions, the ideal information rate for a bandwidth B, received power P_R, and noise N, is $B \log_2(1 + P_R/N)$ bits/sec. A very good, practically achievable value is about one-third of the ideal value. One "bit" is a digit in a binary system, corresponding, e.g., to "yes" or "no." (Indeed, "bit" stands for "binary digit.")

TABLE 1.1

Information rate R (bits/sec)	Task	K
5	Low information rate (about 10 words/min of English text). Telegraph	270
100	Teletype	5.5×10^3
1000	Fast (machine) telegraph	5.5×10^4
4000	Voice communication	2.2×10^5
10^7	Television in real time[a] (One TV picture may consist of 500 × 500 points with 8 shades of grey; as $2^3 = 8$, one picture contains 75×10^4 bits of information; to transmit the picture in 1/13 of one second, we need a bandwidth of $13 \times 75 \times 10^4 \approx 10^7$ bits/sec.)	5.5×10^8
200	One high-quality TV picture per day (2000 × 2000 lines, 16 shades of grey; color: times 3)	1.1×10^4

[a] The minimum information rate for TV in real time is about 5×10^4 bits/sec, for low-quality pictures.

lation technique, but get little or no actual information across (threshhold value). To get the information safely, we need a ratio of signal-to-noise energy of about 100. If $P_R/N = 127$ and $T = 290°K$, then $K = 54.4R$. From this we obtain K as given in Table 1.1. From Eqs. (1.5) and (1.9), we obtain

$$P_R = \left(\frac{P_R}{N}\right) 1.6 \times 10^{-21} \times \frac{3R(T/290)}{\log_2(1 + P_R/N)} = \frac{1.6}{10^{21}} K$$

$$= \frac{P_T}{6.4} \left(\frac{\lambda}{r}\right)^2 \left(\frac{D_T}{\lambda}\right)^2 \left(\frac{D_R}{\lambda}\right)^2 \quad [W].$$

From this equation it follows that

$$P_T = \frac{K}{10^{20}} \left(\frac{r}{\lambda}\right)^2 \left(\frac{\lambda}{D_T}\right)^2 \left(\frac{\lambda}{D_R}\right)^2 \quad [W]. \tag{1.10}$$

As $P_T \sim K$, we should avoid having K unnecessarily large, i.e., we should avoid transmitting any unnecessary information, which is either known or can be deduced otherwise, e.g., predicted from available information.

(Information theory[1] shows that, by applying very advanced methods, often 100 bits of information can be transmitted as one bit.) The Earth's atmosphere is transparent between $\lambda = 10$ and $\lambda = 10^{-6}$ m, and then again below 10^{-12} m. The plasma surrounding a vehicle that enters the Earth atmosphere at more than 100 km altitude, coming with cosmic speed from space, attenuates or reflects electromagnetic radiation. It is only for wavelengths below a few millimeters that communication through this plasma appears to be possible, provided the antenna withstands the environment.[2]

Neglecting communication during high-speed aerodynamic flight, $\lambda = 10$ cm appears to be a possible choice, since much power and experience is

TABLE 1.2

Frequency (Mc/sec)	Transmitter (on Earth surface) gain	Receiver (on target surface) gain
100	1	250
500	1	500
1000	1	1000
3000	2000	2000
10,000	2000	2000
30,000	2000	2000

[1] Information can be useful or useless: if everything is known no useful information can be transmitted; if nothing (code, language, frequency, etc.) is known no useful information can be transmitted. There appears to be an optimum distribution of knowledge in order to result in a maximum content of information per message. The quoted equation connecting information rate and bandwidth does not differentiate between useful and useless information.

As an example of information compression, the following system was described in 1964:

Human speech → Processor → Ten cycle per second bandwidth link
→ Reprocessor → Synthetic language,

where "synthetic language" is a whisper, without accent, inflection, or change in pitch; only timing of words and verbal content are maintained.

The "processor" volume is 820 cm³, its mass is 0.45 kg, it is transistorized and consumes 0.7 W.

[2] Various methods are under discussion to solve the entry radio blackout problem: using a wavelength of about 6×10^{-2} mm or adding water to the plasma are two possible methods. The latter method was tested during entry from the first manned orbital Gemini flight (March 23, 1965) by injecting 16 lb of water.

TABLE 1.3

Transmitter Power for a Conventional Receiver

Frequency (Mc/sec)	Target (power in kW)			
	Moon	Mars	Venus	Jupiter
100	0.13	4.3×10^3	1.25×10^3	1.35×10^5
500	1.53	5×10^3	1.45×10^3	1.6×10^6
1000	3.04	1×10^4	2.95×10^3	3.5×10^6
3000	7×10^{-3}	2.3×10^2	70	8.5×10^3
10,000	8×10^{-2}	2.6×10^3	7.5×10^2	3.6×10^8
30,000	0.72	2.5×10^4	7.5×10^3	7.0×10^8

available, and since external (cosmic) noise is low at such high frequencies. This demands antenna accuracy to about a few millimeters, which is again not too difficult for moderate sizes.

Radio communication between Earth and various heavenly bodies has been investigated elsewhere; we quote some of the results here (Chandra, 1960). Atmospheric influences are taken into account, and the following assumptions are made: signal/noise ratio, 1; bandwidth, 10 kc/sec; distance to celestial object, minimum; transmitter gain and receiver gain for the antenna, as given in Table 1.2.

The main results are given in Tables 1.3 and 1.4, which list the power (in kilowatts) that must be emitted by the transmitter. From these tables,

TABLE 1.4

Transmitter Power for a Receiver Using Maser
Preamplifier of 85°K Noise Input Temperature
(Power in kW)

Frequency (Mc/sec)	Moon	Mars	Venus	Jupiter
100	No masers operating at this frequency			
500	8.13×10^{-2}	2.67×10^2	77.3	8.53×10^4
1000	0.162	5.33×10^2	1.57×10^2	1.87×10^5
3000	3.7×10^{-4}	12.3	3.73	4.53×10^2
10,000	4.26×10^{-3}	1.39×10^2	39.9	1.88×10^6
30,000	No masers operating at this frequency			

a frequency of 3000 Mc/sec corresponding to a wavelength $\lambda = 10$ cm appears to be desirable again. So let us pick $\lambda = 10$ cm, and $D_T = 1$ m, $D_R = 10$ m:

$$P_T \text{ [watt]} \approx \frac{K}{10^{18}} r^2, \tag{1.11}$$

where r is measured in kilometers.

If the smaller antenna is isotropic and the other data are the same as above, then

$$P_T \text{ [watt]} = \frac{5}{10^{16}} K r^2. \tag{1.12}$$

[It should be noted that this result (1.12) does not depend upon λ.] If both antennas are isotropic, then

$$P_T \text{ [watt]} = \frac{2.5}{10^{11}} K r^2. \tag{1.13}$$

Example 1. Earth-Moon, maximum distance $r \approx 400 \times 10^3$ km. For beam antennas, $P_T \approx 1.6K/10^7$ [W], or for voice communication $K = 2.2 \times 10^5$, i.e., $P_T = 3.5/10^2$ [W] output, or about 0.2 W transmitter input, assuming 17% efficiency.[1] For one isotropic antenna, $P_T \approx 8K/10^5$ [W], or with $P_T = 0.16$ W (as it was in the Pioneer IV space probe), $K \approx 2000$, and at double the distance $K = 500$. This still is good for transmission of a low information rate. These conclusions were proved experimentally (Pioneer IV, launched March 3, 1959, by a Juno II vehicle).

Example 2. Earth-Mars, maximum distance $r = 400 \times 10^6$ km. For beam antennas, $P_T = 0.16K$ [W], or for minimum useful information rate, $K = 200$, $P_T = 32$ W, or transmitter power consumption about 160 W. But about 8.8 kW are necessary to transmit one high-quality TV picture per day.

In the case of one isotropic antenna, in order to just detect the signal ($K \approx 10$), we need $P_T = 800$ W, or a transmitter input about 4000 W. Increasing the dish antenna diameter by a factor of 3.2 reduces the transmitter power by a factor of 10. If, in the case of two dish antennas, both are increased by a factor of 3.2, transmitter energy goes down by a factor of 100. Going to the, in 1961, largest steerable antenna[2] (Jodrell Bank,

---

[1] Vanguard I transmitter: 50 mW transmitter input, 5 mW antenna output; 20–30% efficiency can be obtained with different transmitter designs.

[2] In 1962, a movable radio telescope having $D_R = 91.5$ m was put in operation at the National Radio Astronomy Observatory, Green Bank, West Virginia. A fixed radio telescope in Arecibo, Puerto Rico, has a dish diameter of 305 m.

England, $D_R = 75$ m), and assuming an omnidirectional vehicle transmitter, we get, for $P_T = 5$ W, $r = 36 \times 10^6$ km, and $\lambda = 0.78$ m, the result $K = 7.7$ which appears to be the limit of communication. Indeed, the U.S. space probe Pioneer V, launched in March 1960 by a Thor-Able vehicle, fulfilled these expectations. (Pioneer V had a weight of 100 lb, which was distributed as follows: structure 10 lb, instruments 40 lb, power supply 50 lb. Aphelion is near the Earth orbit, perihelion at 121×10^6 km from the Sun, near Venus' orbit. There were two transmitters on board, one with 5 and the other with 150 W output; frequency was 387 Mc. The strong transmitter failed to operate, probably because of battery difficulties. Jodrell Bank could follow the 5-W transmitter up to a distance of 36×10^6 km.) It is seen that, with 100 W, we can have a useful Earth-Mars beamed communication system, and that 1 W is ample in the Earth-Moon system.

Another outstanding example of communication over planetary distances is constituted by Mariner II, the first successful interplanetary vehicle. Data for the Mariner II flight are given in Table 1.5.

Inserting the values for the spacecraft transmitter and the Goldstone receiver from Table 1.5 into Eq. (1.10), we find $K = 848$, which is sufficient to handle the information rate quoted.

Beam width with a 1-m antenna is about $\varphi = 7°$, and with a 3.2-m antenna about $\varphi = 2.2°$, for $\lambda = 10$ cm. With such narrow beams, it may be difficult to get transmitter and receiver in line-of-sight.

Forgetting for the moment the problems of directing a very narrow beam, the high gain of narrow beams is attractive for line-of-sight communication. For given antenna dimensions, this favors short wavelengths —perhaps even down to infrared or visible light. Because of weather influences, this may become useful—if at all—for space vehicle to space vehicle types of communication. Assuming we have a wavelength of 10^{-6} (visible light 0.3–0.7×10^{-6} m) and a transmitter antenna diameter of 0.1 m, then the beam width is down to about 2.5 sec of arc.

A star of 13.3 magnitude has an energy flux density at Earth of 1.4×10^{-17} W/cm². With proper amplification of intensity and contrast (electron-multipliers: "Cateye," typical intensification by a factor of 10^5), this can be received even in the daytime with a telescope of 0.1-m aperture. Therefore, the minimum usable energy input is below 1.1×10^{-15} W. With a Kerr cell, perhaps fast machine telegraph type transmission is possible. The received energy for fast machine telegraph transmissions via radio is around $5.5 \times 10^4 \times 1.6 \times 10^{-21} = 0.88 \times 10^{-16}$ W, about 10 times less. For infrared of about 3×10^{-6} m wavelength, 10^{-11} W is the figure corresponding to the 1.1×10^{-15} W. At a distance of 400×10^6 km, with a

TABLE 1.5

Purpose	Venusian flyby experiment
Duration of flyby	42 min
Launch date	August 27, 1962
Hyperbolic excess speed	Slightly below 0.1 Earth mean orbital speed
Arrival date	December 14, 1962; after 109 days of flight
Hyperbolic excess speed	Slightly below 0.2 Earth mean orbital speed
Closest distance to Venus	34,750 km above sunlit surface
Closest distance to Sun	0.722 a.u. on December 27, 1962
Launch information	NASA Atlas Agena B launch vehicle; the spacecraft was injected from Cape Kennedy, Florida into an intermediate orbit, in which it remained for 13 min
Midcourse	A late vernier or early midcourse maneuver of approximately 30 m/sec was executed on September 4, 1962
Spacecraft	
Structure	77 lb
Solar panels	48 lb (total energy output ~ 167 W)
Electronics	146 lb (total energy requirement ~ 137 W)
Propulsion	32 lb (hydrazine monopropellant)
Launch back-up battery	33 lb
Six scientific experiments	41 lb
Other equipment	70 lb
Total weight	447 lb
Communication system, spacecraft	
Transmitter output	3 W
Transmission rate	8.33 bits/sec (over short distances 33.33 bits per second)
Frequency	960 Mc ($\lambda = 31.25$ cm)
Weight of transmission system	55 lb
Antenna	Parabolic dish, 1.22 m diameter
Beam angle	$\sim 19°$
Receiver temperature	7300°K
Communication system, Earth station (Goldstone)	
Transmitter output	10 kW
Antenna diameter	25.9 m
Frequency	890 Mc ($\lambda = 33.7$ cm)
Tracking accuracy	
Angular	~ 0.01 rad
Radial distance	1.25 m
Radial speed	0.16 m/sec
Distance from Earth at Venusian encounter	60×10^6 km

beam width of 2.5 sec, we have a circle of 2500-km radius or 2×10^{17} cm^2 area. The transmitted energy then must be around $1.4 \times 10^{-17} \times 2 \times 10^{17}$ = 2.8 W, for the optical case. Transmitter input might be about 12 W. In the corresponding radio case with 3.2- and 32-m antennas, the transmitted energy is 88 W with about 400 W transmitter input.

Considering energy, the optical communication machine appears to be superior, and the optical system will be lighter, smaller, and easier to handle. It can be very simple, when the signal consists of reflected solar light. But—to repeat—the problem of correct alignment is formidable.

The optical maser or laser development allows us to generate coherent, monochromatic (bandwidth of the order of 100 cps) light of high intensity within very narrow beams. Using reflected solar light, instead of a laser beam, intensity modulation with a Kerr cell or similar equipment can be imposed. The bandwidth would be very large—with simple filters perhaps about 10^{13} cps. This will, of course, lead to considerable "noise."

One further point against the optical link is that, for weather-independent vehicle-planet communication, radio is used anyhow. So there is little point in carrying a second system, except for emergency use.

In *Aviation Week* of February 22, 1960, it is pointed out that in the far ultraviolet we could go down to wavelengths of 0.04×10^{-6} m. Against this speaks the poor obtainable reflectivity (with an aluminum surface, 95% can be reflected at $\lambda = 10^{-6}$ m, and only slightly less at 0.2×10^{-6} m, but with an optimum germanium surface, only 20% at $\lambda = 0.04 \times 10^{-6}$ m).

For a light source, besides lamps, lasers, solar light, etc., electrically exploded wires could be considered. For 10^{-3} sec duration, a radiation equivalent to a black body of 350,000°K can be created.

For some applications of space-to-space communication, even X-rays or particle jets might find application. A γ-ray communication system can be visualized, e.g., by chopping of γ-radiation from a nuclear reactor; in this area, the simple information theory does not hold because of quantum effects.

At the other extreme, very low frequencies (e.g., 18 kc/sec, $\lambda \approx 17$ km) might be of interest for Earth-satellite communication systems, because they are not limited to line-of-sight contacts. (Lofti, USA, launched February 21, 1961.)

We have looked at omnidirectional and strongly directional antennas. For interplanetary missions, a compromise appears possible, namely, taking advantage of the flatness of the solar system: if we radiate energy only into a band $\pm 5°$ off the ecliptic, instead of omnidirectionally, the transmitter energy consumption drops for the same receiving system to about

20% of the omnidirectional value, but is still, by a factor of about 100, higher than it would be for a $\varphi = 5°$ beam-width parabolic antenna.[1]

Can the range of the transmitter be improved by going to high-energy impulse transmissions? (See, von Braun, 1952.) It is well known that, from a transmitter of 10^3 W constant power output, we can get 10^6 W, if we use it only 10^{-3} of the operating time, e.g., for a thousand impulses per second of 1 μsec each. If the average energy during the impulse is p, and the impulse time is τ, then the energy radiated during one impulse is approximately $E = p\tau = $ constant. To receive an impulse of τ, we need a bandwidth of $B \approx 1/\tau$. Therefore, the received energy is given by $E_r \sim p \sim B$. As receiver noise is also proportional to B, signal-to-noise ratio is independent of B or τ; high-energy impulse operation does not increase range.

If there is a relative motion of magnitude v_r along the line-of-sight between transmitter and receiver, then received and transmitted frequencies are no longer alike (Doppler effect). If the transmitter is approaching the receiver, then, with c the speed of light, the shift in wavelength is obviously $\varDelta\lambda \approx - v_r\lambda/c$. If we call the frequency f, then

$$f\lambda = c,$$

or

$$df\,\lambda + f\,d\lambda = 0,$$
$$\varDelta f\,\lambda = - f\,\varDelta\lambda \approx v_r f(\lambda/c),$$

or

$$\varDelta f \approx v_r/\lambda.$$

If Mars and Earth are at right angles as seen from the Sun, then the relative radial velocity is about 30 km/sec. The orbital velocity of a station around Earth may be directed against Mars, and another station around Mars may just move towards Earth; the velocity between the stations would be about 41 km/sec. At $\lambda = 10$ cm, we have $\varDelta f \approx (41 \times 10^3)/(0.1) = 0.41 \times 10^6$ cps. This shift may be larger than the total bandwidth, which, of course, means that the receiver must be tuned to the arriving frequency. Another annoying factor has to do with the speed of light: even with 300,000 or, more precisely, 299,792.5 $\pm$ 0.1 km/sec, it takes 1.33×10^3 sec ≈ 22.2 min to bridge the maximum Earth-Mars distance of 400×10^6 km. Therefore, if under those conditions we wait for an answer from a Mars expedition, about $\frac{3}{4}$ h elapses for pure round-trip time of the radio signal! In the case

---

[1] This is one example showing that, occasionally, noncircular radiation patterns can be used with advantage.

of the Moon, the round-trip time of the signal is, of course, much shorter —about 2.5 sec. However, this time delay nuisance in communication is not a new problem, e.g., common mail shows this feature.

Obviously, the radio beam has to be aimed at a place ahead of the vehicle, namely, to where the vehicle will be at arrival of the radio signal. Assuming a relative tangential speed of 41 km/sec, we have to aim ahead by $a = 41/300,000$ rad $= 28.2$ sec of arc. This small angle will usually be taken care of by the beam width.

Finally, a remark concerning analog versus digital data transmission appears to be in place here. In analog systems a signal property (e.g., intensity) corresponds directly to a property of the transmitted object (e.g., reflectivity of a surface element of a black-and-white picture). But to stick with the example of black-and-white picture transmission, we could measure the reflectivity of each picture element in some scale and, instead of the intensity itself, transmit the number that resulted from the measurement. This is a more elaborate method, but the result will be better, as there is less interference to be expected in the transmission of a figure than in the transmission of an amplitude. On the other hand, instead of a continuous grey scale, as in the analog picture, there will be a stepwise grey scale in the digital picture. This can improve contrast, but is nevertheless a loss in information.

In another example, instead of a plotted curve, we transmit a coordinate table of a number of points of this curve: the digital transmission will be more elaborate, it will give only some points of the curve, but at better accuracy.

To summarize, digital transmission will give better accuracy and less noise than analog transmission, but at the price of higher complexity. If this and the remarkable development of digital electronic computers after World War II and the accuracy limit of about 1 part in 10^4 for analog computers are taken into account, then it is no longer surprising that the general trend is towards digital systems.

For Earth-to-deep-space-vehicle communication, an orbital relay station appears to have some advantages:

(1) There are no atmospheric influences to worry about between vehicle and orbital station, and the orbital station is, thanks to its closeness, much less dependent upon "weather."

(2) The orbital station can employ a cooled receiving antenna, thus further reducing receiver noise drastically. On the other hand, the receiving antenna will perhaps have to be smaller than it would be on Earth ground.

1.2 Radar

Radar is the technique of bouncing a radio signal back from an object and receiving it again, usually with the same antenna used for transmitting.[1] By measuring the time between transmission and echo, distance can be found. From distance rate or Doppler shift comes the normal velocity component, and the tangential velocity component can be found from distance and angular rate. By getting a point-by-point radar echo from the object, complete radar pictures can be received.

Let us look at the energy flow: the transmitter may send an energy peak P_T during the short time τ. The energy received by a spherical object of effective cross section $F = \pi R^2$ is, corresponding to Eq. (1.5),

$$P_R' = \frac{P_T}{3.2} \left(\frac{2R}{r} \right)^2 \left(\frac{D}{\lambda} \right)^2,$$

when the beam width is larger than the apparent diameter of F, or $2R < 1.26(\lambda/D)r$, $R/r < 0.63\,\lambda/D$. A fraction ξ of this energy is reflected back anisotropically. (In special cases—e.g., corner reflector—an isotropic reflection towards the transmitter can occur.) So the energy received back at the transmitting antenna is equal to

$$P_R = \xi \frac{P_R'}{2\pi r^2} \eta \frac{\pi}{4} D^2,$$

or, for $\eta = \frac{1}{2}$,

$$P_R = \frac{\xi}{13} P_T \left(\frac{R}{\lambda} \right)^2 \left(\frac{D}{r} \right)^4. \tag{1.14}$$

With a bandwidth $B = 1/\tau$ cps we get, from Eq. (1.6),

$$N = 1.6 \times 10^{-21} \frac{1}{\tau} \quad \text{[W]}.$$

We demand that $P_R = KN$, where $K = 1$ for limit of detection possibility and $K = 10^2$ for routine operation. So, finally (for $\tau < \frac{1}{10}$ sec),

$$P_T\tau = \frac{2K}{\xi 10^{20}} \left(\frac{r}{D} \right)^4 \left(\frac{\lambda}{R} \right)^2 \quad \text{watt sec.} \tag{1.15}$$

If the reflector is a perfectly conducting sphere of radius R', then for $R'/\lambda \geq 1$ we have $\xi = 1$. For larger wavelengths, ξ diminishes rapidly.

---

[1] Laser developments will permit us to use optical frequencies.

Example. $P_T = 265 \times 10^3$ W; $\tau = 10^{-3}$ sec (estimated); $P_T\tau = 265$ W sec; $r = 45 \times 10^6$ km; $D = 25.6$ m; $R = 6200$ km; $\xi \approx 0.9$ (est); $\lambda = 60$ cm. (Data are approximately the same as those used in the first Earth-Venus radar contact on February 10, 1958, from MIT Millstone Hill Radar Observatory, Westford, Massachusetts. Radar echos from the Moon were received in 1946, and from the Sun in April 1959,[1] and from Mars on January 21, 1963.)

This leads to $K = 0.13$.

If now the noise figure is 0.02 instead of the 0.2 used to derive Eq. (1.11), we get $K = 1.3$ and this suffices, if extensive cross-correlation techniques and long evaluation times are available. By increasing P_T and D by a factor of 10 (the maximum average power output of a radar transmitter may be 10^6 W; little further increase, because of the expense of \$1 to \$5 per watt, is expected) and going to refined receiver techniques, it has become possible to detect some surface details, and the old mystery of the length of a Venusian day has been solved (253 days, retrograde). The resolving power would be, with $\lambda = 10$ cm,

$$1.26 \frac{\lambda}{D} = 1.26 \frac{10}{256 \times 10^2} = \frac{4.92}{10^4} \quad \text{rad},$$

which would give a resolution of about 22,100 km or 1.8 Venusian diameters; the shape of the surface object cannot be determined. Since polarization and energy of the reflected beam contain further information, the above resolution does not do justice to the capability of radar astronomy.

Indeed, in the Fall of 1964, a crude Venus radar map was in preparation (radar data: 85-ft diameter dish antenna; wavelength 12.5 cm; 100-kW transmitter; average return signal 10^{-22} W; receiver noise temperature 30°K).

The following information is available concerning the structure of the surface where the radar reflections came from:

Venus: rough, of the order of 12.5 cm (comparable to lunar surface)
Mercury: rougher than Venus
Mars: smoother than Venus
Jupiter: smoother than Mars.

---

[1] There is a Soviet claim to have made radar contact with the planet Mercury in the summer of 1962; according to the Soviet announcement, the surface of Mercury has the same reflection properties as the Moon. This was verified by US data obtained in May 1963. In September 1963, Soviet scientists received a radar echo from the planet Jupiter.

For narrow beamwidth φ and large objects, the whole energy may be intercepted by the illuminated object. In other words, the total transmitted energy falls upon the object. So

$$P_T \tau = \frac{2.6K}{\xi \times 10^{20}} \left(\frac{r}{D} \right)^2, \qquad \text{for} \quad \frac{R}{r} \geq 0.63 \frac{\lambda}{D} . \qquad (1.16)$$

This case is applicable for, e.g., an altimeter for a lunar landing vehicle. Let us assume that $K = 10^3$, $\xi = 0.01$ (for the Moon, $\xi = 0.01$ to 0.05, for $\lambda = 10$ cm to 1 m), $r = 200$ km, and $D = 1$ m. Hence,

$$P_T \tau = \frac{1}{10^4} \quad \text{W sec.}$$

Consecutive measurements shall be made about 10^{-3} sec apart (the vehicle moves about 3 m in 10^{-3} sec), which demands 10^3 impulses/sec. Thus, we have to radiate an average power of $\bar{P}_T = 10^{-1}$ W, which calls for an energy input of about 1 W. The impulse length should be short, say, 10^{-7} sec, resulting in a radiated peak power of $P_T = 10^3$ W. Measuring the duration between signal and echo with an error of $\frac{2}{3} \times 10^{-6}$ sec we get an accuracy, in measured distance, of about 100 m. Nonimpulsive methods (e.g., frequency-modulation, smoothing) have to be used to give better accuracy—up to a factor of 10 or 100 better, but at the price of much (factor of 10^2) lower maximum range for the same power, or larger time requirement per measurement.

Relative velocity along the line-of-sight can be measured either from rate of distance change or by comparison of transmitted and received frequency (Doppler shift). The accuracy can be very high (better than 1 m/sec). But we should not forget that both rocket exhaust[1] and ionized gases may act upon the electromagnetic waves of the frequency used.

Sometimes, we read of radar used to detect meteors for protection of space vehicles. Let us assume we have a radar which sweeps the whole surroundings once every second—quite an achievement at narrow beams, large antenna, and high power. Table 1.6 can then be constructed.

At a relative velocity of 100 km/sec, we have to detect meteors at 1000-km distance. The dangerous type is of perhaps 1-mm diameter. Substituting $\lambda = 1$ cm, $K = 10^2$, $\xi = 0.1$, $D = 10$ m in Eq. (1.15), we have

$$P_T \tau = 2 \times 10^5 \quad \text{W sec.}$$

---

[1] Where applicable, the rocket exhaust may generate a dust cloud upon impingement upon a surface. This cloud may disturb measurements.

a long time, the failure rate is higher, because aging sets in. We speak here, and in the following, only about the simple "main operating time." (Generally, $\dot{N}$ might be a function of the history of the component, year of its production, etc. We will disregard this.[1])

The constant T in Eq. (1.17) can easily be understood: The mean lifetime of one of the components is

$$t = -\frac{1}{N_0} \int_{N_0}^{0} t \, dN = \frac{1}{N_0} \int_{0}^{\infty} N_0 \frac{t}{T} \exp\left(-\frac{t}{T}\right) dt = T.$$

The probability p that a given subcomponent is still "alive" after an operating time t_1 is

$$p = \frac{N}{N_0} = \exp\left(-\frac{t_1}{T}\right).$$

If we have n such similar components in the system, the probability that the system will be "alive" at the time t_1 is

$$p = \exp(-nt_1/T). \tag{1.18}$$

If we demand a certain probability p of success, then we have to demand a subcomponent mean lifetime of

$$T = nt_1/\ln(1/p)$$

or

$$T \approx \frac{nt_1}{1-p} \qquad \text{for} \quad 1 \geq p \geq 0.9. \tag{1.19}$$

Because of the high costs involved in space flight, we have to demand high reliabilities (= probability that the subcomponents will work properly). This is even more important for manned missions. Typical requirements might be:

Mission	Reliability p	Number of critical subcomponents n
Unmanned	0.9	100
Manned	0.999	200

[1] The assumption of a constant failure rate is occasionally only a very poor approximation of reality.

TABLE 1.6

	Time
Meteor just out of range	1st secor
First meteor detection	2nd secon
Second meteor detection	3nd secon
Third meteor detection—computer gives alarm	4th second
Lock-on of radar at meteor	5th second
Computation	6th and 7th second
Initiation of maneuver to avoid meteor	8th and 9th seconds
Meteor at former location of vehicle	10th second

For $\tau = 10^{-7}$ and 10^4 impulses/sec, we have

$$P_T = 2 \times 10^{12} \text{ W peak power,}$$
$$\bar{P}_T = 2 \times 10^9 \text{ W average power.}$$

The energy input for our fictitious meteor-warning radar might be 10^{10} W which should be compared to the energy-production rate of a great Eart bound power station of around 10^9 W. Therefore, such a device appears be unfeasible. If, by the way, with such high energies, shorter wa lengths, and therefore, smaller beam angles, could be realized, we co vaporize the meteors before they reach the vehicle, if the meteor absorl noticeable fraction of the impinging energy. The radiation pressure 2×10^9 W is about 0.5 kg—the radar set would at the same time be a us photon propulsion system. This may illustrate how impractical suc radar system is—a conclusion reached as early as 1948 (Clarke, 19

1.3 Reliability

This is a very involved field, and we will consider only a few of th damentals.

If we have a large number N_0 of specimens of the same subcom —say, a radio tube—and we test all of them, then if only random f occur the number N of well working ones at the time t is given by

$$N = N_0 \exp(-t/T).$$

From Eq. (1.17), the failure rate is $(-\dot{N})/N = 1/T = \text{constant}$ this is only true during the main operating time. Initially, the fai is higher because of the errors in manufacturing and material fau

So, for the required mean lifetime of the subcomponent, we have

Unmanned mission: $\qquad T = 10^3 t_1$

Manned mission: $\qquad T = 2 \times 10^5 t_1$

A few typical mean lifetimes are given in Table 1.7. For a manned near-Earth satellite flight, t_1 may be 10^{-3} yr. This then would demand that $T = 200$ yr, and we see that this may just be possible by careful choice of components.

TABLE 1.7

Components	T (yr)
Vacuum tubes	3
Electric motors	5
Switches	16
Microcircuits	20
Relays	23
Capacitor	180
Transistor	230
Resistor	1000

An unmanned lunar flight of $t_1 = 0.1$ yr duration calls for $T = 100$ yr, again bordering on the limit of our capabilities. A digital computer of the type that would be needed for space navigation could, without maintenance, be made to work with a reliability of 0.999 for about 4 days only [1] —even after another decade of work, this time may not yet have reached a year (Unger, 1958). This can be understood by considering that a typical digital computer of the capacity considered here may contain 10,000 diodes, 2000 resistors, 1500 transistors, and 500 capacitors— about 1.4×10^4 parts. Assuming that $(dN/dt)N \approx -5/10^4$ per 1000 hr or $-\dot{N}/N = 5/10^7$ per hr, valid for each of the components (or $T = 228$ yr), we get, for the failure rate of the computer, approximately $(5/10^4) \times 1.4 \times 10^4 = 7$ per 1000 hr, or the mean time to failure for the computer is $1000/7 \approx 150$ hr ≈ 6 days; the probability of successful operation for 4 days is 0.513. This shows that the data quoted above giving a reliability of 0.999 refer to a smaller computer (factor 33) built of the best components ($T = 4500$ yr), or using a large degree of redundancy. Some actual data are given for comparison in Table 1.8.

---

[1] During the 4-day Gemini orbital mission in June 1965, the flight computer failed.

TABLE 1.8

COMPUTER PLUS DATA ADAPTER

Vehicle	Saturn I	Saturn V
Number of components	12,000	80,000
Weight (pounds)	210	253
Volume (ft³)	3.9	5.5
Total power (watts)	540	438
Operations per second	3,200	9,600
Storage capacity (bits)	100,000	460,000
Mean time between failures (hours)	750	45,000 (triple redundancy)
Operational availability	After 1964	After 1968
Manufacturer	IBM	IBM

On the other hand, the assumed model of constant failure rate does not necessarily describe reality. As an extreme example consider 10^3 young men, carefully selected for health and motivation, kept in a carefully controlled environment! I think it could be assured with 98% probability that no fatality would occur during a one-year test period. This group behaves then as if the mean lifetime of a man were $T = 10^3 \times 1/(0.02) = 5 \times 10^4$ yr; so it appears to be at least possible to select components which, for a few years, behave as if they had a lifetime of 10^6 yr. Still the problem remains of how to find such "healthy specimens."

Without additional action the component reliability is clearly not sufficient for interplanetary flights. What can be done in order to improve this situation? The situation may be improved by one the following methods:

(1) Closely supervised materials and production, quality-control, hand-picked components, selection of "healthy specimens."

(2) Improvement or change of component design or material: Such improvements are often difficult to verify, as, e.g., for a 3-yr manned Mars expedition we may need $T = 0.6 \times 10^6$ yr, which we could hardly measure in any test, if we had such components.[1]

(3) Simple, functional system design, with a small number of critical components.

---

[1] This speaks in favor of systems testing instead of components testing. Against systems testing can be held: complexity of operation, high cost, and difficulty in evaluating results.

(4) Nonmarginal system design, so that no component is critically stressed; this usually improves the lifetime of the component.

(5) Provision of a favorable environment.

(6) Redundancy and repair.

(*a*) A switch or a human operator exchanges the bad component. Assuming that a man and a switch have the same reliability of 0.999, then the reliability of 100 switches in series is $(0.999)^{100} \approx 0.9$, acceptable for unmanned flights. If the man replaces the 100 switches, the reliability reaches the value 0.999, as necessary for manned missions. As man has some other qualities (reason, power of decision, communication, high reliability, but requiring complicated means to be kept alive) the decision for or against the man is more difficult than just to replace 100 switches.

(*b*) Parallel components can be arranged so that operation of the system goes on without switches, even if one component fails (Failsafe design).

(7) Decrease payload and increase fuel in order to decrease mission time.

(8) For the future, there is the possibility of using the raw material of the component that failed, to produce a new one. Not quite so advanced, self-healing features or component repair could be used. Of course, special equipment has to be carried to do these things. Methods (4) to (8) will decrease payload capability for a given vehicle and mission. Therefore, marginal vehicles will be inherently less reliable, as certain methods of improvement cannot be utilized. On the other hand, even for large vehicles, reliability will certainly not be higher than demanded by economic and other considerations. There is an "optimum" reliability which leads to minimum overall cost of a program. If a better reliability is desired, then the reduction in losses saves less money than the increase in reliability costs. Generally, this optimum reliability is high for sufficiently large programs. Considerations of endangering human life may make a higher reliability than the "optimum" desirable, and consideration of the time schedule can make a lower reliability acceptable.

(9) Part-time operation can help, but effects of on-off switching may lead to a loss, instead of a gain, in lifetime.

In order to illustrate the power of redundancy [method (6)], let us look at a simple example: The system may consist of n similar elements, of which each one has the reliability α to perform its task. We assume that a failing element will not influence the other elements (no "catastrophic failures") and that k elements can fail without endangering the system.

Letting α be the probability of an element working properly, $1 - \alpha$ gives the probability of failure. The probability that exactly k of the elements fail is given by

$$\binom{n}{k} (1 - \alpha)^k \alpha^{n-k},$$

and, of course,

$$\sum_{\nu=0}^{n} \binom{n}{\nu}(1 - \alpha)^\nu \alpha^{n-\nu} = (1 - \alpha + \alpha)^n = 1.$$

The probability of not more than k of the n elements failing is given by

$$P_k^n = \sum_{\nu=0}^{k} \binom{n}{\nu} (1 - \alpha)^\nu \alpha^{n-\nu}.$$

Many interesting conclusions may be drawn. Let us assume that we need 10 elements, and $\alpha = 0.95$. If we use no redundancy, then

$$P_0^{10} = \alpha^{10} \approx 0.60;$$

with one redundant element,

$$P_1^{11} = \alpha^{11} + 11\alpha^{10}(\alpha - 1) = 0.90;$$

with two redundant elements,

$$P_2^{12} = \alpha^{12} + 12\alpha^{11}(\alpha - 1) + 66(\alpha - 1)^2\alpha^{10} = 0.98.$$

For $\alpha = 0.9$, correspondingly,

$$P_0^{10} = 0.35, \qquad P_1^{11} = 0.70, \qquad P_2^{12} = 0.87, \qquad P_3^{13} = 0.98.$$

So we can conclude that a redundant system can have a reliability P, which is higher than the reliability of a single element. The degree of redundancy k needed to meet the condition $P = \alpha$ goes up as α decreases.

An interesting example for larger elements (say, propulsive engines) is to have one redundant element only and demand that

$$P_1^n \geq \alpha,$$

or

$$\alpha^n + n\alpha^{n-1}(1 - \alpha) \geq \alpha,$$

or

$$n\alpha^{n-2} - (n - 1)\alpha^{n-1} \geq 1.$$

Introducing $\alpha = 1 - \xi$, where $\xi \ll 1$, power series development up to the order of ξ^2 gives finally

$$P_1^n \geq \alpha,$$

for

$$\alpha \geq 1 - \frac{2}{(n + 1)(n - 2)}, \qquad \text{if} \quad n \geq 4.$$

The picture, as given here, is optimistic insofar as a cluster introduces new elements connecting the cluster elements and new control elements to take care of redundancy. These elements introduce a reliability of their own, reducing cluster reliability. We will disregard this effect here. Then, for example, the cluster of eight engines of the mighty Saturn 1 booster is more reliable than a single engine, if $\alpha > 0.964$, and if there is a one-engine-out capability.[1] Since solid propellant engines have very high reliabilities —say, $\alpha = 0.995$— we can cluster them up to $n = 20$, with no loss in reliability, provided we have a one-engine-out capability with the failing engine not effecting other engines. Unfortunately, usually the engine-out capability cannot be realized, as the propellant lost in the failing engine cannot be utilized by the other engines. This difficulty does not exist in liquid propellant vehicles.

Let us return to the liquid-propellant 8-engine cluster: The above result might recommend that we design for a one-engine-out capability. Let us assume that we agree to wind restrictions at launch so that the initial acceleration can be as low as $1.1g_0$, but to have this with 7 out of 8 engines forces us to go to $1.255g_0$ for 8 engines, which brings a reduction in lift-off weight by 14.2%. Since, for the heavier vehicle, the g-losses are larger because of longer burning time, the 14.2% decrease in launch weight will correspond (for larger vehicles) to a smaller payload reduction, say 5%. If we do not want to sacrifice this 5% of the payload by carrying only $95\% = \frac{19}{20}$, then we have to rely on no engine quitting during the first operating seconds Δt, when the vehicle is still too heavy for the thrust of only 7 engines. It is easily derived that $\Delta t < \frac{1}{8}Tr/(r - 1)$, where T is the normal burning time of that stage and r is the mass ratio of that stage.

---

[1] The engine-out capability together with the automatic guidance adaption were demonstrated in the completely successful sixth flight of the SATURN 1 vehicle on May 28, 1964.

Since Δt may be around 20 sec only, one might prefer this risk (except for manned flights or very valuable payloads), as engine reliability during the first seconds can be made better than $(\frac{19}{20})^{1/s} \approx 0.995$ by proper checkout and holddown technique. So, by taking the risk of good engine operation during the time Δt, we might lose less than the voluntary reduction of 5% per flight.

Let us assume that during powered flight one engine out of the eight quits. Since the other seven use up all the fuel (this is an inherent advantage of the liquid propellant system!), we have an increased burning time of at most $1.125T$, which increases the gravity losses during first stage operation by perhaps somewhat less than 100 m/sec. To make up for this, there are at least 6 possibilities:

(1) Fly with reduced payload—again perhaps 5% payload reduction.

(2) Have up to 5% (exact amount function of time of engine failure) of payload jettisonable.

(3) Fly reduced performance mission (e.g., lower circular orbit than planned).

(4) Let about $3\frac{1}{2}$% of the payload be last-stage propellant, which is delivered in orbit (e.g., for refueling missions) in case all engines work, or which is used up by the last-stage propulsion system in case one engine of the booster failed.

(5) This is essentially the same as (4): Carry a flight performance propellant reserve in the last stage that is sufficiently large to cover the performance reduction of an engine failure in the booster.

(6) Another possibility is to uprate the thrust of the remaining engines after one engine failure, so that total thrust stays constant. This means that normally (cruise level) the engines operate not at their full (emergency power) thrust level, which reduces the theoretical payload capability. Again we have to balance a planned payload reduction against a possible payload loss due to failure of the vehicle, because it does not have engine-out capability. Furthermore, if engine-out capability exists and one engine failed, then it is generally very important not to have a second engine failure. This is an argument against uprating of the still operating motors.

Looking, for example, at aircraft, conditions are different. Here engines should usually have long lifetimes, which forces us to operate them generally at a lower than maximum power level. This automatically gives the capability to go to maximum level for short times, such as take-off or emergency conditions. If we have a reusable rocket booster, then similar principles might apply.

Considerations of waiting-orbit technique will complicate the issue of economy of engine-out provision even more. Of course, two-engine-out capability will further increase reliability, but only at higher payload penalty. Control problems might be so severe that, e.g., no two neighboring engines must fail, resulting in a restricted double redundancy. This brief glance into a special problem in the field cluster versus single element might suffice here.

Redundancy is no cure-all. As mentioned, the control and holding, etc., elements for groups have, themselves, reliabilities smaller than one, thus reducing cluster reliability. Nonrandom failures (e.g., running out of gas with a car can hardly be blamed on car reliability) and systems errors (e.g., having a wrong overall mixture ratio) still may occur. The danger of catastrophic failure increases. Low reliability of the element (e.g., poor workmanship) forces us to unrealistically high redundancies.

For another application of reliability considerations, let us test n elements, each with reliability α, and ask for the probability to have exactly k failures:

$$P_k{}^n = \binom{n}{k} (1 - \alpha)^k \alpha^{n-k}. \tag{1.20}$$

For a Laplace or normal distribution, implying that α is neither very close to 0 nor very close to 1,

$$P_k{}^n \approx \frac{1}{(2\pi)^{1/2}\sigma} \exp\left[-\frac{(k-d)^2}{2\sigma^2}\right] \leq \frac{1}{(2\pi)^{1/2}\sigma},$$

where $d = n(1 - \alpha)$ is the most probable number of failures and $\sigma = [n\alpha(1 - \alpha)]^{1/2} = (d\alpha)^{1/2}$ is called "standard deviation of d." The standard deviation for α or $1 - \alpha$ equals $\sigma/n = [\alpha(1 - \alpha)]/n]^{1/2}$ or, in a better approximation, $\sigma/n = [\alpha(1 - \alpha)/(n - 1.5)]^{1/2}$.

For $1 - \alpha \approx 0$, $\alpha \approx 1$ (Poisson):

$$P_k{}^n \approx \frac{d^k}{k!} \exp(-d) \leq \frac{d^d}{d!} \exp(-d) \approx \frac{1}{(2\pi)^{1/2}\sigma},$$

where $d = n(1 - \alpha)$ and $\sigma = d^{1/2}$.

What is the probability W_g that, for a measured value k, $(k - d)/\sigma \leq g$ is valid?

$$W_g = \sum_{d-g\sigma}^{d+g\sigma} P_k{}^n \approx \int_{d-g\sigma}^{d+g\sigma} P_k{}^n \, dk \approx \left(\frac{2}{\pi}\right)^{1/2} \int_0^g \exp(-x^2/2) \, dx.$$

From tables of the error integral we obtain

$$\begin{aligned}
&W_{0.50} = 38\% &&\text{(This means that an observed value } k\\
&W_{0.67} = 50\% &&\text{has } 38\% \text{ probability of being be-}\\
&W_1 \;\; = 68\% &&\text{tween } d - 0.5\sigma \text{ and } d + 0.5\sigma, \text{ etc.)}\\
&W_{1.64} = 90\%\\
&W_2 \;\; = 95\%\\
&W_{2.58} = 99\%\\
&W_3 \;\; = 99.7\%\\
&W_{3.49} = 99.96\%.
\end{aligned}$$

What can we deduce about α if a series of n tests with k failures has been made? We know there is a certain probability W_g that $| k - d | \leq g\sigma$, or $| k - n(1 - \alpha) | \leq g[n\alpha(1 - \alpha)]^{1/2}$. From this comes

$$\frac{1}{n + g^2}\left\{k + \frac{1}{2}g^2 - g\left[k\left(1 - \frac{k}{n}\right) + \frac{g^2}{4}\right]\right\}^{1/2} \leq 1 - \alpha$$

$$\leq \frac{1}{n + g^2}\left\{k + \frac{1}{2}g^2 + g\left[k\left(1 - \frac{k}{n}\right) + \frac{g^2}{4}\right]\right\}^{1/2}. \qquad (1.21)$$

We have now established that α is, with a confidence W_g, between two limits.

Numerical example. In 10 tests, one failure was experienced; that is, $n = 10$, $k = 1$. With the low confidence of 38% (or $g = 0.5$), we can say that

$$0.062 \leq 1 - \alpha \leq 0.158$$

or

$$0.84 \leq \alpha \leq 0.94.$$

With the high confidence of 95% (or $g = 2$) it follows that

$$0.59 \leq \alpha \leq 0.98.$$

So the test would prove that, with 38% confidence, the reliability of the tested element is better than 84%, and with 95% confidence it is better than 59%. Assuming that in 14 tests we had $k = 0$, we only have a confidence of $W = 90\%$ that $\alpha > 0.84$. Therefore at least 14 tests with zero failure are necessary to establish a reliability of 84% with 90% confidence. The application to evaluation and planning of tests is obvious.[1]

---

[1] See problem 1.12.

Another numerical example can show the possible errors in interpretation of test results. In two test series, the results may have been:

$$k = 3, \qquad n = 20,$$

and

$$k = 20, \qquad n = 100.$$

In the first case, the shown reliability appears to be $\frac{17}{20} = 0.85$, in the second case only 0.80. Now let us ask for the reliability limits with 95% confidence. We then have, for the first case, 0.64 to 0.95, and for the second case 0.71 to 0.87. Therefore, the reliability limit, with 95% confidence level, is better in the second case! The reason is, of course, that the ratio k/n is more stable against small variations when the number of tests is large. By increasing the number of tests in the first case, we might reach a better reliability than in the second case, as shown by the upper reliability limits, which represent the "optimistic outlook."

Let us look at this case in a slightly different manner: Let the probability of failure be 0.2. What is the probability of having three or less failures in a sample size of 20?

$$P_0^{20} = \binom{20}{0} \times 0.2^0 \times 0.8^{20} = 0.0115$$

$$P_1^{20} = \binom{20}{1} \times 0.2^1 \times 0.8^{19} = 0.0576$$

$$P_2^{20} = \binom{20}{2} \times 0.2^2 \times 0.8^{18} = 0.1375$$

$$P_3^{20} = \binom{20}{3} \times 0.2^3 \times 0.8^{17} = 0.2050$$

$$\text{Sum} \quad 0.4116$$

We find that the probability of having three or less failures in the sample of 20 is equal to 41.16%, or, in other words, there is quite a high chance that the two test results stem from the same basic population.

This example really shows how careful one has to be when interpreting test results. Results are meaningful only with high confidence level, i.e., for large sample sizes. Reliability is a statistical concept, which cannot easily be applied to small samples or single events. In rocket vehicles, the unit cost is usually so high that it prevents a large number of tests. Furthemore, in a test series the experiences of one test are incorpored in the next one. So, in an already small series, it may happen that all specimens are different, thus finally leading to a reliability figure which is derived from one single experiment. At best, this can be regarded to be an "educated guess."

These brief considerations might explain why some workers in the field of space flight talk of a "reliability barrier" right now.

The problem of crew safety is related only to vehicle reliability, as the crew can be rescued in many mishaps of the vehicle: capsule ejection during launch, abort maneuver during powered flight, rescue from orbit in case of brake rocket failure, etc. Therefore, in a well-planned operation of a well-designed manned vehicle, crew safety should be considerably better than vehicle reliability.

If total mission reliability is R, and reliability of crew rescue in case of failure is r, then crew safety S equals 1 minus the probability that both mission and rescue fail simultaneously, or

$$S = 1 - (1 - r)(1 - R) = r + R - rR.$$

Related to reliability is the concept of maintainability. A measure for maintainability is, e.g., the "mean system downtime per failure instance." For some details, see Slattery (1961).

We considered only two modes, viz., failure and no failure. In reality, many failures can be repaired: novel methods are required for investigations of the reliability of repairable systems. (See, e.g., Goodyear Aircraft Corporation Report No. GER-10848, by G. Nagy.)

For a delightful introduction to statistics, see Moroney (1956).

1.4 Navigation in Space

1.4,1 Fundamentals

The fundamental task of navigation consists of finding position and velocity at a given time and drawing conclusions as to what corrections, if any, should be applied and when, in order to fulfill the mission. If the vehicle is on its ideal course, then no corrections should have to be applied: the guidance system is trying to keep the vehicle "on course."

In space flight using high-acceleration rocket vehicles, we have generally three phases:

(1) From ignition of main engine to the end of the powered phase, which equals injection to the free-flight phase.

This time is usually short—between a few minutes up to perhaps ½ hr. During this time the vehicle is controlled by the injection guidance system, which should make sure that, at the end of the next phase, the vehicle is at the correct initial position for phase (3).

(2) Free-flight phase counting from injection to the beginning of the final phase. During this time, the midcourse guidance system operates and insures that, indeed, a correct position at the beginning of phase (3) is reached. This phase can last between $\frac{1}{4}$ hr in certain satellite ascent cases up to several years in interplanetary flights.

(3) Final phase, which is again a powered phase, at the end of which the vehicle should have fulfilled a main part of the total mission, e.g., landing on the Moon. This phase is controlled by the terminal guidance system. The duration of phase (3) is comparable to, but often shorter than, phase (1).

It goes without saying that injection, midcourse, and terminal guidance systems will use common elements as much as possible, and in some cases it may happen that one system can fulfill all three tasks.

At the end of the launch phase, the acceleration may be 60 m/sec^2 —let us assume cutoff is given for the engine; therefore, fuel flow to the motor is interrupted. Then follows the thrust decay time, during which the thrust chamber just expands its contents of gases. This may last about 1 sec and may add a speed of perhaps 15 m/sec to the vehicle. Unfortunately, this thrust decay time shows fairly large variations, so that the 15 m/sec velocity can vary by ± 3 m/sec. Besides, if the cutoff command is given only $\pm \frac{2}{100}$ of one second wrong, we have another velocity error of ± 1.2 m/sec. One obvious solution to these difficulties is to give cutoff voluntarily early—say, when the velocity is 5 m/sec short of its theoretical value. If all variations are high, then our speed is 0.8 m/sec low, and in the extreme low case we may be 9.2 m/sec low. After the velocity deficit is established, a low-thrust[1] Vernier engine is initiated, and the velocity (of the vehicle, or after a separation the velocity of the payload only) is brought up to its theoretical value. As the acceleration may now be only 1% of 60 m/sec^2, the error can be held to $\pm (4.2/100)$ m/sec = 4.2 cm/sec, if the measurements permit this accuracy. (Of course, no system can be better than the sensors.)

This Vernier phase (or phases) takes place between the launch and the free-flight phase, and may occur several hours after main engine cutoff when these hours can be utilized to determine the necessary correction more precisely. Rather arbitrarily, we will regard the Vernier correction as the final part of the injection phase. Some general remarks on the midcourse part appear to be in place here.

---

[1] More precisely, low acceleration.

We shall see that location can be measured with fairly high accuracy, but velocity often cannot. This is not very serious, since from location and time and initial location and initial time, velocity can be found very accurately from celestial mechanics. There are no unpredictable midcourse disturbances such as, e.g., wind, which simplifies the calculational problem considerably.

Let us assume we find the vehicle at a given time t_1 to be not at its ideal location, but at a place p_1. How do we proceed now? We take a possible arrival time t_2 at the usually moving target (say, Mars), which fixes the position of Mars at p_2. To reach this position we know the allowable flight time $t_2 - t_1$ and the endpoints p_1 and p_2. There is just one velocity $\mathbf{v}_{1\text{th}}$ at the position p_1, which brings us at the time t_2 to p_2. Therefore, we have to correct our velocity $\mathbf{v}_1$, by $\mathbf{\Delta}$ so that $\mathbf{v}_1 + \mathbf{\Delta} = \mathbf{v}_{1\text{th}}$. The correction $\mathbf{\Delta}$ is calculated for all times t_2 around the ideal time of arrival, utilizing time of correction as a parameter. The most convenient $\mathbf{\Delta}$-value (often the smallest, or the one having the least sensitivity to errors) is applied at the proper time with a high acceleration such that only the velocity coordinates, and not the location coordinates, are changed.

A simpler method is to go back to the standard trajectory as soon as a deviation is found.[1] This may, however, bring us to the target place at a wrong time, unless much fuel can be spent on the corrective mancuver. Therefore, this scheme, well proven against stationary targets, appears to be not generally applicable for moving targets, as we have them in space flight. It can be used when time of arrival is of no concern, as will be the case in, e.g., the problem of bringing a new satellite into its orbit, without rendezvous with another satellite being involved.

From the preceding description it is obvious that, usually, time has to be known aboard the ship. A modern time-keeping device can be built for a weight below 100 lb, to keep time to within 1 sec in 10^{13} sec $= 300,000$ yr. But assuming this clock fails, then, by observing the angle planet–Sun–another planet with an accuracy of perhaps 5 sec of arc, the time can be determined to within about 0.5 sec, the exact value depending upon the planets chosen.

If the time is received from Earth via a radio link, travel time of the

---

[1] This method is often referred to as "delta minimum guidance," and the previous method as "Q-matrix guidance." For the sake of completeness, the self-adaptive guidance mode shall be mentioned. This is the most refined system, because it commands the optimum action as a result of the measured conditions (e.g., a deviation from course, or failure of an engine). This mode has been developed for the Saturn space vehicle system.

electromagnetic wave has to be compensated for. As both speed of light and distance from Earth are only known with some error, an uncertainty is again involved—in practical interplanetary cases perhaps about 0.1 sec. This could be considerably reduced by immediate retransmission of the signal to Earth, where the round-trip time for the electromagnetic signal is measured. From this, a very accurate value (namely, half the round-trip time) for the time compensation can be found and given to the vehicle.

1.4,2 The Intercontinental Ballistic Missile

This is a good example of what guidance systems can do. We know that, at 8000-km range, deviations of ± 5 km, or thereabouts,[1] appeared to be the state-of-the-art as early as 1961. The angular accuracy in azimuth is easily established. In a spherical triangle of sides a, b, c and angles α, β, γ we have $\sin a : \sin b = \sin \alpha : \sin \beta$. If now a is the deviation from the target (called Δa) and b is the range of the missile (called 2η), then α is the azimuth error (called simply Δ), and β is approximately $\frac{1}{2}\pi$. So $\sin \Delta a = (\sin 2\eta) \times (\sin \Delta)$, or regarding Δa and Δ as being small and introducing the Earth's radius R:

$$(R\,\Delta a) = \Delta\, R \sin 2\eta.$$

Introducing the linear deviation from target $R\,\Delta a = \delta$ and the actual range $x = R\,2\eta$, we obtain, finally, the allowable azimuth error:

$$\Delta = \left(\frac{2\eta}{\sin 2\eta}\right)\frac{\delta}{x}\,.$$

With $\delta = \pm 3.5$ km, $x = 8000$ km, and $2\eta \approx 1.257 \approx 72°$ it follows that $\Delta = \pm 2$ min of arc. It should be remarked that, if v is the injection speed and α the flight path angle, a normal speed component v_n corresponding to Δ follows from

$$\Delta = \frac{v_n}{v \sin \alpha}\,,$$

or for typical ICBM-values of $v \sin \alpha = 6000$ m/sec and $\Delta = \pm 2' = (2/3440)$ rad, we have, approximately, $v_n = \pm 3.5$ m/sec. It does not appear to be too difficult to keep v_n below this value.

---

[1] The Minuteman ICBM (3 stages, solid propellant, operational since 1962; 16.4 m in length, 1.89 m maximum diameter, launch weight more than 29.5 tons) has an inertial guidance system. The Wing 1 missiles can hit a target the size of an airfield runway, at up to 9300 km distance; Wing 2 missiles will have a range beyond 10,200 km; Wing 6 missiles are even better.

Let us refer back to Fig. 4.8 of Vol. 1. We chose α so that the range 2η is a maximum, or $d\eta/d\alpha = 0$. We expect that the accuracy in α is not critical under this condition:

$$\cos \eta = \cos(180 - \varphi_0) = -\cos \varphi_0 = \frac{1 - v^{*2} \sin^2\alpha}{[1 - (2 - v^{*2})v^{*2} \sin^2\alpha]^{1/2}}.$$

Or, in simpler form,

$$\cos \eta = y = \frac{1 - \beta x}{(1 - x)^{1/2}}.$$

If x_0 and y_0 are the "ideal" values,

$$y = \frac{1 - \beta x_0 - \beta(x - x_0)}{[1 - x_0 - (x - x_0)]^{1/2}} = \frac{1 - \beta x_0}{(1 - x_0)^{1/2}} \frac{1 - [\beta(x - x_0)/(1 - \beta x_0)]}{[1 - (x - x_0)/(1 - x_0)]^{1/2}}$$

or

$$y = y_0 \left\{1 - \frac{\beta \, \Delta x}{1 - \beta x_0}\right\} \left\{1 - \frac{\Delta x}{1 - x_0}\right\}^{-1/2};$$

series development gives

$$\frac{y}{y_0} = \left\{1 - \frac{\beta \, \Delta x}{1 - \beta x_0}\right\} \left\{1 + \frac{1}{2} \frac{\Delta x}{1 - x_0} + \frac{3}{8} \left(\frac{\Delta x}{1 - x_0}\right)^2 + \cdots\right\},$$

$$\frac{y - y_0}{y_0} = \frac{\Delta y}{y_0} = \left[\frac{1}{2(1 - x_0)} - \frac{\beta}{1 - \beta x_0}\right] \Delta x$$

$$+ \left[\frac{3}{8} \frac{1}{(1 - x_0)^2} - \frac{\beta}{2(1 - x_0)(1 - \beta x_0)}\right] \Delta x^2 + \cdots$$

If $d\eta/d\alpha = 0$, we have

$$\frac{\beta}{1 - \beta x_0} = \frac{1}{2(1 - x_0)} \quad \text{and} \quad \frac{\Delta y}{y_0} = \frac{1}{2} \left(\frac{\beta \, \Delta x}{1 - \beta x_0}\right)^2.$$

Since $y = \cos \eta$,

$$\left(\frac{dy}{y}\right)_0 = -\frac{\sin \eta_0}{\cos \eta_0} \, d\eta$$

and

$$\beta x = v^{*2} \sin^2 \alpha$$

If v^* is a constant, then

$$d(\beta x) = 2v^{*2} \sin \alpha \cos \alpha \, d\alpha;$$

so

$$\Delta\eta \approx - \frac{\cos\eta_0}{\sin\eta_0} \times 2\left(\frac{v^{*2}\sin\alpha\cos\alpha\,\Delta\alpha}{1 - v^{*2}\sin^2\alpha}\right)^2.$$

Inserting η_0 and α_{opt} gives

$$\sin\eta_0 = \frac{v^{*2}}{2 - v^{*2}}\,, \qquad \cos\eta_0 = 2\,\frac{(1 - v^{*2})^{1/2}}{2 - v^{*2}}\,,$$

$$\sin^2\alpha_{\text{opt}} = \frac{1}{2 - v^{*2}}\,, \qquad \cos^2\alpha_{\text{opt}} = \frac{1 - v^{*2}}{2 - v^{*2}}\,.$$

Finally,

$$\Delta\eta \approx - \frac{v^{*2}}{(1 - v^{*2})^{1/2}}\,(\Delta\alpha)^2.$$

For an ICBM of 8000 km range, $\eta = 36°$ or $v^{*2} = 0.74$. So, with $\Delta\alpha = 0.1°$ $\approx (1/580)$ rad we have an error in range of $6370 \times 10^3(2\,\Delta\eta) \approx -60$ m. This is indeed negligible. If the altitude of the injection point is wrong by dh, the resulting range error is given by $dh/(1 - v^{*2})^{1/2}$. The simple geometrical derivation is left to the reader.

What about sensitivity to an injection speed error? Maximum range is given by

$$\sin\eta \quad = \frac{v^{*2}}{2 - v^{*2}}\,,$$

$$\ln\sin\eta \quad = 2\ln v^* - \ln(2 - v^{*2})\,,$$

$$\frac{\cos\eta}{\sin\eta}\,d\eta = \left\{\frac{2}{v^*} + \frac{2v^{*2}}{2 - v^{*2}}\right\}dv^*$$

$$= \frac{4}{(2 - v^{*2})v^*}\,dv^*\,,$$

or [1]

$$d\eta = \frac{2}{2 - v^{*2}}\,\frac{v^{*2}}{(1 - v^{*2})^{1/2}}\,\frac{dv^*}{v^*}\,.$$

With $(2\,d\eta) = \pm\,4/8000$ and $v^{*2} = 0.74$, it follows that $dv^* \approx \frac{2}{3}$ m/sec. Therefore, the sensitivity against speed errors is rather high. This may force us to use, for long-range missiles, injection angles that do not give maximum range but are more favorable with respect to sensitivity. In all ICBM-type cases v^* is near 1.

---

[1] From the following equation we have $d\eta/dv^* = \infty$ for $v^* = 1$. For global ranges, minimum energy trajectories become impractical from a sensitivity point of view.

The guidance system will correct for wind influences, and effects of variation of specific impulse, flow rate, and thrust from their nominal values
during the powered flight. The same is true for deviation of the ignition
point from its ideal condition. Earth oblateness effects cannot be neglected—they give range alterations dr of the order of $dr/r = J$ or K [see Eq.
(4.55) of Vol. 1]. Gravitational effects due to other celestial bodies (a
few meters) or due to the relativistic effects (a few centimeters) are negligible. But during entry there are uncorrected wind effects, making the
margin for error for the injection conditions even more stringent. This
effect may also place limitations upon nose-cone shape such that extremely blunt shapes have to be avoided. Other physical uncertainties are
mainly due to Earth's gravitational constant and gravitational anomalies,
which may add up to 0.5 km deviation. Earth is possibly a three-axial
ellipsoid—this will, if neglected, give a deviation from target not larger
than 1 km. This completes our survey of the performance that can be
expected from purely inertial navigation of ballistic vehicles upon Earth.

Injection time is usually of no concern for an ICBM. Not so in space
flight. If, e.g., a flight to the Moon is planned, then the Moon must be there
when the vehicle reaches Earth-Moon distance. This, for a given trajectory,
and hence, given time of transit, determines the time of injection. Therefore,
we have to carry a clock aboard the vehicle,[1] so that the guidance system
can check actual against ideal time of cutoff and induce a proper correction.

If the target for an IRBM- or ICBM-type rocket vehicle is closer than
the full range of the missile, many possibilities exist: one can use the full
vehicle performance in velocity and take an either high or flat trajectory.
Another way is not to utilize the full velocity capability, but cut off the
engine early[2] and fly the minimum-velocity-trajectory corresponding to
the distance. Furthermore, two flight paths exist for every cutoff velocity
above the minimum for the distance.

Which solution is actually adopted to get to the short-distance target
is determined by guidance-system compatability, considerations to minimize impact deviations due to injection errors, and tactical considerations
as to flight time, enemy defense, etc.

From our investigation of the accuracy which the guidance system of
an ICBM actually has to have, and from the fact that the Atlas ICBM has
been declared operational (in September 1959), we can conclude that, for
a multistage space rocket vehicle, injection errors not larger than $\pm 0.3°$

---

[1] Or give a proper radio command from the ground.

[2] Conceivably, a first stage of a multistage vehicle might not be used.

in pitch angle, and $\pm 0.15°$ in azimuth, and ± 5 m/sec in speed can be expected, if the guidance system controls the vehicle up to the final stage, and if ICBM-type accuracy is reached in every step. If liftoff time is a few seconds wrong, and a few more seconds of error compile during powered flight, then injection time should be accurate to better than ± 30 sec, which we expect to be corrected for as described, but some residual error will remain—perhaps corresponding to ± 1 sec. Uncompensated deviation of the injection point from ideal will hardly be more than 1 km in any direction.

A three-stage Saturn 1B-type vehicle having a full guidance system in the last stage, and going from launch directly to injection at near-parabolic speed, is expected to have the following errors at cutoff:

Range	~ 1 km
Altitude	~ 1 km
Cross range	~ 1 km
Speed	~ 2 m/sec
Injection angle	0.02 deg
Azimuth	0.01 deg

If an intermediate satellite orbit is entered, the final injection will have larger errors unless the guidance information is updated (e.g., by tracking information from Earth) during the orbital part of the mission.

If, after main-engine cutoff, the vehicle is observed for a certain time —e.g., a few hours— and then a Vernier correction is applied, the corresponding residual errors can probably be reduced by a factor of 10.

This may be sufficient to describe the degree of injection accuracy we can expect.[1]

1.4,3 Guidance Systems (*ARS Journal*, 1959)

In an "inertial system" we measure accelerations on board the vehicle. This is done by measuring the force between, say, the vehicle hull and a freely movable mass—forces that act equally upon the freely movable mass and the vehicle cannot be measured. As gravity is in this class, we cannot measure it, but we can calculate its value. The procedure is as follows:

Initial conditions are known. The gravity vector at the initial location is calculated and added to the measured acceleration vector. Two integrations with respect to time give velocity vector and location, and thus new

[1] Gemini II (Sept. 1966) performed the most accurate landing within the Mercury and Gemini manned satellite programs: automatic mode, 3.2-km deviation.

initial conditions which allow us to go through the same procedure again, etc. To measure the acceleration vector, we need a coordinate system on board the vehicle, the timewise behavior of which is known. One well-proven method is to use a gyro-stabilized space-fixed [1] (inertial) platform and mount the accelerometers upon this platform. The measurements are then automatically within an inertial coordinate system (Mueller, 1960).

Of course, the measurements can be made in a coordinate system which is vehicle-fixed, and the attitude of the vehicle-fixed system, with respect to the inertial platform, can be utilized to transform the measurements to the inertial system. This simplifies the mechanical part of the guidance system, but makes the computation more complicated. We can go one step further and eliminate the mechanical platform, if vehicle turning rates are measured and properly integrated; we can then calculate vehicle attitude with respect to the inertial system. This, in effect, replaces the mechanical platform by a computed one. At the present time, mechanical platforms appear to be more accurate.

The art of gyro-manufacturing is highly developed, with precision and elimination of friction being the goal. Ways to reach it are airbearings, floating the rotor in some liquid, or magnetic suspension of a superconducting rotor in vacuum; the magnetic field penetrates only about 10^{-4} mm deep into a superconductor, and no energy is necessary to maintain the magnetic field generated from a current within a superconducting coil. If the superconducting rotor approaches the coil, an additional current is induced, which makes the system stable. Metals neither expand nor contract in the low temperature environment, which results in high precision. In the absence of external torque, a gyro will maintain its orientation. As we cannot exclude all external torques (e.g., imbalances, friction, pick-up force), a practical gyro will have a random precession, or random drift. Today, under $1g$ acceleration, a random drift rate as low as 20 sec of arc per hour $\approx 0.15°$ per day has been achieved (Unger, 1958). Very large improvements appear potentially possible. [2] But today values ten times as

---

[1] References other than space-fixed ones can be used also.

[2] Advanced gyro types may use: electromagnetic suspension in high vacuum; electrostatic suspension in high vacuum; cryogenic and magnetic suspension in high vacuum, as discussed above. Two types of gas bearings are utilized: hydrostatic or hydrodynamic. Molecular gyroscopes depend upon the gyroscopic properties of molecules or atoms; output sensors are difficult. Two types of gimballess platforms have been described in the literature: (1) concentric spheres, where the inner sphere is completely free for angular motions, and (2) the "computed platform" as mentioned above. Electrostatic gyros did obtain 8 sec of arc/day at $1g$. The listing in this footnote shows that many principles are explored in order to obtain improvements in guidance

large must still be regarded as good. And it should be mentioned that, under the zero-gravity condition of unpowered flight in space, the gyro-drift rate will be much smaller than its value under nonzero acceleration.[1] On the other hand, high g-loads will increase drift.

Usually three accelerometers measure acceleration in three axes, and care must be taken not to have any deflections in the accelerometer mounting to prevent cross-coupling between the measurements. Several types of accelerometers are used: With a seismic mass, $\ddot{x}$ can be measured. If we give a torque proportional to $\ddot{x}$ upon a gyro, then the angular rate of precession is proportional to $\ddot{x}$, and the total angle of precessional turn is proportional to $\dot{x}$. (Integrating gyro; actually the housing of the instrument is turned so that the gyro keeps measuring the x-component.) In the same manner, the y, z-components are determined.

Accelerometers have an accuracy to about 0.1% of their dynamic range. Therefore, it may pay to have two accelerometers for each direction: one for the higher g-loads (e.g., during main engine burning or near cutoff) and one for the lower accelerations. (For example, at ignition of main engines, or during Vernier engine operation.)

We have shown in Chap. 4 of Vol. 1 that the gravity gradient in the case of Earth satellites can be utilized to stabilize the attitude of a satellite vehicle. Therefore, it is feasible to measure the gravity gradient aboard a vehicle, and from the gravity gradient, the gravitational acceleration itself can be calculated. This is a modification of the statement that the gravitational acceleration cannot be measured aboard the vehicle. On the other hand, such a gravity-gradient meter is not yet available, and the accuracy aspect appears not to be very promising (Oberth, 1958).

The autopilot is an important element of the full guidance system. It keeps the vehicle in a stable flight position and can, together with a preprogrammed tilt initiation, keep a vehicle approximately along a pre-computed trajectory. But the vehicle has no information as to where it

---

system accuracy. Other desirable improvements have to do with economy, lifetime, weight, power and volume requirement, environmental insensitivity, operational flexibility, reliability, maintainability, etc. Properly arranged laser beams can assume surprising duties, e.g., those which have conventionally been performed by gyro-scopes (see *Aviation Week*, February 11, 1963, p. 98). According to S. Tilson in "The New Navigation" (*International Science and Technology*, July 1963) gyro drift rates are probably below 0.5"/h. See also "Unconventional Inertial Sensors," by J. T. Lavan, in *Space/Aeronautics*, Dec. 1963.

[1] The superconducting gyro may achieve, under zero gravity condition, the low drift rate of 0.01 arc sec per year.

actually is; it is an open-loop system, whereas a full guidance system has
the loop closed since the vehicle derives information about its coordinates
(location, velocity) and concludes from these what actions to take in order
to reach the target. These conclusions are given to the autopilot which
initiates proper action, say, a jet deflection. So if, e.g., thrust were to deviate
somewhat from its nominal value, then a simple autopilot system would
fly a "wrong" trajectory, but a full guidance system would force the vehicle
to fly along a "correct" one.

The attitude control system makes sure that the attitude of the vehicle
equals the attitude as required by the guidance system, unless overriding
considerations (e.g., angle of attack which can endanger vehicle stability,
it may be measured aerodynamically; sloshing can threaten structural in-
tegrity) force a deviation. Self-adaptive control systems are under development.

Angle of attack may be measured aerodynamically. It is a very important
quantity concerning missile stability. Cutoff speed may be controlled even
in an autopilot system, or may be determined by depletion of one of the
propellant components even in a full guidance system. The latter procedure
should, e.g., be used for lower stages of step rockets, thereby utilizing boosters to their fullest extent. Only the final stage for each maneuver should
have controlled cutoff. The main advantage of an inertial guidance system
is that it is completely contained within the vehicle and does not need any
links to the outside. A disadvantage is the basic accuracy limitation, which
has to do with sensor error and stability limits. Even at the expense of
longer observation time, we cannot "buy" better guidance information.
This is not true for the radio-inertial guidance system, which we will consider next.

Here location is measured from an observer sitting on Earth. By comparing two location measurements at different times, a mean velocity is
computed. This becomes more accurate as the time of observation increases.
The Earth-measured mean velocity is utilized to improve the velocity as
measured aboard the vehicle by a simple inertial system.

Of advantage are the high accuracy (in distance, easily to ± 1 m, and
in distance rate, easily to ± 0.1 m/sec![1]) and the fact that, thanks to
the radio link, most of the computation can be done on Earth, thus saving
complexity, weight, and power within the vehicle. Disadvantages are that
a complex and costly worldwide tracking net is necessary to cope with all
situations, and that the vehicle depends upon a link to the outside, which

---

[1] With effort, an improvement by one order of magnitude may be obtained.

may fail or be interferred with. Furthermore, radio guidance is based upon the assumption that the path of the radio signal between transmitter and receiver is accurately known. Mainly because of atmosphere influences, this is not completely true.

In the field of space flight, the main application of radio guidance may occur during the Vernier phase, where high accuracy is very helpful and where only a few ground stations are necessary for one launch complex.

It goes without saying that additional localization may be done by optical observation from Earth. Angular accuracy—relatively poor in radio systems[1]—would increase tremendously, but weather dependence makes this method alone less attractive. But there may be special cases of application, e.g., for a lunar satellite, where some other method establishes a coarse orbit around the Moon, which is exactly observed from Earth during the following days. Then a convenient correction maneuver to enter the desired orbit is calculated, and the appropriate commands are given to the vehicle. Furthermore, optical tracking can be attractive in connection with some other method, where it is used to improve or verify the data obtained otherwise.

In pure radio guidance, all necessary observations (velocity and location vector) are done from Earth, and commands are given to the vehicle. Apart from still greater simplicity within the vehicle, this method has no advantage over radio-inertial guidance. It is less accurate, as it is not possible to derive a good value for the instantaneous acceleration from the location measurements because of the errors of the latter.

Again, optical means could be utilized in place of the radio-ranging.

A special case of a radio-guided vehicle is a beam rider, where the vehicle moves along a narrow radio beam.

In all methods where some or all of the guidance information is collected at Earth, accuracy decreases with distance. The long travel time of an electromagnetic signal from Earth to the vehicle may make such methods useless—e.g., when a lunar landing vehicle goes into an undesirable maneuver, this is known on Earth about 1.3 sec later, and the command for the reaction maneuver can reach the vehicle only 2.6 sec after the undesired maneuver began, which may be too late. For interplanetary distances, the two-way signal time may be of the order of a half-hour; no further comment is necessary. We can conclude that guidance from Earth is not attractive for large distances, say, above 100,000 km, at least for the target-centered terminal guidance phase.

---

[1] For example, interferometer technique.

Pure inertial guidance becomes worse with time because of gyro drift. At cutoff, the alignment error may be 0.02°, and n days of gravity-free flight later, $(0.02 + 0.05n)$ deg. Allowing a maximum error of 0.1 deg, we get $n_{max} = 1.6$ days, or pure inertial guidance might be adequate for lunar missions, if very high accuracy (as, e.g., landing at a predetermined spot) is not demanded at the target.

Assume that a special terminal guidance system takes over to control the final powered maneuver, e.g., lunar landing. In the same way as there is a "natural" flight path for a launch, namely, a gravity tilt, there is a "natural" trajectory for the landing. Because of considerations of fuel consumption, only limited deviations from this "natural" trajectory are possible, which means that the ignition point for the landing maneuver has to be close to its theoretical position, if the actual landing point shall be at the predetermined spot. When the powered flight path length for this final maneuver is S, then we can estimate a reasonable terminal guidance system to correct for not more than 10% of S deviation from the desired end location. To consider further the example of the lunar lander: If a spot landing at a point P is desired, then the ideal braking maneuver has to start at a certain point in space so that the natural powered descent just leads to P. If now S is 200 km, then the actual starting point of the powered trajectory may be 20 km off its ideal location, and we can expect the terminal guidance system to correct for these 20 km and still bring the vehicle to P. Close to the ground a hovering time may be included for fine control, survey of actual touchdown spot, etc. If the injection-guidance system from the Earth launch phase is to bring the vehicle to within $\pm$ 20 km of the target, then an angular accuracy of about $\pm (20/380{,}000)$ rad $\approx \pm 10$ sec of arc is required, assuming a straight-line trajectory. In fact, even with a Vernier system, we can expect an accuracy of only $\pm 0.03° \approx \pm 100''$, as estimated before. So, it follows from this example that, generally, besides injection, Vernier, and terminal, a midcourse guidance system has to be used. This requirement will be even more important for interplanetary transfers than it is for flights in the Earth-Moon system.

The main problem concerning the terminal guidance system, to determine location and velocity with respect to the landing area, has a number of possible solutions. If location and time are known, then velocity can be established very accurately from theory, as mentioned before. Therefore we must consider further the measurement of location. A coordinate system can be determined by the local vertical, and some fixed stars, or planets, or the Sun. The local vertical can be found by scanning the target's horizon, and taking the mean value of this direction. Since perhaps the full horizon will not be in sunlight, infrared technique has to be used. Radar, or the apparent diameter of the target or of some well-known mark on the surface of the target, will give distance, and direction can be found by looking at the position of the target relative to the background of stars. Or direction might be established by looking at the surface of the target and comparing this to a map, either by a man in the vehicle, or by automatic map-matching equipment (a practical difficulty lies in the, as a function of distance, varying scale of the picture), or via a TV link with Earth. Looking down to the target's surface does not necessarily require sunlight: infrared or active radar technique or an artificial flare might be used, and with modern light-intensifying methods (photoelectron multipliers) mere starlight will suffice to illuminate the landscape.

If velocity has to be measured, its normal component can be found from the rate of altitude change, and the lateral one from altitude and rate of change of the line-of-sight to some surface mark upon the target.

As the rocket exhaust might interfer with some or all of the guidance measurements, and to smooth the operation, it will be advisable to use the measurements only to adjust an inertial guidance system, and do the actual final maneuver under control of this inertial system. Because of its sensitivity and importance for, say, a lunar landing, the very final phase might be controlled differently.

Assistance from the target should not be ruled out. If the target is manned, the inhabitants there can observe and perhaps even control the maneuver. Even if the target is unmanned, one or a number of conveniently placed radar or radio responders or infrared sources, etc., can be of help.[1]

Much of what has been said in Chapter 5 of Vol. 1 about vehicles landing from space can be applied to the general problem of terminal guidance.

It goes without saying that a sufficiently dense atmosphere can be used for control of stability, attitude, and directional changes, as is similarly done within the Earth's atmosphere.

1.4,4 On Midcourse Guidance (Unger, 1958; Moskowitz and Weinschel, 1964)

The task for the midcourse guidance system is to bridge the gap between the accuracy that can be obtained from the injection phase and that which is required for the terminal phase. Because of gyro drift, generally a pure inertial system will not suffice. But it may still be used for smoothing, if

---

[1] Velocity Sensing for Spacecraft Docking, by R. Zito Jr., in *Space/Aeronautics*, Dec. 1963: relative speed can be measured down to mm/sec, using the Mössbauer effect.

it is adjusted continuously or occasionally by some other means. This adjustment is most important with regard to attitude (drift!) and position. (If the acceleration measurement is in error only by 10^{-3} m/sec², then the inertial system gives in 60 h $\approx 22 \times 10^4$ sec a position error of $\frac{1}{2} \times 10^{-3}$ $(22 \times 10^4)^2 \approx 25 \times 10^3$ km!) Since we want radio contact between Earth and an interplanetary vehicle, radio navigation appears promising at first sight. But there are many drawbacks, such as correction for Earth rotation, ionospheric refraction, loss of line-of-sight for one particular station, and possible communication failure.

Accuracy in radial distance could be established to about 10^{-4} using a responder in the vehicle, receiving the radio signal back on Earth and measuring signal travel time.[1] Angle may be measured to about 2 min of arc, giving a positional error of the order of 6×10^{-4} times radial distance d from Earth. Then the total positional error may be about $10^{-3}d$. Optical position finding promises to be approximately one order of magnitude better.

If we could place three sets of automatic radio equipment into known positions in space, certain types of radio navigation become applicable, such as, e.g., Loran. The accuracy of the position determination could be of the order of 10^{-4} of the length of the radius vector. Whether this is worth the effort is at least doubtful, since optical methods promise to give the same accuracy. On the other hand, the radio method can be automated quite easily.

Optical position finding may be done from Earth, or from the vehicle. The former promises very high accuracy, but over-all, the reliability may be too low because of weather, line-of-sight position, radio link, brightness of vehicle. So let us look into the potentially most promising method of long-range midcourse navigation, namely, completely vehicle-contained celestial-optical navigation.[2]

Of course, position cannot be found by looking at the fixed stars alone —their distances are too great. Only attitude can thus be established.

An error of about 1 sec of arc appears to be the state-of-the-art for instruments of, say, 13 cm objective diameter. Large specialized, Earth-based instruments can be up to 3 orders of magnitude better. A 13-cm telescope will easily reach stars of magnitude 12 or brighter, and the theoretical resolution is

$$1.22 \frac{\text{wavelength}}{\text{objective diameter}} = 1.22 \frac{5 \times 10^{-5}}{13} = 5 \ \mu\text{rad} \approx 1''.$$

---

[1] Using a different technique, considerably better than 10^{-4}.

[2] Not necessarily in the visible area of the electromagnetic spectrum.

By measuring the apparent angular diameter α of an object of known diameter D, distance R can be established:

$$R \approx D/\alpha,$$

and the error is

$$\frac{\Delta R}{R} \approx \left|\frac{\Delta D}{D}\right| + \left|\frac{\Delta \alpha}{\alpha}\right|.$$

$\Delta D/D$ may be due to insufficient knowledge of the diameter of the object, or may be due to a varying diameter, say, because of oblateness of a planet. Let us estimate $\Delta D/D = 2 \times 10^{-4}$, and we allow $\Delta R/R \leq 10^{-3}$, then follows $\Delta \alpha/\alpha \leq 8 \times 10^{-4}$, or for $\Delta \alpha = 1''$ we have $\alpha \geq 1.25 \times 10^{3''} \approx 20$ min of arc. This gives, as a limiting distance for this type of ranging, $R_{max} \approx 160\,D$, which is, for Earth, 2×10^6 km; for the Moon, 0.61×10^6 km; for Mars, 1×10^6 km; and for the Sun, 220×10^6 km. So, for interplanetary distances, only the Sun is usable, but at 150×10^6 km the error is about 10^5 km. If a planet is in a convenient position, this error may be reduced by two orders of magnitude. If the angular accuracy is $1'' \approx 5\,\mu$, then lateral position is known with an error of only $\Delta R_l \approx (5/10^6)R$, which is two orders of magnitude better than the distance R. To find directions, the object— e.g., a planet—is observed with respect to the known background (occultation method) of stars, and direction of the vehicle with respect to that planet is found using a star table. The proper motion of the fixed stars is not negligible, but well known (around $\frac{1}{100}$ – 1 sec of arc per year, for many convenient stars) and can be corrected for. Aberration angle δ can be fairly large:

$$\delta \approx \frac{\text{speed of observer} = v \sin(\mathbf{v}, \mathbf{c})}{\text{speed of light} = c} \approx \frac{30 \sin(\mathbf{v}, \mathbf{c})}{300,000} \approx 20'' \sin(\mathbf{v}, \mathbf{c}),$$

but since only difference-angles between neighboring objects at the celestial sphere will be measured, we have for two stars, Nos. 1 and 2,

$$|\,\delta_1 - \delta_2\,| = 20'' \,|[\sin(\mathbf{v}, \mathbf{c}_1) - \sin(\mathbf{v}, \mathbf{c}_2)]\,|$$
$$\approx 20'' \,|\,(\mathbf{c}_1 - \mathbf{c}_2)\,|\cos(\mathbf{v}, \mathbf{c}_1),$$

where $(\mathbf{c}_1 - \mathbf{c}_2)$ denotes the small angular difference between the two objects. If this is one degree of arc, and $\cos(\mathbf{v}, \mathbf{c}_1)$ is one, then $|\,\delta_1 - \delta_2\,| \approx 0.33''$.

If, in case of the Sun, we cannot observe the background of stars because of differences in brightness, then—as has been proposed—the star field in the opposite direction to the Sun can be observed, from which, again, direction can be found. Now aberrations will add up and give errors of the order of 40″. But approximate correction should not be difficult.[1]

It may be necessary to correct for parallactic effects due to motion of the vehicle within the solar system, which may amount up to 1″. In measuring position of a planet with respect to fixed stars, both the reference stars and the planet should be within the field of view of the instrument. This insures high accuracy of the measurement and reduces or eliminates the need to correct for the difference in aberration, which will be more difficult for automatic star trackers, where one telescope follows the planet and another one looks at a fixed star, and the angle between the telescopes is measured. Measuring one planet with respect to the star background gives the apparent position of this planet at the time of observation. The position of the planet at a particular time, in the coordinate system used, is known, e.g., from tabulations. Therefore, the position of the vehicle is determined to one degree of freedom (Fig. 1.3).

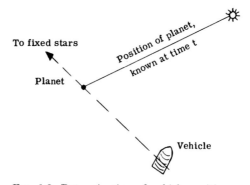

FIG. 1.3. Determination of vehicle position.

If we establish a second such line, then the vehicle is at the cross point of these lines. Accuracy will be very high: If the distance to the planets is 200×10^6 km, and the angular accuracy 1″, then the positional error is about $\pm 2 \times 10^3$ km with respect to the planet. But it migh be simpler to measure the distance from the planet. If the planet has a satellite going around at distance D, and the angle α between satellite and planet is meas-

---

[1] Because speed is not of much concern, for manned space vehicles we can think of photographic observations followed by evaluation of the photographs with high-precision measuring equipment; optical means can be used to obtain a point-like picture of the Sun, thus increasing accuracy. It appears to be possible to have an observational error below 1″.

ured to only $2''$ because of the difficulty of establishing the centers of the observed discs, then the distance error is given by

$$\left|\frac{\Delta R}{R}\right| = \left|\frac{\Delta D}{D}\right| + \left|\frac{2''}{\alpha}\right|.$$

Assuming $\Delta D/D = 10^{-4}$, and allowing $2''/\alpha = \frac{1}{2} \times 10^{-3}$, then $\Delta R/R \approx \frac{1}{2} \times 10^{-3}$, and $\alpha \geq 4 \times 10^{3''} \approx 1.1°$. For $D = 100{,}000$ km we have $R_{max} = 5 \times 10^6$ km and $\Delta R_{max} = 2.5 \times 10^3$ km. Again, the range is not large enough for truly interplanetary flight.

If R is the distance from the Sun, then solar radiation flux is $\sim 1/R^2$. Reradiation from a surface of some material of temperature T is $\sim T^4$; so, in equilibrium, we have $T^4 \sim 1/R^2$, or $R = \text{const}\ 1/T^2$ and

$$\left|\frac{\Delta R}{R}\right| \approx \left|\frac{\Delta \text{const}}{\text{const}}\right| + 2\frac{\Delta T}{T}.$$

As $\Delta \text{const}/\text{const}$ is hardly better than 5×10^{-4} (the solar radiation varies slightly, and the constants of nature, or of the materials, may not be known exactly, or vary slightly), and as we may have

$$2\frac{\Delta T}{T} \approx 2 \times 10^{-4},$$

so follows

$$\frac{\Delta R}{R} \approx 7 \times 10^{-4},$$

up to perhaps Martian distance—then T becomes too low. Even up to Pluto the error may be below 1%. In view of the simplicity, this is a very useful method to measure continuously the distance from the Sun just by measuring a temperature (Press, 1958).

Measurement of velocity or speed is again much more difficult than measuring position. Just differentiating position data, even including a practical smoothing time, is out of the question with position errors of several thousand kilometers. Two effects have been proposed to measure velocity: aberration of light and Doppler measurement. As shown, aberration angle can be about $40''$ for 30 km/sec. With a measuring accuracy of about $1''$, this results in a speed error of about 1 km/sec—completely insufficient. Doppler measurement using the light of stars or radioastronomical measurements of the sharply defined hydrogen absorption line ($\lambda = 21$ cm) might allow us to determine speed to about ± 10 m/sec. But the low energy density of these radiations makes such measurements very difficult. Optical

Doppler measurements of solar radiation with a smoothing time of about 2 min (too long smoothing times are not applicable because of instrument stability reasons) might be a practical way to determine the radial velocity component to about 1 m/sec. If we have a transponder in the vehicle, and a Doppler measurement is made on Earth using the Earth-vehicle-Earth radio communication link, then about $\pm$ 0.2 m/sec will be the error of the radial speed relative to Earth. But Earth's speed itself is not known very accurately—($\pm$ 1 m/sec)—this brings us to a very important problem, namely, the question of the accuracy of the astronomical data. We proceeded so far as if the necessary information (e.g., Sun-planet distances) were available without error, which is of course not true. Many astronomical data are known, with relative accuracy of about 10^{-3}–10^{-5}. We will pursue this subject further in Sec. 1.4,9.

The situation with regard to velocity measurements being what it is, it appears again best to calculate the velocity from theory, time and position being known. We need the navigational general purpose computer anyway. To simplify the problem, perturbation technique against a precomputed "standard" trajectory should be used. Because of the required accuracy [1] (one part in 10^8, e.g., in case of time, 1 sec in 3 yr), a digital computer is a "must." Measured data have then to be presented to the computer in digitized form, of course. Analog elements might be used with advantage.

A large number of data have to be stored in the computer (astronomical data, precalculated trajectory, ephemeris of celestial bodies). To save power, magnetic storage devices might be utilized.

In most cases, high computational speed will not be necessary in the midcourse phase. This might simplify the very difficult task of developing such a computer having a high reliability (0.999) for a long lifetime (3 yr). Today, we may get such a computer to work with high reliability for a few days only. A 300-lb vehicle, completely self-sustained, is described by Laning et al. (1958), which is to return to Earth after a passage of Mars. The computer is highly versatile and reliable, and has a large degree of decision-making capability. It has a large permanent program composed of individual elementary commands. Magnetic core storage is utilized. The computer has two rates of operation—300,000 cps (fast; 3000–5000

---

[1] The computational inaccuracy should be equal to about one-third of the observational inaccuracy, as shown in *Astronautica Acta*, Vol. VI/4 (1960) by D. F. Lawden. Consult this paper also for a method to optimize the midcourse correction maneuver. Typical analog computer accuracy is 1 in 10^4; digital computer accuracy is limited by number of digits and numerical integration step size.

additions per second with a power consumption of the order of 10 W)
and 300 cps (slow; 3–5 additions per second with a consumption of below
1 W). The fixed program consists of 4096 words at 20 bits each. The erasable
portion of storage may consist of 256 words at 20 bits, also. The computer
will be in complete control of the vehicle. If, e.g., a command given by
the computer takes 0.2 sec to execute, then the computer will wait for
0.4 sec and then order some action, which will depend upon whether the
command has been executed as judged by a feedback loop, or whether the
command has not been executed. In the latter case, the computer will
proceed with the surmise that some piece of equipment has failed, and
initiate some corrective action, if possible.

In the case of total power shutdown, the computer has automatic restart
capability, should power return. It can reset its clock to within 15 min
accuracy by evaluation of planet-tracker positions.

The computer weight is about 20 lb, to which a power supply for 1 W continuous output must be added. This consists of 8 lb of solar battery weight,
giving 4 W at Earth and 2 W at Mars vicinity. Furthermore, 20 lb of storage batteries for peak loads are present.

In the case of manned space flight, the task is considerably simplified
by the possibilities of maintenance, repair, and control, and by the fact
that the computer itself can be simpler because of the presence of the human brain. Most studies assume the use of an electronic computer, but
other types (e.g., pneumatic, optical) may find application (Wood and Fox,
1963).

1.4,5 Considerations Pertaining to Fuel Consumption

A few general considerations can be made with regard to fuel consumption:

(1) *Fuel consumption and guidance accuracy.* We will look at a highly
simplified picture (Fig. 1.4): A vehicle A is moving between two points
p_1, p_2. The speed $|\mathbf{v}|$ is correct and constant. The flight path is a straight
line between consecutive impulses, and there are no external forces.

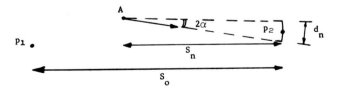

Fig. 1.4. Guidance model.

From a distance S_n we can aim only to a target diameter

$$d_n = 2\alpha S_n ,$$

where α is the angular accuracy of the guidance system. Within the target area, the velocity vector may point at every point with equal probability. Let us assume $\mathbf{v}$ points at d_{np}, then

$$\left(\frac{\pi}{4}\right) d_{np}^2 = \frac{1}{2}\left(\frac{\pi}{4}\right) d_n^2$$

or

$$d_{np} = \frac{1}{2^{1/2}} d_n .$$

Now let us assume that we chose

$$S_{n+1} = \tfrac{1}{2} S_n .$$

Then

$$d_{n+1} = \tfrac{1}{2} d_n$$

and

$$d_{(n+1)p} = \frac{1}{2 \cdot 2^{1/2}} d_n .$$

From Fig. 1.5 follows:

$$2x = \left[\left(\frac{1}{2^{1/2}} d_n\right)^2 + \left(\frac{1}{2^{1/2}} d_{n+1}\right)^2\right]^{1/2} = \left(\frac{5}{8}\right)^{1/2} 2\alpha(2S_{n+1})$$

or

$$\frac{x}{S_{n+1}} = (2.5)^{1/2}\alpha .$$

So the angle through which $\dot{\mathbf{r}}$ has to be turned is about $(2.5)^{1/2}\alpha$—this needs a kick of magnitude $\Delta v_n = (2.5)^{1/2}\alpha\,|\mathbf{v}|$. We consider the task of the midcourse guidance fulfilled when $d_m = d = $ miss distance, from which the terminal guidance system can take over.

How many corrections have to be applied? Obviously, at launch (p_ι), there is $d_0 = 2\alpha S_0$, and $d_1 = \tfrac{1}{2} d_0$, $d_2 = \tfrac{1}{2} d_1 = (\tfrac{1}{2})^2 d_0$, ..., $d_m = (\tfrac{1}{2})^m d_0$ $= d$, or $2^m = d_0/d = 2\alpha S_0/d$, or

$$m = 1 + 3.32 \log_{10}(\alpha S_0/d). \qquad (1.22)$$

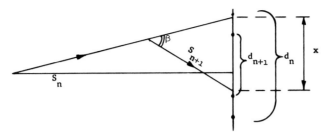

FIG. 1.5. Guidance correction.

The total velocity requirement for the m corrections is

$$\Delta v = (2.5)^{1/2} \alpha \mid \mathbf{v} \mid \{1 + 3.32 \log_{10}(\alpha S_0/d)\}.$$

On the other hand,

$$\Delta v = I_{sp} g_0 \ln(M_0/m_1) = I_{sp} g_0 \ln(1 + \Delta m_f/m_1),$$

where M_0 is the initial mass, m_1 the cutoff mass, and Δm_f is the propellant mass required.

Let us assume we allocate 10% more propellant than the calculation gives, and futhermore let $\Delta m_f/m_1$ be sufficiently small so that

$$\ln(1 + \Delta m_f/m_1) \approx \Delta m_f/m_1 .$$

Then, finally,

$$\frac{\Delta m_f}{m_1} \approx 1.74 \frac{v}{I_{sp} g_0} \alpha \left\{1 + 3.32 \log_{10} \frac{\alpha S_0}{d}\right\}. \tag{1.23}$$

This is a slightly modified version of Unger's formula (Unger, 1958). Assuming now $v = 30$ km/sec, $I_{sp} g_0 = 3$ km/sec, $S_0 = 500 \times 10^6$ km, and $d = 10$ km, then follows

$$\frac{\Delta m_f}{m_1} = 58\alpha(8 + \log_{10}\alpha).$$

For $\alpha = 2'' \approx 10^{-5}$ rad we have $\Delta m_f/m_1 = 1.74 \times 10^{-3}$. This is not much propellant and is spent in $m = 10$ kicks.

If $\alpha = 3' \approx 10^{-3}$ rad, then m goes up to 17, and $\Delta m_f/m_1$ goes up to 0.29, which is already high for practical application. We see from this example how accuracy (α) and energy (Δm_f) can be mutually exchanged; it is the old story of brains versus muscles.

(2) *Optimum time for a maneuver.* Let us assume that the energy per unit mass of a vehicle shall be changed by action of a rocket motor. If the burning time is very short, we can write

kinetic energy before kick + addition of kinetic energy + potential energy
= energy after kick = kinetic energy after kick + potential energy,

or

$$\Delta E = \text{energy addition} = \text{addition of kinetic energy only.}$$

For a kinetic energy per unit mass of $\frac{1}{2}v^2$, we have $\Delta E = \mathbf{v} \cdot \Delta\mathbf{v}$. Now

$$\Delta\mathbf{v} = \mathbf{I}_{sp}g_0 \ln\left(1 + \frac{\Delta m_f}{m_1}\right).$$

So, finally,

$$\Delta E = (\mathbf{I}_{sp}g_0) \cdot \mathbf{v} \ln(1 + \Delta m_f/m_1). \tag{1.24}$$

From this we see that $\Delta\mathbf{v}$ and $\mathbf{v}$ shall be parallel (or antiparallel), and an optimum time for the maneuver is when $|\mathbf{v}|$ is a maximum. If we want to turn through some angle α without changing $|\mathbf{v}|$ then, from Fig. 1.6, we have $\sin(\alpha/2) = \frac{1}{2}\,|\Delta\mathbf{v}|\,/\,|\mathbf{v}|$, or $\alpha \approx \Delta v/v$. For a given Δv, we should carry out the maneuver when v is a minimum.

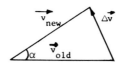

FIG. 1.6. Velocity change diagram.

A problem similar to this one is that of obtaining the maximum lateral displacement at the end of a trajectory. The vehicle is moving from p_1 to p_2 (Fig. 1.7) with a varying velocity $v = v(S)$. We apply a kick at some point S so that, for a given kick, d is a maximum:

$$\alpha \approx \Delta v/v$$

and

$$d = (S_0 - S)\Delta v/v\,;$$

from $\partial d/\partial S = 0$, the optimum point $S = S_1$ can be calculated.

For example, $v = A/S^n$, where A is constant:

$$d = (S_0 - S) \frac{\Delta v}{A} S^n = \frac{\Delta v}{A} (S_0 S^n - S^{n+1}),$$

$$\frac{\partial d}{\partial S} = \frac{\Delta v}{A} [nS_0 - (n+1)S]S^{n-1} = 0,$$

$$S_1 = \frac{n}{n+1} S_0 \quad \text{and} \quad d_{max} = \frac{\Delta v}{A} \frac{1}{n+1} \left(\frac{n}{n+1}\right)^n S_0^{n+1}.$$

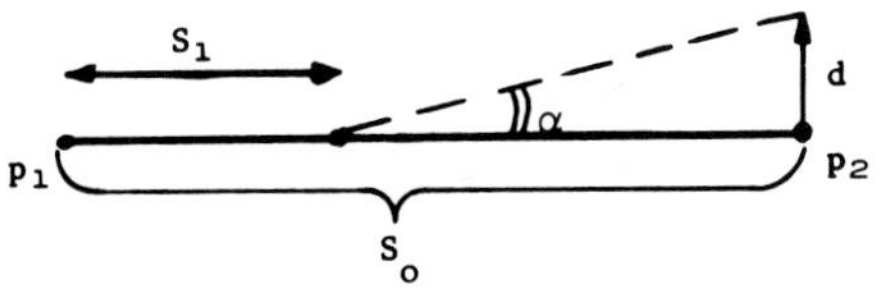

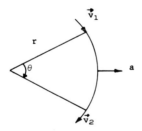

FIG. 1.7. Lateral displacement diagram.

Here the optimum is no longer given by the minimum of speed, and obviously the real case will be still much more complicated than the idealized problem we have considered. But the rule of carrying out a maneuver as early during the flight as possible does not necessarily hold (see above example for $n \neq 0$).

FIG. 1.8. Turning in space $|\mathbf{v}_1| = |\mathbf{v}_2|$.

(3) *Turning in space.* Centrifugal acceleration is given by $a = v^2/r$, and angular speed or turning rate is $\dot\theta = v/r$ (see Fig. 1.8). Therefore,

$$a = \dot\theta v.$$

For $\dot\theta = \text{const}$ (or $v = \text{const}$ for $r = \text{const}$), we get

$$v\theta = at.$$

For rockets, we write $at = I_{sp}g_0 \ln(1 + \Delta m_f/m_1)$. So, finally,

$$\theta \approx \frac{I_{sp}g_0}{v} \ln\left(1 + \frac{\Delta m_f}{m_1}\right).$$

If Δm_{fl} is the total propellant aboard the vehicle, then we can conclude

$$\theta_{max} \leq \frac{I_{sp}g_0}{v} \ln\left(1 + \frac{\Delta m_{fl}}{m_1}\right). \tag{1.25}$$

In a practical case, $\Delta m_{fl}/m_1$ may be 0.1, and v equal to $I_{sp}g_0$—then θ_{max} $\leq 5.5°$. The example above is, as are all cases of this section, somewhat artificially construed, but serves to demonstrate the limited maneuverability of a space rocket vehicle. This again demands high initial accuracy.

With $\Delta m_{fl}/m_1 = (3.55)/100$, $v = 12$ km/sec, and $I_{sp}g_0 = 3$ km/sec, we can alter the flight path angle by only $0.5°$; this shows the typical capability of a small corrective rocket system (about 4% of the total vehicle weight) to change the flight path angle of an interplanetary vehicle returning to Earth shortly before the beginning of atmospheric entry. Since the permissible deviation from optimum conditions is so small (see Chapter 5, Vol. 1) and since the corrective capability is small also, there follows again the demand for high navigational accuracy.

1.4,6 The Problem of Attitude Control (Roberson, 1960; Haeussermann, 1962)

1.4,6,1 ATTITUDE PERTURBATIONS

We often want to have the attitude of the vehicle controlled—reasons can be, e.g., addition of a velocity vector Δv, controlled attitude of some instruments (optical observations, radio antennas, power plants using solar energy, radiators for cooling to be directed away from the Sun, astronomical telescope in satellite, tankage containing low-temperature liquid propellants should point only with a small area toward the Sun to minimize evaporation losses, etc.) The desired accuracy may be about $\frac{1}{10}$ of a degree of arc during the duration of the mission, but wide variations are possible. Photocells may be directed toward the Sun, perhaps within 10 deg, and still operate properly. The orbiting astronomical satellite, on the other hand, will have a star-referenced pointing accuracy of $\frac{1}{10}$ of a second of arc, or better, to be maintained during many hours. A wide-beam radio antenna may require an accuracy of only a few degrees for a few minutes.

Perturbations of attitude can come from initial alignment errors, or initial uncompensated angular rates of motion, or from gradients of the gravity field, or from interaction with electric or magnetic fields,[1] radiation pressure, unsymmetrical residual aerodynamic forces, meteor hits, motion within the vehicle, and thrust misalignments. Let us consider these perturbations in greater detail.

(1) *Initial alignment/initial angular rate.* Initial alignment is mainly governed by thrust directions at cutoff. This can be far from the desired flight attitude, when, e.g., a particular attitude with respect to the Sun is desired.

At main engine cutoff, unsymmetric nozzle flow may introduce an angular moment; but if thereafter we take a sufficiently long smoothing time, and if a sufficiently stable attitude reference (e.g., stars) is available, then the remaining initial angular rate can be kept arbitrarily small, provided the control system is sufficiently powerful and sensitive.

(2) *Force fields in space.* We will consider only the effects of the gravity field gradient. For the magnetic or electric field the influences depend strongly upon properties (e.g., structure, materials, current loops) of the vehicle itself. Some effects of the magnetic field upon a rotating vehicle have been described earlier (Chap. 4 of Vol. 1).[2]

For the extreme case of the dumbbell satellite (Fig. 4.24 of Vol. 1), we found for the moment 2μ due to the gradient of the gravity field

$$2\mu \approx 2\,\frac{m}{2}\,\omega^2 \left(\frac{l}{2}\right)^2 2\alpha = \frac{m}{2}\,\omega^2 l^2 \alpha \;.$$

Using Eq. (4.36), of Vol. 1,

$$2\mu \approx (ml^2)\,\frac{\gamma M}{a^3}\,\frac{\alpha}{2}\;.$$

In this equation, m is the mass of dumbbell satellite, l the length of dumbbell satellite, M the mass of central body, γ the gravitational constant, a the distance from central body, and α the angle from local vertical.

Introducing $g_0 = \gamma M/R^2$, we get

$$2\mu \approx (mg_0) \left(\frac{R}{a}\right)^3 \left(\frac{l}{R}\right)^2 R\,\frac{\alpha}{2}\;.$$

---

[1] The satellite may have a magnetic moment due to permanent magnetism, induced magnetism, internal circuitry, and eddy currents.

[2] It should be mentioned that eddy currents which reduce the spin rate, as shown in Chapter 4 of Vol. 1, may generate a torque in asymmetric cases.

Introducing an acceleration $\ddot{x}$, we can write

$$2\mu \approx 2\,\frac{m}{2}\,\ddot{x}\,\frac{l}{2}\;,$$

or

$$\ddot{x} \approx g_0 \left(\frac{R}{a}\right)^3 \frac{l}{R}\,\alpha\;. \tag{1.26}$$

For an Earth satellite, we may have $a/R = 1.1$, $R/l = 10^6$, $\alpha = 1(\approx 57°)$, resulting in $\ddot{x} \approx 10^{-6} g_0$. The resulting torque for $mg_0 = 100$ kg would be $2\mu \approx 3 \times 10^{-4}$ mkg. This should be compared to about 5×10^{-3} mkg, which is necessary to turn a telephone dial.

For practical nondumbbell satellites, torques would be even lower. A test satellite (200 lb weight having a 5 lb weight at the end of a 100 ft boom) was orbited on November 15, 1961, but apparently the boom did not extend. A similar experiment was repeated on June 16, 1963 (polar orbit, 741 km altitude), with success. For such stabilization systems a main problem is the damping of satellite oscillations, which has been solved by addition of a coil spring with a high energy loss rate (up to 50% per cycle) and magnetic hysteresis rods. Passive gravity-gradient stabilization appears to be practical for all altitudes up to the 24-h orbit, for careful designs. (See R. B. Kershner, Gravity-Gradient Stabilization of Satellites, *Astronautics and Aerospace Engineering*, September 1963).

The torque from the solar field is, at Earth distance from the Sun, many millions of times smaller than the value computed above. Therefore, it is negligible.

(3) *Radiation pressure.* Radiation pressure due to radiation eminating from the vehicle shall be disregarded.

Pressure due to solar radiation in the vicinity of the Earth is not larger than 0.8×10^{-6} kg/m². The torque resulting from this should not be larger than 10^{-5} mkg, since, by careful design, balancing should not be difficult.[1]

As this effect does not change markedly with distance from Earth, for moderate distances, it may well be, for deep-space missions, more important than the gravity-gradient influence.

(4) *Residual aerodynamic forces.* Assuming we have an effective area of 2 m² at a lever arm of 5 m, at an angle of 90° to the velocity $\mathbf{v}$, and we demand that the aerodynamic moment be larger than 3×10^{-4} mkg, then

---

[1] For control purposes, focusing might be helpful. See R. R. Hibbard, *ARS Journal*, June 1961, p. 844.

for a coefficient $c_D \approx 2$ and for altitudes between 130 and 1000 km the following equation is valid:

$$c_D(\varrho/2)v^2 \times 2 \times 5 \sin 90 \approx (g_0\varrho) \times 6 \times 10^7 > 30 \times 10^{-5}$$

or

$$(g_0\varrho) > 5 \times 10^{-12} \quad \text{kg/m}^3.$$

This means that, for altitudes below 450 km, the aerodynamic torques may be important.[1] Again, by careful design, much of the torque can be avoided.

(5) *Meteor hits.* The total Earth is hit by hardly more than 2×10^9 gm/day of meteors, representing a meteor flux of about 2×10^{-7} gm/m² h. Let us increase this figure by a factor of 10. The average speed may be 30 km/sec. Again for a reference area of 2 m² at a lever arm of 5 m, the torque cannot be larger than 2×10^{-8} mkg when, namely, each meteor delivers all its impulse to the vehicle.[2]

The resulting figure is extremely low. But it should not be overlooked that very large deviations from the figure may occur in the rare case when a larger meteor hits and transfers momentum.

(6) *Motion within the vehicle.* A rotating wheel within the satellite may easily have a momentum of 2 mkg sec—e.g., when the wheel has a radius of 1 m and a weight of 10 kg resulting in a moment of inertia of 1 kg sec² m, and rotates once every 3 sec. If now the buildup time for this rotation were 2 sec, then the average torque would be 1 mkg. It is easily seen that internal motion may be the strongest source of attitude perturbations.

(7) *Thrust misalignment.* This perturbation is only effective during engine operation, of course. For a distance of 20 m between engine and center of gravity, a misalignment of one minute of arc, and 10^3 kg thrust results in a moment of 6 mkg, or a side force of 0.3 kg at a lever arm of 20 m length. To control this is not difficult when the proper means (e.g., thrust directional control, or Vernier engines) are provided.

1.4,6,2 ATTITUDE CONTROL METHODS

We have, so far, looked into causes of attitude perturbation. Let us now consider the methods of attitude control. Of course, many of the perturbations can be utilized for this. Generally, we have to pay attention to interference possibilities between several control methods—e.g., aerodynamic

---

[1] Below 500 km altitude, attitude control by aerodynamic force may be simpler to realize than by gravitational gradient.

[2] Back-sputtering might increase the torque by a factor of ten or so.

torque may upset a control method based upon gravity gradient. But let us look into it in greater detail.

(1) *Gravity field gradient.* If a satellite has equal moments of inertia around its three main axes, then there is no resulting gravity torque. If now two weights are shifted, we can create some small torque for control; this gives a method of very fine attitude control to correct very small perturbations. A good example of application might be given by the orbiting telescope, where demands as to control accuracy are extremely high.

With three different moments of inertia, a completely passive stabilization system is possible, as described in Chap. 4 of Vol. 1. As calculated there, the gravity torques will lead to oscillations, which have to be damped in order to reach equilibrium. One practical method of damping is to have a liquid contained within the satellite so that the oscillation creates motion of the liquid, the energy of which is dissipated in internal friction reap' pearing, of course, as heat which finally has to be radiated away. Oscillations can be damped, if the moment of inertia of the vehicle is kept constant. Spin and oscillations can be "worked off" or increased by proper variation of the moment of inertia.

(2) *Other fields.* It should be mentioned that a moment can be generated by interaction between, e.g., a current loop within the vehicle or a permanent magnet within the vehicle, and the magnetic field of the Earth. Such a control system appears to be quite applicable up to the 24-h-orbit altitude. It is used very successfully is the spinning Tiros II satellite (launched November 1960).

(3) *Air resistance: fins for satellites.* By putting fins, or by attaching a drag body, behind the satellite, some attitude control should be obtainable in the upper atmosphere. This is especially true for bodies in the not-so-high atmosphere, as satelloids (satellites that have to compensate for air drag by some means of thrust to obtain a reasonable lifetime; the thrust may come from exhaust of some auxiliary power system, or some low-thrust chemical or nonchemical rocket engine, or bursts of a high-thrust rocket engine), or airscoopers (satellites that collect upper atmosphere gases and liquefy them, in order to use them for orbital refueling of chemical or nonchemical rocket propulsion systems). The question now is, what is the limiting altitude for such aerodynamic controls?

Let the control moment be $\mu = K\alpha$, where α is the angle between fin and velocity vector. If θ is the moment of inertia, then $T = 2\pi(\theta/K)$ gives the period of the resulting oscillation. Again, the oscillation has to be damped artificially, because the aerodynamic damping is only very slight in the thin atmosphere. Assuming that T shall be a fraction k of the orbital satellite period, we have

$$K = \frac{1}{k^2} \, \theta \, \frac{\gamma M}{a^3} \, .$$

On the other hand,

$$\mu = 2 \, \frac{\varrho}{2} \, v^2 A L \alpha$$

$$\approx \varrho \, \frac{\gamma M}{a} \, A L \alpha \, ,$$

so, $k^2 a^2 A L \varrho = \theta$.

Writing, for the moment of inertia, $\theta = 2(m/2)(L/3)^3$ we get

$$(g_0 \varrho) = \frac{(mg_0)L}{9k^2 a^2 A} \, .$$

For a numerical example, put $mg_0 = 1000$ kg, $L = 20$ m, $A = 20$ m², $a = 6600$ km, $9k^2 = 1$:

$$g_0 \varrho = \frac{2.3}{10^{11}} \quad \text{kg/m}^3,$$

and the corresponding altitude is about 340 km. According to our computations in Chap. 4 of Vol. 1, the lifetime, in a circular orbit of 340 km altitude is shorter than a year, under reasonable assumptions.

The effect of interplanetary gas appears to be negligible; but long travel times and the possibility of existence of denser areas or some kind of "winds" may alter this conclusion.

(4) *Radiation pressure.* It is possible—especially for interplanetary flights—to develop a system to control vehicle attitude with respect to the Sun, utilizing the solar radiation pressure. Again, damping has to be provided.

(5) *Control jets.* With control jets, spin can be removed from a vehicle by applying a torque. Care must be taken so that only a torque acts, and not a resultant force, which would alter the velocity vector (unless such alteration were desired). To have true couples only, 4 vehicle-fixed control nozzles are necessary for each axis, or 12 such nozzles in total. If the nozzles can be turned in a plane, 4 nozzles can suffice. Possibly, each nozzle should have two or more thrust levels (or, more accurately, each control system should have two or more torque levels), one for fast or coarse maneuvers and one for fine control, with the lower thrust level being the more important one.[1] To have very precise couples only, the thrust magnitude of at least

---

[1] For a discussion of microrocket technology, see Sutherland and Maes (1966).

6 of the 12 nozzles should have the capability to be finely controlled. This thrust control should occur automatically, governed, e.g., by translatorial zero-reading accelerometers, which are positioned in the center of gravity of the vehicle. We see again how a conceptually simple system tends to become difficult in engineering detail. There are several possibilities of creating the necessary control force:

(a) Jet from compressed gas or evaporated liquid or subliming solid. The gas might be heated before expansion, or not. The specific impulse is usually low (around 65 sec, in a typical case for nitrogen gas with a chamber pressure of 20 atm, and no additional heating), the exception being solar-heated hydrogen.

(b) Jet from exhaust of some internal power plant. If this power plant is required anyhow, no special mass has to be carried along to form the impulse carrier. For improvement, the exhaust may be heated externally or by after-burning.

(c) Jet from chemical propellants, usually liquid propellants, as neither solid nor gaseous propellants appear promising here. Self-igniting (hypergolic) or non-self-igniting (catalytic, thermal ignition), mono- or bipropellant, storable or nonstorable (cryogenic), or hybrid (lithergolic) systems, special propellants or the same propellants as in the main engine can be used. The feed system (pressure, pump) has to be developed carefully, as multiple restart capability under zero-g or artificial g conditions is mandatory.

(d) During main engine burning, attitude (except roll, if only one nozzle operates) control can be achieved by jet deflection. For roll control, the turbine exhaust is convenient.

(e) Thermal or explosive nuclear engines do not appear promising, as these tend toward high thrust. But all types of low thrust high specific impulse devices (arc-jet, ion, MHD) seem to be especially suitable, because already a thrust acceleration as low as $10^{-6}g$ might suffice in controlling the attitude of the vehicle, as has been shown in the previous part on the magnitude of the attitude perturbations. Obviously, no fast maneuvers can be done with such small forces.

All such very high specific impulse engines utilize electric energy to accelerate the exhaust jet. Therefore, these systems will be specially attractive for space vehicles that need a large supply of electrical energy anyhow for their operation, and that can use this electric energy to operate the control jets neglecting their other functions during such periods. Active communication satellites can be put in this class.

A fundamental disadvantage—which is minimized for the high specific impulse systems—of all attitude controls by thrust is that they use mass, and therefore will run out of impulse carrier unless some sort of supply can be established. Another disadvantage is that the jet might disturb the operation of the space vehicle itself, e.g., disturb communication, or astronomical or other observations or measurements (e.g., interplanetary gas), or decrease the quality of some special surfaces (e.g., windows, optics, radiators, highly reflective areas, photocells).

(6) *Flywheel controls.* Rotational momentum can be transferred from the vehicle to a flywheel or other type of gyro within the vehicle. Thus rotation of the vehicle can be stopped at the expense of rotating a gyro, or—and this will be a very important application—a vehicle can be brought to change its attitude by spinning of a gyro, and when the new desired attitude is reached, all motion can be stopped just by stopping the gyro. Behind all these applications is, of course, the law of conservation of rotational momentum.

The fundamental advantage of this type of control is that no mass is jettisoned and that it does not depend on the presence of some exterior field. Therefore, lifetime depends only upon energy, which can be supplied fairly easily over long times. (Solar energy, or a man spinning up the gyro, or nuclear energy.) The basic disadvantage is that a gyro can only "soak up" a certain amount of spin before it is mechanically destroyed; therefore a given gyro under certain circumstances might not be sufficient to control the attitude of a vehicle, or after some time the spin capacity of a gyro might be satured. This will usually not happen when the torque inputs to the vehicle are random, because then the spin of the gyro will only move around zero, and the gyro would effectively be used to smooth the results of the torque inputs. Disconnecting and discarding a saturated gyro is another way of carrying spin away from the vehicle, again at the price of loss of mass.

For a three-axis attitude control system, it appears as if we need three gyros. But it is possible to construct such a system, because of cross-coupling effects, with only two gyros. The gyros themselves can be built in many ways, e.g., flywheel, or a liquid that is pumped around in a circular tube, or a metal ball, contained with the aid of an air bearing in a hollow sphere. Two counter rotating gyros may be used for differential fine control.

(7) *Combined systems.* Many combinations of attitude control system are possible. One of the most promising seems to be to combine a flywheel and a jet control system. The flywheel system is used generally, and only when

the spin of one of the gyros reaches a certain limiting value is the gyro stopped and the torque balanced by the jet system. Besides, the jet system can be used for faster maneuvers than allowed by flywheels. For Earth satellites, the flywheel system might profitably be replaced by a magnetic field coupling system.

1.4,6,3 ATTITUDE SENSING METHODS

After describing the attitude perturbances and the attitude control means, we now consider attitude sensing. To do so we have to compare the orientation of the vehicle-fixed coordinate system to a convenient reference coordinate system. There are many possibilities to establish such a reference system: gravity field gradient direction, magnetic or electric field direction, optical or infrared horizon scanning, observation of cosmic radiation and thus finding the Earth's shielding effect, looking for a star, the Moon, Sun or a planet, a planetary surface, determination of the wavefront of a radio signal by phase comparison, or otherwise finding the direction to a known transmitter, relying upon the direction kept by a spinning gyro, or measuring and integrating angular accelerations—these are some of the methods to determine a reference direction in space, not all of which are generally applicable. For example the Earth's shielding effect against cosmic radiation can be measured comparatively close to the Earth only.

Whenever a not-permissible deviation of a controlled vehicle axis from the desired direction is measured, a corresponding action must be taken by the control system; what this action consists of may be decided by the computer, which is, for guidance purposes, already on board (or on Earth).

A spinning gyro tends to keep its space-fixed direction when no disturbing moments are present. If such moments $\mathbf{N}$ cannot be avoided, gyro precession results; the gyro rotational momentum vector $\mathbf{q}$ and the vector $d\mathbf{q} = \mathbf{N}\, dt$ add. The moment $\mathbf{N}$ may be due to forces $\mathbf{f}$ acting upon the gyro axis $\mathbf{l}$ so that $\mathbf{N} = [\mathbf{l}\, \mathbf{f}\,]$. This leads to the familiar behavior of gyros, where $d\mathbf{q}$ is vertical upon $\mathbf{f}$. So if we want to put a spinning gyro into a new position, which has to be done occasionally in guidance systems or with spinning vehicles, we have to apply forces vertically upon the desired motion of the axis, i.e., we precess the gyro into its new position.[1]

Knowing that the perturbing moments in space are small, we can make the whole space vehicle a gyro by spinning it, thus stabilizing it along a

---

[1] Observing the precession (e.g., by evaluation of radio signals from the vehicle antenna, or telemetry of Sun, etc., position) the moments can be found. This could be used to perform local air density measurements, for instance.

space-fixed direction for a short time. It is known from mechanics that both the body axis of minimum and that of maximum moment of inertia are possible stable axes of rotation, the former being of labile and the latter of stabile equilibrium for nonrigid bodies. Let us assume that the moments of inertia are I_{max} and I_{min}, and the vehicle is spinning around the I_{min} axis with a frequency ω_1. The rotational momentum is $I_{min}\omega_1$, and if the vehicle would flip over to the stabile position without external moments acting, then the rotational momentum would be preserved: the spin frequency would change to ω_2 so that $I_{min}\omega_1 = I_{max}\omega_2$. The energy was $E_1 = \frac{1}{2}I_{min}\omega_1^2$, and would be now $E_2 = \frac{1}{2}I_{max}\omega_2^2 = \frac{1}{2}I_{max}(I_{min}\omega_1/I_{max})^2 = \frac{1}{2}I_{min}\omega_1^2(I_{min}/I_{max})$, which shows that $E_2 < E_1$. So in the absence of external moments the "flipover" can only occur when the energy of the rotating vehicle is dissipated. An energy loss rate, which is often quite high, is due to the following effect (see Fig. 1.9):

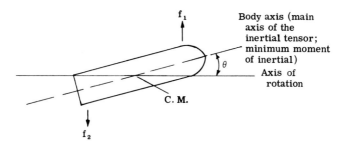

FIG. 1.9. Alignment of axes.

There will be a small, nonzero angle θ between body axis and axis of rotation due to technical-practical inaccuracies. This introduces forces $\mathbf{f}_1$, $\mathbf{f}_2$, which form a moment that wants to make the body rotate around its axis of maximum moment of inertia. (For a rotation around this maximum axis, the corresponding moment would tend to reduce θ, this is why those axes are called labile and stabile axis of rotation, if energy can be dissipated. Otherwise, both are stabile in the absence of exterior moments. A precession results, which generates vibrations in the rotating body (or especially in whip antennas, when such are attached; this happened to Explorer I. Explorer III did not have them—the "flipover" occurred much later) which are damped. This is the looked-for loss of rotational energy. Finally, when a flat spin has developed, the spin rate is slowly decreasing[1] because of interaction with the magnetic field; simultaneously, a precession

---

[1] There can be a spin fluctuation due to a coupling between spin and precession.

is occurring, which is mainly due to interaction between permanent magnetic moments of the satellite and the magnetic field of the Earth, as long as θ has not yet reached 90°. After θ has reached 90°, the main cause of precession is the torque due to the gravitational field gradient (Gudzent, 1961; Neumann, 1962). A full understanding of this complicated field was obtained during studies of Explorer XI (launched on April 27, 1961, by Juno II vehicle; γ-ray astronomical satellite).

A practical conclusion of these considerations is that, for a spin-stabilized vehicle, the rotation should be around the axis of maximum moment of inertia right from the beginning.

It can be derived approximately from a solution presented by Naumann, (1959):

$$\tan \frac{\theta}{2} = \tan \frac{\theta_0}{2} \exp\left[\alpha \, \frac{P}{L(R-1)^4} t\right] = \tan \frac{\theta_0}{2} \exp(At),$$

where θ is the opening angle of the tumble, i.e., precession angle, θ_0 the initial value of θ, L the initial angular momentum of the spinning satellite, P describing the energy dissipation rate,

$$R = \frac{\text{moment of inertia around final axis of spin}}{\text{moment of inertia around initial axis of spin}}$$

(for $R < 1$, the spin is stable and no unstable tumble occurs), α is a constant, and t is the time. If the time is measured in minutes, then A is usually between 0.1 and 0.0001.

From this we have for the time T in hours, to go from a small angle θ_0 (in degrees) to flat spin ($\theta = 90°$) $T = (1/60 \, A) \ln(120/\theta_0)$. For $\theta_0 = 1°$, we get $T = 0.08/A$, or $T = 1$ to 1000 h. (In the satellite Explorer I, launched Jan. 31, 1958, θ went from a small value θ_0 to $\theta \approx 60°$ in one revolution; from this follows $A = 0.0466 - 0.011 \ln \theta_0$, or $A = 0.045 \pm 0.025$ can be estimated.)

There are a number of reasons why, in some cases, the spin of a space vehicle has to be changed. For example, the spin required for stabilization during ascent may be too high for the operational phase, or, in other cases, injection may occur without spin but the operational phase may require a spin rate different from zero. To change the spin rate, tangential rocket thrust can be applied. Another method is to change the moment of inertia around the spin axis. The moment of inertia can be changed by masses moving in a radial direction on rigid rods, in tubes or on flexible wires.

The moment-of-inertia change has the advantage that large radii of gyration can be obtained with small concentrated masses at the ends of the cables, thus resulting in an uncomplicated system of low total weight. On the other hand, only spin reductions relative to the initial spin rate can be accomplished.

A simple method of spin reduction by mass release on strings is to wind the strings around the circumference of a cylindrical part of the space vehicle, opposite to the direction of spin. Upon release the masses will move outward in the direction of spin, each describing an involute of a circle. After the complete extension, the strings must be separated from the body; otherwise they would wind around in the opposite direction and restore the spin rate to its original value. Such a system may have a very light weight for a desired spin reduction.

The main disadvantage of this method is that after separation of the spin reduction system no subsequent restoration is possible. This may limit the useful lifetime of the space vehicle.

A more complex method, avoiding this disadvantage and yielding an additional advantage of nutation damping, is as follows: the mass-shifting strings are run through fixed holes in the outer shell of the space vehicle, unwinding from one or more reels inside the body (Kuebler, 1959). The reels may be controlled by several types of braking systems (for example, force-controlled, or velocity-controlled). Since here the wires stay attached spin can again be increased by rewinding the wires. The wires can have a second function as antennas. But then their lengths must remain fixed.

If the masses are on flexible wires or strings, etc., no purely radial extension can occur because of unbalanced tangential forces (e.g., Coriolis). By balancing these (e.g., extension along rods or pumping liquids within tubes), purely radial extension can be forced. But the increased weight makes such systems unattractive, generally. Even in the case of weights on strings, the extension will be nonradial only during the process of extension. When the radial speed becomes zero, the Coriolis force vanishes and an oscillation around the radial position sets in, which is damped by wire flexing. Finally, the strings point radially outward and the vehicle spins again as if it were rigid.

Some simple theoretical considerations provide more insight:

(1) *Extension of weights along rods or on wires* (see Fig. 1.10). The conservation of rotational momentum is given by

$$\omega_0\{I_0 + 2mR^2\} = \omega_1\{I_0 + 2mD^2\}.$$

Let satellite mass be M and satellite moment of inertia be $I_0 = \frac{3}{4}MR^2$.

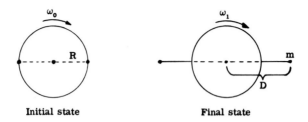

Initial state   **Final state**

Fig. 1.10. Extension of weight along rods or wires.

We have

$$\frac{\omega_1}{\omega_0} = \frac{1 + 8m/3M}{1 + (8m/3M)\,(D/R)^2}.$$

Assume $D/R = 10$, $m/M = \frac{5}{100}$, then $\omega_1/\omega_0 \approx 1/12.65$. The total weight of the system may be estimated:

Weights		5%		of M
Wire (rods)		3%	(10%)	of M
Wire release, etc.		5%	(5%)	of M
Total		13%	(20%)	of M

(2) *Wrap-around wires.* This quite complicated case is treated very clearly by Thomson (1961).

We assume that m is only a small fraction of the mass of the total system (Fig. 1.11). The rotating coordinate system rotates such that the y-axis passes always through the tangent point of the unwinding wire. Initially (for time $t = 0$), we demand that m be in contact with the cylinder at the X-axis. Then $s = R\varphi$. In the rotating system

$$\mathbf{r} = R\varphi\mathbf{i} + R\mathbf{j}.$$

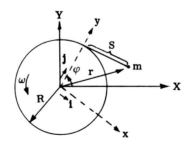

Fig. 1.11. Wrap-around wire system. X, Y, inertial system; x, y, rotating system; $\mathbf{i, j, k}$, unit vectors such that $\mathbf{k} = [\mathbf{ij}]$.

The velocity of m in the inertial system is given by

$$\mathbf{v} = \dot{\mathbf{r}} + (\omega + \dot{\varphi})\,[\mathbf{k}\mathbf{r}]$$
$$= -R\omega\mathbf{i} + R\varphi(\omega + \dot{\varphi})\mathbf{j}.$$

The rotational momentum of m is, in the inertial coordinate system,

$$\mathbf{h} = [\mathbf{r}\,m\,\mathbf{v}]$$
$$= mR^2\,[\omega + \varphi^2(\omega + \dot{\varphi})]\mathbf{k},$$

and the total rotational momentum is obviously,

$$\mathbf{H} = I\omega\mathbf{k} + \mathbf{h}\,,$$

where I is the moment of inertia of the spinning cylinder.

The kinetic energy of the spinning system is again in the inertial coordinate system,

$$E = \tfrac{1}{2}I\omega^2 + \tfrac{1}{2}mv^2$$
$$= \tfrac{1}{2}I\omega^2 + \tfrac{1}{2}mR^2[\omega^2 + \varphi^2(\omega + \dot{\varphi})^2].$$

Initially (at time $t = 0$), we have

$$E_0 = \tfrac{1}{2}(I + mR^2)\omega_0{}^2$$

and

$$H_0 = (I + mR^2)\omega_0\mathbf{k}\,.$$

Putting $E = E_0$ and $H = H_0$ we get, with the abbreviations $C = I/mR^2 + 1$, and $\varphi_0 = 0$, $\varphi_{\max} = S/R$, where S is the total length of the wire: $\dot{\varphi} = \omega_0$, and $\omega = \omega_0(C - \varphi^2)/(C + \varphi^2)$.

To obtain the limiting value[1] of $\omega_{\min} = 0$, we need to have

$$\varphi^2_{\max} = \left(\frac{S_m}{R}\right)^2 = C$$

or

$$S_m = \left(\frac{I}{m} + R^2\right)^{1/2};$$

for $I = \tfrac{3}{4}MR^2$ comes

$$S_m = R\left(1 + \frac{3}{4}\frac{M}{m}\right)^{1/2},$$

[1] For $\varphi \to -\infty$ we have $\omega = -\omega_0$; it can easily be shown that $\dot{\omega}_{\max} = 1.3\omega_0{}^2 C^{-1/2}$.

or with $M/m = 100$, we have

$$S_m = 8.72R.$$

So we obtain a complete despin for the following weight penalty:

Weights	1% of M
Wires	2% of M
Wire release etc.	1% of M
Total	4% of M

Figure 1.11 shows, for simplicity only, one weight of mass m, unwinding from the rotating cylinder. In reality, for symmetry reasons, two weights of mass of $m/2$ each are used.

1.4,7 Some Satellite Problems

What is the minimum accuracy to establish a vehicle in an orbit around a celestial body? [Vehicle in orbit (initial conditions) is shown in Fig. 1.12.] It is easy to compute the geometrical elements of the resulting orbit.

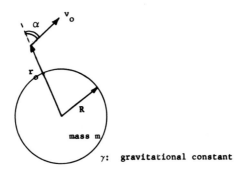

FIG. 1.12. Vehicle in orbit, initial conditions.

(1) Check whether or not the orbit is parabolic or hyperbolic. For elliptic orbits,

$$|\mathbf{v_0}| < v_{op},$$

where v_{op} is the parabolic velocity at the distance r_0. From Eq. (4.25) of Vol. 1,

$$v_{op}^2 = 2\gamma m/r_0.$$

(2) If the orbit is an ellipse, then, from Eq. (4.30) of Vol. 1,

$$c = r_0 v_0 \sin \alpha \; ;$$

and from Eq. (4.22) of Vol. 1,

$$v_0^2 = \gamma m \left(\frac{2}{r_0} - \frac{1}{a} \right)$$

or

$$\frac{a}{r_0} = \frac{1}{2 - v_0^2/(\gamma m / r_0)} \; .$$

From these we obtain, for the energy E per unit mass of the satellite vehicle:

$$E = - \frac{\gamma m}{2a} \; , \qquad \text{[Eq. (4.20) of Vol. 1]}$$

and for the eccentricity ε:

$$\varepsilon^2 - 1 = \frac{2 E c^2}{\gamma^2 m^2} \; , \qquad \text{[Eq. (4.18) of Vol. 1]}.$$

From the geometry of conic sections, the pericenter distance of the ellipse is given by

$$r_{min} = (1 - \varepsilon) a.$$

Substituting the previous results and introducing $v_0^2/(\gamma m / r_0) = \bar{v}_0^2$, we have

$$\frac{r_{min}}{r_0} = \frac{1 - [1 - (\sin^2 \alpha) \bar{v}_0^2 (2 - v_0^2)]^{1/2}}{2 - \bar{v}_0^2} \; . \tag{1.27}$$

Usually, we demand $r_{min} \geq kR$, where k is larger than or equal to 1 to take care of an atmosphere, if any. Equation (1.27) is, for $r_{min} = kR$, a function between $\bar{v}_0^2$ and $\sin^2 \alpha$, which gives those values of $\bar{v}_0$ and α which will still just produce an orbit. Four general results are:

(1) For $\bar{v}_0^2 \to 2$ (parabolic orbit) we have

$$\frac{r_{min}}{r_0} = \sin^2 \alpha = \cos^2(\tfrac{1}{2}\pi - \alpha).$$

The minimum of the radius vector occurs before or behind the injection point, depending upon whether α is smaller or larger than $\tfrac{1}{2}\pi$.

On the other hand, the polar equation of a parabola is $r = p/(1 + \cos \varphi)$, or for $r_{\min} = \frac{1}{2}p$,

$$\frac{r_{\min}}{r_0} = \frac{1 + \cos \varphi}{2} = \cos^2 \frac{\varphi}{2} .$$

So follows $\frac{1}{2}\varphi = \frac{1}{2}\pi - \alpha$.

This simple result has been derived before in Chap. 4 of Vol. 1.

(2) For given $r_{\min}$, any increase in $\bar{v}_0{}^2$ will increase the maximum allowable deviation of α from $\frac{1}{2}\pi$. Therefore, it is of benefit to inject satellites with a planned "excess velocity"

$$\varDelta\bar{v}_0 = |\,\bar{v}_0\,| - 1 > 0.$$

(3) It does not matter whether $\alpha = \frac{1}{2}\pi + \varDelta\alpha$, or $\frac{1}{2}\pi - \varDelta\alpha$.

(4) For $\bar{v}_0{}^2 = 1$ we get $r_{\min}/r_0 = 1 - \cos \alpha$, or

$$\cos \alpha = \frac{r_0 - r_{\min}}{r_0} = \cos\left(\frac{\pi}{2} + \varDelta\alpha\right) = \sin \varDelta\alpha ;$$

for

$$\frac{r_0 - r_{\min}}{r_0} = \frac{200 \text{ km}}{6600 \text{ km}} ,$$

we have $\varDelta\alpha \approx 1.7°$.

If the planned injection velocity were $v_0 = (\gamma m/r_0)^{1/2} + 100 \text{ m/sec}$, then we have, besides the $\pm 1.7°$ angular margin, a velocity margin of about $\pm 100 \text{ m/sec}$: Satellite injection conditions are not very critical, if just an orbit, and not an orbit of some exactly prescribed properties, is the goal.

By using a higher injection velocity excess, and not utilizing all of the excess as margin for velocity error, the allowable angular error $\varDelta\alpha$ can be further increased (see remark No. 2).

This was a look at the maximum tolerable errors to accomplish the orbiting of a satellite, and we see that these are large compared to allowable errors for an ICBM.

But now a glance at another example, namely, at the equatorial circular 24-h satellite. This vehicle is meant to be sitting Earth-fixed over the same point of the Earth's equator so that it is always in the narrow beam of a fixed antenna upon Earth.

Of course, we have to allow for some technical imperfections—let us assume that we tolerate a yearly motion of 1 deg of arc. This means that inclination of the orbit must be smaller than, say $\frac{1}{2}$ deg, which is not too difficult to achieve. Later there will be more about the perturbation of inclination.

Now let us allow $\frac{1}{2}$ deg = 0.00874 rad of oscillatory motion of the sub-satellite point around its design value; from Eq. (4.76) of Vol. 1 we have

$$\varepsilon_{\max} = 0.00437.$$

In Sec. 4.1,6 of Vol. 1, the interesting equation is derived that $\cos \delta = \varepsilon$ (see Fig. 4.7 of Vol. 1), if the injection speed is exactly circular, or introducing $90° - \delta = \delta'$ it follows that $\sin \delta' = \varepsilon$. With $\varepsilon = \frac{1}{2}\varepsilon_{\max} = 0.00219$ we have $\delta' \approx 7'31''$ as the maximum allowable deviation of the injection velocity from the horizontal direction.

From Eq. (4.19) of Vol. 1, we get, for a deviation of the magnitude of the injection velocity Δv from circular speed, and correct horizontal injection angle:

$$(v \pm \Delta v)^2 \approx v^2 \pm 2 \, \Delta v \, v \approx \frac{\gamma m}{a}(1 + 2\varepsilon); \qquad \text{or} \qquad \frac{\Delta v}{v} \approx \pm \, \varepsilon;$$

from this we get $| \, \Delta v/v \, | = (0.219)/100$ as maximum deviation, or for the 24-h satellite: $| \, \Delta v \, | < 6.7$ m/sec.

Another half a degree yearly may be allowed for secular drift, or per revolution $1/(2 \times 365) = (1/730)$ deg. Because 24 h correspond to $360°$, this corresponds to a time of $1/(15 \times 730) = 1/10{,}950$ h deviation per revolution or because of $\Delta T/T = \frac{3}{2} \, \Delta a/a$; $\Delta a/a = \frac{2}{3}[1/(10{,}950 \times 24)] \approx 1/395{,}000$; from this comes, for the allowable altitude error, $\Delta a \approx 0.107$ km.

So the 130-m maximum variation in altitude for inclined orbits as calculated in Chap. 4 of Vol. 1 is not negligible, but this correction does not appear for equatorial orbits.

Let us summarize the allowable simultaneous errors for a 24-h satellite in order to have a drift rate along its orbit smaller than $1°/\text{yr}$ away from the desired Earth-fixed location over the equator:

maximum inclination error is $\qquad\qquad\qquad\qquad \pm \frac{1}{2}$ deg of arc;

maximum altitude error, deviation from ideal value
(radius $\approx 42{,}000$ km) is $\qquad\qquad\qquad\qquad \pm 107$ m;

maximum injection velocity magnitude error from
circular speed (circular speed ≈ 3 km/sec) is $\qquad \pm 6.7$ m/sec;

maximum injection velocity direction error, from
horizontal is $\qquad\qquad\qquad\qquad\qquad\qquad \pm 7\frac{1}{2}$ min of arc.

We see that the margin for error for an exactly prescribed orbit can be quite narrow.

According to Eq. (4.53) of Vol. 1, there is, due to the Moon, a monthly oscillation of $\Delta r/r \approx 2.5 \times (1/81) (42{,}000/380{,}000)^3 \approx 1/24{,}000$, or the angular oscillation is 1/24,000 rad or 8.6''. Similarly, we get a yearly oscillation due to the Sun of $\Delta r/r \approx 1/55{,}000$, or 3.7''. As seen from the surface of the Earth, larger oscillations may occur due to lunar or solar perturbations, as these effects sometimes tend to speed the satellite up somewhat, and sometimes tend to slow it down. Furthermore, secular or long-periodic terms will result. Regression of nodes, etc., due to Earth oblateness are smaller by a factor of ~ 326 than they would be for the same inclination in the 2-h orbit [from Eq. (4.59) of Vol. 1].

Let us assume that the pole of the ecliptic is, at the same time, the pole of the lunar orbit (see Fig. 1.13).[1]

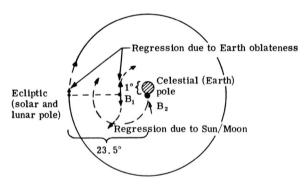

FIG. 1.13. Regression of poles. B_1 and B_2 are poles of two 24-h orbits.

Then, for an inclination of approximately 7°, such that B_1 is between the ecliptic and celestial pole, the two regressions would just about cancel each other.

Starting with zero degrees inclination, B_2 would approximately move as indicated, thus reaching a maximum of about 14° inclination (more exactly, 14.6°), and be back to zero inclination after about 106 yr. The initial rate of change of inclination, around zero degrees inclination, is 0.8 deg per year, not quite negligible. This then means that the equatorial 24-h satellite should have initially its B-point in the hatched area: this is no more than 1 deg away from the ideal zero-inclined position, and guarantees, from the point of view of inclination change, a time of at least $1/(0.8)$

[1] For explanation of Fig. 1.13, see Fig. 4.19 of Vol. 1.

= 1.25 yr of less than 1 deg inclination. We can just fulfill the specification of not more than one degree of motion per year in inclination. Therefore, for operational lifetimes of several years, perturbations necessitate an orbital correction system, even for perfect injection.

In reality, matters are even more complicated as the pole of the ecliptic and the lunar pole do not coincide.

The annual speed requirement to correct for this perturbation by about 20 small impulses per year is estimated to be 40 m/sec, keeping the maximum deviation to less than $1/20°$ from the desired position.

Another perturbation stems from the ellipticity of the Earth equator. A satellite will be in stable equilibrium only at the endpoints of the minor axis; from other points, an oscillation starts around these stable points. At the endpoints of the major axis, there is unstable equilibrium. From Allan (1963), some results are quoted:

If φ is the angular distance from a point of stable equilibrium, g the gravitational acceleration at the orbital radius a, and R the radius of the central body, then the equation of apparent motion is

$$\ddot{\varphi} = -18 \frac{g}{a} \left(\frac{R}{a} \right)^2 J_{22} \sin 2\varphi;$$

in short,

$$\ddot{\varphi} = -\tfrac{1}{2}k^2 \sin 2\varphi.$$

Integrated,

$$\dot{\varphi}^2 - k^2 \cos^2\varphi = \text{constant} = c.$$

To have a true oscillation and not a continuous motion we have to demand that $c < 0$, i.e., $|k \cos \varphi_0| > |\dot{\varphi}_0|$, where the index zero designates initial conditions. If this condition is fulfilled, we have an amplitude below $\pi/2$, and a period of oscillation larger than $2\pi/k$. The apparent angular speed is $\dot{\varphi}$, leading to an apparent velocity $v = \dot{\varphi}a$. To null this apparent velocity, the speed requirement[1] is $\varDelta = \tfrac{1}{3}v$.

Let us assume that a 24-h-orbit satellite has been injected such that $\dot{\varphi}_0 \approx 0$, and φ_0 is so small that $\sin 2\varphi_0 \approx 2\varphi_0$. For this case the period is, exactly, $2\pi/k$. But we permit the satellite to oscillate for the brief time interval dt only:

Apparent acceleration: $\ddot{\varphi} = \tfrac{1}{2}k^2 \sin 2\varphi_0 = A$.
Apparent speed after the time dt: $\dot{\varphi}a = Aa\,dt$.
Speed requirement[1] to reverse the motion: $\tfrac{2}{3}Aa\,dt$.

[1] See footnote on p. 77.

Number of such impulses, to be fired per year T: $|T/2|\,dt$.

Total yearly speed requirement: $\varDelta = \frac{1}{3}AaT = (aTk^2/6)\sin 2\varphi_0$.

Numerically, $J_{22} = 2 \times 10^{-6}$, $k^2 = 0.9 \times 10^{-14}\,\text{sec}^{-2}$, $2\pi/k = 2.1$ yr, $aTk^2/6 = 2m/\text{sec}$; thus $\varDelta$ is quite small.

Altogether, the annual speed budget for an equatorial 24-h satellite is not larger than 50–60 m/sec, for both station-keeping and attitude control requirements.

An interesting question is, what are major axis and speed for the ideal 24-h satellite? Obviously, the sidereal period for an equatorial orbit is equal to one sidereal day if the satellite is to be stationary with respect to the Earth surface. (With respect to the Sun, the period equals one solar day. A slightly different period is necessary for inclined orbits with the exception of polar orbits, as discussed in Chap. 4 of Vol. 1.) So, for the period,

$$P = 24^{\text{h}} - 3^{\text{m}}\,55.909^{\text{s}} = 23^{\text{h}}56^{\text{m}}4.091^{\text{s}}$$

$$= 0.997269566(1 \pm 10^{-8}) \quad \text{days.}$$

For Earth,

$$\gamma m = 3.9862 \times 10^{20}(1 \pm 0.0002) \quad \text{cm}^3/\text{sec}^2.$$

Because of the Earth's shape, a correction factor, for Kepler's third law, for circular orbits of inclination β and radius r is

$$\mu = \left\{ 1 + J\left(\frac{R_{\text{earth}}}{r}\right)^2 (1 - 1.5\sin^2\beta) \right\}.$$

Here $\mu = 1.0000375(1 \pm 10^{-6})$. Assuming that the satellite is of negligible mass, we write Kepler's third law as $P^2(\gamma m)\mu = 4\pi^2 a^3$.

From this equation, $a = 42,165(1 \pm 0.7 \times 10^{-4})$ km. This means that the altitude is known to ± 3 km, but, as determined previously, it has a margin for error of 0.107 km only!

According to Eq. (4.54) of Vol. 1, the solar and lunar influence can be approximated by assuming a reduced mass for the Earth, where the reduction factor is

$$k = 1 - \frac{\gamma m_1}{\gamma m_2}\left(\frac{r}{d_1}\right)^3 - \frac{\gamma m_3}{\gamma m_2}\left(\frac{r}{d_3}\right)^3,$$

where $r \approx 42,000$ km (Earth-satellite), $d_1 \approx 150 \times 10^6$ km (Earth-Sun), $d_2 \approx 384,000$ km (Earth-Moon), $\gamma m_1/\gamma m_2 \approx 332,000$ km (solar mass), $\gamma m_3/\gamma m_2 \approx 1/81$ (lunar mass).

Therefore,

$$k = 1 - \frac{7.28}{10^6} - \frac{6.91}{10^6} = 1 - \frac{1.419}{10^5}.$$

From Kepler's third law, $P^2 = 4\pi^2(r^3/\gamma m)$, or

$$2 \ln P = 2 \ln 4\pi + 3 \ln r - \ln \gamma m.$$

For $P =$ constant we get, by differentiation,

$$0 = \frac{3\,dr}{r} - \frac{d(\gamma m)}{\gamma m}$$

or

$$\frac{dr}{r} = \frac{1}{3}\frac{d(\gamma m)}{\gamma m} = -\tfrac{1}{3}(1 - k).$$

Numerically,

$$\frac{dr}{r} = -\frac{4.73}{10^6} \qquad \text{or} \qquad dr = -0.2 \text{ km.}[1]$$

Even this small correction is of the same order as the allowable margin for error. Therefore, the practical realization of a 24-h satellite is only possible by fine corrections of a satellite which has been established in an approximate orbit.

Speed in the 24-h orbit is $v_0 = 2\pi a/P = 3.0747(1 \pm 0.7 \times 10^{-4})$ km/sec only known to ± 0.2 m/sec. This is an example to illustrate the inadequacy of our knowledge of the fundamental astronomical constants. We will find more such examples in the next sections.

Now we will investigate the relative motion of two satellites that are near each other (Fig. 1.14).

The satellite is at p in a circular orbit, and a supply vehicle is nearby. (If the supply vehicle is in a somewhat different orbital plane, then it crosses the plane of the satellite motion twice each period. Such a crossing can be utilized for a rocket maneuver to equalize the planes of motion. Thereafter, the initial situation, as assumed here, is realized. How orbital planes can be changed will be described in greater detail later in this section.) In the rotating coordinate system, according to Sec. 4.2,1 of Vol. 1,

$$\ddot{\mathbf{r}} + 2[\boldsymbol{\omega}, \dot{\mathbf{r}}] = -\gamma m \frac{\mathbf{r}}{r^3} + \omega^2 \begin{cases} x' \\ y' \\ 0 \end{cases} + \text{other accelerations (e.g., thrust, drag).}$$

[1] By analogy to a footnote in Section 4.4,3,2 of Vol. 1 this estimated value might be high by a factor of 2.

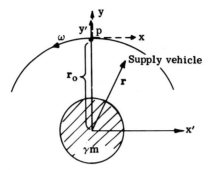

FIG. 1.14. Relative motion of two satellites.

(1) We introduce an x-, y-coordinate system[1] so that

$$x' = x,$$
$$y' = r_0 + y,$$
$$z' = z.$$

(2) We regard the planar problem only:

$$z = z' = 0.$$

(3) The angular velocity $\boldsymbol{\omega}$ points in the z-direction; we take

$$\omega^2 = \gamma m / r_0{}^3;$$

this assures that the satellite remains fixed at the point p.

(4) The other accelerations shall be called F_x, F_y.

Under these assumptions, we have

$$\begin{pmatrix} \ddot{x} \\ \ddot{y} \end{pmatrix} + 2\,\omega \begin{pmatrix} -\dot{y} \\ +\dot{x} \end{pmatrix} = \omega^2 \left[1 - \frac{1}{\{(1 + y/r_0)^2 + (x/r_0)^2\}^{3/2}} \right] \begin{pmatrix} x \\ r_0 + y \end{pmatrix} + \begin{pmatrix} F_x \\ F_y \end{pmatrix}.$$

Assuming that $y \ll r_0$, $x \ll r_0$, then

$$\left\{ \left(1 + \frac{y}{r_0}\right)^2 + \left(\frac{x}{r_0}\right)^2 \right\}^{-3/2} \approx 1 - 3\,\frac{y}{r_0};$$

---

[1] An improvement is obtained by measuring x not along the tangent to the path of motion, but along the actual path of motion instead. If we do this, the following approximations can be applied for distances between the two satellites up to several hundred kilometers.

therefore,

$$\begin{pmatrix} \ddot{x} \\ \ddot{y} \end{pmatrix} + 2\omega \begin{pmatrix} -\dot{y} \\ +\dot{x} \end{pmatrix} = \omega^2 3\, \frac{y}{r_0} \begin{pmatrix} x \\ r_0+y \end{pmatrix} + \begin{pmatrix} F_x \\ F_y \end{pmatrix}.$$

We can say that, approximately[1] (Anthony and Sasaki, 1965)

$$\ddot{x} - 2\omega\dot{y} = F_x, \tag{1.28}$$
$$\ddot{y} + 2\omega\dot{x} = 3\omega^2 y + F_y.$$

If $F_x = F_y = 0$, then $\dot{x} - 2\omega y = C$, where C is a constant, and

$$\ddot{y} + 2\omega C + \omega^2 y = 0.$$

Introducing the new variable y^+, such that $y = y^+ - 2C/\omega$, yields

$$\ddot{y}^+ + \omega^2 y^+ = 0;$$

integrating,

$$y^+ = C_1 \cos \omega t + C_2 \sin \omega t$$

or

$$y = C_1 \cos \omega t + C_2 \sin \omega t - 2C/\omega. \tag{1.29}$$

Inserting this into $\dot{x} - 2\omega y = C$ and integrating, we get

$$x = -3Ct + 2C_1 \sin \omega t - 2C_2 \cos \omega t + C_3. \tag{1.29a}$$

The initial conditions are

$$x_0 = C_3 - 2C_2,$$
$$y_0 = C_1 - 2C/\omega,$$
$$\dot{x}_0 = 2\omega C_1 - 3C,$$
$$\dot{y}_0 = \omega C_2.$$

From these we get

$$C = \dot{x}_0 - 2\omega y_0,$$
$$C_1 = 2\dot{x}_0/\omega - 3y_0,$$
$$C_2 = \dot{y}_0/\omega,$$
$$C_3 = 2\dot{y}_0/\omega + x_0.$$

---

[1] If $z \neq 0$, then $\ddot{z} + \omega^2 z = F_z$; for $F_z = 0$ the motion is oscillatory, where for $z = 0$ we have $\dot{z}_{max} = (\dot{z}_0^2 + \omega^2 z_0^2)^{1/2}$.

Generally, rendezvous will not occur between the supply vehicle and the satellite, because if $C \neq 0$ we have a secular term in x, which will tend to increase the distance, even if initially the two vehicles approach each other.

A special case occurs when an object is thrown[1] "up" from a space station:

$$x_0 = y_0 = \dot{x}_0 = 0, \qquad \dot{y}_0 = A\omega;$$

then $C = 0$, $C_1 = 0$, $C_2 = A$, $C_3 = 2A$, and

$$x = 2A - 2A \cos \omega t,$$
$$y = A \sin \omega t.$$

This trajectory is an ellipse (see Fig. 1.15). The object will hit the space station again exactly after one revolution—but from the bottom! It is interesting to speculate that, if the velocity y_0 were 10 m/sec from an orbit

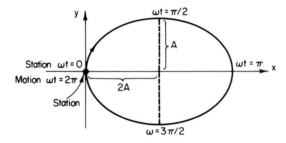

FIG. 1.15. Elliptic trajectory of object thrown vertically from satellite.

of $\omega = 10^{-3}$ sec^{-1} (or period of about 105 min), then $A = 10^4$ m, and the maximum distance of the thrown object from the space station is only 40 km, and the altitude difference is never more than 10 km. This effect has been applied in one of Clarke's short stories as early as 1953 (Clarke, 1953).

If such a moving object could be observed for very small values of A within the station, without any disturbances, then the direction of the local vertical can be determined by looking at the orientation of the ellipse of motion. It is easy to determine whether or not $\dot{x}_0 = 0$, because only for $\dot{x}_0 = 0$ (for $x_0 = y_0 = 0$) is $C = 0$, i.e., no secular motion is observable.

---

[1] Throwing an object from a space station could be realized, e.g., by releasing the object from a rotating satellite at the proper time.

With the different initial conditions $x_0 = y_0 = \dot{y}_0 = 0$, $\dot{x}_0 = A\omega$, it follows that (see Fig. 1.16)

$$x = -3A\omega t + 4A \sin \omega t$$

and

$$y = -2A + 2A \cos \omega t.$$

There is a strong secular effect: the object is, after one period, $18.85A$ in front of the satellite[1] which is 188.5 km for a velocity of only $A\omega = 10\,\text{m/sec}$.

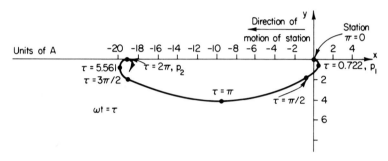

FIG. 1.16. Observed motion of object thrown horizontally from satellite. $\omega t = \tau$.

By the way, this is a typical example of a "secular effect," being just a long-period one. (If the satellite has enough mass, its attraction may strongly perturb this secular effect: see "Lunar Satellites," in Chapter 5 of Vol. 1.) The value $\dot{x} = 0$ occurs for:

$\omega t = \tau$	x	y
0.722	0.48A	$-$ 0.5A
5.561	$-$ 19.35A	$-$ 0.5A

Assume that a guidance system has placed the vehicle in the vicinity of a satellite, and the relative velocities are small. Now the task of the vehicle shall be to get to the satellite and to match both location and velocity at some, not specified, time (satellite rendezvous docking phase). Obviously, we have to choose some time, functions of thrust F_x, F_y, so that the vehicle comes to rest very close beside the satellite. A final third phase of the

[1] The average speed is $\bar{\dot{x}} = -3A\omega = -3\dot{x}_0$.

maneuver consists of actual physical contact, which may perhaps be made with the aid of a rope connecting vehicle and satellite, or an extremely low acceleration system, and some hydraulic or other shock absorbers. As objects still have their mass, this third phase is quite tricky, and a space-man moving in some kind of protective suit between satellite and vehicle had better be careful.

In rendezvous maneuvers, the origin of the coordinate system is placed at the target. The chaser has to adjust twelve coordinates at some time t, which generally is a free parameter, available for optimization purposes. The twelve coordinates are:

Location	$x = 0,$	$y = 0,$	$z = 0.$
Speed	$\dot{x} = 0,$	$\dot{y} = 0,$	$\dot{z} = 0.$
Attitude (pitch, yaw, roll)	$\alpha = 0,$	$\beta = 0,$	$\gamma = 0.$
Angular speed	$\dot{\alpha} = 0,$	$\dot{\beta} = 0,$	$\dot{\gamma} = 0.$

The target has to control

$$\alpha = 0, \qquad \beta = 0, \qquad \gamma = 0;$$
$$\dot{\alpha} = 0, \qquad \dot{\beta} = 0, \qquad \dot{\gamma} = 0.$$

To control eighteen variables so that all are zero at one time t, which can be adjusted to the initial situation, describes the control problem involved.

A word may be allowed about military satellite interception: this is a simpler problem, since only location has to be matched within limits, determined by the mission, whereas the velocity vector including planes of motion for vehicle and satellite can be different.[1] On the other hand, time of intercept may be specified, and the satellite may carry some defense of its own, or at least will give no active assistance to the incoming vehicle. Now back to the second phase of a rendezvous flight, viz., the determination of the functions F_x and F_y: x, y, z and $\dot{x}$, $\dot{y}$, $\dot{z}$ are all measured either from the satellite or from the vehicle, the satellite being at the origin of the coordinate system. Both can be in radio contact and, in order to save weight in the vehicle, all of the more complicated computations can be done on a computer within the satellite (or on Earth), and given to the vehicle via a radio command link.

Assuming the two-dimensional problem only, then [from Eq. (1.29) or

---

[1] For satellite inspection, however, both location and velocity must be matched within limits, which are prescribed by the mission and capability of the inspector and, possibly, the satellite.

from the non-approximated initial equation] the motion of the vehicle with respect to the satellite can be calculated. With some short (impulsive) thrusts F_x, F_y, the velocity $\dot{x}_0$, $\dot{y}_0$ can be changed by $\Delta\dot{x}_0$, $\Delta\dot{y}_0$ without noticeably changing x_0, y_0. Only three tasks—easy for a computer—remain:

(1) To calculate $\Delta\dot{x}_0$, $\Delta\dot{y}_0$ values so that vehicle and satellite meet at some later time.

(2) Reject those combinations $\Delta\dot{x}_0$, $\Delta\dot{y}_0$ in which the time to intercept is too long. "Being too long" is, of course, arbitrary, and a numerical value might be given to the computer, e.g., by a human operator.

(3) Compute the relative arrival velocities $\dot{x}_E$, $\dot{y}_E$ and form the sum $\Delta v = (\Delta\dot{x}_0{}^2 + \Delta\dot{y}_0{}^2)^{1/2} + (\dot{x}_E{}^2 + \dot{y}_E{}^2)^{1/2}$ for all acceptable $\Delta\dot{x}_0$, $\Delta\dot{y}_0$ combinations. The value Δv is the required velocity to make the rendezvous.

In order to minimize fuel consumption, that combination of $\Delta\dot{x}_0$, $\Delta\dot{y}_0$ should be picked which minimizes Δv. In case of several similar solutions, the shorter time to intercept might be preferred,

These decisions being made, final values $\Delta\dot{x}_0$, $\Delta\dot{y}_0$ are known, and the motor adds impulsively the velocity $\Delta\mathbf{v}_1 = (\Delta\dot{x}_0, \Delta\dot{y}_0)$. On arrival at the station, $\Delta\mathbf{v}_2 = -(\dot{x}_E, \dot{y}_E)$ has to be added impulsively, in order to equalize the velocity between vehicle and station.

The thrust program as a function of arrival time has been determined for two impulsive maneuvers. The above procedure gives minimum fuel consumption only under the assumption that this minimum is contained within the class of two-impulse trajectories.

The special case of intercept—where velocity match is not required, and only one impulse has to be fired—is treated elsewhere (Eggleston, 1960). If s is the range and $\dot{s}$ the range rate from interceptor to satellite, and the time t is zero at the instant of observation of s and $\dot{s}$, then the optimum time of intercept is approximately $\tau \approx -s/\dot{s}$. To be exact, $\cot \omega\tau = -\dot{s}/\omega s$. Hornby (1961) treats the two-impulse rendezvous case, outlined before. The main results are:

First impulse: $\Delta v_1{}^2 = (\omega s \cot \omega\tau + \dot{s})^2 + E$, where E is a positive definite quadratic form, dependent only upon initial conditions. The total speed $\Delta v_1 + \Delta v_2$ is a minimum if the rendezvous occurs at a time τ, which follows from

$$\cot \omega\tau = -\frac{\dot{s}}{\omega s + E^{1/2}} = -\frac{\dot{s}}{\omega s + \Delta v_{1\text{min}}},$$

and

$$\Delta v_2 = \frac{\omega s}{\sin \omega\tau}.$$

It can be written approximately:

$$\cot \omega\tau \approx - \dot{s}/2\omega s$$

or, for

$$\left| \frac{2\omega s}{\dot{s}} \right| < 0.5,$$

$$\tau \approx - 2s/\dot{s}$$

and

$$\Delta v_2 \approx \omega s \left[1 + \left(\frac{\dot{s}}{2\omega s} \right)^2 \right]^{1/2} \approx \frac{\dot{s}}{2} .$$

When should the rendezvous maneuver be initiated? A good strategy is as follows: compute $\Delta v_{\min} = \Delta v_1 + \Delta v_2$; likewise, compute $\Delta \dot{v}_{\min} = a$. If $a > 0$, initiate rendezvous immediately, and if $a < 0$, then wait and initiate maneuver at the instant when $a = 0$.

In the coplanar case, the situation is simpler: let s be the vector from satellite to chaser; γ is defined by $\gamma = \frac{1}{2}\pi -$ angle (s, $\dot{\text{s}}$). Then [1] $E = (v \cos \gamma - \omega s)^2$, and, for the case $\omega s > v \cos \gamma$, we have

$$\cot \omega\tau = - \frac{v \sin \gamma}{\omega s - v \cos \gamma} \qquad \text{and} \qquad \Delta v_{\min} > v,$$

and for $\omega s \leq v \cos \gamma$ we have

$$\omega\tau = \tfrac{1}{2}\pi + \gamma, \qquad \text{and} \qquad \Delta v_{\min} = v.$$

Obviously, the best strategy to initiate the rendezvous is, in the latter case, to wait till v is a minimum.

A practical difficulty is introduced by the fact that purely impulsive thrusts, or velocity changes in zero time, are physically impossible, but this just means that the computation is more complicated since, during the thrust maneuver, not only velocity, but location changes also. The principle remains unchanged.

Referring to Fig. 1.16, we see that, if the satellite is at 0.0, and the vehicle at p_1, then we have to establish the negative of the velocity which the object in Fig. 1.16 has at p_1 for the vehicle, and it will arrive shortly later with a relative velocity equal to $A\omega$ at the satellite. (Intercept in the near zone.)

---

[1] We write s for $|\,\text{s}\,|$, and v for $|\,\dot{\text{s}}\,|$. The symbol ω stands for the angular motion of the target satellite around the central body, as before.

If the vehicle is at p_2, then again we have to establish the negative of the object's velocity in Fig. 1.16 at p_2, which is away from the target; but in spite of this, the target is approached one period of the satellite later, coming from above and behind with an "overvelocity" of only 10 m/sec, if the distance were 188.5 km. (Intercept in the far zone; the dividing line between near and far zone is at about $0.5A$ distance. The value of A is arbitrary, but transfers in the near zone need relatively much propellant and short times, and transfers in the far zone relatively little propellant, but long times.)

In a practical case, one might have a far zone, coarse, intercept phase first, and then a near-zone, fine, intercept phase to correct for the small remaining errors, before the third, terminal, contact phase.

Taking s and $\dot{s}$ information between satellite and vehicle, it is possible to design a continuous thrust program so that the desired rendezvous (location and velocity match) is reached. Propellant economy of such a maneuver is worse than for the described two-kick intercept phase. Besides, thrust magnitude control may be necessary.

This may suffice on the rendezvous problem as seen from the satellite. Let us look at this problem from the planet Earth. Some additional information on this point of view follows at the end of this section.

When the point of departure is I (see Fig. 1.17) and II is the point of arrival, then we talk of a Hohmann transfer if the central angle between I and II is 180°, if the powered maneuvers at I and II both take place in zero time, if both departure and arrival are tangential to the circular orbits, and if all three trajectories are in one plane. In orbit I, the circular velocity is $v_I = (\gamma m / r_1)^{1/2}$, and the energy per unity mass is $E = \frac{1}{2} v_I^2 + E_{pot} = - \frac{1}{2} \gamma m / r_1$. [Generally, from Eq. (4.20) of Vol. 1: $E = - \frac{1}{2} \gamma m / a$.] At location I, we change the velocity by Δv_I, added parallel to v_I, and ask for the change in a:

$$v_I \, \Delta v_I \approx \frac{1}{2} \frac{\gamma m}{r_1^2} \, \Delta a.$$

We want to have $\Delta a = \frac{1}{2}(r_2 - r_1)$; so

$$\Delta v_I \approx \frac{1}{4} v_I \frac{r_2 - r_1}{r_1}.$$

We have $\omega_I = 2\pi / T_I = v_I / r_1$, where T_I is the period in orbit No. I. So finally,

$$\Delta v_I \approx \frac{1}{4} \omega_I (r_2 - r_1).$$

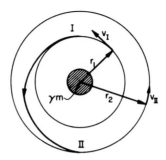

FIG. 1.17. Interorbital transfer.

On the other hand, if $\Delta v_{\mathrm{I}} = \omega_{\mathrm{I}} A$, then $r_2 - r_1 = 4A$, which is in agreement with conditions shown in Fig. 1.16. The circular velocity a tradius r is,

$$v^2 = \gamma m / r,$$

and

$$2v\,\Delta v \approx -\frac{\gamma m}{r^2}\,\Delta r$$

or

$$\Delta v \approx -\frac{1}{2}\frac{2\pi r}{T}\frac{\Delta r}{r} = -\tfrac{1}{2}\omega\,\Delta r.$$

This equation gives the difference in circular velocities for an altitude difference Δr. By comparison, we find

$$|\,\Delta v_{\mathrm{I}}\,| \approx \tfrac{1}{2}|\,\Delta v\,|.$$

We might as well have gone from point II to point I. Therefore, because of symmetry we have

$$|\,\Delta v_{\mathrm{I}}\,| + |\,\Delta v_{\mathrm{II}}\,| \approx |\,\Delta v\,|. \tag{1.30}$$

This surprisingly simple result is, of course, only approximately true. In chapter 6 of Vol. 1, we have looked in greater detail into energy requirements. Here we have the result that the total velocity requirement for an altitude change Δr via Hohmann transfer is given by

$$|\,\Delta v_{\mathrm{I}}\,| + |\,\Delta v_{\mathrm{II}}\,| = \tfrac{1}{2}\omega\,\Delta r.$$

The time duration for this maneuver is about half a period. The approximations are valid for $\Delta r \ll r$.

Let us assume there is a satellite at point I (Fig. 1.17), from which a vehicle separates to go along the trajectory I–II, but no maneuver is carried out at II, and the vehicle comes back to point I.

The period T in the elliptic orbit is larger than in the circular orbit:

$$\left(\frac{T_1}{T_2}\right)^2 = \left(\frac{a_1}{a_2}\right)^3$$

or

$$\frac{\Delta T}{T} \approx \frac{3}{2}\frac{\Delta a}{a} \, .$$

To separate the vehicle from the satellite, a velocity increment Δv is used: We had

$$\frac{\Delta v}{v_{\mathrm{I}}} \approx \frac{1}{4}\frac{2}{r_1}\frac{\Delta a}{}$$

Therefore,

$$\frac{\Delta T}{T_{\mathrm{I}}} \approx 3\,\frac{\Delta v}{v_{\mathrm{I}}} \, .$$

The angular speed of the satellite is ω_{I}; in the time ΔT, the satellite has passed through the angle

$$\Delta\varphi = \Delta T\, \omega_{\mathrm{I}} \approx 3\,\frac{\Delta v}{v_{\mathrm{I}}}\, T_{\mathrm{I}}\, \frac{2\pi}{T_{\mathrm{I}}}$$

or

$$\left(\frac{\Delta\varphi}{2\pi}\right) \approx 3\,\frac{\Delta v}{v_{\mathrm{I}}} \, . \tag{1.31}$$

If now, after one revolution, the vehicle circularizes again at I, it has used in total the velocity $2\,\Delta v$, and is, by an angle $\Delta\varphi$, behind the satellite—or, to apply this to a practical problem: if the vehicle has been leading the satellite by $\Delta\varphi$, then rendezvous can be accomplished after the maneuver. The time duration is about on period. By waiting two periods, we can make up for an angle of $2\Delta\varphi$, etc. This technique is called "chasing technique" (Barker and Straly, 1959). If we are willing to wait for many periods of "chasing," then large angles, $\Delta\varphi$, can be compensated for by small velocity requirements ($2\,\Delta v$). Here is a good example where time can be bought at the expense of more energy. This is fairly common in transportation problems, of course.

The angle $\Delta\varphi$ corresponds to a linear distance

$$\Delta x \approx r_1\,\Delta\varphi = 3\,\frac{\Delta v}{v_{\mathrm{I}}}\,2\pi r_1 = 3\,\frac{\Delta v\,T_{\mathrm{I}}\,2\pi r_1}{2\pi r_1} = 6\pi\,\frac{\Delta v}{\omega_1}\,,$$

or for $\Delta v = \omega_1 A$, we get

$$\Delta x = 6\pi A.$$

This, again, is in agreement with the secular effect, shown in Fig. 1.16.

For the rendezvous phase vehicle-satellite, we obtain the following three-step procedure:

(1) Circularize the vehicle orbit.

(2) Equalize altitudes and circularize again by a Hohmann-transfer, bringing vehicle and satellite, possibly, close together.

(3) Bring vehicle and satellite together by applying chasing technique. In general, chasing technique utilizes the difference in periods between a "final orbit" and a "waiting orbit," which is, at one place, tangential to either the final orbit, or to the transfer orbit leading to the final orbit. There are several possibilities of realizing this:

(a) The transfer orbit in Fig. 1.17 can be used to be at the same time the waiting orbit, which means: the kick at II is not fired at the first opportunity.

(b) At II (Fig. 1.17), only partial circularization (or over-circularization, if some energy loss is accepted; the loss is due to the overspeed, which must first be added, and then be braked again) is accomplished, leading to the waiting orbit, from which the final orbit is entered at the proper opportunity.

(c) In leaving orbit I (see Fig. 1.17), at first a waiting orbit is entered (which can be inside orbit I, completely between orbit I and II, or partially or completely outside orbit II; in the second case, the waiting orbit leads to no energy loss). From the waiting orbit, injection to the transfer orbit is initiated leading to orbit II. Clearly, combinations employing several different waiting orbits are possible. The beginning of the transfer need not be at orbit I, but may be, e.g., at the surface of the central body.

This three-step procedure is but a slight variation of the method described in connection with the rendezvous as seen from the satellite. It is very reassuring that, basically, the same procedure emerges, independent of the point of view.

An even simpler rendezvous guidance scheme is:

(1) Circularize the vehicle orbit; let the satellite orbit be Δr higher.
(2) Wait till the vehicle is, by an angle

$$\frac{\Delta\varphi'}{2\pi} \approx \frac{3}{8}\frac{\Delta r}{r},$$

behind the satellite (per period, the vehicle gains $4\Delta\varphi'$ on the satellite). Then fire an acceleration impulse $\Delta v_\mathrm{I}/v = \frac{1}{4}\,\Delta r/r$, coast up to the correct altitude and meet the satellite.

(3) Circularize, by firing a second kick, to increase the speed approximately by

$$\frac{\Delta v_\mathrm{II}}{v} \approx \frac{1}{4}\frac{\Delta r}{r}.$$

The waiting time in step 2 can be fairly long: for example, if $\Delta r = 400$ km and $r = 7000$ km, then $4\Delta\varphi' \approx 31°$, and about 12 periods, or 20 h, are necessary to catch up $360°$. If the motion of vehicle and satellite are coplanar at the beginning of the chasing time, then they may not be coplanar at the end of it, because of the different rate of regression of the nodes [Eq. (4.59) of Vol. 1]. This effect can be precalculated, and has to be taken into proper consideration. One way to compensate for this differential effect is, of course, to start with proper noncoplanar orbits so that the orbits are coplanar at the time of the final transfer maneuver.[1] To accomplish relative motion between two satellites we used, so far, either different orbits, or we applied a small "kick" to one of the two vehicles. Another possibility would be to have purely internal forces acting—e.g., we provide for a rope connecting the two bodies and start pulling. We will not calculate the relative orbits, but we will derive a result from the laws of conservation of momentum and energy, which will give good insight into the problem. For simplicity, the satellites shall be regarded as mass points, as we usually did, and shall be in coplanar orbits being not far distant from each other, and going around the center body in the same direction. When these satellites pass one over the other, they shall be connected by a rope, thus forming only one satellite. What is the resulting motion? Some physics first:

Let us consider n mass points, m_i and m_k being two of them. An arbitrary

---

[1] First rendezvous in space: Gemini 7 and 6, both manned; long duration formation flight, closest approach one foot, December 16, 1965. First docking accomplished on March 16, 1966, by Gemini 8 (manned) and Agena target (unmanned). Gemini 10 actually used the docked Agena for orbital change (July 19, 1966).

space-fixed point 0 is used from which we measure the radius vector, $\mathbf{r}_i$, of mass point m_i. Upon m_i act exterior forces $\mathbf{K}_i$, and interior forces $\mathbf{K}_{il}$ coming from the mass point number l; obviously, $\mathbf{K}_{ii} = 0$. We use three axioms:

(1) $\mathbf{K}_{ik}$ is parallel to $\mathbf{r}_i - \mathbf{r}_k$.

(2) $\mathbf{K}_{ik} = -\mathbf{K}_{ki}$.

(3) $m_i \ddot{\mathbf{r}}_i = \mathbf{K}_i + \sum_{k=1}^{n}{}' \mathbf{K}_{ik}$,

where the prime is a reminder that $\mathbf{K}_{ii} = 0$.

We will derive three important results:

(1) *Momentum law.* The center of gravity, or center of mass (CG), is defined by the vector $\mathbf{r}^*$. Then, if $\mathbf{g}$ is an acceleration:

$$\sum_i [\mathbf{r}_i m_i \mathbf{g}] = [\mathbf{r}^* \sum_i m_i \mathbf{g}],$$

or

$$[\{\sum_i m_i \mathbf{r}_i - \mathbf{r}^* \sum_i m_i\}\, \mathbf{g}] = 0,$$

or

$$\mathbf{r}^* = \frac{1}{M} \sum_i m_i \mathbf{r}_i\,,$$

where $M = \sum_i m_i$. From axiom (3),

$$\sum_i m_i \ddot{\mathbf{r}}_i = \sum_i \mathbf{K}_i + \sum_i \sum_k{}' \mathbf{K}_{ik}\,,$$

with

$$\sum_i m_i \ddot{\mathbf{r}}_i = M \ddot{\mathbf{r}}^* \qquad \text{and} \qquad \sum_i \mathbf{K}_i = \mathbf{K},$$

and from $\sum \sum'_{ik} \mathbf{K}_{ik} = 0$ (from axiom 2), we obtain

$$M \ddot{\mathbf{r}}^* = \mathbf{K}.$$

This says in words that the CG of a system of mass points moves as if all exterior forces were acting upon the CG. Integration for $\mathbf{K} = 0$ gives the law of conservation of momentum.

(2) *Spin law.*

$$m_i \ddot{\mathbf{r}}_i = \mathbf{K}_i + \sum_k{}' \mathbf{K}_{ik} \qquad \text{[from axiom (3)]},$$

$$[\mathbf{r}_i m_i \ddot{\mathbf{r}}_i] = [\mathbf{r}_i \mathbf{K}_i] + [\mathbf{r}_i \sum_k{}' \mathbf{K}_{ik}],$$

or

$$\sum_i [\mathbf{r}_i m_i \ddot{\mathbf{r}}_i] = \sum_i [\mathbf{r}_i \mathbf{K}_i] + [\sum_i \mathbf{r}_i \sum_k{}' \mathbf{K}_{ik}].$$

Of course,

$$[\mathbf{r}_i m_i \ddot{\mathbf{r}}_i] = \frac{d}{dt} [\mathbf{r}_i m_i \dot{\mathbf{r}}_i] = \dot{\mathbf{G}}_i \,,$$

and

$$\Sigma \mathbf{G}_i = \mathbf{G}_i \,.$$

Let us call $[\mathbf{r}_i \mathbf{K}_i] = \boldsymbol{\vartheta}_i$ (moment) and $\Sigma \boldsymbol{\vartheta}_i = \boldsymbol{\vartheta}$. The expression $[\Sigma \mathbf{r}_i \Sigma \mathbf{K}_{ik}]$ consists of terms

$$[\mathbf{r}_i \mathbf{K}_{ik}] + [\mathbf{r}_k \mathbf{K}_{ki}] = [\mathbf{r}_i - \mathbf{r}_k, \mathbf{K}_{ik}] \qquad \text{[from axiom (2)]}$$
$$= 0 \qquad \text{[from axiom (1)].}$$

Therefore,

$$\dot{\mathbf{G}} = \boldsymbol{\vartheta}.$$

Integration for $\boldsymbol{\vartheta} = 0$ gives the law of conservation of spin, or rotational momentum.

(3) *Energy law.* Kinetic energy $T = \sum_i (m_i/2) \dot{\mathbf{r}}_i^2$. Let us write

$$\mathbf{r}_i = \mathbf{r}^* + \mathbf{R}_i, \qquad \dot{\mathbf{r}}_i = \dot{\mathbf{r}}^* + \dot{\mathbf{R}}_i \,;$$

then

$$T = \frac{1}{2} M \dot{\mathbf{r}}^{*2} + \dot{\mathbf{r}}^* \sum m_i \dot{\mathbf{R}}_i + \sum_i \frac{m_i}{2} \dot{\mathbf{R}}_i^2.$$

The location of the center of gravity in the $\mathbf{R}$ coordinate system is

$$\mathbf{R}^* = \frac{1}{M} \Sigma m_i \mathbf{R}_i = 0,$$

as the center of gravity is the origin of the $\mathbf{R}$ system. Thus, $\Sigma_i m_i \dot{\mathbf{R}}_i = 0$, and

$$T = \frac{1}{2} M \dot{\mathbf{r}}^{*2} + \sum_i \frac{m_i}{2} \dot{\mathbf{R}}_i^2,$$

$$\sum_i m_i \ddot{\mathbf{r}}_i \dot{\mathbf{r}}_i = \sum_i \mathbf{K}_i \dot{\mathbf{r}}_i + \sum_i \sum_k{}' K_{ik} \dot{\mathbf{r}}_i \,,$$

or

$$d\left(\sum_i \frac{m_i}{2} \dot{\mathbf{r}}_i^2 \right) = dT = \Sigma \mathbf{K}_i d\mathbf{r}_i + \sum_i \sum_k{}' \mathbf{K}_{ik} d\mathbf{r}_i.$$

Since $\mathbf{K}_{ik} \parallel \mathbf{r}_i - \mathbf{r}_k$, $\mathbf{K}_{ik}$ is a central force from m_k to all m_i. Therefore, there is a potential such that

$$\mathbf{K}_{ik} = -\operatorname{grad}_i V_{ik} \, .$$

Because of axiom (2),

$$V_{ik} = V(\mid \mathbf{r}_i - \mathbf{r}_k \mid) = V_{ki} \, ,$$

or V_{ik} shall be a function only of the distance between m_i and m_k.

We demand that $\mathbf{K}_i = -\operatorname{grad} V_i$; then finally

$$T + \sum_i V_i + \frac{1}{2} \sum_i \sum_k{}' V_{ik} = \text{constant},$$

or

$$\text{kinetic energy} + \text{potential energy} = \text{constant}.$$

The internal forces do not drop out, as they obviously can do work. Let us apply these results to the problem of the connected satellites (see Fig. 1.18):

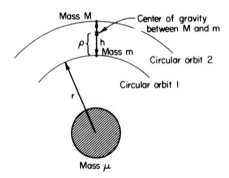

Fig. 1.18. Two connected satellites. $\varrho = [M/(M+m)]h; \; h \ll r$.

(1) *Impulse law.*

$$(M + m + \mu) \, \ddot{\mathbf{r}}^* = 0,$$

or, the center of gravity of the 3-body system stays at rest in the proper coordinate system.

Considering just the two satellites, the center of gravity moves uninfluenced by whether M and m are connected or not:

$$M\left(\frac{\gamma\mu}{r+h}\right)^{1/2} + m\left(\frac{\gamma\mu}{r}\right)^{1/2} = (M + m)v. \qquad (A)$$

(2) *Spin law*. As we have interior forces only,

$$\mathbf{G} = \text{constant.}$$

Before the satellites are connected,

$$G = |\sum_i [\mathbf{r}_i m_i \dot{\mathbf{r}}_i]| = mr \left(\frac{\gamma\mu}{r}\right)^{1/2} + M(r+h)\left(\frac{\gamma\mu}{r+h}\right)^{1/2}$$

or $\qquad\qquad\qquad\qquad\qquad\qquad\qquad\qquad\qquad\qquad$ (B)

$$G = (\gamma\mu)^{1/2} \{mr^{1/2} + M(r+h)^{1/2}\}.$$

After the vehicles are connected, some spin Ω of the satellites about their center of gravity and an elliptic orbit of major axis $r + H$ may result. Let us first consider the values of $\mathbf{G}$ for a point system using the knowledge about the center of gravity:

$$\mathbf{G}_i = [\mathbf{r}_i m_i \dot{\mathbf{r}}_i],$$
$$\mathbf{G} = \sum [\mathbf{r}^* + \mathbf{R}_i, \, m_i(\dot{\mathbf{r}}^* + \dot{\mathbf{R}}_i)]$$
$$= M[\mathbf{r}^*, \, \dot{\mathbf{r}}^*] + \sum m_i [\mathbf{R}_i \dot{\mathbf{R}}_i],$$

because of the definition of the center of gravity. Thus, here

$$G = (m+M)(r+\varrho)v + \frac{mM}{m+M} h^2\Omega. \qquad (B)$$

(3) Finally, the energy law with the "new" major axis, $r + H$, is

$$-\frac{\gamma\mu}{r} m - \frac{\gamma\mu}{r+h} M = -\frac{\gamma\mu}{r+H}(m+M) + \frac{mM}{m+M} h^2\Omega^2. \qquad (C)$$

In the Eqs. (A), (B), and (C) there are three unknowns: v, Ω, and H. It follows from (A), approximately to the second order with $x = h/r$,

$$v = \left(\frac{\gamma\mu}{r}\right)^{1/2}\left\{1 - \frac{M}{M+m}\left(\frac{1}{2}x - \frac{3}{8}x^2\right)\right\}. \qquad (D)$$

This is slightly larger than circular velocity for $r + \varrho$. From (B),

$$mr^{1/2} + Mr^{1/2}\left(1 + \frac{1}{2}x - \frac{1}{8}x^2\right)$$

$$= (m+M)\left(1 + \frac{M}{M+m}x\right)r^{1/2}\left\{1 - \frac{M}{M+m}\left(\frac{1}{2}x - \frac{3}{8}x^2\right)\right\}$$

$$+ \frac{1}{(\gamma\mu)^{1/2}} \frac{mM}{m+M} r^2 x^2 \Omega.$$

From this

$$\Omega = - \frac{1}{2} \frac{(\gamma\mu/r)^{1/2}}{r} . \qquad (E)$$

From the energy law comes, by series development for $x = h/r$ and $y = H/r$ to the second order, a quadratic equation for y which can be solved, again to the second order, to give

$$H = \frac{M}{M+m} h \left(1 - \frac{5}{4} \frac{m}{M+m} \frac{h}{r} \right).$$

We also have

$$\varrho = \frac{M}{M+m} h. \qquad (F)$$

So the major axis $r + H$ will be smaller than $r + \varrho$. The resulting orbit of $(m + M)$ is elliptic, with the point of contact $(r + \varrho)$ being apocenter and the pericenter being

$$2(\varrho - H) = \frac{5}{2} \frac{m}{M} \varrho \frac{\varrho}{r}$$

below the altitude, $r + \varrho$.

Now let us pull the satellites m, M together, using the connecting rope. The initial distance is h, the final is l. Conservation of spin[1] is given by

$$\Omega = - \frac{1}{2} \frac{(\gamma\mu/r)^{1/2}}{r} \left(\frac{h}{l} \right)^2 .$$

The energy of the rotating system is $E_r = \frac{1}{2}[mM/(m+M)]l^2\Omega^2 = \frac{1}{8}[mM/(m+M)]/(\gamma\mu/r^3)h^2(h^2/l^2)$, or the energy increases by

$$\Delta E_r = \frac{1}{8} \frac{mM}{m+M} \frac{\gamma\mu}{r} \left(\frac{h}{r} \right)^2 \left\{ \left(\frac{h}{l} \right)^2 - 1 \right\}.$$

Centrifugal acceleration of m is

$$A_1 = \frac{M}{M+m} l\Omega^2 = \frac{1}{4} \frac{M}{M+m} \frac{\gamma\mu}{r^2} \frac{h}{r} \left(\frac{h}{l} \right)^3 .$$

As the forces are in equilibrium, we get, for the acceleration of M,

---

[1] The moment of inertia of the connected satellite system is given by $\dfrac{mM}{m+M} h^2$.

$A_2M = A_1m$. So, for a distance shortening from h to l, the work done is

$$\Delta E = \int_h^l A_1 m \, dl = \frac{1}{8} \frac{mM}{m+M} \frac{\gamma\mu}{r} \left(\frac{h}{r}\right)^2 \left\{\left(\frac{h}{l}\right)^2 - 1\right\}.$$

This explains exactly the energy increase ΔE_r. As found in the energy law, the work of internal forces has to be considered.

Introducing $g_0 = \gamma\mu/R^2$, we have, acting upon m,

$$\frac{A_1}{g_0} = \frac{1}{4} \frac{M}{M+m} \left(\frac{R}{r}\right)^2 \frac{h}{r} \left(\frac{h}{l}\right)^3,$$

and acting upon M

$$\frac{A_2}{g_0} = \frac{m}{M} \frac{A_1}{g_0}.$$

With

$$\frac{M}{M+m} = \frac{7}{8}, \qquad \frac{h}{r} = \frac{10 \text{ km}}{7000 \text{ km}}, \qquad \left(\frac{R}{r}\right)^2 = 0.8,$$

we have for $h/l = 20$ that $A_1/g_0 = 2$, and l is still 0.5 km. The rope has to hold the load $2mg_0$ at least.

Let us assume that a man in a space suit has left a space station to work 2000 m below it. He circularizes there, and because of failure of his propulsion unit he is pulled back to 25 m distance at his safety line: he experiences then $\sim 29 \, g$'s. He is going around the station once every 1.84 sec with a speed of 96 m/sec $\approx$ 308 km/h: the "pulling-in" may not be so easy. Of course, these problems can be avoided if external forces (e.g., rocket thrust) are available or if he "traps" spin by separating a small mass on a long thin line. This may suffice on the field of relative motion.

The maneuver of changing the direction of flight of a vehicle by application of rocket power is commonly called "dog-legging." It has to be applied whenever a satellite is to be placed in an orbit, the inclination of which is smaller than the latitude of the launch site. In some other cases, it has to be used because of range safety considerations.

There are many possibilities for accomplishing "doglegging": Assume we have, already, a circular orbit (1), and we fire a kick $\Delta = 2 \, |\mathbf{v}_1| \sin \frac{1}{2}\alpha$ so that a new circular orbit (2) results (Fig. 1.19). By doing this, the inclination changes from γ_1 to γ_2, and the right ascension of the ascending node changes by $\Delta\Omega$. From spherical trigonometry, after some rearranging of terms, we obtain

$$\cos \gamma_2 = \cos \alpha \cos \gamma_1 - \sin \alpha \sin \gamma_1 \cos \varphi,$$

$$\tan \Delta\Omega = \frac{\sin \varphi}{\sin \gamma_1 \operatorname{ctn} \alpha + \cos \gamma_1 \cos \varphi}. \qquad (1.32)$$

The first equation can be written as

$$\cos \gamma_2 = \cos(\gamma_1 + \alpha) + 2 \sin \alpha \sin \gamma_1 \sin^2 \tfrac{1}{2} \varphi.$$

If the kick is given at the node (i.e., $\varphi = 0$), then, and only then, $\Delta\Omega = 0$, and $\gamma_2 - \gamma_1 = \alpha$ is the maximum possible inclination change. For a very small kick we get from $\Delta = 2 \,|\mathbf{v}_1| \sin \tfrac{1}{2} \alpha$ that $d\Delta = v_1 \, d\alpha$, and from Eq.

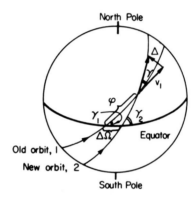

FIG. 1.19. Changing of vehicle flight direction.

(1.32) by putting $\gamma_2 = \gamma_1 + d\gamma$ it follows that $d\gamma = \cos \varphi \, d\alpha$ and $d\Delta\Omega = (\sin \varphi / \sin \gamma_1) d\alpha$. Let us assume the small speed increment $d\Delta$ is the result of a constant, continuous, small acceleration $\dot{v}$, then

$$d\Delta = \dot{v} \, dt = \dot{v} \, \frac{d\varphi}{\omega} \approx \dot{v} \, \frac{T}{2\pi} \, d\varphi,$$

where T is the period in the circular orbit. If at $\varphi = \pm \tfrac{1}{2}\pi$, $\dot{v}$ reverses its sign, then we get for one period

$$\Delta\gamma = 2 \int_{-\frac{1}{2}\pi}^{+\frac{1}{2}\pi} d\gamma = \frac{2}{\pi} \frac{\dot{v}}{v_1/T} = 4\dot{v} \frac{r^2}{\gamma m} = 4 \frac{\dot{v}}{g_0} \left(\frac{r}{R} \right)^2, \qquad (1.33)$$

where Eq. (4.36) of Vol. 1 and $g_0 = \gamma m / R^2$ have been utilized.

If the constant acceleration $\dot{v}$ is due to a rocket engine thrust, then the total velocity required for this angular change $\Delta\gamma$ is $\dot{v}T$. If this same velocity had been applied as a nodal kick, then the inclination change α would have been

$$\alpha = 2 \text{ arc sin } (\dot{v}T/2v_1) \approx \dot{v}T/v_1 .$$

By comparison it is seen that the continuous thrust-method is only $2/\pi = 0.636$ as effective as the kick method.[1] For $\dot{v}/g_0 = 10^{-4}$ follows, for $(r/R)^2 \approx 1.18$, a possible inclination change of $\Delta\gamma = 0.027°$ in 96 min, or $0.4°/\text{day}$. For $(r/R)^2 = 44$ follows $\Delta\gamma = 1°/\text{day}$. (Generally, everything but the altitude being equal follows $\Delta\gamma \sim r^{1/2}$ per day.) Therefore, inclination change by continuous low-thrust is attractive only if long duration of the maneuver can be tolerated, and if the specific impulse is high enough for the higher speed requirements to be fulfilled.

From Eq. (1.33) follows, for the time t required to achieve a given $\Delta\gamma$ value, $t = \frac{1}{2}\pi \Delta\gamma (v_1/\dot{v})$, or the velocity requirement is $\dot{v}t/v_1 = \frac{1}{2}\pi \Delta\gamma$. For $\dot{v}t/v_1 = 1$ follows only $\Delta\gamma = 2/\pi$, corresponding to 36.5°: Inclination changes are costly energywise, since $\dot{v}t = v_1$ is, of course, a high requirement. Therefore, dogleg maneuver should be avoided whenever possible.

The change of the right ascension of the node for the same low-thrust maneuver[2] is, per period T,

$$\Delta\Omega = 2 \int_{-\frac{1}{2}\pi}^{+\frac{1}{2}\pi} d \Delta\Omega = \frac{1}{\pi} \frac{\dot{v}T}{v_1} \int_{-\frac{1}{2}\pi}^{+\frac{1}{2}\pi} \frac{\sin \varphi}{\sin \gamma} d\varphi,$$

$$\sin \gamma = \sin (\gamma_1 + \Delta\gamma) \approx \sin \gamma_1 + \Delta\gamma \cos \gamma_1 ,$$

and

$$\Delta\gamma \approx \frac{2}{\pi} \frac{\dot{v}t}{v_1} = \frac{2}{\pi} \frac{\dot{v}t}{v_1} \frac{\varphi}{2\pi} .$$

Therefore,

$$\Delta\Omega \approx \frac{1}{\pi} \frac{\dot{v}T}{v_1} \int_{-\frac{1}{2}\pi}^{+\frac{1}{2}\pi} \frac{\sin \varphi}{\sin \gamma_1 + \cos \gamma_1 (2/\pi)(\dot{v}T/v_1)(\varphi/2\pi)} d\varphi,$$

$$\Delta\Omega \approx \frac{1}{\pi} \frac{\dot{v}T}{v_1} \int_{-\frac{1}{2}\pi}^{+\frac{1}{2}\pi} \frac{\sin \varphi}{\sin \gamma_1} \left(1 - \text{ctn } \gamma_1 \frac{2}{\pi} \frac{\dot{v}T}{v_1} \frac{\varphi}{2\pi}\right) d\varphi ,$$

$$\Delta\Omega \approx \frac{2}{\pi^3} \left(\frac{\dot{v}T}{v_1}\right) \frac{\cos \gamma_1}{1 - \cos^2\gamma_1} . \tag{1.34}$$

So far, we have described two methods to change inclination when a cir-

---

[1] The described method of change of inclination with low acceleration is not optimized, because the radius r has been kept constant. See Sec. 6.4 of Vol. 1 for some details.

[2] With the exception that the direction of $\dot{v}$ has to be changed at $\varphi = 0$ and $\varphi = \pi$.

cular orbit has already been obtained, namely, by one kick or by a continuous thrust maneuver. Care has to be exercised when a required velocity $v_r = \dot{v}T$ is transformed into a mass ratio, r, because the equation $v_r = c \ln r$ holds for $c = $ constant only. There is more on this question in Chap. 2.

A third, less energy-consuming method consists of changing the inclination during the ascent. The vehicle goes first to a circular "waiting orbit," which shall be, for energy reasons, as low as possible, and which shall have an inclination equal to the latitude of the launch place in order to take full advantage of Earth rotation.

At one of the equator crossings of this waiting orbit a Hohmann transfer up to the final orbital altitude is initiated. At apocenter of the transfer ellipse, which is, of course, also over the equator, a kick is fired with a dual function, namely, both to circularize the orbit and to give it the desired inclination. If the location of the vehicle within the final orbit is not the required one, a chasing maneuver has to be initiated.

If part of the inclination change is performed during the pericenter kick and only the remaining part need be carried out at the apocenter then an energy savings can be obtained. This subject was considered in Chap. 6 of Vol. 1.

A fourth way is to go farther away from Earth first and carry out the inclination change there. This takes advantage of the low speed of a vehicle far from Earth, which makes changes of the velocity direction easy. After the change, the vehicle returns to the desired altitude and enters the desired orbit. This method is the least energy-consuming one if applied correctly, but it is complicated and, sometimes, the flight time involved is very long, and guidance and accuracy requirements are very severe; this renders the method often impractical.

When the inclination of a desired orbit is equal to, or larger than, the latitude of the launch place, then the vehicle launch azimuth and launch time are chosen so that, at injection to the Hohmann transfer ellipse, the injection velocity vector lies wholly in the desired orbital plane. (A small deviation between the plane containing Earth center and injection velocity vector, and Earth center—launch point—cutoff point could hardly be termed a dog-leg, but perhaps a "launch maneuver"; the cross-over point is arbitrary.) At apocenter of the transfer ellipse, either circularization occurs, or a chasing maneuver starts by not fully circularizing, either leaving a speed deficiency if the vehicle is behind the desired location in the final orbit, or giving some excess speed if the vehicle has to drop back. Some remarks on the timing of launch from Earth to a satellite orbit can be found in the next section for the special case of a "waiting orbit."

To initiate landing upon the central body, the satellite has to apply some braking thrust, if the altitude is not low enough for aerodynamic braking alone to suffice. The flight path will be altered such that denser atmosphere is traversed, and from there aerodynamic forces are relied upon. (In the case of an atmosphereless central body, of course, all the braking has to be done by rocket action. As shown in Chap. 5 of Vol. 1, drag braking is much more attractive.) To reach a desired final landing area, and to have neither excessively high deceleration forces, nor an excessively high total heat input or heat input rate, demands that the landing trajectory be closely controlled. This means that the braking impulse has to be applied at the correct time in the correct direction with the correct magnitude, and the less control we have during the aerodynamic phase, the more precision is required for the entry kick. Since correct time simply means correct location within the orbit with respect to the central body, it appears obvious to give the landing-initiation signal from the central body, or deduce it from observation of the central body from the satellite.

To summarize, satellite guidance problems are in two fields: firstly, to get the satellite to its proper orbit, and secondly, to control satellite motion thereafter. In the latter case, the satellite has to have a propulsion and attitude control system of its own. There are many reasons for such maneuverable satellites: to change major axis, eccentricity, inclination, epoch or other elements from a preliminary value to the final one, or even to change the mission of a satellite (multipurpose satellite), for fine corrections after a long observation time, to assist in rendezvous flights, to compensate for air resistance, for station-keeping purposes (e.g., 24-h satellites) to initiate return to the central body, to initiate escape into space, or to fulfill military objectives. This listing is not meant to be complete.

To close this section, we would like to show that the information contained in Fig. 1.15 can be derived in an Earth-centered coordinate system too (see Fig. 1.20):

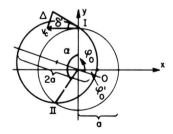

FIG. 1.20. Relative satellite motion in an Earth-centered coordinate system.

A satellite ejects an object with a small radial kick Δ at I; the major axis a remains (nearly) unchanged, but eccentricity (Sec. 4.1,6 of Vol. 1) changes: $\varepsilon = \sin \delta' \approx \Delta/v_c$;

$$\sin (\varphi_0 - 90°) = \sin \varphi_0' = \varepsilon; \quad \alpha = \pi - 2\varphi_0' \approx \pi - 2\varepsilon;$$

$$\varphi_0 - \tfrac{1}{2}\pi = \varepsilon; \quad \varphi_0 = \tfrac{1}{2}\pi + \varepsilon; \quad \tfrac{1}{2}\varphi_0 = \tfrac{1}{4}\pi + \tfrac{1}{2}\varepsilon;$$

$$\tan \left(\frac{\pi}{4} + \frac{\varepsilon}{2} \right) = \frac{\sin (\tfrac{1}{4}\pi + \tfrac{1}{2}\varepsilon)}{\cos (\tfrac{1}{4}\pi + \tfrac{1}{2}\varepsilon)} = \frac{\sin \tfrac{1}{4}\pi \cos \tfrac{1}{2}\varepsilon + \cos \tfrac{1}{4}\pi \sin \tfrac{1}{2}\varepsilon}{\cos \tfrac{1}{4}\pi \cos \tfrac{1}{2}\varepsilon - \sin \tfrac{1}{4}\pi \sin \tfrac{1}{2}\varepsilon}$$

$$\approx \frac{1 + \tfrac{1}{2}\varepsilon}{1 - \tfrac{1}{2}\varepsilon} \approx 1 + \varepsilon.$$

From Eq. (4.38) of Vol. 1,

$$\tan \frac{v_0}{2} = \left(\frac{1 - \varepsilon}{1 + \varepsilon} \right)^{1/2} \tan \frac{\varphi_0}{2} \approx (1 - \varepsilon^2)^{1/2} \approx 1 - \frac{1}{2}\varepsilon^2,$$

or

$$\frac{v_0}{2} = \frac{\pi}{4} - \frac{1}{4}\varepsilon^2, \quad v_0 = \frac{\pi}{2} - \frac{1}{2}\varepsilon^2,$$

and from Eq. (4.39) of Vol. 1 we obtain, for the flight time t_1, along the ellipse from 0 to I,

$$\frac{2\pi}{T} t_1 \approx \frac{\pi}{2} - \frac{1}{2}\varepsilon^2 - \varepsilon \sin \left(\frac{\pi}{2} - \frac{1}{2}\varepsilon^2 \right) \approx \frac{\pi}{2} - \varepsilon.$$

Therefore, the time t_2 from I to II through the elliptic orbit is $t_2 = T - 2t_1 = (\tfrac{1}{2} + \varepsilon/\pi) T$; the satellite has moved through an angle $\alpha_s = (2\pi/T)t_2 = \pi + 2\varepsilon$. So, we get, for the maximum angular distance between satellite and ejected object, $\alpha_s - \alpha = 4\varepsilon$ or linearly, $x = 4\varepsilon a = 4(\Delta/v_c) a$.

"Altitudewise," the maximum distance between object and vehicle is about

$$y = r_{max} - a = (1 + \varepsilon)a - a = \varepsilon a = \tfrac{1}{4}x.$$

1.4,8 Some Problems of Lunar Flight

Much has already been said both about the mechanics and about the guidance scheme of lunar flights; only a few more considerations are to be given here.

Let us first consider a parabolic coplanar trajectory from Earth to the Moon; injection altitude shall be 200 km, with exactly parabolic speed in the horizontal direction. We will neglect the lunar influence first (see Fig. 1.21).

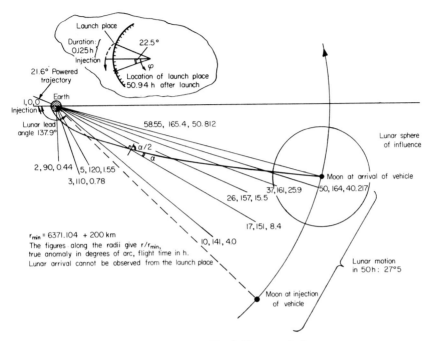

Fig. 1.21. Coplanar Earth-Moon trajectory.

For the powered flight path, cutoff altitude shall be 200 km; powered flight time is 450 sec at an average acceleration $\dot{v}$ of 2.4 g_0, and powered trajectory length is about 2500 km, which gives a ground travel of about 2400 km $\approx$ 21.6°.

From Eq. (1.27) we obtain

$$\frac{r_{\min}}{r} = \cos^2 \frac{\varphi}{2} = \cos^2 \left(\frac{\varphi}{2} - \alpha \right)$$

or

$$\tan \frac{\varphi}{2} = \left(\frac{r}{r_{\min}} - 1 \right)^{1/2};$$

from Eq. (4.25) of Vol. 1 we have

$$v_0 = \left(\frac{2\gamma m}{r_0} \right)^{1/2};$$

and, generally,

$$v = \left(\frac{2\gamma m}{r} \right)^{1/2}.$$

From Eq. (4.35) of Vol. 1,

$$\tan\frac{\varphi}{2} + \frac{1}{3}\tan^3\frac{\varphi}{2} = \frac{(2\gamma m/r_{\min})^{1/2}}{2r_{\min}}\,t,$$

where

$$\frac{(2\gamma m/r_{\min})^{1/2}}{2r_{\min}} = \frac{11.01467\ \mathrm{km/sec}}{2\times 6571.104\ \mathrm{km}} = \frac{1}{0.33146}\ \mathrm{h}^{-1}.$$

To include the lunar influence approximately, let us calculate the values for 40.217 h flight and refer these conditions to the Moon (Fig. 1.22).

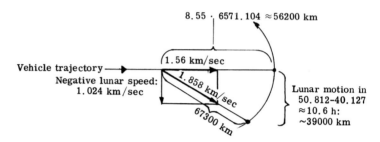

FIG. 1.22. Vehicle-lunar rendezvous.

Now we have the simple problem of vertical drop to the lunar surface from 67,300 km distance from lunar center, with an initial velocity of 1.858 km/sec. According to the solution of one of the problems of Chap. 4 of Vol. 1,

$$E = \frac{1}{2}(1.858)^2 - \frac{4.89848\times 10^3}{67.3\times 10^3} = 1.651 = \frac{1}{2}(1.818)^2\ \mathrm{km^2/sec^2};$$

$y = 0.338x$, where x is the distance from lunar center in 10^3 km; $\tau = 2.21t$, where t is the flight time in hours; and the final conditions $y = 0.586$, $t = T$, and the initial condition is $y_0 = 22.75$, $t = 0$.

From the equation for the hyperbolic case, $T = 9.4$ h instead of $50.812 - 40.217 \approx 10.6$ h, or the lunar attraction shortens the fall by 1.2 h to a total flight time of 49.6 h. Impact velocity follows, from the energy law, to be 2.985 km/sec. This should be compared to the more accurate figures given in Chap. 4 (51 h, 2.884 km/sec). In 50 h, the Moon moves through an angle of 27.5 deg. So, at injection, the "lead angle" of the Moon is 137.9 deg, as shown in Fig. 1.21.

As the leading, Earth-facing quarter of the lunar surface is favored for an impact, we expect that the deviation resulting from an injection error will be a nonlinear function of the injection error. In this case, a point of the lunar surface should be selected for target so that the allowable tolerance is the same in each direction.

Now let us consider a grazing hyperbolic trajectory around the Moon (see Chap. 4 of Vol. 1, geometry of conic sections):

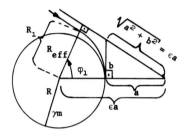

FIG. 1.23. Grazing hyperbolic Moon trajectory.

We call R_{eff} the maximum miss distance from the target which will still result in a grazing impact (Fig. 1.23):

$$\frac{R_{\text{eff}}}{\varepsilon a} = \frac{b}{(a^2 + b^2)^{1/2}}.$$

Inserting $b^2 = a^2 (\varepsilon^2 - 1)$,

$$R_{\text{eff}} = b = a(\varepsilon^2 - 1)^{1/2}.$$

Comparing the derivation of Eq. (4.26) of Vol. 1, it follows that

$$R_{\text{eff}} = \frac{v_{\max} R}{v_r}. \tag{1.35}$$

This important equation—which can be read directly from Kepler's second law—gives the effective diameter of the target. It is seen that slower trajectories give a larger effective target radius, because v_r is smaller. In our example, $v_r \approx 1.818$ km/sec and $v_{\max} = 2.985$ km/sec. So, $R_{\text{eff}}/R \approx 1.64$.

What happens if we inject the vehicle at the Earth launch, by error, with some upward angle α deg, but with correct speed? This moves the point of interception of the lunar trajectory by 2α in the sense opposite of the lunar motion, and reduces the flight time approximately by

$$\Delta t = \frac{(\alpha/360)2\pi \times 6571 \text{ km}}{11 \text{ km/sec}} = 10.4\,\alpha \quad \text{sec}$$

The lunar angular motion in this time is $\alpha' \approx 1.6 \times 10^{-3}\alpha$ deg. Therefore, the deviation of the intersection point between trajectory and lunar path is $(2–1.6 \times 10^{-3})\alpha$. In order to still have an impact, we can allow a maximum deviation of 1.64×0.26 deg from the lunar center, because 0.26 deg is the apparent half-diameter of the lunar disk.

So we have $\alpha_{max} = 0.214°$, or the well-known but fairly surprising result: if we aim for the Moon, then the allowable angular errors behave approximately as if the flight path were a straight line. A slower trajectory will be less (permissable errors larger by up to a factor of larger than 2), and a faster one more (up to factor of $\frac{1}{2}$), sensitive. Generally, arrival speed will hardly be influenced, arrival time only a little.

What happens if the injection angle is without error but the injection speed is, by Δv, high? For the parabolic case, the energy can be expressed as

$$E = v_p\,\Delta v + \tfrac{1}{2}\,\Delta v^2 \quad \text{m}^2/\text{sec}^2,$$

where v_p is the parabolic speed. Again

$$r_{min} = 6571.104 \times 10^3 \quad \text{m}$$

$$v_{max} = v_p + \Delta v = 11{,}015 + \Delta v \quad \text{m/sec}.$$

From Eq. (4.27) of Vol. 1, we have

$$v_r^2 = 2E,$$

and from Eq. (4.27) of Vol. 1,

$$E = v_p^2\,\frac{r_{min}}{4a} \quad \text{or} \quad \frac{a}{r_{min}} = \frac{1}{4\,\Delta v/v_p + 2(\Delta v/v_p)^2}\,,$$

and from Eq. (4.26) of Vol. 1,

$$\varepsilon = \frac{v_{max}^2 + v_r^2}{v_{max}^2 - v_r^2} = 1 + 4\,\frac{\Delta v}{v_p} + 2\left(\frac{\Delta v}{v_p}\right)^2.$$

equation of a conic section is

$$\frac{r}{r_{min}} = \frac{1 + \varepsilon}{1 + \varepsilon \cos \varphi_H} = \frac{2(1 + \Delta v/v_p)^2}{1 + \{1 + 4\,\Delta v/v_p + 2(\Delta v/v_p)^2\} \cos \varphi_H}\,.$$

On the other hand, for the parabola we have

$$\frac{r}{r_{min}} = \frac{2}{1 + \cos \varphi_p}\,;$$

writing $\varphi_H = \varphi_p + \Delta\varphi$, we get

$$(1 + \cos \varphi_p) \left(1 + \frac{\Delta v}{v_p}\right)^2 = 1 + \left\{1 + 4 \frac{\Delta v}{v_p} + 2 \left(\frac{\Delta v}{v_p}\right)^2\right\} \cos(\varphi_0 + \Delta\varphi).$$

From this, for small $\Delta\varphi$, linear in $\Delta v/v_p$:

$$\Delta\varphi = - 2 \frac{\Delta v}{v_p} \tan \frac{\varphi_p}{2}. \tag{1.36}$$

In the lunar case, $\varphi_p = 165.4°$, so,

$$\tan (\varphi_p/2) = 7.8 \quad \text{and} \quad \Delta\varphi \text{ (deg)} = - 0.081 \, \Delta v \text{ (m/sec)}.$$

By what time, Δt, is the flight time decreased, as a consequence of increasing the launch speed by Δv? We will answer this question for the rectilinear orbit of near-parabolic launch speed only. From one of the problems of Chap. 4 of Vol. 1,

$$\tau = (1 + y)^{1/2} y^{1/2} - \ln[(1 + y)^{1/2} + y^{1/2}],$$

where

$$\tau = 2^{1/2} \frac{E^{3/2}}{\gamma m} t \quad \text{and} \quad y = \frac{E}{\gamma m} d,$$

where t is the time to move from the attracting mass point out to the distance d.

By series development:

$$(1 + y)^{1/2} = 1 + \frac{1}{2} y - \frac{1}{8} y^2 + \frac{1}{16} y^3 - \cdots,$$

$$\ln(1 + \varepsilon) = \varepsilon - \frac{1}{2} \varepsilon^2 + \frac{1}{3} \varepsilon^3 - \frac{1}{4} \varepsilon^4 + \frac{1}{5} \varepsilon^5 - \frac{1}{6} \varepsilon^6 + \cdots,$$

and

$$\varepsilon = y^{1/2} + \frac{1}{2} y - \frac{1}{8} y^2 + \frac{1}{16} y^3 \cdots.$$

Therefore, τ is given by (including terms up to y^3)

$$\tau = \frac{2}{3} y^{3/2} \left(1 - \frac{3}{10} y - \frac{3}{8} y^{3/2}\right).$$

For the parabolic case, we have $\tau_p = \frac{2}{3} y^{3/2}$; so,

$$\frac{\tau_p - \tau}{\tau_p} = \frac{\Delta t}{t_p} = - \left(\frac{3}{10} y + \frac{3}{8} y^{3/2}\right).$$

Using first terms only,

$$y = \frac{E}{\gamma m}\, d = \frac{2E}{v_p^{\,2}}\, \frac{d}{r_{\min}} = \left\{ 2\,\frac{\Delta v}{v_p} + \left(\frac{\Delta v}{v_p}\right)^2 \right\} \frac{d}{r_{\min}} \approx 2\,\frac{\Delta v}{v_p}\, \frac{d}{r_{\min}}\,.$$

So,

$$\frac{\Delta t}{t_p} \approx -\,0.6\,\frac{\Delta v}{v_p}\, \frac{d}{r_{\min}}\,. \qquad (1.37)$$

Numerically, for the lunar near-parabolic flight,

$$\Delta t \approx -\,\frac{\Delta v[\text{m/sec}]}{6.16}\quad \text{h}\,.$$

This time corresponds to an angle of lunar motion

$$\Delta\varphi_2 = -\,0.089\,\Delta v\quad \text{deg}\,.$$

As seen relative to the lunar target, the miss distance, taking into account the focusing factor 1.64, is approximately

$$\left(\frac{0.089 - 0.081}{1.64}\right)\Delta v = 0.00487\,\Delta v\quad \text{m/sec}$$

degrees in front of the Moon. The maximum allowable miss from the lunar center for a lunar impact shot is about $\pm\,0.26$ deg, resulting in a maximum allowable speed error of $\Delta v = \pm\,53.4$ m/sec. The lunar impact would occur, instead of in the lunar center, at the "edge" of the Moon.

We notice a very interesting feature in this coplanar, near-parabolic, horizontally injected flight: the self-cancellation of errors. It so happens that a slight excess in velocity makes the vehicle intersect the lunar path ahead of the design point. But the flight time is reduced, too, thus causing the Moon to be ahead of the design intersection, so that the Moon is just nearly at the actual intersection: lunar position change due to changed flight time and change of intersection-point between vehicle and lunar orbits nearly cancel each other.

This is not the case at other than near-parabolic injection speeds. Let us assume that, for a given condition ① (Fig. 1.24), the shown trajectory leads to a lunar hit at ②. Increasing injection speed shifts the point of impact upon the lunar surface, until the trajectory passes in front of the Moon, depicted here for the parabolic trajectory 2. Further increase in injection speed again can result in a lunar impact ③, while, after further injection speed increases, the vehicle passes behind the Moon, ④. From

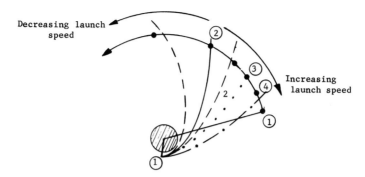

Fig. 1.24. Lunar trajectory as a function of launch speed.

Fig. (1.24), the variation of the miss distance as a function of injection speed is shown in Fig. (1.25).

At near-parabolic speed, the reversal of the trend of miss distance as a function of injection speed still takes place just upon the lunar surface. Let us assume, in our example, that this would occur for an injection error of 53.4 m/sec, then, approximately, another + 53.4 m/sec increase will

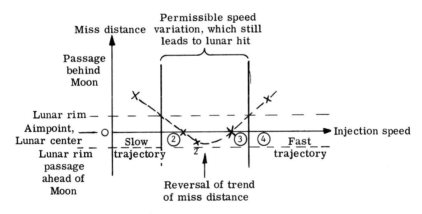

Fig. 1.25. Lunar miss distance as a function of injection speed.

bring us back to the original impact point: we have an allowable injection-speed error of ± 106.8 m/sec! Indeed, the maximum for horizontal injection is around ± 80 m/sec; for steeper injection, this can increase to ± 300 m/sec and more.

About the worst possible assumption is that no self-correction takes place whatsoever. Since we had $\Delta\varphi_2 \approx 0.09 \, \Delta v$, and the target radius is about 0.26°, we get, for the worst case, $\Delta v = \pm 2.9$ m/sec. Slow trajectories (with transfer times of 80 h or longer) can indeed reach such sensitivity. The fast trajectories are generally less sensitive to small injection speed errors.

Decreasing the horizontal injection speed from our standard parabolic trajectory, by 50 m/sec, to 10,965 m/sec will increase the flight time by about 12 h [8.1 h given approximately by Eq. (1.37)]. The free-flight path angle increases by about $6.7°$ [Eq. (1.36): $3.7°$]. The margin for error just to hit the Moon is still ± 20 m/sec. From Fig. 1.21 we see that at vehicle impact, the Moon will be $6.7°$ ahead of the drawn position but that the launch point will be $180°$ further on, which means that the Moon will be $20°$ off the zenith of the launch place. This is, of course, a very desirable condition for observation, and tends to make an approximately 60 h (or ~ 37 h, where the same favorable observational conditions exist at a higher trajectory energy level) trajectory quite attractive.

Let us look into the question of variation of the impact speed upon the Moon. From Eq. (4.43) of Vol. 1 we obtain the approximation (index 1 is at launch, index 2 is at lunar impact, d is the Earth-Moon distance)

$$\frac{v_1{}^2}{2} - \frac{\gamma m_1}{r_1} \approx \frac{v_2{}^2}{2} - \frac{\gamma m_2}{R_2} - \frac{\omega^2}{2} d^2 .$$

Differentiating v_1 and v_2 yields

$$\Delta v_2 \approx \frac{v_1}{v_2} \Delta v_1 . \tag{1.38}$$

For the parabolic trajectory, we have $v_1 = 11{,}015$ m/sec and $v_2 = 2884$ m/sec, thus $\Delta v_2 \approx 3.82 \, \Delta v_1$. Therefore, a reduction in Δv_1 of 50 m/sec reduces Δv_2 by 191 m/sec (accurately: 197 m/sec). In the case of a soft lunar landing mission, this is a strong argument in favor of the 62-h trajectory,[1] which appears to be a good all-around compromise for such a mission. For lunar impacts or lunar misses, the 37-h trajectory might be considered. From Eq. (1.37), for an injection-speed error of only 1.7 cm/sec, a transfer time deviation of 10 sec results. This high sensitivity makes it impractical to use a preset timer in the vehicle to start the braking rocket engine for a soft landing or a similar maneuver. But by simply measuring the deviation of the arrival time for the actual, compared to the nominal, trajectory, a value Δv_2 to correct the impact speed can be found,

$$\Delta v_2 \, \frac{\mathrm{m}}{\mathrm{sec}} \approx - \frac{\Delta t}{2.55} \quad \min ,$$

---

[1] Or still slower trajectories, if their other problems—e.g., error sensitivity— can be handled.

for the near-parabolic case. For the case of a small injection-speed error the direction of the impact speed stays nearly space-fixed, but varies considerably with respect to the lunar surface (often vertical for the nominal trajectory, becoming more flat—to perhaps 45°—towards the rim of the Moon). It might be possible to utilize the insensitivity of the "inertial" impact velocity direction—e.g., by utilization of spin-stabilized vehicles that are correctly oriented right after the injection propulsion period, as proposed in a Rand Corporation study (Buchheim, 1956). But, generally, measurements shortly before ignition of the braking engine, with respect to the Moon, are more promising, though obviously also more complicated.

Let us assume a firing to the Moon from the Kennedy Space Center (Florida, latitude $+ 28.3°N$) with an injection velocity horizontally, due East, using a parabolic trajectory. We first go to a waiting orbit, being 28.3° inclined to the equator, and perhaps only 150 km high, where circular velocity is about 7840 m/sec. To reach 11,015 m/sec, a speed of 3175 m/sec has to be added. At an average flight acceleration of 2.4 g_0 follows, for this maneuver, a duration of $\Delta t \approx 135$ sec, with a total path length of about $[(11,015 + 7840)]/2] \times 135 = 1272 \times 10^3$ m, corresponding to a central angle of 11.1°. As described in Sec. 4.4,3,3 of Vol. 1 the outward velocity comes out to be (with an average outward acceleration of 4.7 m/sec²) 727 m/sec, and the altitude gain is approximately 50 km from 150 to 200 km altitude. The injection angle would be 86.2° against the vertical—the free-flight path angle from the injection to the Moon is then (see Fig. 1.21) 165.4°—2(90° − 86.2°) = 157.8°, plus 11.1° of powered trajectory giving a total path angle of 168.9°.

The projections of the waiting orbit and lunar orbit have the two points N_1 and N_2 in common. When the Moon is 50 h before, say, point N_1, we start the propulsion system of the vehicle, which has to be 180° − 168.9° = 11.1° past point N_2. About 50 h later, the vehicle reaches the Moon; see Fig. 1.26. The vehicle trajectory plane and the waiting orbit plane are identical.

The angle α is the inclination of the lunar orbit and δ is the angle between vehicle plane and lunar plane of motion. Then, by simple spherical trigonometry, $\cos \delta = \cos(28.3 − \alpha) − 2 \sin 28.3 \sin \alpha \sin^2(\Delta/2)$. The angle α is between the limits $\alpha = 23.2 \pm 5.1°$. For the special case $\Delta = 0$ we see that the angle δ is between 0° and 10.2°. Let us use the less favorable limit $\delta = 10.2°$.

The problem is no longer two-dimensional. Of course, we need not dogleg into the lunar plane of motion, because the lunar gravity is dominating the vehicular motion anyway when the vehicle is close enough to the target. Figure 1.27 is an attempt to show the relative approach velocity $\mathbf{v}_r$ of the

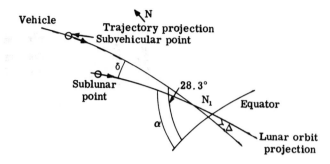

FIG. 1.26. Projections of lunar orbit and vehicle trajectory.

vehicle, as seen from the Moon. From the figure we see that, for the illustrated case the Earth-facing, leading, northern eighth of the lunar surface is favored for an impact area.

Returning to Fig. 1.26, we find that for a lunar impact the maximum allowable miss distance, vertical from the lunar plane of motion, is $d/2 = 0.26°$. From $d\bar{d} = (\pi/4)d^2$, "mean" apparent lunar diameter $\bar{d}$ it follows that the

$$\bar{d} = (\pi/4)\,d = 0.408°,$$

giving

$$\bar{d}/2 = 0.204°.$$

Taking again a focusing factor of 1.64, we get the corrected value $\frac{1}{2}\bar{d}_c = 0.335°$. At $\delta = 10.2°$ follows an allowable miss distance from the line

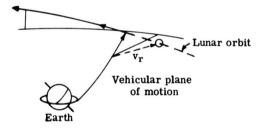

FIG. 1.27. Relative approach velocity as seen from the Moon.

of intersection between the lunar and vehicular plane of motion, $\Delta\varphi \approx 0.335°/\sin 10.2° = 1.93°$. Therefore, even if we have perfect self-compensation of injection-speed errors for the coplanar case, we can benefit only for $\Delta\varphi \leq 1.93°$, or [Eq. (1.36)]. $0.081\,\Delta v < 1.93°$, $\Delta v < 24$ m/sec in the 3-dimensional case.

For larger angles between vehicle and lunar plane of motion (which sometimes have to be used when a waiting orbit has to be avoided) conditions
are, of course, worse: for $\delta = 25°$, Δv goes down to ± 10 m/sec!

In the fairly extreme case of $\delta = 90°$, there is no longer any self-cancel-
ling error effect: the Moon takes 0.47 h to move a distance equal to its own
radius. Using again a focusing factor of 1.64, this gives, for an impact, a
maximum arrival time error of 0.77 h, corresponding to a maximum allowable injection-speed error of 4.75 m/sec [Eq. (1.37)]. The advantage of
such a trajectory is the easy accessibility of the lunar polar areas, if such is
desired. Still worse is the limiting case of $\delta = 180°$: the self-cancellation
effect is now an "automatic error increasing effect."

Let us consider the consequence of injection time errors. The planet
Earth rotates through 1 deg in 4 min. Therefore, ± 1 min injection
time deviation gives a trajectory end-point deviation of $\pm \frac{1}{4}$ deg, which
is the maximum allowable deviation for impact upon the Moon, taking
a focusing factor of one, only. But by correcting injection angle and azimuth, as a function of injection time, this error can be made negligible.
Assuming a 1 deg correcting capability, we can correct for about ± 8 min
since in a parabola a change in injection angle corresponds to double the
change in central angle; this leaves $\pm 7\frac{1}{2}$ min for launch time deviation
since no more than $\frac{1}{2}$ min of error should accumulate during the powered
flight phase. Half a minute of time corresponds to $\frac{1}{8}°$ of error; to turn a
velocity of 11,000 m/sec through $\frac{1}{8}°$ demands 24 m/sec of required speed.
As this error can probably be detected during ascent already, perhaps 12
m/sec are necessary for correction. But to take into account the conceivably
less favorable total trajectory at $7\frac{1}{2}$ min launch time deviation, about
30 m/sec should suffice for the correction of the injection-time deviation,
if this is less than ± 8 min.

Timing is more critical for a launch from a waiting orbit, by a factor of
(angular velocity in orbit)/(angular velocity of Earth) ≈ 16, and additionally by a factor of 2.5 due to the higher average speed of the vehicle between orbital and escape conditions. Thus for a corrective speed capability
of 30 m/sec, this leaves ± 12 sec allowable error of injection time. But if no
corrections are made for it, and lunar impact shall occur, only ± 1.5 sec
remain as margin—and only if no other injection errors occur!

Let us summarize the performance penalties involved in launch from a
satellite orbit to reach the Moon: The "pushbutton error" is the time between actual injection and ideal injection for the revolution, during which
the launch occurs. We have found that 60 m/sec should suffice for pushbutton errors up to ± 24 sec.

We may launch not during the most favorable revolution, but—e.g., forced by a minor launch delay—during one of the neighboring revolutions. To compensate for this time error, three basic strategies may be applied.

(1) Keep the flight duration, between launch and lunar arrival, constant. If the launch time error is Δt, then, upon arrival, the Moon will be, by the time Δt, away from its node,[1] i.e., the trajectory is not in the plane of the initial orbit. Thus, a dogleg angle μ is introduced during the orbital launch maneuver. Since such dogleg maneuvers are, energywise, quite costly, this is, generally, not a favorable strategy.

(2) Another way to compensate for the time error Δt is to hold the arrival point fixed at the node, i.e., to make up for the time Δt during the transit to the Moon, by changing both injection speed v and injection angle δ. If the launch speed is increased by Δv, the arrival speed goes up by 4.5 Δv, and, because of some losses, the total speed budget has to be increased by about 6 Δv. On the other hand, in order to decrease the flight time from 70 to 50 h, we have to increase the injection speed by only 67 m/sec. Therefore, to compensate for $\pm$ 1 revolution or $\pm$ 1.5 h, the velocity penalty is ($\pm$) 6 $\times$ 5.1 $\approx$ 30 m/sec.

(3) The optimum strategy is a combination of the two cases discussed above with some generalization: change all quantities, μ, v, δ in the optimum fashion during the powered phase, so that, considering the possibility of one or more midcourse maneuvers, the launch time error is compensated such that—compared to the ideal trajectory—minimum increase in the speed budget is incurred.

A summary for launch from orbit is given in Table 1.9. Data for an equivalent launch from Earth surface are given in Table 1.10.

The midcourse correction for the case of orbital launch is somewhat smaller, because a part of it is used up during the process of establishing a good launch orbit.

Comparing the data of Tables 1.9 and 1.10 we see that the speed requirement for orbital launch is somewhat higher (+ 60 m/sec) and that the launch tolerances are considerably smaller; furthermore, the restriction to go from Earth surface to the Moon, via a circular orbit phase, does not permit rigorous powered trajectory optimization, compared to the case without this restriction. Fortunately, this "loss" is small. Easing of the orbital launch problem occurs since only a comparatively small speed increment has to be added.

---

[1] The lunar motion in its orbit is about 0.55 deg/h.

TABLE 1.9

Launch time error	Speed budget effect (m/sec)
± 2 revolutions, "late"	± 60
± 24 sec, "pushbutton"[a]	± 60
Inclination change, midcourse correction	± 30
Total	± 150

[a] If α is the elevation angle at injection in degrees, and if Δ_0 is the injection speed for $\alpha = 0$, then, approximately, $(\Delta - \Delta_0)/\Delta_0 \approx (\frac{1}{2}\alpha/20)^2$. This equation is derived on p. 368 of Vol. 1. For a parabola, $\alpha = \frac{1}{2}$ (true anomaly), and if T is the half-launch window in minutes, then the maximum true anomaly in a low Earth orbit is given by $4T$. Using $\Delta_0 = 3225$ m/sec yields finally $\Delta - \Delta_0 \approx 16.13T^2$ m/sec; this value represents the lower limit of the velocity penalty for a given T value; numerically it follows, for $T = \pm 0.5$ min, that the velocity penalty will be a little larger than 4 m/sec, and for a velocity penalty of 60 m/sec the launch window will be smaller than ± 1.9 min. From these considerations it can be seen that the estimate for the "pushbutton error penalty" as given in the main text above is quite conservative. (From numerical studies of a Mars mission, launched from a 420 km circular Earth stellite orbit: $\Delta - \Delta_0 \approx 20\, T^2$.)

TABLE 1.10

Launch time error	Speed budget effect (estimated) (m/sec)
± 2 days, "late"	± 20
± 8 min, "pushbutton"	± 30
Inclination change, midcourse correction	± 40
Total	± 90

How often can we fire at the Moon? If we launch from the Kennedy Space Center to the Moon when the Moon is at its maximum southern declination, then, perhaps 5 days per month, and a total of 16 min per day are favorable. From the equator, one chance of 16 min duration would exist every day. From a low-altitude waiting orbit, there will be a good chance of ± 24 sec for about 5 consecutive orbits. There will be two such periods per month, if there is no regression of the nodes of the launch orbit. With a nodal regression of 6.6°/day, we get about 3.33 firing chances per month.

It is well worthwhile to look into this question of launch window in some depth (Fig. 1.28).

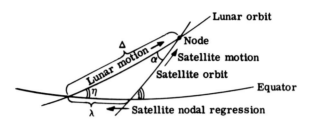

FIG. 1.28. Orbital projections. Lunar motion in orbit is 13.176°/day. Nodal regression in 96-min circular Earth satellite orbit, for $i = 28°$, is 6.6°/day.

By spherical trigonometry we know that

$$\tan \Delta = \frac{\sin i \sin \lambda}{\cos i \sin \eta - \sin i \cos \eta \cos \lambda} .$$

From this equation, regarding λ as variable due to regression of the nodes, we obtain

$$\dot{\Delta} = f(i, \lambda, \eta) \, \dot{\lambda} = F(t) \, \dot{\lambda},$$

where i and η are constants and λ is a function of t. The time duration T_L between launch chances is equal to the time duration between lunar nodal positions:

$$T_L \approx \frac{180}{13.176 + | F(t) \times 6.6 |} \quad \text{days.}$$

The average of $F(t)$, over one period T equals $\overline{F(t)}$. It is easily determined that:

$$\overline{F(t)} = \frac{1}{T\dot{\lambda}} \int_0^T F(t) \, \dot{\lambda} \, dt = \frac{1}{T\dot{\lambda}} \int_0^T \frac{\dot{\Delta}}{\dot{\lambda}} \, \dot{\lambda} \, dt = \frac{1}{2\pi} \int_0^{2\pi} d\, \Delta = 1.$$

Thus follows, on the average, that

$$T_L = \frac{180}{13.176 + 6.6} \approx 9.1 \quad \text{days,}$$

or we have, on the average, 3.33 launch chances per month, as stated before.

If the particular value of $F(t)$, instead of its average, is accounted for, then we find that T_L is, typically, between 3 and 11 days. The relative inclination α between satellite and lunar orbit is given by

$$\cos \alpha = \cos(i - \eta) - 2 \sin i \sin \eta \sin^2(\lambda/2).$$

Thus, the extremes of α are given by $|\, i - \eta\, |$ and $|\, i + \eta\, |$. The particular value of α determines the size of the launch window in the case of a constant flight-time-to-the-Moon strategy; in the case of the nodal-arrival strategy, the value of α does not effect the launch window size.

Of course, there is one launch chance daily from Earth to the waiting orbit, if this has been established by an eastward firing. The inclination of the waiting orbit should be slightly (a few degrees) larger than the latitude of the launch site because, with only a small dogleg angle ("launch maneuver"), the favorable time of launch may be as long as a sixth of the day! (See Fig. 1.29.) This presumes that it suffices just to enter the correct

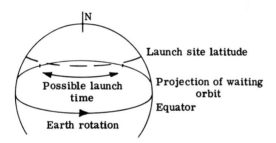

Fig. 1.29. Launch window from Earth surface to satellite orbit.

orbital plane, and that central angle and altitude within this plane are controlled otherwise, e.g., by chasing technique.[1] If exactly at injection orbital plane, central angle, and altitude shall be correct to accomplish rendezvous without further maneuvering, then firing chances are rare, unless the orbit under consideration has been chosen carefully to be "rendezvous compatible" (Petersen and Swanson, 1959).

With more inclined orbits, two launch chances each day exist, obviously, but the added duration of both of them will be shorter than the single, maximum duration (Barker and Straly, 1959).

[1] W. E. Miner and R. Silber give an exact solution in ARS preprint 2626–1962, according to which the launch window for 50 m/sec penalty extends from -1.25 to $+1.1$ h, and for 100 m/sec penalty from -1.5 to $+1.35$ h around the optimum launch time, when inclination and latitude are equal.

The trajectory requirements for a lunar impact and the available accuracies as established in Sec. 1.4,2 of this chapter are compared in Table 1.11.

TABLE 1.11

TRAJECTORY REQUIREMENTS

Injection error	Effect at lunar arrival
$\pm$ 8 min from Earth, $\pm$ 12 sec from orbit Speed $\pm$ 5 m/sec	None, if compensated (30 m/sec required speed penalty) Time $\mp$ 49 min Speed $\pm$ 19 m/sec Location: $\pm$ 1/2 R off (Lunar radius $R = 1738$ km)
Pitch angle $\pm 0.3°$	Time: $\mp$ 6 sec Location $\pm$ 1.2 R off
Azimuth $\pm 0.15°$ Radius vector 5 km	Location $\sim$ 0.4 R off Location 5 km off

We see that under the assumptions made the expected deviation would be

$$ R \left[\left(\frac{1}{2} \right)^2 + 1.2^2 + 0.4^2 \right]^{1/2} \approx 1.36R $$

or nearly all (99.7%) of the shots would lie within $\pi(1.36\ R)^2$ instead of πR^2, assuming that the listed deviations in speed, etc., were 3σ values. Then, 1 R deviation would correspond to a 2σ deviation, or 95% of the shots would hit the Moon.

Applying a vernier correction a few hours after injection should bring the deviation down to $0.3R \approx 500$ km, thus enabling an "area landing" upon the Moon. (The Soviet Lunik 2 claimed about 500 km deviation of the real from the theoretical impact point; reaching the Moon September 14, 1958 around 0° Moscow time.) One midcourse correction should easily bring us to within 50 km, and two to within 10 km of the desired landing location. From there, the terminal guidance system will compute a braking maneuver so that the landing place is less than 1 km off the desired location, and a final hovering phase will enable the vehicle to make a "spot landing" within only meters of the zero point.

The astronomical constants of the Earth-Moon system are not known with certainty. For Earth alone, $\gamma m/R$ is known not better than within $\pm \frac{1}{50}$ of 1%. This gives an uncertainty of the escape velocity of about

$\frac{1}{100}$ of 1%, or ± 1.1 m/sec. From this effect alone, there results a lunar impact speed uncertainty of 4 m/sec, an arrival time uncertainty of 10.7 min, and an impact location uncertainty of 0.01 deg or 72 km. To this must be added an uncertainty due to the solar mass (a few kilometers), due to the oblateness of the Earth (again a few kilometers), and due to the lunar mass (in spite of the relatively poor known lunar mass— $\pm 0.05\%$ uncertainty— less than 1 km). Clearly, here is a field for more fundamental research to determine astronomical constants.[1] But for the time being, midcourse guidance appears to be the simplest way to overcome this difficulty.

It is quite interesting to speculate about the requirements of a Moon-Earth flight. Since Earth appears to be nearly sky-fixed as seen from the Moon, and flight time and Earth arrival speed are quite insensitive to small initial errors Δv m/sec,

$$\Delta v_{\text{arrival}} \approx \frac{1}{3.82} \Delta v \quad \text{and} \quad \Delta T = -\frac{\Delta v}{25.5} \text{ h,}$$

the problem of just hitting Earth does not appear to be difficult.

Let us look into the geometry of a return flight. Figure 1.30 approximately describes the situation. The conditions are quite similar to those depicted in Fig. 1.22, from which the numbers have been taken.[2] We know that the return trajectory is hyperbolic with respect to the Moon, with the hyperbolic excess speed being $v_r = 1.818$ km/sec, and $v^* = 2.985$ km/sec. The speed at the injection point at 100 km altitude follows from the energy law to be 2.935 km/sec. From Eq. (4.27) of Vol. 1 we have, for the major axis, $a = 1.481 \times 10^3$ km.

The computation of the injection angle is fairly cumbersome:

(1) Assume an injection angle α_1 (for example, 45°).
(2) From Eq. (4.30) of Vol. 1: $v_1 r_1 \sin \alpha_1 = v_r a (\varepsilon^2 - 1)^{1/2}$ follows ε (1.733).
(3) From $r_1 = a(\varepsilon^2 - 1)/(1 + \varepsilon \cos \varphi_1)$ follows φ_1 (69.2°).
(4) From $r_2 = a(\varepsilon^2 - 1)/(1 + \varepsilon \cos \varphi_2)$ follows φ_2 (123.4°).
(5) From $v_2 r_2 \sin \alpha_2 = v_r a (\varepsilon^2 - 1)^{1/2}$ follows α_2 (1.75°).

If $180 - [\beta + \Delta + (\varphi_2 - \varphi_1) + \alpha_2] = 56.8°$, then α_1 was correctly chosen. In the sample case of $\alpha_1 = 45°$, we had to have $\beta + \Delta = 67.25°$. Assuming $\Delta = 3.25°$, then $\beta = 64°$, which may be quite acceptable. At cutoff, the "aiming angle" is $\beta + \Delta + \alpha_1 - 90° = 22.25°$ "below" the center of Earth. This is not difficult to instrument with the help of an Earth tracker,

---

[1] See H.G.L. Krause, On a consistent system of astrodynamic constants. NASA-G.C.M.S.F.C., MTP-P&VE-F-62-12; also, Tross (1960).

[2] Correct figures are slightly different, as mentioned in connection with Fig. 1.22.

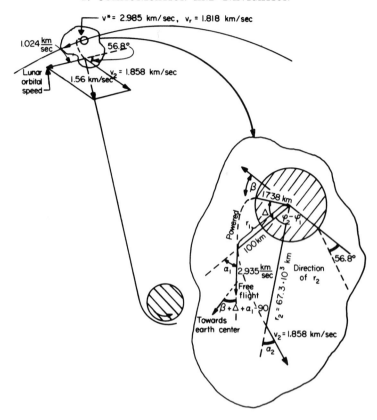

FIG. 1.30. Moon-to-Earth trip.

and a star seeker: the former is utilized to determine the angle of 22.25°, the latter to determine the flight plane. These instruments do not have to fly in the return vehicle—they might just set an inertial guidance system, and be left at the lunar surface.

Of course, atmospheric entry conditions are quite critical for a manned return vehicle, as described in the previous chapter. The return flight path

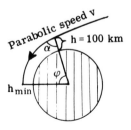

FIG. 1.31. Parabolic reentry trajectory. $\Delta h = h - h_{min}$.

has to miss Earth at a closely determined altitude, with little margin for error. We have (see Fig. 5.9 of Vol. 1) without lift: $\alpha = 84.4 \pm 0.2°$, and with a ratio of lift/drag $= 0.5$: $\alpha = 83.7 \pm 1.7°$ We will transform these angular variations into altitude variations (see Fig. 1.31.)

The equation of the parabola is

$$r = \frac{2r_{\min}}{1 + \cos \varphi};$$

from this

$$1 - \frac{2\Delta h}{R+h} = \cos \varphi,$$

or differentiating Δh and φ:

$$\delta(\Delta h) = \frac{R+h}{2} \sin \varphi \, \delta\varphi.$$

We know that

$$90 - \alpha = \tfrac{1}{2} \varphi$$

or

$$\varphi = 2(90 - \alpha),$$

and $\delta\varphi = -2 \, \delta\alpha$:

$$\delta(\Delta h) = -(R + h) \sin(180 - 2\alpha) \, \delta\alpha. \tag{1.38a}$$

This gives a margin for error for the ballistic entry of $\Delta h_{\min} \approx \pm 4.4$ km, and for the lifting entry, ± 42 km. With midcourse and terminal guidance, such accuracies seem achievable,[1] the purely ballistic case being perhaps somewhat marginal.

Earth landing location uncertainty for the ballistic entry body is shown in Table 1.12. (Total travel during aerodynamic entry is of order of 10^3–10^4 km without "skipping".) Therefore, we can expect the ballistic body to land upon Earth, timewise, not more than ± 5 min off, and locationwise, in a strip being ± 250 km long and perhaps ± 50 km wide around the theoretical location.

Applying lift, the landing time error may go up to ± 15 min, but it should be possible, with only a little control, to bring the vehicle down not more than a few kilometers (parachute drift) from the intended location. If the lift stems from wings, the accuracy of landing may be the same as in today's aircraft.

---

[1] The Apollo command module has 43 km entry corridor, returning from the moon. For coarse control of landing area, one skip is planned.

TABLE 1.12

Earth Landing Location Uncertainty

Source of error	Corresponding variation in central angle,[a] $\Delta\varphi$
Entry point to Earth atmosphere, variation	$\pm\,0.1°$ ($\pm$ 11 km)
Atmospheric parameters, variation	$\pm\,0.5°$ ($\pm$ 55 km)
Entry angle $\Delta\alpha$, variation ($\pm\,0.25°$)	$\pm\,0.5°$ ($\pm$ 55 km)
Lunar launch injection time error uncorrected $\pm\,\frac{1}{2}$ min (error due to Earth rotation during this time)	$\pm\,0.1°$ ($\pm$ 11 km)
Trajectory, transfer time variation for 1.3 m/sec injection speed variation: $\pm\,3$ min	$\pm\,0.8°$ ($\pm$ 90 km)
Total uncertainty	$\pm$ 2° ($\pm\,225$ km)

[a] Central angle of landing point, measured from Earth center.

For lunar satellites we have accuracy requirements similar to those for lunar impacts.

Circumlunar flights can have less, or more, stringent requirements, depending on characteristics of the mission. Some details have been given in Chap. 4 of Vol. 1.

Generally, errors will be corrected as soon as detected. But this is not always true—think of an example (Sec. 1.4,5 of this chapter) of directional correction with varying speed! Another exception happens for a circumlunar shot. If we plan to correct for *both* lunar approach *and* Earth return errors in one corrective impulse, then this should be given either immediately after cutoff or more than 100,000 km away from Earth. It is simpler, although energywise usually considerably worse, to give dual corrections:

(1) Correct for Moon approach only, as soon as deviations are detected.

(2) Correct for Earth return after lunar circumnavigation, again as soon as deviations are detectable, because the correction becomes rapidly more demanding in required speed (roughly, n-fold fuel requirement when the same error is corrected at $1/n$ of Earth-Moon distance instead of immediately after the circumlunar mission), and it may cost up to a hundred times more propellant than a correction right at launch would have required.

There is a "best" spot (with respect to minimum propellant) to correct for Earth return errors, which is before the lunar encounter. Unfortunately, this best spot is different, depending upon whether minimum altitude of the return trajectory or return time is corrected, and a correction of return time can influence return location adversely, and vice versa. There is the possibility to correct, e.g., return time only, without effecting return location, but such separate corrections for time and location do not lead to minimum propellant consumption.

If the closest distance to the lunar surface is equal to one lunar radius, and the total round-trip flight time is approximately equal to 160 h, then the displacement of the minimum altitude of the Earth return leg is about 300 km for 0.02° injection angle deviation, 600 km for 0.1 km injection altitude deviation, and 650 km for 0.2 m/sec injection speed deviation.

This high sensitivity demands that we make corrections soon after injection. But there are other reasons which demand corrections later:

(*a*) The information on the actual trajectory becomes better after some time due to, e.g., smoothing of tracking data.

(*b*) The deviation due to the uncertainty in our knowledge of the lunar mass can only be corrected after the lunar passage. Because of being forced to make corrections later instead of at the time of injection, about 50 m/sec ideal speed are necessary to correct for 1 m/sec initial deviation. Therefore, about 200 m/sec ideal speed may be required for corrections for a circumlunar voyage with subsequent atmospheric entry at Earth. The return conditions should have deviations from ideal in minimum altitude of not more than a few kilometers and in return time, of the order of 1 min.

The major part of the Table 1.13 stems from Líeske (1958). These values are, of course, only typical, and, in detail, they depend strongly upon the particular trajectory chosen.

Let us again draw attention to the error amplification, which occurs in close circumlunar flights. This has been described in some detail in Chap. 4. of Vol. 1. Because of the error magnification effect, the "neglected factors" from the end of Chap. 4 are of increased importance.

In order to simplify the guidance problems, the vehicle should approach the Moon only as close as is necessitated by its missions. On the other hand, trajectory sensitivity is not all bad: large arrival point shifts can be effected with little propellant consumption, if high-accuracy guidance systems are available. The final effect of a given correction, or likewise, of a given error, can be about 1–2 orders of magnitude higher when it occurs before the lunar encounter, as compared to the case when it occurs after the lunar encounter.

In this context, it should be noted that a given injection error produces, generally, a larger final deviation for a slow than for a fast trajectory. This does not necessarily mean that a larger midcourse correction speed is required, because the higher sensitivity of the slower trajectory results in a larger correction for a given midcourse maneuver.

TABLE 1.13

Lunar Mission Accuracy Requirements

Mission	Permissible errors at injection, if astronomical constants were completely known		Midcourse/terminal guidance required
	Δv(m/sec)	$\Delta \gamma$	
Just hit the Moon	± 25	± 0.5°	No
Hit within ± 170 km	1.3	0.01	Yes
Hit within ± 1 min	0.1	0.01	Yes
Lunar satellite, altitute variation ± 170 km	1.3	0.02	Yes
Final orbit not specified	Similar to "Just hit the Moon"		No, except for initiation of braking to enter orbit
Circumlunar return to Earth			
Return location not specified	50	10	No
Return within ± 1700 km	0.08	0.03	Yes
Return tangentially, with altitude variation less than ± 17 km	0.3	0.001	Yes
Hit Earth from Moon,[a] location unspecified	400	5	No
Hit tangentially, altitude variation less than ± 17 km, impact point variation less than 250 km	1	0.005	Yes

[a] Generally, the data given here agree with results quoted by Gunkel and Shulte (1960). It is discussed there that the allowable errors are a function of the lunar launch location, and to a lesser degree, of the Earth landing location.

1.4,9 Some Problems of Interplanetary Flight

Let us first look at some of the astronomical constants of the solar system. [See Herrick et al. (1957), Swanson (1957), Ehricke (1959), and Aeronutronic Publication U-583, September 1959.]

(1) *Unit of time.* This is based upon the tropical year (1900), divided by 365.24219879 days. The result is called "ephemeris mean day." The ephemeris mean second is an ephemeris mean day, divided by 86,400. These

results are in close agreement with a "mean solar day," or a "mean solar second." A "sidereal year" equals 365.25636042 mean solar days.

(2) *Masses.* Usually, the solar mass is taken to be unity. Then the ratios of the masses are:

Sun: Earth $\quad \dfrac{m_{\odot}}{m_{\oplus}} = 332{,}488 \ (1 \pm 0.00013)$

Earth: Moon $\quad \dfrac{m_{\oplus}}{m_{\mathbb{C}}} = 81.375 \ (1 \pm 0.0003)$

and $\quad \dfrac{m_{\odot}}{m_{\oplus} + m_{\mathbb{C}}} = 328{,}452 \ (1 \pm 0.00013)$

Mars: Earth $\quad \dfrac{m_{\mathring{\jmath}}}{m_{\oplus}} = 0.1072 \ (1 \pm 0.003) \qquad$ [Mariner IV: $0.107303(1 \pm 0.00015)$]

Venus: Earth[1] $\quad \dfrac{m_{\varphi}}{m_{\oplus}} = 0.8136 \ (1 \pm 0.005)$

For absolute data, we use for the gravitational constant,

$$\gamma = 6.671(1 \pm 0.0007) \times 10^{-8} \ \text{cm}^3/\text{g sec}^2,$$

and

$$m_{\oplus} = 5.975(1 \pm 0.0007) \times 10^{27} \ \text{g}.$$

The product[2]

$$k_e{}^2 = \gamma m_{\oplus} = 3.9862 \times 10^{20} \ \text{cm}^3/\text{sec}^2$$

is good to a factor of (1 ± 0.0002).

An improvement, by more than an order of magnitude, can be expected from precision observations of artificial Earth satellites.

With the mean Earth radius of

$$R_{\oplus} = 6371.104 \ (1 \pm 0.00001) \quad \text{km},$$

we get

$$\left(2 \ \frac{\gamma m_{\oplus}}{r_{\oplus}} \right)^{1/2} = 11.185 \ (1 \pm 0.0001) \quad \text{km/sec},$$

or, escape speed from Earth surface is known only to within[3] ± 1.1 m/sec.

---

[1] From Mariner II: $0.81485(1 \pm 0.00015)$.
[2] More recent data: $\gamma m_{\oplus} = 398{,}601 \pm 1$; $\gamma m_{\mathbb{C}} = 4902.60 \pm 0.12$.
[3] An order of magnitude better, using the best available data of 1965.

(3) *Radii*. This is shown in Table 1.14.

TABLE 1.14

Mean Spherical Radius

Planet	Radius (km)
Sun	696000 (1 ± 0.001)
Earth	6371.104 (1 ± 0.00001)
Moon	1738 (1 ± 0.001) [At Ranger VI, VII impact: 1735.5 ± 0.3]
Mars	3415 (1 ± 0.0075) (equatorial: 3355)
Venus	6100 (1 ± 0.01)

(4) *Orbital data*. This is shown in Table 1.15.

TABLE 1.15

Orbital Data

Planet	Major axis	Eccentricity	Inclination	
			Equator to ecliptic	Orbit to ecliptic
Earth	1.000000230 a.u.[a]	0.01673	23°27′	0
Moon	384403 ± 1 km	0.0549	1°32′	5°8′ (±10′)
Venus	0.723332 a.u.	0.00679	30° ? [b]	3°24′
Mars	1.523691 a.u.	0.09336	25°12′	1°51′

[a] a.u. = astronomical unit.

[b] Data from radar astronomy, from the Arecibo telescope: 253 ± 5 days retrograde (announced August 27, 1964). Inclination less than 6° to the vertical upon its orbital plane; actual apparent day about 119 ± 1 day.

(5) *Period of rotation*. This is shown in Table 1.16.

TABLE 1.16

Period of Rotation

Planet	Period
Earth	23 h 56 min
Moon	27 days 7 h 43 min
Mars	24 h 37 min
Venus	∼ 250 days retrograde [a]

[a] See footnote (b) of Table 1.15; also, Richardson (1958).

(6) *The Astronomical Unit.* A massless body at one astronomical unit (a.u.) distance from the Sun would have a sidereal period of

$$P = 365.2568983263$$

mean solar days (Gaussian year). From this, its speed—or the gravitational constant for the Sun—would be

$$k_s = \frac{2\pi}{P} = 0.01720209895 \, (1 \pm 2 \times 10^{-9}) \, \frac{\text{a.u.}^{3/2}}{\text{mean solar day}}.$$

With the help of Kepler's third law, the other heliocentric speeds can be expressed very accurately in such units.

Unfortunately, the length of an astronomical unit in laboratory units is not very well known. Taking recent data it appears that we know it hardly better[1] than

$$a = 149.50 \times 10^6 \, (1 \pm 0.0002) \, \text{km}.$$

Thus follows

$$k_t = 1.1510 \times 10^{13} \, (1 \pm 0.0003) \, \text{cm}^{3/2}/\text{sec}.$$

Here are only 4 significant figures against about 9 in the astronomical system of units! Further development of radar ranging of planets promises to improve our knowledge of a, by more than one or two orders of magnitude.

The mean speed of Earth going around the Sun is given by

$$v_\oplus = \frac{2\pi \times 1.00000023 \times 149.50 \times 10^6}{(1 + 1/328452) \times 365.25636042 \times 86400}$$

$$= 29.765 \, (1 \pm 0.0002) \quad \text{km/sec}.$$

So we know that value to ± 6 m/sec.[2]

By radio astronomical means, Earth's orbital speed can be measured directly. As this speed is known very accurately in (astronomical units)/ (unit of time), this is a new method to determine the length of the astronomical unit in laboratory units. Thus, the measurement of a with an error below 600 km seems possible.

---

[1] Evaluation of radar ranging of Venus gave 149.5995×10^6 km (USSR), and 149.59882×10^6 km (USA, JPL), and 149.59785×10^6 km (USA, Lincoln Lab.). (These data are as of October 1961.) From these data comes, as a mean value, $149.5987 \times 10^6 \, (1 \pm 0.000005)$ km.

[2] More recent data (December 1962): 29.785 km/sec, ± 1 m/sec.

These are, of course, just a few of the constants pertaining to the solar system. More can be found, e.g., in the quoted references.

Evidently, for numerical calculations, there is a choice as to what units to take—e.g., in a system using the astronomical unit to measure distance, we enjoy a high accuracy. More familiar to the engineer, but five orders of magnitude less accurate, is the use of a kilometer or similar laboratory unit instead. Of course, when the "accurate" result utilizing the a.u. is converted to laboratory units, the same final inaccuracy results as if we had used such units right from the start. But

(1) Sometimes the conversion to laboratory units is not necessary (e.g., in comparisons).

(2) Any improvement in the knowledge of the length of the astronomical unit does not necessitate a new computation—just the final conversion step has to be repeated.

Therefore, the suggested procedure appears to be:

In precision orbit work, use the astronomical unit, and in feasibility orbit work, a convenient laboratory unit to measure distances.

The basic requirements of a system of laboratory units are twofold:

(a) The units should be well-defined. The foot, yard, mile, etc. (British, American, international foot, etc.), obviously do not fulfill this requirement as good es the meter, kilometer, etc., do.

(b) The units should permit ease of conversion. Any decimal system has this feature. Unfortunately, there is no decimal system of time, unless we use, e.g., an hour, or day, etc. as basic unit and express every other time interval as a decimal fraction thereof.

It is a fallacy to assume that actual numbers become "more practical" (meaning less digits) in one of the possible systems: the number of digits to be written is determined only by the desired accuracy.

This may suffice on the very important subjects of basic units, and our physical knowledge about the structure of the solar system.

Now we consider the problem of hyperbolic approach to a planet:

From Fig. 1.23 and Eq. (1.35) we obtain, for the effective radius R_{eff}, with $v_{\max}^2 = v_r{}^2 + v_{\mathrm{esco}}^2$, where v_{esco} is the escape speed at the surface of the central body and v_r is the relative approach speed measured very far away from the planet:

$$\frac{R_{\mathrm{eff}}}{R} = \frac{(v_r{}^2 + v_{\mathrm{esco}}^2)^{1/2}}{v_r} = \left(1 + \frac{v_{\mathrm{esco}}^2}{v_r{}^2}\right)^{1/2}. \qquad (1.39)$$

(In the case of a launch, v_r was called "residual speed." The term "hyperbolic excess speed" is frequently used.)

For φ_1 (Fig. 1.23), we have

$$\cos \varphi_1 = \frac{R_{\text{eff}}}{\varepsilon a} = \frac{(\varepsilon^2 - 1)^{1/2}}{\varepsilon}.$$

We know that [Eq. (4.17) of Vol. 1]

$$r = \frac{a(\varepsilon^2 - 1)}{1 + \varepsilon \cos \varphi}.$$

Hence, it follows that

$$R_1 = \frac{a(\varepsilon^2 - 1)}{1 + (\varepsilon^2 - 1)^{1/2}}.$$

Whereas R_{eff} was the effective radius to hit the central body of radius R regardless of hit location, we can interpret R_{eff} also as the effective radius to hit the front side of a central body of radius R_1.

The energy per unity mass of the approaching body is known: from Eq. (4.27) of Vol. 1 we have

$$E = \frac{1}{2} v_r{}^2 = \frac{\gamma m}{2a} = \frac{1}{2} \frac{\gamma m}{R_1} \frac{R_1}{a} = \frac{1}{4} v_{\text{esco}}^2 \frac{R_1}{a},$$

or

$$\frac{a}{R_1} = \frac{1}{2} \frac{v_{\text{esco}}^2}{v_r{}^2}.$$

The constant for Kepler's second law is, from Eq. (4.26) of Vol. 1,

$$C = r_{\min} v_{\max} = v_r \, a \, (\varepsilon^2 - 1)^{1/2} = v_r \, R_{\text{eff}}.$$

From these equations,

$$(\varepsilon^2 - 1)^{1/2} = 2 \frac{R_{\text{eff}}}{R_1} \frac{v_r{}^2}{v_{\text{esco}}^2},$$

and now

$$R_1 = R_{\text{eff}} \left(1 + \frac{1}{2(R_{\text{eff}}/R_1) \, (v_r/v_{\text{esco}})^2}\right).$$

From this

$$\frac{R_{\text{eff}}}{R_1} = \frac{1}{2} (\pm) \frac{1}{2} \left(1 + 2 \, \frac{v_{\text{esco}}^2}{v_r{}^2}\right)^{1/2}. \tag{1.40}$$

Using the ratio

$$\frac{R_1}{R} = \frac{2(1 + v_{esco}^2/v_r^2)^{1/2}}{1 + [1 + 2(v_{esco}^2/v_r^2)]^{1/2}},$$

we easily obtain the result $1 \leq R_1/R \leq 2^{1/2}$, for the same effective radius R_{eff}. For the same true radius $R_1 = R$, of course, $(2^{1/2}/2) \leq [R_{eff(1)}/R_{eff}] \leq 1$, which shows that the effective radius for a hit upon the front side of the central body is somewhat smaller than for a hit regardless of hit location upon the central body.

The maximum unbraked impact speed is always given by $v_{max} = (v_{esco}^2 + v_r^2)^{1/2}$. This changes the above equations to

$$\frac{R_{eff}}{R} = \frac{v_{max}}{v_r}$$

and

$$\frac{R_{eff}}{R_1} = \frac{1}{2} + \frac{1}{2}\frac{v_{max}}{v_r}\left(2 - \frac{v_r^2}{v_{max}^2}\right)^{1/2}.$$

In the lunar example of the previous section, we had $v_r = 1.82$ km/sec and $v_{max} = 2.985$ km/sec, resulting in

$$\frac{R_{eff}}{R} = 1.64 \qquad \text{and} \qquad \frac{R_{eff}}{R_1} = 1.547,$$

which means here

$$\frac{R_{eff(1)}}{R_{eff}} = 0.944.$$

To hit the Moon on the front side is not much more difficult than to hit the Moon at all.

If—for example, for atmospheric reasons (see Fig. 1.32)—we want to arrive at a specified altitude R_2 with no more error than $\pm dR_2$, what is dR_{eff}? Since

$$\frac{R_{eff}}{R_2}\left(1 + \frac{v_{esco}^2}{v_r^2}\right)^{1/2} = \left(1 + \frac{2\gamma m}{R_2 v_r^2}\right)^{1/2},$$

we have, after differentiating

$$\frac{dR_{eff}}{dR_2} = \frac{1}{2}\left(\frac{R_{eff}}{R_2} + \frac{R_2}{R_{eff}}\right). \tag{1.41}$$

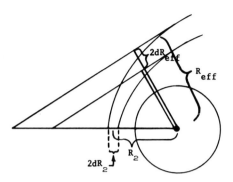

Fig. 1.32. Effective radius of central body.

Areawise, we have to compare

$$dA = (2\pi R_2)(2dR_2)$$

and

$$dA_{\text{eff}} = (2\pi R_{\text{eff}})(2dR_{\text{eff}}),$$

or

$$\frac{dA_{\text{eff}}}{dA} = \frac{R_{\text{eff}}}{R_2}\frac{dR_{\text{eff}}}{dR_2} = \frac{1}{2}\left[\left(\frac{R_{\text{eff}}}{R_2}\right)^2 + 1\right] = 1 + \frac{1}{2}\frac{v_{\text{esco}}^2}{v_r^2}.$$

According to the derivation, v_{esco} has to be taken here at R_2, which will, now, no longer be at the surface of the body. Of course,

$$(v_{\text{esco}}^2)_{R_2} = (v_{\text{esco}}^2)_{\text{surface}}\frac{R}{R_2},$$

and $\frac{1}{2}v_{\text{esco}}^2$ equals the square of the circular velocity at the same location. Again, $dA_{\text{eff}}/dA > 1$ makes the aiming problem easy.

After Eq. (5.25) of Vol. 1 we had derived, approximately, the braking from one path through the Earth's atmosphere:

$$\frac{\Delta v}{v} = - 690 \exp(- h_{\min}/H).$$

Assuming $v = 12$ km/sec, $\Delta v = - 2.4$ km/sec (or about 4 km/sec for two paths), $H = 8.5$ km, we get $h_{\min} \approx 69$ km. Assuming that we allow Δv to vary as much as ± 0.4 km/sec, allows a variation of $h_{\min}$ by ± 1.5 km. With $R_{\text{eff}}/R \approx 5$—which is approximately true for a return from Venus to Earth using a Hohmann profile—we obtain $dR_{\text{eff}} = \pm 3.8$ km. This is a very thin ring to hit from Venus; but if it can be hit, then, after two atmospheric passes, the speed is reduced to 8 ± 0.8 km/sec, and a satellite orbit can be established with little fuel consumption. Just to hit Earth, we have a much larger target of $R_{eff} \approx 32{,}000$ km. Only, approximately, 5×10^{-4} of this area is available for atmospheric braking missions!

As mentioned in Chaps. 5 (Vol. 1) and 3 (Vol. 2), there are variations in atmospheric density at a given altitude, depending upon latitude, "weather," tides, solar activity, etc. Fortunately, the unpredictable variations do not appear to be strong below 100 km altitude, but nevertheless this will further complicate atmospheric entries, and probably cut down the available entry margin. On the other hand, employing lift will widen the entry corridor. Even more complicated would be to have a rendezvous between the returning Venusian vehicle and an already existing Earth Space Station, because not only altitude, but also the other elements of the final orbit of the vehicle have to agree with prescribed values. No doubt the vehicle would need the capability to change orbital elements in order to get to the space station, or a ferry might be employed between space station and vehicle.

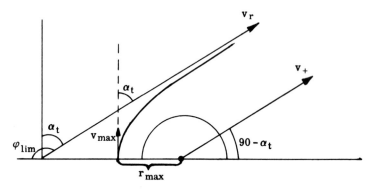

FIG. 1.33. Hyperbolic departure trajectory.

For a hyperbolic departure computation, let us assume we know the pericenter distance r_{min} and velocity v_{max}. [See Fig. 1.33.] Then ε and a follow easily [from Eqs. (4.28) and (4.34) of Vol. 1, respectively]:

$$v_{max}^2 = \gamma m \left(\frac{2}{r_{min}} + \frac{1}{a} \right)$$

and

$$C = r_{min} v_{max} = [\gamma m a (\varepsilon^2 - 1)]^{1/2}.$$

Introducing $2\gamma m/r_{\min} = v_{\text{esco}}^2$, we have

$$\frac{r_{\min}}{2a} = \frac{v_{\max}^2}{v_{\text{esco}}^2} - 1$$

and

$$\varepsilon^2 - 1 = 4 \left(\frac{v_{\max}}{v_{\text{esco}}}\right)^2 \left[\left(\frac{v_{\max}}{v_{\text{esco}}}\right)^2 - 1\right]. \tag{1.42}$$

Since

$$v_r^2 = v_{\max}^2 - v_{\text{esco}}^2 = v_{\text{esco}}^2 \frac{r_{\min}}{2a} ,$$

and the maximum angle of turn, $\varphi_{\lim}$, of the velocity vector is given by

$$\cos \varphi_{\lim} = -1/\varepsilon,$$

we obtain

$$\cos(\varphi_{\lim}) = \cos(\alpha_t + \tfrac{1}{2}\pi) = -\sin \alpha_t = -1/\varepsilon,$$

or

$$\operatorname{ctn} \alpha_t = (\varepsilon^2 - 1)^{1/2} = 2 \frac{v_{\max}}{v_{\text{esco}}} \left[\left(\frac{v_{\max}}{v_{\text{esco}}}\right)^2 - 1\right]^{1/2}. \tag{1.43}$$

It is often required that $\mathbf{v}_r$ be parallel or antiparallel to the planetary velocity $\mathbf{v}_\oplus$ around the Sun. Now think of the plane of motion of the vehicle shortly after launch—this is a plane containing $\mathbf{v}_r$ and the mass center of the planet. Since $\mathbf{v}_r$ and $\mathbf{v}_\oplus$ are parallel, and $\mathbf{v}_\oplus$ goes through the planetary mass center, this plane also contains $\mathbf{v}_\oplus$ (Fig. 1.34). Look at the great circle which this plane traces along the surface of the planet: along this circle lies the projection of the flight path upon the nonrotating planet. Now let us rotate this plane around $\mathbf{v}_\oplus$ or around the AB axis—all these planes are possible planes of motion. All the traces upon Earth form a net similar to the net of the longitudinal circles, but the poles P here are the two places A and B at which $\mathbf{v}_\oplus$ and the surface intersect. If α_t is known in degrees of arc, then injection to the free-flight trajectory must be along one of such traces, $(90 - \alpha_t)°$ away from one of the "poles" A or B, directed away from the "pole." [Which pole, is determined by whether $\mathbf{v}_r$ and $\mathbf{v}_\oplus$ are parallel, or antiparallel] To every plane belong two launch sites; one of these permits, usually, us to take advantage of the Earth's rotation, the other is hindered by the Earth's rotation. All of these launch points give the "locus of launch sites." For a given fixed launch place upon the rotating Earth, launch time and azimuth are now fixed: namely, when the launch point is carried, due to

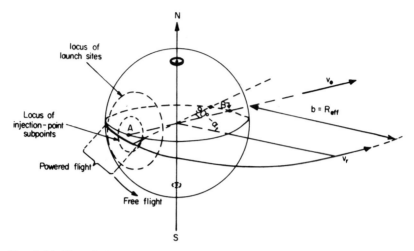

FIG. 1.34. Hyperbolic injection plane. $\mathbf{v}_\oplus$ shall be parallel to $\mathbf{v}_r$. The resulting speed relative to the Sun is $\mathbf{v}_\oplus + \mathbf{v}_r$.

Earth rotation, through the locus of launch sites, determines the launch time, and the plane containing this point, the "pole" A and the Earth's center, determines azimuth (Fig. 1.34). Favorable launch times usually occur twice every day, where one of the launchings is better with respect to getting assistance from Earth rotation.

It is interesting that the plane of the ecliptic does not enter these considerations at all. Indeed, under some circumstances the trajectory may go over the planetary poles! The same geometrical considerations are true for arrivals; the arriving vehicle will, indeed, usually not arrive within the ecliptic, or any other special plane. These considerations have a bearing upon the selection of an ideal space-port latitude upon any planet. For the much-advertised equatorial base it is valid that:

(1) For artificial satellites, no advantage compared to any latitude φ exists, if the inclination of the orbital plane is equal to or larger than φ. There is a definite advantage in order to establish an equatorial 24-h staellite. Compared to other missions, not many of these will be fired. Therefore, the dog-leg penalty may be acceptable for larger or advanced vehicles, which, in spite of dog-legging, still maintain sufficiently high payload capability.

Landing from, and supply to, an equatorial space station is somewhat simpler with an equatorial base than any other combination. Regression of nodes is not present.

(2) For lunar flights, coplanarity with the lunar plane of motion can be reached easily only from latitudes equal to or smaller than approximately

18°. Full advantage of the Earth's rotation can be taken by launching from the equator for noncoplanar flights, resulting in 18–25.75° inclination between lunar and vehicular planes of motion.

(3) For interplanetary operations, near-equatorial launch sites usually will allow the largest possible gains due to Earth rotation, with the actual maximum generally occuring for a launch site that is being of the order of 10 deg (generally, half of inclination of ecliptic) away from the equator (see Fig. 1.34).

To answer the question of whether an equatorial site should be used or not, the following considerations are pertinent:

(1) You need a general space-flight program to investigate and evaluate the operation of such a base.

(2) Make a survey of possible near-equatorial launch sites having transportation, availability, range safety, hazardous operations (e.g., nuclear propulsion), recovery of boosters and upper stages, range instrumentation, climate, earthquakes, accessibility, natural resources, sufficient size, ownership, political aspects, etc., in mind.

(3) Estimate cost of acquiring and building of the launch site in a time frame consistent with the space flight program, and compare this to the cost of extending an available base to handle the program.

(4) Estimate additional costs of operation of the equatorial base compared to the extended available base.

(5) The equatorial base will result in economic savings due to higher payload capability (Earth rotation), higher reliability of some flights (no doglegging), and sometimes simpler overall operation (supply of equatorial space station).

The grand total of the influence of the use of an equatorial base for the space-flight program can be established now, and it is seen whether savings or higher costs result. Still, the question is not solved:

(1) Is the suggested base, indeed, available?

(2) Can the available base, indeed, be extended to handle the space flight program?

(3) How sensitive is the resulting cost to changes in the program?

(4) How likely are developments that make the economic advantage of the "better" base insignificant (e.g., nuclear or solar propulsion, advanced guidance systems), thus giving more weight to other criteria?

(5) Will dangerous experiments (e.g., nuclear propulsion tests) favor (range safety) or disfavor (secrecy) an equatorial base?

(6) Will the equatorial base cost (building, etc.) or save (simplified recovery) time for an important project (e.g., man on the planets)? How much?

Indeed, the problem of the utility of an equatorial base is a very involved one, deserving close and thorough study because of the high costs and important possible consequences involved. Any answer may well be complex —e.g., the high cost of building an equatorial base may initially delay the space flight program, but later the existence of that base may accelerate it. By what yardstick should one decide? Could or should such an equatorial base be the first step towards an "International Space-Port-Earth"? If yes, how much is it worth to take the leading step in this direction? This shall suffice on the equatorial launch site.

Instead of from the planet's surface, an interplanetary trajectory may start from a planetary satellite orbit. In order to avoid excessive doglegging, the satellite plane should contain the axis AB (Fig. 1.34) at launch of the interplanetary vehicle.[1] Therefore, such satellite orbits have to be chosen carefully with respect to the final mission, and detailed investigations are required in this area to determine important operational aspects, as e.g., the utility of an established "orbital service station" or the practicality of entering the initial launch orbit upon return from the interplanetary space mission.

Launch window considerations are similar to those given in Sec. 1.4,8:

(1) The target planet-launch planet relationship has to be correct; this will occur every synodic period, and a typical window length equals 4% of the synodic period.

(2) The satellite orbital plane has to contain the axis AB (Fig. 1.34). With a nodal regression rate of 6.6°/day this occurs once every 27.3 days, assuming the direction AB to be fixed within the equator. In order to lengthen this window, one might either stop the regression by propulsive means[2] (station keeping) or one might set up the satellite in a correct plane of zero regression rate (polar plane, according to Sec. 4.4,2,4 of Vol. 1).

(3) The true anomaly has to be correct ("pushbutton error").

(4) In the case of launch from an elliptic orbit, there is the additional constraint to launch from or near the pericenter.

Some numerical data are given in Table 1.17 (Brice, 1963). Launch win-

---

[1] This means, the inclination shall not be smaller than the latitude of the points A, B. This is a necessary, but not a sufficient condition.
[2] Generally, not practical.

dow for above condition (2) is shown in Table 1.18. Pushbutton launch window [above, condition (3)] for the best revolution is shown in Table 1.19.

TABLE 1.17

Nominal Trajectory

Mission	Earth-Mars flight
Launch date (nominal)[a]	18.5 March 1975
Arrival date	4 November 1975
Trip duration (nominal)	231 days
Initial orbit	Circular
Altitude	420 km
Inclination	28.5 deg
Ideal impulsive launch speed	7.82 km/sec

[a] On the nominal launch date, the satellite orbital plane contains the axis AB (Fig. 1.34) [i.e., condition (2) above is satisfied].

TABLE 1.18

Launch Window around Nominal Date

Days-before till days-after nominal date	4.4–3.7	1.4–1.3	0.92–0.92
Speed penalty (m/sec)	500	100	50

TABLE 1.19

Pushbutton Window

Minutes-before till after best moment	3.5–4.5	1.82–2.09	1.3–1.5
Speed penalty (m/sec)	400	100	50

Since these penalties of Tables 1.18 and 1.19 represent idealized lower limits, realistic penalties will be larger.

Launch window No. 2 can be increased considerably by multi-impulse maneuvers, at the price of increased complexity. Such multi-impulse maneuvers can be described as follows:

Two-impulse. One impulse to depart from orbit, and a second impulse later. Inclination change and injection energy are distributed between these two maneuvers.

Three-impulse.

IMPULSE No. 1. Injection into an elliptic orbit, at pericenter of ellipse, plus some inclination change.

IMPULSE No. 2. At apocenter, correct inclination and—if applicable— change pericenter slightly.

IMPULSE No. 3. At pericenter, injection into final trajectory.

Four-Impulse.

IMPULSE No. 1. As 1 above.

IMPULSE No. 2. At apocenter, correct inclination and circularize.

IMPULSE No. 3. Inclination change, and initiation of an elliptic orbit back to low altitude.

IMPULSE No. 4. As 3 above.

To give numerical data, the three-impulse maneuver can reduce the penalty for an angle of 50° between orbital and flight plane to 200 m/sec, having a ratio of (apocenter)/(pericenter) < 50.

The four-impulse maneuver is similar to the three-impulse one; but in addition to increasing launch window No. 2, it practically eliminates window No. 4 by permitting rotation of the line of apsides.

For an exact study of the single-impulse interplanetary launch window, we introduce

(1) Hyperbolic excess velocity, determined by direction AB and speed, or right ascension α, declination δ, speed v_∞, which are slowly varying functions of time T (days).

(2) Assembly orbit, determined by right ascension of ascending node $\Omega(t)$, inclination γ (constant), argument of pericenter $\omega(t)$, major axis a (constant), eccentricity ε (constant), which are medium fast variable functions of time t (hours). The usual choice is a circular orbit, i.e., $\varepsilon = 0$ and ω undefined.

(3) Motion of vehicle in assembly orbit up to launch, determined by its true anomaly $\varphi(\tau)$, being a function rapidly changing with time τ (seconds).

For a given time instant, all elements are determined, and the solution for finding the required speed increment Δv to launch the vehicle is uniquely defined, assuming launch occurs in the general direction of orbital motion.

Finding the best location within the orbit (or best φ value) is the problem of the pushbutton window.

Finding the best value of Ω constitutes the problem of the plane window.

Generally, this means that the trace of the assembly orbit shall go through the point (α, δ). If δ is not very different from γ, this condition can be approximately fulfilled for quite a long time period (several days), or for two briefer time periods being separated by a few days.

The interplanetary window is, of course, determined by the minimum of v_∞.

In reality, matters are more complicated than described so far. Let us assume we want to optimize a vehicle for a simple Earth-Mars flyby-Earth mission. There is one particular instant of launch T_0 coupled with a particular instant of return T_1 for which the overall initial mass in Earth orbit is minimized. Let us say that the launch window limits are $\pm \Delta T$, from the optimum launch time T_0. We can find for all given launch dates between $T_0 - \Delta T$ and $T_0 + \Delta T$ the corresponding Earth return dates $T_1{}'$ so that the initial mass in Earth orbits is minimized for each case. Then we pick the case leading to the largest Earth braking requirement, load the spacecraft life support system, etc., according to the largest mission duration, and provide an orbital booster sufficient for this payload and the largest orbital injection requirement. This vehicle would indeed be capable of covering the entire launch window. But it will be unnecessarily heavy, if largest orbital launch requirement and largest Earth return braking requirement do not occur for the same flight. This is easily seen: picking, e.g., the flight leading to largest Earth return requirement, we would not quite use up the propellants in the orbital booster. Conceivably, we could utilize part of this propellant excess for a non-optimum injection such that the Earth return requirement is reduced, i.e., the braking stage becomes smaller. Now we have a lighter vehicle than before, still covering the total launch window.

At higher complexity, even more improvement will result if unused injection stage propellants can be transferred to the braking stage for later usage.

Above considerations become considerably more complex for stopover missions. But the principle is now clear:

(A) In general, there is a launch time T_0 and return time T_1 leading to minimum initial mass. (This is true for given mission duration; or given stay-time at target: or without such restrictions.)

(B) For a given time $T_0{}'$ near T_0 there is a return time $T_1{}'$ leading to minimum initial mass, for given launch time ("optimum mission").

(C) The vehicle of minimum initial mass for a given launch window $T_0 - \Delta T$ to $T_0 + \Delta T$ will have to fly nonoptimum missions, generally.

(D) For a vehicle having a launch window, it will not always be possible to use up all available propellants.

As to the problem of compatibility of flight mechanics between an orbital launch facility and interplanetary trajectories, it was shown by Croft [1965] that an arbitrarily chosen facility (circular orbit of 485 km altitude and 32° inclination) was compatible with all 27 Mars/Venus launch window, which were investigated for a 15 year time period.

The reader should by now have a good comprehension of the launch window problem. Its operational importance can hardly be overestimated and many supporting concepts (e.g., orbital support facility, orbital launch base, etc; and orbital operations around the target planet) have to be closely integrated with it. Only after this integration has been performed can the true utility or practicality of such supporting concepts be assessed properly.

Let us go back to a typical example of interplanetary flight. We will pick an Earth-to-Mars coplanar near minimum-energy or Hohmann transfer, with Mars being, upon arrival, at its pericenter, and the vehicle intending to impact upon Mars (see Fig. 1.35). First, we regard only the two-body

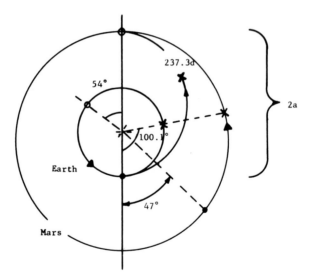

Fig. 1.35. Earth-to-Mars low energy coplanar trajectory.

problem Sun-vehicle where, for the Sun-Earth (circular orbit), $r_{\min} = 1.000\ 000$ a.u.; for Sun-Mars (pericenter of Mars = apocenter of transfer orbit) $r_{\max} = (1 - \varepsilon_\delta)a_\delta = 1.381439$ a.u.; $a = \frac{1}{2}(r_{\min} + r_{\max}) = 1.190720$;

eccentricity of trajectory ε: $1.000\,000 = a(1 - \varepsilon)$, or $\varepsilon = 0.160172$. The period equals double the Earth-Mars travel time, T. From Kepler's third law:

$$(2T)^2 = a^3,$$

or

$$T = \tfrac{1}{2}a^{3/2} = 0.6496612 \quad \text{Gaussian years}$$
$$= 237.3 \quad \text{days.}$$

The Earth rotates, in this time, through an angle of

$$360 \times \frac{237.3}{365.26} \approx 234°.$$

The Martian period is

$$P = (1.5237)^{3/2} \times 365.257 = 687.5 \text{ days.}$$

Question. How far did Mars move during 237.3 days?
   From Eq. (4.39) of Vol. 1,

$$\frac{2\pi}{687.5} \times 237.3 = \nu - 0.09336 \sin \nu,$$

therefore,

$$\nu = 128.9°;$$

and from Eq. (4.38) of Vol. 1,

$$\tan \frac{\varphi}{2} = \left(\frac{1.09336}{0.90664} \right)^{1/2} \tan 64.45,$$

$$\varphi = 133.0°,$$

or

$$180 - \varphi = 47°.$$

Opposition of Earth-Mars occurs some time after launch. When? We will look very roughly into this:
   Since the Earth mean angular speed is $(360)/(365.256) = 0.98561$ degrees per day, and the Mars mean angular speed is $(360)/(687.5) = 0.52364$ degrees per day, Earth is catching up at the rate of 0.46197 degrees per day. To catch up by 47° takes 101.7 days, or 100.1 degrees of Earth motion after launch. Therefore, the proper launch time is 101.7 days before opposi-

tion. Using Earth (average) speed $v_\oplus$, we get for the solar-centered launch speed, for the vehicle,

$$v_p{}^2 = v_\oplus{}^2 \frac{a_\oplus}{a} \frac{1 + \varepsilon}{1 - \varepsilon}.$$

Since

$$a(1 - \varepsilon) = a_\oplus,$$

we get, finally,

$$v_p = v_\oplus(1 + \varepsilon)^{1/2}$$

or, numerically,

$$\frac{v_p - v_\oplus}{v_\oplus} = (1 + \varepsilon)^{1/2} - 1 = 0.0771125 \approx \frac{\varepsilon}{2}.$$

The speed $v_r = v_p - v_\oplus$ is that which the vehicle has to add to Earth's velocity. We look now upon the two-body problem, vehicle-Earth, and arrange conditions so that, after a hyperbolic launch from Earth, we have residual speed v_r just equal to $v_p - v_\oplus$. Doing so, we treat the 4-body problem (Sun, 2 planets, vehicle), as three two-body problems. The results are obviously only an approximation—hopefully, a good one.

Therefore, we desire

$$v_r = v_p - v_\oplus = 2.2953 \ (1 \pm 0.0002) \quad \text{km/sec.}$$

So this value is known to about ± 0.5 m/sec.

The mean Martian orbital speed is, taking $v_\oplus$ for unity,

$$v_\delta = v_\oplus \left(\frac{1.000000}{1.523691} \right)^{1/2} = v_\oplus \times 0.810125,$$

and

$$v_{\delta \, \text{max}} = v_\delta \left(\frac{1 + \varepsilon}{1 - \varepsilon} \right)^{1/2} = v_\oplus \times 0.889644.$$

Apocenter speed of the vehicle in its orbit around the Sun is, from Kepler's second law,

$$v_A = v_p \times \frac{1.000000}{1.381439}$$

$$= v_\oplus \times \frac{1.0771125}{1.381439} = v_\oplus \times 0.779704.$$

Therefore, Mars is faster than the vehicle by

$$v_{r2} = v_{\vartheta} - v_A = v_{\oplus} \times 0.109940 = 3.27236 \ (1 \pm 0.0002) \quad \text{km/sec.}$$

Again, changing to a vehicle-Mars two-body problem, unretarded impact speed upon Martian surface follows from

$$v_{\max 2}^{\,2} = v_{\text{esco }\vartheta}^2 + v_{r2}^2,$$

or, numerically, with

$$v_{\text{esco }\vartheta}^2 = 25.003 \ (1 \pm 0.011) \quad (\text{km/sec})^2$$

and

$$v_{\text{esco }\vartheta} = 5.000 \ (1 \pm 0.006) \quad \text{km/sec,}$$

we obtain

$$v_{\max 2} = 5.975 \ (1 \pm 0.004) \quad \text{km/sec.}$$

The effective Martian radius for impacts from Earth is, therefore,

$$R_{\text{eff }\vartheta} = R_{\vartheta} \frac{v_{\max}}{v_r} \approx 6230 \quad \text{km.}$$

The ideal minimum launch speed from Earth v_m (for zero altitude, neglecting air drag) is, similarly,

$$v_m = (v_{\text{esco }\oplus}^2 + v_r{}^2)^{1/2} = 11.418 \quad \text{km/sec,}$$

or only 233 m/sec more than the Earth escape speed. The effective radius (b in Fig. 1.34) $b \approx 31720$ km. As this is even larger than the numerical uncertainty of the astronomical unit, precision computations have to take this translation of the vehicle, with respect to Earth, into account. We will neglect it here.

The launch consists of two maneuvers: Earth escape and providing for v_r. Here we have combined these propulsion periods. Another possibility would be to do an Earth escape and add v_r sufficiently far away from Earth; this second method is energywise worse as it violates the principle of depositing propellant clouds at low potential energy, or in other words. it violates the rule to avoid burning at (extreme) altitudes. Indeed, the minimum requirement would then be the full value of v_r over escape speed, or 2.062 km/sec more than in the "combined" case.

In 1928, Oberth described very clearly this advantage of "combination of propulsive periods" (Oberth, 1928).

But the "two-propulsive-periods" method has one advantage: the direction of the first maneuver (Earth escape) is no longer important at all.

This means that the escape can be made taking full advantage of any velocity which the vehicle may already possess, e.g., any orbital speed around Earth, and $\mathbf{v}_r$ is added correctly, when the vehicle is sufficiently far away from Earth. Therefore, when launching for Mars from an Earth satellite orbit, the spatial orientation of which is completely "wrong," there are no larger losses involved than 2.062 km/sec. Still, this loss appears to be unbearably high for chemical propulsion systems.

We have

$$v_r^{\,2} = v_m^{\,2} - v_{\text{esc}\,\oplus}^2 ,$$

or differentiating, and having $\partial v_m = 0$:

$$| \,\partial v_r \,| = \frac{v_{\text{esc}\,\oplus}}{v_r} \,| \,\partial v_{\text{esc}\,\oplus} \,| \,.$$

The astronomical uncertainty of $\partial v_{\text{esc}\,\oplus}$ was ± 1.1 m/sec—so, from this source,

$$| \,\partial v_r \,| = \pm \, 5.4 \text{ m/sec.}$$

Adding the ± 0.5 m/sec of astronomical uncertainty of v_r itself, we wind up purely from the point of view of lack of precision of astronomical data with an uncertainty value of ± 6 m/sec for the heliocentric apocenter speed $v_p = 32.060$ km/sec. It is interesting to remark that the uncertainty of $v_\oplus$ (6 m/sec) does not greatly effect the computation. The reason is that we take this speed as reference speed, and presumably a vehicle speed could precisely equal Earth speed around the Sun without knowing the exact the numerical value of it.

From Eq. (4.20) of Vol. 1, we have

$$\frac{1}{2} v^2 + E_{\text{pot}} = - \frac{\gamma m}{2a} = - \frac{v_\oplus^{\,2}}{2} \frac{a_\oplus}{a} .$$

Differentiating a with respect to v yields

$$\frac{da}{a} = 2 \left(\frac{v}{v_\oplus} \right)^2 \frac{a}{a_\oplus} \frac{dv}{v} . \qquad (1.44)$$

With

$$\frac{v}{v_\oplus} = \frac{v_p}{v_\oplus} = 1.0771125,$$

$$\frac{a}{a_\oplus} = \frac{1.190720}{1.000000} ,$$

and

$$\frac{dv}{v} = \frac{dv}{v_p} = \frac{6}{32060} = 0.000187,$$

we obtain

$$\frac{da}{a} = 0.000519 \qquad \text{or} \qquad da \approx \pm\, 77{,}500 \text{ km.}$$

Let us assume that v_p is, indeed, 6 m/sec high. What is the error angle δ (Fig. 1.36)?

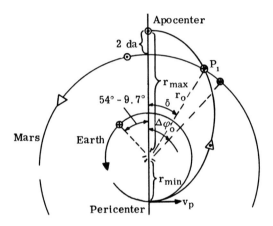

FIG. 1.36. Earth-Mars half-ellipse trajectory. $2a' = 2(a + da)$; $r_{\min} = a'(1 - \varepsilon')$; $\varepsilon = 1 - r_{\min}/a$; $d\varepsilon = (r_{\min}/a)\, da/a$.

The polar equations of the elliptic orbit are [from Eq. (4.37) of Vol. 1]

$$r = \frac{a(1 - \varepsilon^2)}{1 + \varepsilon \cos \varphi} = a(1 - \varepsilon \cos \nu).$$

Substituting $\varphi = \tfrac{1}{2}\pi - \delta$, $r = r_\delta$, $a = a'$, $\varepsilon = \varepsilon'$, we have

$$\cos \varphi = -\cos \delta = -(1 - \sin^2 \delta)^{1/2} \approx -1 + \tfrac{1}{2} \sin^2 \delta,$$

and

$$r_\delta \approx \frac{a'(1 - \varepsilon'^2)}{1 - \varepsilon' + \tfrac{1}{2}\varepsilon' \sin^2 \delta} = \frac{a'(1 + \varepsilon')}{1 + [\varepsilon'/2(1 - \varepsilon')] \sin^2 \delta}$$

$$= \frac{r_{\max}}{1 + [\varepsilon'/2(1 - \varepsilon')] \sin^2 \delta}.$$

From this we easily obtain

$$\frac{r_{max} - r_\delta}{r_{max}} = \frac{\varepsilon'}{2(1 - \varepsilon')} \delta^2$$

and, after rearranging,

$$\delta \approx 2 \left\{ \frac{1 - \varepsilon}{\varepsilon} \frac{da}{r_\delta} \right\}^{1/2} \tag{1.45}$$

Similarly, the correction for the eccentric anomaly ν is

$$\mu \approx 2 \left\{ \frac{1 + \varepsilon}{\varepsilon} \frac{da}{r_{max}} \right\}^{1/2} \tag{1.46}$$

$$= 2 \left\{ \frac{1}{\varepsilon} \frac{da}{a} \right\}^{1/2}. \tag{1.47}$$

Thus[1]

$$\frac{\delta}{\mu} = \left\{ \frac{1 - \varepsilon}{1 + \varepsilon} \right\}^{1/2}.$$

The flight time through the half-ellipse has changed from T to $T' = T + dT$, where $T = \frac{1}{2} a^{3/2}$, and $dT/T = \frac{3}{2} da/a$.

From Eq. (4.39) of Vol. 1 follows, for the flight time dt from the apocenter to the point P_1,

$$\frac{dM}{d\nu} = \frac{r}{a},$$

or

$$\frac{2\pi}{2T} \frac{dt}{\mu} = -\frac{r_{max}}{a},$$

$$dt = -\frac{T}{\pi}(1 + \varepsilon)\mu.$$

Calling the "ideal" flight time T, the "new" flight time from pericenter to P_1 is equal to

$$t = T + dT + dt$$

$$= T \left(1 + \frac{3}{2} \frac{da}{a} - \frac{1 + \varepsilon}{\pi} \mu \right),$$

---

[1] The following relation follows also from Eq. (4.38) of Vol. 1, by putting $\varphi = 180 - \delta$ and $\nu = 180 - \mu$.

or the shortening of the flight time is

$$\frac{T-t}{T} = \frac{\Delta t}{T} = \frac{1+\varepsilon}{\pi}\mu - \frac{3}{2}\frac{da}{a}. \tag{1.48}$$

How far does Mars move in the time Δt? For Mars, there is again, from Eq. (4.39) of Vol. 1,

$$\Delta v_\delta = \frac{2\pi}{1-\varepsilon_\delta}\frac{\Delta t}{P_\delta},$$

or

$$\Delta\varphi_\delta = \left(\frac{1+\varepsilon_\delta}{1-\varepsilon_\delta}\right)^{1/2}\Delta v_\delta \approx \frac{(1+\varepsilon_\delta)}{(1-\varepsilon_\delta)} \times 2\pi \times \frac{T}{P_\delta}\frac{\Delta t}{T}. \tag{1.49}$$

How does this look numerically? We started out with a heliocentric over-speed of 6 m/sec. This resulted in [from Eq. (1.44)]

$$\frac{da}{a} = 0.000519.$$

The angle μ is (using for r_δ, the Martian pericenter value; for precision computation, an iteration must be applied), from Eqs. (1.45) and (1.46),

$$\mu = 0.1138 = 6.51° \quad \text{and} \quad \delta = 0.0967 = 5.54°$$

From Eq. (1.48), we obtain

$$\frac{\Delta t}{T} = 0.0420 - 0.0008 = 0.0412,$$

$$\Delta t = 0.0412 \cdot 237.3 = 9.8 \text{ days.}$$

(Hence, the Earth is $0.98561 \times 9.8 = 9.66°$ before the Hohmann arrival position.) Since, from Eq. (1.49),

$$\Delta\varphi_\delta = 0.1076 = 6.16°$$

the vehicle passes in front of Mars by an angular distance

$$\Delta\varphi_\delta - \delta = 0.0109 = 0.625°$$

or

$$0.0109 \times 1 \cdot 3814 \times 149.5 \times 10^6 = 2.25 \times 10^6 \text{ km.}$$

Mars is, thereafter, catching up, and vehicle-Mars pass each other at a distance of about 2 da = 150,000 km, shortly before the vehicle has reached its apocenter. During passage, the vehicle is farther away from the Sun than Mars. The vehicle starts dropping back towards the Sun, and when it again passes the Martian orbit, Mars is leading more than 0.625°, disregarding Martian perturbations upon the vehicle trajectory.

Therefore, the astronomical uncertainty alone is such as to induce a miss of 150,000 km for the chosen example, mainly due to lack of knowledge pertaining to k_e.

Let us now assume that the astronomical data were completely known. At launch from Earth, maximum geocentric cutoff speed may be 1.2 m/sec h gh (Ehricke, 1958). Because

$$v_r{}^2 = v_{\max}^2 - v_{\mathrm{esc}\ \oplus}^2,$$

we get

$$| \, \partial v_r \, | = \frac{v_{\max}}{v_r} | \, \partial v_{\max} | \, ,$$

or, here,

$$\partial v_r = + 6 \quad \mathrm{m/sec}.$$

If the geocentric cutoff angle were correct, Eq. (1.43) (see Fig. 1.33 for α_T) would read

$$\mathrm{ctn}\, \alpha_T = 2 \frac{v_{\max}}{v_{\mathrm{esco}}} \left[\left(\frac{v_{\max}}{v_{\mathrm{esco}}} \right)^2 - 1 \right]^{1/2},$$

$$d\alpha_T = - 2 \sin^2 \alpha_T \frac{2(v_{\max}/v_{\mathrm{esco}})^2 - 1}{[(v_{\max}/v_{\mathrm{esco}})^2 - 1]^{1/2}} \frac{dv_{\max}}{v_{\mathrm{esco}}},$$

and

$$\sin^2 \alpha_T = \frac{1}{4(v_{\max}/v_{\mathrm{esco}})^2[(v_{\max}/v_{\mathrm{esco}})^2 - 1] + 1} \, .$$

Approximately, for $v_{\max}/v_{\mathrm{esco}} \approx 1$,

$$d\alpha_T \approx - \frac{2(v_{\mathrm{esco}}/v_{\max})^4}{[(v_{\max}/v_{\mathrm{esco}})^2 - 1]^{1/2}} \frac{dv_{\max}}{v_{\mathrm{esco}}}.$$

Here,

$$d\alpha_T \approx - \frac{2[11{,}185/(11{,}185 + 233)]^4}{[(1 + 233/11{,}185)^2 - 1]^{1/2}} \frac{1.2}{11{,}185}$$

$$\approx - \frac{1.00}{10^3} \, \mathrm{rad} \approx - 0.06°.$$

Therefore, $\mathbf{v}_r$ and $\mathbf{v}_\oplus$ are no longer parallel—as seen from the Sun $\mathbf{v}_r$ has an outward component of $1.00 \times 10^{-3} v_r \approx 2.33$ m/sec. So, the solar centered initial speed v_p is not only approximately 6 m/sec high, but inclined outward by an angle of about

$$\frac{2.33}{32{,}060} = \frac{0.73}{10^4} \approx 15''.$$

We have the interesting result that a pure speed error introduces an angular error also. But, because of the smallness of the angle, we expect the effect to be comparable to the effect of the astronomical uncertainty.

Similarity, if $\mathbf{v}_{max}$ is off by $1°$, then $\mathbf{v}_r$ is off by about $2°$, and finally v_p off by about

$$d\beta \approx 2 \frac{v_r}{v_p} \approx 0.15°,$$

and speedwise short by

$$v_r(1 - \cos 2°) \approx v_r \times \tfrac{1}{2} \sin^2 2° \approx 1.4 \quad \text{m/sec.}$$

So, the purely angular error induces a speed error also. Let us consider this case further. From Eq. (4.153) of Vol. 1 we have

$$d\beta = \frac{\varepsilon}{1 + \varepsilon} d\varphi ,$$

if φ is zero and both $d\beta$ and $d\varphi$ are sufficiently small. Thus

$$d\varphi = \frac{1 + \varepsilon}{\varepsilon} d\beta .$$

For $\varepsilon = 0.16$ and $d\beta = 0.15°$, the vehicle is at an anomaly of $d\varphi = 1.088°$, or about $S = 149.5 \times 10^6 \times (1.088/57.3) \approx 2.83 \times 10^6$ km past its pericenter. There is the relationship

$$\frac{dr}{r \, d\varphi} = d\beta ,$$

or

$$dr = r \frac{1 + \varepsilon}{\varepsilon}(d\beta)^2 = S \, d\beta \approx 6100 \quad \text{km,}$$

which is equal to the distance of the pericenter of the heliocentric trajectory from the orbit of Earth.

We found before that 2 da equalled 150,000 km for a 6-m/sec heliocentric speed deviation.

For a speed deficit of 1.4 m/sec, we expect an approximately 35,000-km trajectory apocenter deviation, which leaves the apocenter 35,000 − 6100 ≈ 29,000 km inside Mars' orbit.

Since the speed error builds up as the square of the angular error, about 2.275 deg of geocentric injection-error are equivalent to $(2.275)^2 \times 29,000$ ≈ 150,000 km deviation, or in other words, equivalent to a geocentric speed error of 1.2 m/sec. We see that control of cutoff speed appears to be more critical than control of cutoff angle.

If we want to hit Mars, the deviation at arrival at the target has to be below the effective radius of 6230 km. This leaves about

$$\frac{6250}{150,000} \times 1.2 \approx 5 \text{ sec/cm}$$

for geocentric injection speed error, if no other errors are present, or

$$\left(\frac{6250}{29,000}\right)^{1/2} \times 1 \approx 0.465°$$

geocentric injection angle error, if this is the only deviation.

At very high speeds there is an interesting reversal: the trajectory is a straight line from Earth to Mars. The flight time is of the order of distance d divided by speed v, and the time variation dt due to a speed error dv is $dt/t = -\ dv/v$. The allowable time variation is approximately the time Mars takes to move one radius: $\Delta t = \pm\ 141$ sec, since, for high speeds, effective and geometric radius are equal. So, for the allowable maximum speed error,

$$|\ \Delta v\ | = \frac{v^2}{d} \times 141.$$

or for $v = 100$ km/sec and $d = 150 \times 10^6$ km, $\Delta v = \pm\ 9.4$ m/sec, instead of 5 cm/sec.

But the maximum allowable angular error is only $\pm\ (3415)/(150 \times 10^6)$ rad ≈ $\pm\ 4.6''$, instead of 0.46°. This shows how dangerous it is to generalize results.

Timing of launch from Earth is not much more critical for interplanetary than for lunar flights.

During one day, Earth rotation is the decisive factor. If injection angle is corrected for Earth rotation, there should be a time span of several minutes in which to launch. Of course, if we leave from a low satellite orbit, timing is more critical by a factor of[1] about 30—but there are 15 chances per day.

The flight trajectory is very sensitive to small geocentric cutoff speed variations. Due to the astronomical uncertainties alone, the transfer time varies by about ± 1 week. Therefore, small cutoff velocity adjustments should make launch easily possible for a time duration of about ± 10 days around the "design" day.

We can draw the following conclusions:

(1) Energywise, a minimum energy voyage to Mars demands hardly more than a lunar trip—even less, if aerodynamic braking to land is used for Mars, and rocket braking for the Moon. Travel times are fairly long.

(2) A good injection guidance system[2] (including Vernier phase; without it about 3 times as much deviation) may get us within 0.5×10^6 km of Mars, with a noticeable fraction of this deviation being due to lack of knowledge about astronomical data.

(3) So a midcourse guidance system is required to improve on this deviation by a factor of 10^2, leaving 5000 km deviation. This enables Martian impacts.

(4) Furthermore, a two-phase terminal guidance system is necessary for precision-type missions: the first phase reduces the deviation to 50 km, and the second phase to perhaps 2 km. Controlled touchdown, correction of a Martian satellite orbit, etc., would enable us to finally terminate a mission with only a negligible deviation.

There are many more considerations which have to be made for interplanetary flights. Let us, very coarsely, look at a few:

(1) *Flight objective.* Let us consider a flight from Earth to Mars. The objective might be

(a) Planetary probe. To measure data in interplanetary space; perhaps a planet shall be passed at some, usually not rigidly specified, distance, and

---

[1] A factor of 15 due to the higher angular speed and a factor 2 due to the higher average speed, making directional corrections more propellent consuming.

[2] Mariner II—discussed in Sec. 1.1— has demonstrated that a single impulse late vernier or early midcourse maneuver, based on radio tracking and commanded from Earth, together with a fairly simple inertial injection guidance system and a likewise simple celestial reference attitude control system, can provide sufficient accuracy for flights to the close vicinity of the near planets. A corrective speed capability of 45 m/sec would have been sufficient for 99% of the launch cases; Mariner II actually provided 61 m/sec, and required 31.16 m/sec.

some measurements be done regarding this planet. Test of guidance and communication equipment, improvement on astronomical constants, etc.

(b) Planetary impact.

(c) Planetary satellite. Specifications might be just to establish any satellite orbit, or a more or less rigidly defined one (e.g., any circular orbit up to rendezvous with an already existing artificial or natural satellite). Perturbations from natural satellites may present serious stability problems—think, e.g., of Jupiter's system. From the satellite, one or several landers or satelloids proceed to the planetary surface. For energy economy, the planetocentric plane of arrival and the final satellite orbital plane should be identical. The sense of motion in the satellite orbit should be determined by the direction of the unbraked vehicle speed at the planetocentric pericenter. The planetocentric plane of arrival can be controlled by spending only a very little energy, as described (see Fig. 1.34) in some detail for the departure from a planet. The direction of the unbraked vehicle speed, at planetocentric pericenter, is controlled by the side of the planet, at which—being already in the correct plane—the planet is approached by the vehicle.

(d) Planetary landings. Corresponding considerations are valid for landing upon the planetary surface, either directly or via a satellite orbit: directions and planes of motion should be chosen so as to benefit from the planet's rotation.

(e) Landing upon a natural planetary satellite. Apart from research pertaining to the corresponding planet, these satellites present a field of their own. Besides, this would eliminate the stability problems mentioned under (c) and might provide some meteor and radiation protection in addition to a firm base for certain instruments (say, astronomical telescopes).

(f) Return mission for the preceding cases. As shown, there has to be a certain relative position between launch and target planet in order to launch for a connecting flight. Therefore, we have to wait after arrival at the other planet until such a favorable position, with respect to Earth, occurs.

Instead of having a return flight, a much larger payload could be carried for a simpler one-way mission, enabling, e.g., longer payload lifetime, higher component reliability, and better communication. This has to be carefully evaluated, an dtrade-off studies have to be performed to plan unmanned missions.

(g) Flyby missions. Flyby trips are planned such that the vehicle passes reasonably close to one or several planets or fulfills some other interplanetary mission, and returns to Earth or its vicinity without a waiting period at any of the target planets. Whether return to Earth, or Earth vicinity only, is anticipated, is a question of guidance accuracy and whether the capability for aerodynamic entry or rocket braking exists. En route, propulsion may or may not be required. After return to Earth vicinity, the vehicle would pass Earth and again go out into interplanetary space, but not, usually, come close to any other planet for a long time.

(2) *Trajectory types* (Figs. 1.37 and 1.38). This is a short survey only. This subject is considered more fully in Chapter 7 of Vol. 1.

(a) Hohmann ellipses. These trajectories are characterized by a transfer angle of 180° and are, both at launch and arrival, tangential to the planetary orbits. Energy requirements are often minimum.

(b) Cutting ellipses. The flight trajectories are ellipses which are at one or both ends, nontangential to the planetary orbits. Flight time can be reduced, energy requirement is higher, compared to (a).

(c) Parabolic/hyperbolic orbits. Similar to (a) and (b), a time reduction results at the price of higher energy requirements.

(d) Roundtrips. We have to mention the Hohmann roundtrip of about $1\frac{1}{2}$ yr duration, which is composed of 3 Hohmann trajectories. It requires enroute propulsion maneuvers.

More recently, the 1 yr Crocco roundtrip has been proposed (VII International Astronautical Congress, Rome, 1956). Similarly, modified Crocco or resonance flights are possible, where m vehicle periods equal n Earth periods. For energy reasons, the angle β should be as small as possible; in the $m \neq n$ cases, $\beta = 0$ can be useful.

Straight-line or symmetric trips should be listed. Out-of-the-ecliptic flights might be of interest.

(3) *General remarks concerning trajectories.*

(a) Trajectories can be flown in the same direction as the planets move, or in the opposite way. Energy requirements go up very much at no advantage—therefore, such "opposite" trajectories are impractical, and of theoretical interest only.

(b) Periodic orbits may have the property that the vehicle has to go through more than one period before the objective is accomplished. Long flight times can be involved, but sometimes more favorable geometric conditions between Earth and target during vehicle-target rendezvous can be obtained. The possibility of modification of trajectories by close encounters (gravitational maneuvering) has to be mentioned.

(c) In the Mars sample computation, it was shown that a very small

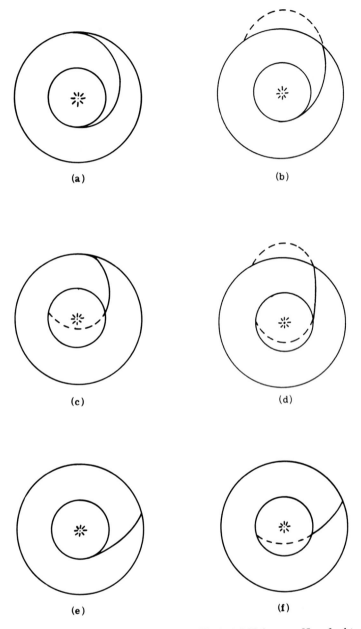

Fig. 1.37. Interplanetary trajectory types. *Elliptic*: (a) Hohmann; No. of subtypes, 1. (b) One side cutting; No. of subtypes, 2. (c) One side cutting; No. of subtypes, 2. (d) Both sides cutting; No. of subtypes, 4. *Parabolic/hyperbolic*: (e) Tangential; No. of subtypes, 1. (f) Cutting; No. of subtypes, 2. Total number of subtypes: 12.

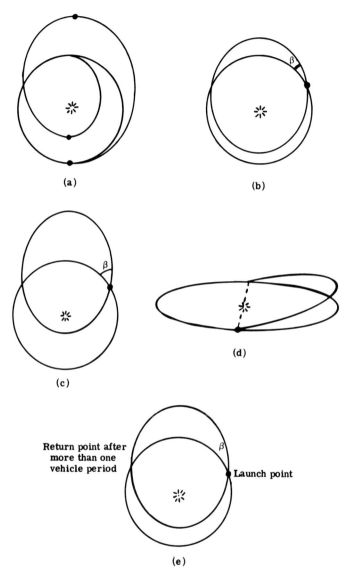

FIG. 1.38. Interplanetary round trip trajectories. (a) Hohmann (● designates thrust application). Duration: $1\frac{1}{2}$ yr. (b) Crocco, 1 yr. (c) Modified Crocco or resonance. n vehicle periods equal m Earth periods, where n, m are integers. β may be, but does not have to be, zero. (d) Half-year or out-of-ecliptic flight. (e) Symmetric or straight-line flight. After some flight duration T, the following conditions must be fulfilled for symmetry reasons: (1) the vehicle is at one of the apsides; (2) vehicle, Sun, and planet form one straight line. After a total duration $2T$, the vehicle returns to the planet. Again, β may or may not be zero.

increase in geocentric launch speed decreases flight time considerably (1.2 m/sec brought a reduction of 9.8 days!). But how does this influence arrival conditions? Hohmann heliocentric arrival speed in units of Earth's orbital speed $v_{\oplus}$ was $v = 0.779704$, parallel to the Martian orbital speed of $v_{\delta} = 0.889644$. Solar-centric launch velocity was $v_p = 1.0771125$ and shall now be 6 m/sec $= 0.0002015$ or 0.01873% higher. Because of Kepler's second law, at arrival, the component parallel to v_{δ} is

$$v_A' = 0.779704(1 + 0.0001873) = 0.779850.$$

At solar-centric launch, kinetic energy is increased by

$$v_p{}^2[(1.0001873)^2 - 1].$$

Because of the energy law, and because potential energies are independent of whether a fast or Hohmann trajectory is flown, kinetic energy is, at target, still higher by the same amount, or the speed is higher by $\varDelta v$:

$$(0.779704 + \varDelta v)^2 = (0.779704)^2 + (1.0771125)^2 (1.0001873^2 - 1).$$

Roughly,

$$\varDelta v = 1.0771125^2 \frac{0.0001873}{0.779704} \approx 0.0002785.$$

Total arrival speed then is $v_A = 0.779983$, with v_A being inclined outward by an angle β, so that

$$\cos \beta = (1 - \sin^2 \beta)^{1/2}$$

$$\approx 1 - \frac{\beta^2}{2} = \frac{0.779850}{0.779983}$$

$$\approx 1 - \frac{0.000133}{0.779983},$$

or

$$\beta \approx 0.01847 \text{ rad} \approx 1.05°.$$

The relative speed v_r with respect to Mars is (see Fig. 1.39)

$$\varDelta v_1 \approx v_A \beta = 0.0144,$$
$$\varDelta v_2 \approx v_{\delta} - v_A' = 0.1098,$$

and

$$v_r = (\varDelta v_1{}^2 + \varDelta v_2{}^2)^{1/2} = 0.11074.$$

The Hohmann value was $v_{r2} = 0.10994$. So we have an increase, by 0.0008 ≈ 24 m/sec, to $v_r = 3.296$ km/sec. With the value of the escape speed, at zero altitude, $v_{esco} = 5$ km/sec, we get, finally, $v_{max2} \approx 5.99$ km/sec. If the vehicle just passes or impacts on Mars (probe), the difference from the Hohmann value of $v_{max} = 5.98$ km/sec might not be significant. For aerody-

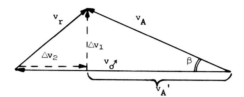

FIG. 1.39. Velocity relative to Mars.

namic braking, we might need $(5.99/5.98)^2 \approx 1.003$ times as much ablation material for heat protection, which for a typical entry vehicle (heat protection 30%, structure 20%, guidance and control 30%, payload 20%) reduces the payload by 0.5% of its original value.

If a Martian satellite in a low circular orbit is the objective, and we wish to enter the satellite orbit by rocket braking, then the maximum braking for the Hohmann case is $5.98 - 5/2^{1/2} = 2.45$ km/sec, but for the faster trajectory $5.99 - 5/2^{1/2} = 2.46$ km/sec. This again will reduce payload slightly. (Initial weight of the vehicle before braking to enter the satellite orbit is 1.000; for 2.45 km/sec and a jet velocity of 3 km/sec the mass ratio is 2.265, giving a cutoff weight of $1/(2.265) = 0.442$, or a fuel consumption of 0.558. Total hardware weight may be 0.256, leaving 0.186 for payload. For 2.46 km/sec, the corresponding values are 2.271, $1/(2.271) = 0.440$, $1 - 0.44 = 0.56$, hardware 0.257, leaving 0.183 or 1.6% less than 0.186 for payload). What is the distance between Earth and Mars during arrival of the vehicle (Fig. 1.40)?

With d the distance between Earth and Mars, we get

$$d^2 = 1^2 + r^2 - 2r \cos \varphi,$$

$$\frac{d}{r} \delta d = \left(1 - \frac{\cos \varphi}{r}\right) \delta r + \sin \varphi \, \delta \varphi .$$

Inserting the indicated data we have (both δr and $\delta \varphi$ are negative!)

$$d = 1.1318$$

and

$$\delta d = -0.0586,$$

or

$$100 \times \frac{\delta d}{d} = -4.2\% .$$

The distance d is decreased by 4.2% by increasing the geocentric injection speed by 1.2 m/sec or about $\frac{1}{100}\%$!

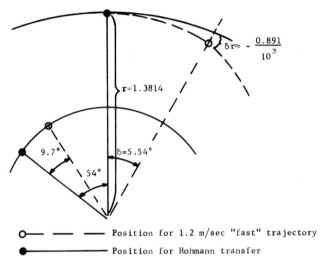

Fig. 1.40. Earth-Mars distance diagram.

Assume now, for the last stage of the launching vehicle, the data are as given in Table 1.20.

TABLE 1.20

Payload	1000 lb
Guidance and control	1000 lb
Rocket motor, tankage, structure	2000 lb
Cutoff weight	4000 lb
Vacuum specific impulse	420 sec

Then, for a 1.2 m/sec speed gain, we have a propellant consumption of about 1.2 lb. The radio transmission system may be 300 lb of the 1000 lb of payload. This weight can be taken to be roughly proportional to the square of the transmission distance. Therefore, a reduction of this distance by 4.2% will reduce the 300 lb by 9% or 27 lb.

There may be some mice on board with a life support system of 100 lb weight, 60 lb of which is consumable. This is proportional to the flight time, therefore reduced by 4.12% or 2.5 lb.

On the other hand, the passage of Mars occurs now slightly faster (order of 0.2%), which may require us to increase data storage device capacity by, say, 0.2% of 100 lb or 0.2 lb. Furthermore, "faster" instruments (e.g., larger apertures in optical systems) may be necessary, bringing an increase in weight by 20 lb. Adding up, the faster trajectory gives us, in this case, a savings of about 8 lb, which may allow some more redundancy, more sturdy design, addition of another or a more refined experiment, etc.

This discussion of a quite artificial case shows that the energy minimum transfer is not necessarily the system optimum trajectory. Usually, this system optimum trajectory is shifted towards the faster transfers, as was recognized very early (G. v. Pirquet, *Die Rakete*, June 1928). In addition to the above weight considerations we have that, because of the shorter transfer time, overall reliability will be higher, even for the same system. Chances of meteor hits are reduced, etc. But for rocket vehicles using chemical propulsion throughout, generally, the optimum trajectory is very close to the minimum energy transfer case. (For example, for a typical Martian satellite the payload loss of 1.6% would overshadow the gain of 8 lbs, which represented about 0.8%.)

We have touched only upon the difficulties of computation of fast trajectories—e.g., optimization for a given flight duration shorter than the Hohmann flight duration was not discussed. In the last chapter of Vol. 1, we discussed these problems to an accuracy sufficient for preliminary design purposes.

(d) If the standard velocity requirement for some mission is v_{id}, and for some reason we have investigated the influence of an increase of v_{id}, by Δv, upon the trajectory (reduction of flight time, etc.) then the question arises: how can we gain the excess speed Δv? Two practical ways exist: reduction of payload and replacement of it by fuel, or addition of a new stage. Forgetting for the moment about complexity and reliability, engine availability, cost, etc., we will prefer that method which results in the higher payload. Following Unger (1959), a very coarse answer can be obtained. The last stage weight for tanks and engine, at cutoff condition, is Q; for payload + guidance + structure, on standard trajectory, is M; for payload on fast trajectory is m; the structure ratio for propellant tanks is S, or in other words,

$$S = \frac{\text{propellant tank weight} + \text{unusable propellant residuals/propellant}}{\text{tank weight} + \text{propellant weight}}$$

Also let m_p be the weight of propellants available through the reduction of M to m, and

$$M - m = m_p + S(M - m),$$

and let c be the vacuum jet exhaust velocity. Then

$$\mathit{\Delta}v = c \ln \left[\frac{M + Q}{m + S(M - m) + Q} \right],$$

or, with $h = \exp(\mathit{\Delta}v/c)$, we have

$$\frac{m}{M} = \frac{1}{1 - S} \left[\frac{1}{h} - S + \frac{Q}{M} \left(\frac{1}{h} - 1 \right) \right].$$

With the typical values of $Q/M = 1$ and $S = 0.05$,

$$\left(\frac{m}{M} \right)_{\text{case 1}} = \frac{2.1}{h} - 1.1$$

or

$$\frac{m}{M} \leq 0 \qquad \text{for} \quad h \geq 1.9$$

or

$$\frac{\mathit{\Delta}v}{c} \geq 0.64.$$

Therefore, the method of payload replacement cannot be used for high speed additions.

If an additional stage is provided, the change in velocity is given by

$$\mathit{\Delta}v = c \ln \left[\frac{M}{m + m_e + S(M - m - m_e)} \right],$$

where m_e is the weight of the additional engine. With $m_e = (1/30)$ (of the thrust, where thrust $= 7 [m + m_e + S(M - m - m_e)]$, we estimate $m_e \approx \frac{1}{2}m$, and then

$$\left(\frac{m}{M} \right) = \frac{1/h - S}{1.5(1 - S)}.$$

Again taking $S = 0.05$, we get

$$\left(\frac{m}{M}\right)_{\text{case 2}} = \frac{0.7}{h} - 0.035 .$$

Hence if follows that $m/M \leq 0$ only for $h \geq 20$, or $\Delta v/c \geq 3$.

We can conclude that the method of adding another stage allows fairly large increases, Δv, in speed. From $(m/M)_{\text{case 1}} = (m/M)_{\text{case 2}}$ is easily found that higher remaining payload results from method 1 for $\Delta v/c < 0.272$, and method 2 is superior for $\Delta v/c > 0.272$.

(e) For the Mars flight example we calculated the minimum energy transfer and its sensitivity to initial errors. This can be done for other transfers, also, and we ask whether there are transfers which show less error sensitivity (minimum guidance trajectories). Results of such studies are (Magness *et al.*, 1958):

(1) Near-minimum (very slightly fast) energy transfers are favorable with respect to sensitivity against small injection errors, compared to many other trajectories.

(2) With respect to injection angle β, there are no less sensitive trajectories than the minimum-energy ones (miss distance $\sim \Delta \beta^2$).

(3) With respect to injection speed v, there are trajectories for which the deviation at target is only proportional to $(\Delta v/v)^3$. These have a large margin for error but are sensitive with respect to angles. Comparison (in brackets minimum-energy case) data are given in Table 1.21. See Fig. 1.41 for symbols.

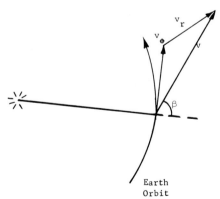

Fig. 1.41. Velocity diagram for injection from Earth. $\mathbf{v}_{\oplus}$, speed of Earth; $\mathbf{v}$, heliocentric injection speed of vehicle; $\mathbf{v} = \mathbf{v}_{\oplus} + \mathbf{v}_r$; $\mathbf{v}_{\infty}$, Earth escape speed at zero altitude; then the geocentric injection speed of vehicle is $v_L = (v_{\infty}^2 + v_r^2)^{1/2}$.

Table 1.21

β (deg)	$\pm \Delta\beta$ ($\times 10^{-2}$ deg)	v (km/sec)	v_r (km/sec)	v_L (km/sec)	$\pm \Delta v_L$ ($\times 10^4$ cm/sec)	One way travel time, T(days)
Mars (At Pericenter)						
80 (90)	1(50)	33.75 (32.06)	6.88 (2.29)	13.12 (11.42)	5(5 × 10⁻⁴)	110 (240)
Venus						
97 (90)	2(75)	26.55 (27.37)	4.79 (2.40)	12.16 (11.44)	3(12 × 10⁻⁴)	78 (146)

These fast trajectories may be of interest for probes, or for vehicles propelled by high-thrust nuclear rocket engines. Near the target, there is a considerable excess speed compared to the Hohmann transfer case. Kinematically, these trajectories show the self-canceling effect of injection speed error similar to the corresponding case in Earth-Moon transfers. Therefore, all the considerations here are exactly valid only for coplanar cases.

(4) Comparing various planets for Hohmann transfers, the margin for injection error in speed is roughly for

Jupiter : Venus : Mars = 200 : 2 : 1.

So far, the inclinations of the planetary planes of motion have been completely neglected. This is not possible in practical cases, as even small angles result in large deviations over the large interplanetary distances.

To cope with the inclination change, one may proceed in the following manner: at launch, we throw in an inclination change γ_1 towards the target. About halfway, we fire an impulse resulting in a second inclination change γ_2. Both γ_1 and γ_2 are chosen so that the target is intercepted. Other schemes are possible—e.g., we can demand $\gamma_1 = 0$, $\gamma_2 \neq 0$ or $\gamma_1 \neq 0$, $\gamma_2 = 0$, or the vehicle moves in the plane of the ecliptic, until it reaches the nodal line of the target planet plane of motion. Then the change to the target plane is effected by rocket engine action.

Generally, the method described above uses the least propellant among these simple methods when γ_1 and γ_2 are chosen properly. In the last chapter of Vol. 1, we looked into the energy necessary for the plane change, and we saw that this is not negligible for near-minimum energy transfers (order of 0.1 to 1 km/sec velocity requirement).

With the above $\gamma_1\gamma_2$ scheme, arrival at the target planet occurs generally under a small, nonzero angle γ_3. This again, increases relative speeds some-what, but does not decide the plane of approach motion, as described be-fore.

The reader is referred back to Fig. 1.34, and should visualize $\mathbf{v}_\oplus + \mathbf{v}_r$ as being not parallel to $\mathbf{v}_\oplus$. The plane of approach motion is determined by $\mathbf{v}_\oplus + \mathbf{v}_r$, vehicle location, and location of the planet's center. For com-plete energy optimization, γ_3 can enter the problem, as this angle would, e.g., demand some increase in weight of the heat protection material for an aerodynamic lander.

(g) All perturbations have been neglected in the previous discussion We ought to list them at least:

(1) Lunar perturbations. These can be very strong, as can be seen from the discussion of perturbational maneuvering. Because of its high sensitivity, and because of the fairly low energy gain, this appears to be more of a nuisance than of real value except in special cases. But there are trajec-tories in which perturbations before and after the encounter cancel each other, thus enabling a fairly close lunar passage with still no resulting per-turbation. For the sake of completeness it should be mentioned that, by gravitational maneuvering, Mars could be utilized to assist in a Jupiter journey, and Jupiter could help to return faster to Earth, or throw the vehi-cle further out. This topic is considered further in Section 1.5.

For some interplanetary flyby-type missions, the planetary encounter promises to be very useful. This was considered in greater detail in Chapter 7 of Vol. 1.

(2) Earth oblateness. Reference is made to point (7) of the discussion at the end of Chap. 4 (Vol. 1). The effect is not quite negligible (may be of the order of a few meters per seconds geocentric cutoff speed variation for Earth to Mars transfers).

(3) Planetary gravitational fields [from end of Chap. 4 (Vol. 1), point (2)]. Jupiter's influence results, very roughly, in a deviation smaller than $r_{p\,\max} \approx 1.2T^2$ km, where T is the flight time in days. For $T = 250$ we have $r_{p\,\max} \leq 75 \times 10^3$ km.

Another way of looking at Jupiter's influence is to say that Jupiter may decrease the solar gravitational attraction, which we may interpret as a re-duction in the solar mass by $1/20{,}000$ of its value. Circular speed around the Sun would be effected by about $1/40{,}000$ or 0.75 m/sec in 1 a.u. distance. An injection-speed error near the orbit of Earth of 0.75 m/sec leads, at the distance of Mars, to an error of about $150{,}000 \times (0.75/6) \approx 20 \times 10^3$ km. Obviously, the effects of the planets cannot be neglected.

(4) Radiation pressure. Solar radiation pressure acts exactly as if

the solar mass were smaller by a factor given by[1]

$$\frac{\text{acceleration due to radiation pressure}}{\text{solar gravitational attraction}} \leq \frac{0.8 \times 10^{-6} \, \text{m}/\text{sec}^2}{6 \times 10^{-3} \, \text{m}/\text{sec}^2} \approx 1.3 \times 10^{-4}.$$

This is larger than Jupiter's effect but should not be difficult to handle because of its predictability and because of its dependence upon $(1/\text{distance})^2$. Besides, for the planets, we measure, of course, only the difference between gravitational force and radiation pressure.

Vehicle radiation and Poynting-Robertson effect appear to be unimportant. [Compare the end of Chap. 4 (Vol. 1), point (3).]

(5) Electric and magnetic fields. Input data are insufficiently known; see point (6) of discussion at end of Chap. 4 (Vol. 1). Probably these effects are not very important.

(6) Resistance of interplanetary gas and impulse transfer from meteor impacts are negligible; compare end of Chap. 4 (Vol. 1), points (4) and (5).

(7) The error in the location of the actual injection point, compared to the ideal one, results in some deviation at target. But we can regard this location as being correct and interpret all errors as errors in velocity by comparing actual and ideal injection velocity for the actual injection point. Anyhow, this error is considered to be of minor influence, if the injection velocity is corrected correspondingly.

(h) Considerations for optimization. There are several criteria for the optimization of interplanetary trajectories. Some are:

(1) Minimum required energy (more precisely, minimum overall speed requirement) to do the mission (Burns, 1959; Lawden, 1959).

(2) Minimum launch weight to do the mission.

(3) Maximum allowable injection errors—sometimes called "minimum guidance trajectories."

(4) Optimum communication trajectories are such that, during vehicle-target encounter, the transmission distance vehicle-Earth is a minimum.

(5) Timing can be optimized in many respects: for example, stay time near target, total mission duration, one-way flight duration. Launch time can be optimized for many aspects—e.g., expected solar activity; or for emergency missions, timing may not be a free variable, leading to new types of problems.

---

[1] Solar radiation pressure on a reflecting surface near Earth is equal to $0.8 \times 10^{-6} \, \text{kg}/\text{m}^2$.

(6) Simplicity of a trajectory will increase the reliability of accomplishing the mission; the number of propulsive periods, critical planetary encounters, or total duration for a given mission can be yardsticks to measure trajectory complexity.

For many of these criteria, we have discussed solutions—e.g., Hohmann trajectories, minimum launch weight, minimum guidance, optimum communication (which can be among the symmetric or straight-line flyby trips), launch time for Hohmann transfers, simplicity (Crocco round-trip: one major impulse only).

In practical cases, the important criteria will be a mixture of the above mentioned and "compromise solutions" must be found. Such solutions will hardly be of a general nature. They will depend on the target planet, mission objective, utilized propulsion system, state-of-the-art of many subsystems (e.g., communication, life support, internal power, environmental protection), etc.

There are 12 fundamentally different trajectories connecting two planets (see Fig. 1.37). As any trajectory type may be combined with itself or any other type for the return leg, $12 \times 12 = 144$ fundamentally different two-way mission profiles result (since cutting trajectories are not uniquely defined, the number of mission profile possibilities is infinite). Among these, favorable combinations should be found and investigated. This immense task cannot be completed once and for all, but can only be performed on a case to case basis, as just outlined. Tools for such a task are available (Ehricke, 1959; Moeckel, 1958; Breakwell *et. al.*, 1959). A general method of great usefulness has been developed by Vertregt (1958). This is applied, and somewhat extended, by Dugan (1960). Extensive charts allowing the determination of the main characteristics of mission profiles have been developed by Ehricke (1962).

A practical method of great power has been described and applied in the last chapter of Vol. 1.

1.5 Gravitational Maneuvering

The fundamental concept of "gravitational maneuvering" (or "perturbation maneuvering") has been discussed in Vol. 1, Section 4.2,1,3. Since the practical application of this technique rests to a great degree upon the guidance accuracy attainble, some additional information of importance shall be developed here (Niehoff, 1965 and 1966).

The nomenclature is adopted from Fig. 4.17 of Vol. 1 We shall investigate first the energy change during encounter. The vehicle experiencing the propulsionless encounter shall have constant mass, and for simplicity its mass shall be unity. With respect to the central mass m_1, we assume that the potential energy is the same at location 0 and at location 1. Therefore, in order to determine the change in energy due to the encounter, it suffices to consider kinetic energy only:

$$E_0 = \tfrac{1}{2}\mathbf{v}_0{}^2,$$
$$E_1 = \tfrac{1}{2}\mathbf{v}_1{}^2.$$

Gain in energy due to encounter is

$$\varDelta E = \tfrac{1}{2}(\mathbf{v}_1{}^2 - \mathbf{v}_0{}^2)$$

We have

$$\mathbf{u}_0 = \mathbf{v}_0 - \mathbf{v}_k \qquad \text{and} \qquad \mathbf{u}_1 = \mathbf{v}_1 - \mathbf{v}_k.$$

(To be exact, we should differentiate between $\mathbf{v}_{k0}$ and $\mathbf{v}_{k1}$; for simplicity, however, we put $\mathbf{v}_{k0} = \mathbf{v}_{k1} = \mathbf{v}_1$).
  Since $u_0{}^2 = u_1{}^2$, we have

$$\varDelta E = \mathbf{v}_k(\mathbf{u}_1 - \mathbf{u}_0).$$

If we introduce three unity vectors $\mathbf{a}$, $\mathbf{b}$, $\mathbf{c}$ so that

$$\mathbf{v}_k = \mathbf{a}v_k, \qquad \mathbf{u}_1 = \mathbf{b}u_0, \qquad \mathbf{u}_0 = \mathbf{c}u_0,$$

then

$$\varDelta E = 2v_k u_0 \frac{\mathbf{a}(\mathbf{b} - \mathbf{c})}{2}.$$

We know that

$$|\,\mathbf{b} - \mathbf{c}\,| = 2 \cos \tfrac{1}{2}(180 - a) = 2 \sin \tfrac{1}{2}\,a$$

Using Eq. (4.49) of Vol. 1 we obtain

$$|\,\mathbf{b} - \mathbf{c}\,| = 2[1 + (v_0/v_c)^2]^{-1},$$

where $v_c{}^2 = \gamma m_2/d_{\min}$. If we call the angle between $\mathbf{v}_k$ and the axis of the hyperbola (see Fig. 4.17 of Vol. 1) β, then finally

$$\varDelta E = v_k v_c \cos \beta \, \frac{2x}{1 + x^2}, \qquad \text{where} \quad x = \frac{u_0}{v_c}.$$

This shows the maximum energy gain (for $x = 1$) to be $\varDelta E_{\max} = v_k v_c \cos \beta$.

Instead of the energy change ΔE, the velocity change $|\,\Delta \mathbf{v}\,|$ can be investigated as well:

$$\Delta \mathbf{v} = \mathbf{v}_1 - \mathbf{v}_0 = (\mathbf{v}_1 - \mathbf{v}_k) - (\mathbf{v}_0 - \mathbf{v}_k) = \mathbf{u}_1 - \mathbf{u}_0 ,$$

$$(\Delta \mathbf{v})^2 = u_1{}^2 + u_0{}^2 - 2u_1 u_0 \cos \alpha$$
$$= 2u_0{}^2(1 - \cos \alpha) = 4u_0{}^2 \sin^2 \tfrac{1}{2}$$

or

$$|\,\Delta \mathbf{v}\,| = \Delta v = 2u_0 \sin \tfrac{1}{2}\alpha = v_c \frac{2x}{1 + x^2} ,$$

where $x = u_0/v_c$ and $v_c{}^2 = \gamma m_2/d_{\min}$. Again, the maximum occurs for $x = 1$ and is given by $\Delta v_{\max} = v_c$. Of course, this velocity change need not be associated with any energy change; viz., if $|\,\mathbf{v}_1\,| = |\,\mathbf{v}_0\,|$, then $\Delta E = 0$; but if at the same time $\mathbf{v}_1$ is not parallel to $\mathbf{v}_0$, then $\Delta v \neq 0$. By the same reasoning, any $\Delta E \neq 0$ is associated with a value $\Delta v \neq 0$.

The more significant question than the mere determination of ΔE or Δv is often: which launch speed increment Δ did I save?

Let us show some aspects of this question with the help of an example: a space probe is launched from Earth, using a Jupiter encounter in order to reach Saturn, after a flight time T (or some other goal).

(1) The solar centered two-body vehicle trajectory between Jupiter and Saturn is such that this trajectory could not have been entered from Earth directly (because no point of this two-body trajectory comes as close to the Sun as one astronomical unit).

In this case, to enter the same trajectory without a Jupiter encounter would require a midcourse propulsion maneuver with the speed capability Δv.

(2) If A is the injection speed at Earth for the probe as described for this example, and B is the injection speed for a probe going in the time T from Earth to Saturn directly, the difference $\Delta = B - A$ could be called "saved by gravitational maneuvering." In this sense, typical numbers for Δ are of the order of one or a few km/sec savings to reach the outer solar system via Jupiter encounters.

(3) Unfortunately, such gravity-assisted trajectories lead to higher target encounter speeds by typically 3–4 km/sec. There are many missions where this penalty is not significant—e.g., flyby's, solar probe, out-of-ecliptic mission, solar system escape; and highly developed aerodynamic braking at the target. In other cases, the penalty will outweigh the gain.

(4) If an Earth-launched probe uses a Jupiter encounter to reach the

Sun, then—at the price of significantly increased mission duration (e.g., 3 years vs. 2 months)—significant reductions in injection speed (18 vs 32 km/sec) are possible.

(5) A 90° out of the ecliptic plane flight can be achieved via a Jupiter encounter; compared to direct injection from Earth, the injection speed is reduced by 25 km/sec.

(6) After the Jupiter encounter, the vehicle on its way to Saturn is in a trajectory of the energy $E + \Delta E$. If the vehicle would have been launched into a trajectory of this energy right from Earth, what additional speed increment δ would have been required?

If the solar-referenced initial speed (near Earth, but outside of Earth's sphere of action) is V_0, then the energy increment ΔE corresponds to a speed increase Δ so that $(V_0 + \Delta)^2 - V_0{}^2 = 2\,\Delta E$. From this for, sufficiently small Δ/V_0, we easily obtain

$$V_0\Delta \approx \Delta E \left[1 - \frac{1}{2}\,\frac{\Delta E}{V_0{}^2} \right].$$

If the Earth escape speed is 11.2 km/sec, then the hyperbolic excess speed is given by $v_r = (v^2 - 11.2^2)^{1/2}$, where $v =$ geocentric cutoff speed. Increasing v to $v + \delta$ increases v_r by Δ, so that $v_r\Delta \approx v\,\delta$.

So, finally, the launch speed increment δ saved by gravitational maneuvering is given by

$$\delta \approx \frac{v_r}{v}\,\frac{\Delta E}{V_0} \left[1 - \frac{1}{2}\,\frac{\Delta E}{V_0{}^2} \right]$$

In a practical case, typical for a mission from Earth to Saturn via a Jupiter encounter: $v = 15$, $v_r = 10$, $\Delta E = 250$ (km/sec)^2, $V_0 = 40$ km/sec, $\delta = 3.8$ km/sec.

(7) It should not be overlooked that these six ways of looking at the energy gain may not describe the full picture: relative location of targets, duration and frequency of launch windows, overall mission duration, trajectory location for the direct and gravity-assisted flight, accuracy requirements, power supply, considerations of communications and telemetry, and effects upon reliability assessment are some of the areas which have to be investigated before a valid comparison between a direct mission and a gravity-assisted mission can be made.

A special case is lunar gravitational maneuvering, increasing the energy of an Earth-launched (or decreasing the energy for an Earth-returning) mission:

(1) Define the hyperbolic excess speed v_r from the cutoff speed v:

$$v^2 = 11.2^2 + v_r^2.$$

(2) Assuming vertical intersection between $\mathbf{v}_r$ and the lunar velocity yields

$$u = (1.024^2 + v_r^2)^{1/2}.$$

(3) The approach angle γ can be defined from $\tan \gamma = v_r/1.024$.

(4) As a consequence of the encounter, the direction $\mathbf{u}$ turns by an angle α so that $\sin \frac{1}{2}\alpha = [1 + (u/1.67)^2]^{-1}$ for a very close lunar encounter [Eq. (4.49) of Vol. 1].

(5) The departure speed v_1 as measured from Earth is given by

$$v_1^2 = 2 \times 1.024^2 + v_r^2 - 2 \times 1.024(1.024^2 + v_r^2)^{1/2} \cos(\alpha + \gamma).$$

(6) A naive gravitational speed gain is given by $\Delta = v_1 - v_r$. But we are rather interested in the equivalent change δ required of the launch speed v, which would correspond to the same energy change. This follows from

$$\delta = (11.2^2 + v_1^2)^{1/2} - v.$$

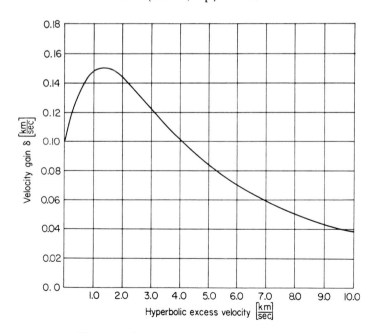

FIG. 1.42. Lunar gravitational maneuvering.

A special case can be investigated easily:

$$v_r = 0, \qquad v = 11.2 \text{ km/sec}, \qquad u = 1.024, \qquad \gamma = 0,$$

$$\sin \tfrac{1}{2}a = 0.72675, \qquad 1 - 2 \sin^2 \tfrac{1}{2}a = \cos a = -0.05632,$$

$$v_1^2 = 2.2153, \qquad \varDelta = 1.488 \text{ km/sec}, \qquad \delta = 98.5 \text{ m/sec}.$$

Indeed it was shown in Vol. 1 (Sections 4.2,2 and 4.4,3,2) that for Earth launch speed close to and below parabolic speed, the equivalent encounter gain is not larger than about 100 m/sec.

If above computation is performed for various values of v_r, then Fig. 1.42 can be drawn. It is seen that the maximum speed gain is $\delta_{max} = 151$ m/sec, occurring for $v_r = 1.4$ km/sec. For many planetary missions $v_r = 5$ km/sec, giving $\delta = 80$ m/sec.

Whether it is worthwhile to realize lunar gravitational maneuvering can only be determined in a detailed and specific study, taking into account demands as listed under (7) above.

Problems

1.1. What is the maximum range r of a communication link with the following properties: $D_T = 20$ m, $D_R = 200$ m, $\lambda = 0.05$ m, $P_R/N = 1$, $T = 2.9°$K, $B = 2$ cps, a safety factor of 2, and $P_T = 10$ kW?

1.2. (a) Derive Eq. (1.21).

(b) Show how, for $n \gg g$, $k \gg g$ we derive

$$k - g \left[n \frac{k}{n} \left(1 - \frac{k}{n} \right) \right]^{1/2} \leq n(1 - \alpha) \leq k + g \left[n \frac{k}{n} \left(1 - \frac{k}{n} \right) \right]^{1/2}.$$

(c) Hence for $k/n \to 1 - \alpha$ deduce

$$(1 - \alpha) - g[n(1 - \alpha)\alpha]^{1/2} \leq (1 - \alpha) \leq (1 - \alpha) + g[n(1 - \alpha)\alpha]^{1/2}$$

or

$$(1 - \alpha) - g\sigma \leq (1 - \alpha) \leq (1 - \alpha) + g\sigma.$$

What conclusions can you draw about the "confidence limits" from this result? [*Hint.* Consider a large sample.]

1.3. What is the relationship between geocentric and geodetic latitudes?

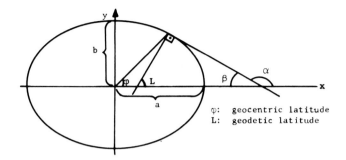

φ: geocentric latitude
L: geodetic latitude

1.4. Determine the range of applicability of a horizon scanner for altitude measurements.

1.5. A vehicle is in a circular orbit of speed v_1. An inclination change can be made by kick maneuvers in two ways:

(a) apply one kick to change the inclination,

(b) apply a kick to go to infinity, change inclination there, return to the circular orbit.

Under what condition is (b), energy-wise, superior?

1.6. Show that, in braking ellipses, apocenter kicks are effective to displace the pericenter.

1.7. An interesting example applying reliability theory is as follows: Two vehicle types are available having a payload capability of 1 and 10, respectively. Both shall be based upon the same technology, same state of the art, etc; thus the lift-off weights will have a ratio of about 10:1, also. The yearly transport volume is 100.

How many vehicles have to be planned assuming

(a) 100% reliability,

(b) 80% reliability, naively,

(c) 80% reliability, 99.7% confidence level, and a normal distribution of failures.

1.8. Let us assume that the measurements of a quantity X are $x_1, x_2, \ldots, x_n$. As an approximation for X, we use $\bar{x} = (1/n) \sum_1^n x_i$. This defines errors of the measurement, namely, $\delta_i = x_i - X \approx x_i - \bar{x}$.

Define the standard deviation for x_i and $\bar{x}$, and develop a rational criterion by which measurements should be rejected.

1.9. Assume that a vehicle antenna of area A has, per unit area, a weight W, and a transmitter of power output P has a weight G per unit of power output. Minimize the weight S of the communication system, assuming that this consists of antenna and transmitter only, and that, for a given transmission distance, the energy flux at the receiver shall be given, i.e., $AP = $ constant.

1.10. Assume that electric noise follows the same distribution as the distribution of kinetic energy in a thermal group of molecules. Equate the average energy $\bar{E}$ with the "noise." Assume that the signal-to-noise ratio is given by $S/\bar{E} = R$, and that, whenever the statistic variable E is larger than S, a transmission error occurs.

Compute the probability of transmission error as a function of signal-to-noise ratio.

1.11. *Power of redundancy.* Assume that the reliability of an element as a function of operating time is given by $R_E = e^{-t/T_0}$, with T_0 a constant. Two such elements shall be considered in the circuits:

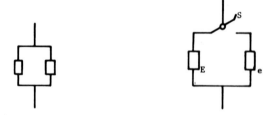

The circuit fails if both elements fail. If the element E fails, the switch S operates and inserts the element e; the reliability of the switch is given by r, which we will assume to be a constant.

Compute the reliability of these two circuits, i.e., compute the probability of these two circuits to function properly for a time T.

What is the minimum permissible r-value so that active redundancy gives the same result as passive redundancy?

1.12. *Confidence limits.* After Sec. 1.21, a numerical example is given which is—strictly speaking—not accurate. It says: "So the test would prove that, with 38% confidence, the reliability of the tested element is better than 84%," whereas from the computation follows that with 38% confidence the reliability is better than 84% *and less than* 94%. Let us assume a symmetric distribution, and $\alpha_L \leq \alpha \leq \alpha_H$ with confidence C

has been shown, where $2\alpha = \alpha_L + \alpha_H$. What is the confidence C_1 such that $\alpha_L \leq \alpha \leq 1$ (true lower limit) and the confidence C_2 such that $0 \leq \alpha \leq \alpha_H$ (true upper limit)?

1.13. *Reliability.* A very practical problem shall be treated, which compares "system testing" and "component testing." Let us assume that the system consists of two components only (e.g., a two-stage rocket vehicle), having reliability r_1 and r_2, and standard deviation σ_1 and σ_2. For the complete system, $R = r_1 r_2$, and the standard deviation of R is σ_R.

Some theoretical fundamentals:

(A) If $f = f(x_1, x_2, \ldots, x_e)$, then

$$df = \sum_{j=1}^{e} \frac{\partial f}{\partial x_j} dx_j \quad \text{and} \quad \sigma_f^2 = \sum_{j=1}^{e} \left(\frac{\partial f}{\partial x_j} \sigma_{x_j} \right)^2.$$

(B) Having n tests, k failures, reliability (naively) $\alpha = 1 - k/n$; mean deviation of number of failures is given by $\sigma^2 = n\alpha(1 - \alpha)$, and mean deviation of α is given by $\sigma_a = [n/(n-1)]^{1/2} (\sigma/n)$. (The $n - 1$ is replaced by $n - m$, if m measurements are the minimum number to determine a numerical value for α.)

In our problem, determine reliability R and standard deviation σ_R from the following information:

(1) 100 system tests; 10 failures;
(2) 100 tests of component 1, 5 failures and 100 test of component 2, 5 failures;
(3) 100 tests of component 1, 10 failures and 100 tests of component 2, zero failures.

1.14. Two vehicles move in circular orbits of the same altitude around one central body. At some instant of time, t_0, their velocities are exactly parallel and the distance between them is d. A quarter of a period later they hit each other. What is the impact speed Δ?

THE USE OF NONCHEMICAL ENERGY FOR PROPULSION

A study of the more advanced possibilities for space-flight propulsion systems is made here. For a chemical rocket, the total available energy is proportional to the amount of propellant carried and is, therefore, limited when possibilities of collecting energy during the mission are neglected. The energy rate (or power) is considered to be unlimited since it is dependent only on the rate of propellant consumption.

If the energy comes from a nonchemical source, e.g., a nuclear reactor or a solar power plant, the energy rate is limited, but total energy is (nearly) unlimited. This fundamental difference is the reason that a special chapter for power-limited flight is necessary.

The main improvement over chemical propulsion systems is expected from increased specific impulse. Equation (1.5) of Vol. 1 shows why this generally leads to a reduced acceleration, which, for extreme cases, requires again special treatment (namely, for acceleration below one local g, down to about 10^{-6} local g's).

2.1 Propulsion Systems and Vehicles

2.1,1 Photon Propulsion

The jet of exhaust gas is replaced by a light beam ("photon gas jet"). The "ultimate" specific impulse of 30×10^6 sec appears to be very promising. But the difficulties are such that even the practical feasibility cannot be regarded as proven.

2.1,1,1 THE ENERGY SOURCE (Saenger, 1953a, 1955)

Let us assume the energy for the propulsion system comes from a nuclear reactor, which comprises 20% of the vehicle mass. About $\frac{1}{2}$ of this 20% shall be uranium U^{235}, of which 0.1% is converted to energy; thus we have

$$\frac{\text{mass converted to energy}}{\text{total mass of vehicle}} = \frac{\Delta m}{m_0} = \frac{1}{5} \times \frac{1}{2} \times \frac{1}{1000} = \frac{1}{10^4}.$$

From the impulse law we have, for the vehicle speed,

$$\Delta v \approx c\frac{\Delta m}{m_0} \approx 3 \times 10^8 \times 10^{-4} \approx 30 \times 10^3 \quad \text{m/sec.}$$

If we take the available energy $\Delta m \times c^2$ and convert it into kinetic energy of some mass m' equal to about $\frac{1}{2}m_0$ with an efficiency η, then $\eta(\Delta m/m_0)c^2 \approx (m'/2m_0)v^2$ or with $\eta = \frac{1}{2}$ follows $v = (\Delta m/m')^{1/2}c = 4200$ km/sec, and $\Delta v = 4200 \ln 2 = 2900$ km/sec, a big improvement (about a factor of 100).

We can deduce that not too small a fraction of the mass of a photon vehicle has to be converted to photons in order to become attractive—say, to reach relativistic speeds. To do so we need, ideally, a nuclear process in which the total (total photon rocket) of the participating masses, or at least a notable fraction of them (partial photon rocket), is converted into radiation. The only known process of this type for the total photon rocket is matter-antimatter interaction (Miller, 1965). No way can be seen today for technical utilization of such matter annihilation energy. But a large fusion reactor may be an attractive power source, with $\Delta m/m_0 \approx 5 \times 10^{-4}$, without giving the capability of reaching relativistic speeds (partial photon rocket). In a partial photon rocket, the unradiated fraction of the "propellant" ("ashes") may remain on board the vehicle, or—resulting in improved performance—may be dumped overboard.

2.1,1,2 THE RADIATION SOURCE (Saenger, 1959a)

Let us assume that somehow the energy could be made available. How do we convert the energy to radiation? We need a radiation pressure of about 10 atm to get accelerations of about one Earth gravity, and 10^{-3} atm for $10^{-4}g$. If an electromagnetic radiation beam transports an energy S through unit area, normal to the beam, in unit time, then the impulse is $I = mc = mc^2/c = S/c$. For complete reflection, the radiation pressure is $P_r = 2S/c$. For a black-body radiator of a temperature T degrees Kelvin, we get (Stefan-Boltzmann's law)

$$S = \frac{1.37}{10^{15}} T^4 \quad \text{kcal/cm}^2 \text{ sec.}$$

From this (with reflection), $P_r \approx 3.8 \times 10^{-21} T^4 \text{ kg/cm}^2$. Some numerical values are given in Table 2.1.

TABLE 2.1

T ($^\circ$K)	P_r (kg/cm^2)	S (kcal/cm^2 sec)
3×10^{-3}	4×10^{-7}	0.111
10^4	4×10^{-5}	13.7
5×10^4	2.5×10^{-2}	8.57×10^3
10^5	0.4	1.37×10^5
3×10^5	32	1.11×10^7
10^6	4×10^3	1.37×10^9
10^8	4×10^{11}	1.37×10^{17}

Thus the radiator has to be in a gaseous state. A hydrogen plasma at a pressure of 100 atm and a thickness of the radiating layer of at least 1 m behaves nearly like a black body from 10,000 to 30,000°K, resulting in radiation pressures of $P_r = 10^{-5}$ to 10^{-3} kg/cm^2.

From Wien's law, the energy maximum of a black-body radiation of T°K occurs for a wavelength λ_{max}, where $\lambda_{max} T = 0.29$ cm deg. For $T = 30 \times 10^3$°K we get $\lambda_{max} \approx 0.97 \times 10^{-5}$ cm, or the ultraviolet part of the spectrum. The energy flow is, for 30,000°K, $S = 600$ kcal/cm^2 sec. If higher radiation pressures are required, heavier elements have to form the plasma. For uranium plasma of, again, 100 atm pressure and only 1 cm layer thickness we can get $P_r = 10$ atm with a temperature of 3×10^5°K. Increasing the layer thickness to 1 m and the temperature to 8×10^5°K, the radiation pressure goes up to 500 kg/cm^2. Now λ_{max} is 10^{-6} cm (border line ultraviolet X-ray), or even 3.8×10^{-7} cm (X-ray), and the energy flow is $S = 5 \times 10^6$, or 2×10^8 kcal/cm^2 sec. Therefore, it appears possible to reach the radiation intensity needed if the energy can be provided and if the radiation source can be maintained.

If, without such a "gaslamp," the photons resulting from annihilation of matter are directly utilized, the wavelength is between 10^{-10} cm (for electrons) and 10^{-15} cm (for uranium atoms), or in the area of γ-rays and cosmic rays. There appears to be little chance of finding an efficient method to transform this to longer wavelengths.

2.1,1,3 THE WALLS OF THE RADIATION SOURCE (Saenger, 1959b)

These walls have to maintain the source of the radiation, which is the gas or the nuclear reaction itself. Obviously, because of the very high temperatures, direct contact with the walls has to be avoided; hydrodynamic or magnetohydrodynamic methods may make this possible.

Even with these methods radiation will reach the walls. Only at some area ("nozzle") the radiation has to go out: we either make this part of the wall transparent, or have it open and prevent the gas from flowing out by hydrodynamic or magnetohydrodynamic confinement. The latter possibility has the advantage that the problem of energy absorption in the transparent wall is absent. At the walls radiation other than the nozzle radiation has to be either reflected or absorbed.

What is the maximum heat flow which the wall can absorb? In modern rocket nozzles, up to 2 kcal/cm² sec have been measured. But because of the much smaller mass-flow rates, this figure cannot be tolerated here since the walls can only be cooled by radiation. Again, from Stefan-Boltzmann's law, when we assume that the wall is a black-body radiator on both sides for the wall temperature, but a reflector for the propulsive radiation, the maximum radiation from the wall is $S_w = 2 \times 1.37 \times 10^{-15} T_w^4$ kcal/cm² sec, where T_w is the wall temperature. With $T_w = 2 \times 10^3 °$K it follows that $S_w = 4.3/100$ kcal/cm² sec.

A good reflector in the near-visible spectral region absorbs perhaps 1% of the incident energy. (Reflectivity for a surface-silver mirror for white light is 0.95 and with specially complicated precautions, 0.995.) This means that we can tolerate incident energies up to only 4.3 kcal/cm² sec. This limits the gas temperature to $T \approx 7.5 \times 10^3 °$K, which is too low to be practical.

There is one way to overcome this difficulty, namely, to improve the reflectivity from 0.99 up to about

$(1 - 10^{-4})$ for a radiation pressure $P_r = 10^{-3}$ kg/cm²,

$(1 - 10^{-8})$ for a radiation pressure $P_r = 10$ kg/cm²,

$(1 - 10^{-10})$ for a radiation pressure $P_r = 500$ kg/cm².

Such high reflectivities have been observed only in the visible spectrum for the phenomenon of total reflection (up to about $1-10^{-7}$). But it does not appear impossible that, even for much shorter wavelengths, very high reflectivities as needed here can be realized, utilizing strong compression shocks in a gas plasma, or in a pure electron gas, giving the required high electron density of the order of 10^{27} electrons/cm³. This result is not yet proven.[1] Even if it were, it is not known how to keep the compression shocks stationary. (It is interesting to remark that, ultimately, conductive, convective, and radiative heat transfer may be prevented by nonsolid walls.)

2.1,1,4 The Photon Beam (Saenger, 1953b)

Such high-intensity radiation beams are outside our general experience. Let us just assume that we have an engine of 100 tons thrust, requiring a "nozzle throat area" of about 1 m². Energy flux on Earth from solar radiation equals $2/(60 \times 10^3)$ kcal/cm² sec. At the photon nozzle, there is transported by the "jet" $S = 5 \times 10^6$ kcal/cm² sec. We have to spread this per cm² throat area over an area of 1.5×10^{11} cm², to equal the flux of solar radiation. At a "jet beam angle" of about 5.7 deg of arc, the beam of 1 m² area at the "nozzle throat" covers 1.5×10^{11} m² at a distance of 3.87×10^3 km; evidently, this "photon jet" is an effective weapon, and launches of such a high-thrust vehicle from Earth surface, or landings by rocket braking, appear problematic.

Impulse is equal to $\dot{m}c$; the energy rate or power for a photonic system is given by $\dot{m}c^2 = $ thrust $\times c$. Thus, it follows that for 100 tons thrust a power of 3×10^{13} m kg/sec, or 3×10^8 MW is needed. The total electric power production of Earth in 1960 was only 3.5×10^5 MW, of which about 23% was produced within the United States.

The total solar energy intercepted by Earth equals 1.8×10^{11} MW (thermal).

The kinetic energy of the jet of a large chemical rocket propulsion system (thrust 5000 tons, exhaust speed 3 km/sec) equals 0.75×10^5 MW (of which about 1% may appear in the form of noise). A successful MHD generator might convert 60% of this to electric power, resulting in 0.45×10^5 MW (electric), about 50% of the total electric output of the United States. Therefore, rocket engines, together with proper generators, can be very useful for delivering large electric power for relatively short time periods.

---

[1] According to Peschka (1960), reflection of intense photon beams by electron gas mirrors is impossible.

2.1,1,5 RELATIVISTIC FLIGHT MECHANICS[1] (Saenger, 1957; Krause, 1956 and 1962)

Here we want to indicate that the ultra-high performance vehicles require relativistic performance treatment. It appears as if even other galaxies could be reached within the lifetime of a human crew (but, of course, not within the lifetime of observers remaining behind). Again, there are many phases that are not sufficiently clear (for example, navigation; general, instead of special, theory of relativity; interaction between vehicle and cosmic matter, cosmic dust and meteors). Some interesting considerations can be found in Rytov (1961).

This shall suffice here as a survey on the status of the "ultimate photon rocket." For more details, the referenced literature should be consulted.

2.1,2 Propulsion Directly from Radioactive Material

This goes back to a proposal made by G. Gamov (in "Atomic Energy in Cosmic and Human Life," Cambridge University Press, New York) on a simple system, utilizing radioactive materials for propulsion as shown in Fig. 2.1. A radioactive material is spread so thin over a thrust plate that no self-absorption occurs. The radiation toward the thrust plate is absorbed; the other radiation delivers the impulse.

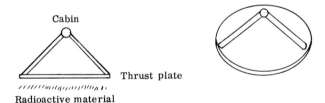

FIG. 2.1. Propulsive system utilizing radioactive material.

Let us assume that the radioactive material emits α-particles of constant energy. The speed of ejection is c.

The probability of ejection is equal for all directions. If the particle is ejected outward—which occurs for half the ejected particles—then the probability to be ejected under an angle φ to $\varphi + d\varphi$ is equal to (see Fig. 2.2)

$$\frac{2\pi r \sin \varphi \, r \, d\varphi}{2\pi r^2} = \sin \varphi \, d\varphi \, ;$$

[1] For historic reasons the early study by Esnault-Pelterie (1928) is mentioned.

the useful impulse carried per unit ejected mass is $c \cos \varphi$. Therefore,

$$\bar{c} = c \int_0^{\pi/2} \sin \varphi \cos \varphi \, d\varphi = \tfrac{1}{2} c.$$

If we have n atoms decaying per second and per cm² thrust plate, and if m is the mass of one α-particle, then the thrust per cm² thrust plate is, assuming one α-particle is created per decay,

$$f = \frac{n}{2} m \frac{c}{2} = \frac{n}{4} mc.$$

(With radioactive chains, about five α-particles per decay can be expected.

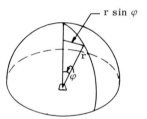

FIG. 2.2. Particle ejection from thrust plate.

This has no influence on the conclusions reached.) The energy absorbed per square centimeter is

$$e = \frac{n}{2} \frac{m}{2} c^2 = \frac{n}{4} mc^2 = fc.$$

In the previous section we saw that a solid wall cannot radiate more than about $4.3/100$ kcal/cm² sec away into space. With 1 kcal = 427 mkg, we have

$$fc < 18.5 \quad \text{mkg/cm}^2 \text{ sec,}$$

or, with c expressed in meters per second,

$$f < 18.5/c \quad \text{kg/cm}^2.$$

Let us assume that we have 5×10^{16} atoms per cm², which can decay. For a high-thrust system, about 2×10^{16} may decay in 600 sec, giving 3×10^{13} α-particles per second, or $3 \times 10^{13} \times 6.6 \times 10^{-27} \approx 2 \times 10^{-13}$ kg/sec cm². If the weight of the vehicle is about 2×10^{-3} kg/cm², then we want a thrust of about 2×10^{-3} kg/cm^2: thus follows the required value for

$$c = \frac{4f}{nm} = \frac{4 \times 2 \times 10^{-3}}{2 \times 10^{-13}} g_0 \approx 4 \times 10^{11} \; \frac{m}{sec} .$$

As this is above the speed of light, we should have used relativistic mechanics. Because of Geiger-Nuttal's relation, the lifetime of very energetic α-radiators becomes very short. The above inequality cannot be fulfilled. Without actually going into the details, we can conclude that this method cannot propel a high-acceleration space vehicle.

For a low acceleration system, the weight may only be 10^{-5} kg/cm^2, and the required thrust at least 10^{-9} kg/cm^2. (This is only a factor of 10 larger than solar radiation pressure in Earth vicinity.) However, we need propulsion times of the order of one year. Now the 2×10^{16} particles have a decay time of the order of 3×10^7 sec, or about 7×10^8 α-particles/cm^2 sec $= 4.5 \times 10^{-18}$ kg/sec cm^2. This forces us to have

$$c = \frac{4 \times 10^{-9}}{4.5 \times 10^{-18}} g_0 \approx 10^{10} \; \frac{m}{sec} ,$$

this is still 30 times faster than the speed of light, so that relativistic treatment would be necessary; but for such high energies the necessary lifetime cannot be provided. The "cooling inequality" was fulfilled.

A "practical" case would be to use radiothorium:

$$\mathrm{Rdth}^{90}_{228} \xrightarrow[\alpha]{T=1.9 \text{ yr}} \mathrm{Th \, X}^{88}_{224} \xrightarrow[2e^- \text{ and } 4\alpha]{\text{fairly fast}} \mathrm{Pb}^{82}_{208} \qquad (T : \text{half-life.})$$

The average α-particle energy in this chain is about 7 MeV $\approx 1.14 \times 10^{-13}$ mkg, giving $c \approx 1.86 \times 10^7$ m/sec. Of 6×10^{16} particles, about 3×10^{16} decay in 2 yr giving a flow rate of $(15 \times 10^{16})/(2 \times 3 \times 10^7)$ α-particles/cm^2 sec, or 1.66×10^{-17} kg/cm^2 sec. The thrust comes out to be

$$\frac{1}{2} \frac{1.66}{10^{17}} \frac{1.86}{2} \times 10^7 \frac{1}{g_0} \approx \frac{0.8}{10^{11}} \; \frac{kg}{cm^2} .$$

In spite of all the favorable assumptions made, this is still, by a factor larger than a hundred, smaller than the bare minimum of 10^{-9} kg/cm^2: propulsion directly from radioactive material does not appear to be a promising method. [A different conclusion is reached by Short and Sabin (1960).]

2.1,3 Nuclear Thermodynamic Rocket Engines with High Thrust (Shepherd and Cleaver, 1948-1949; Bussard and DeLauer, 1958; Schmidt and Decker, 1960)

The technique of solid-core nuclear fission reactors is highly developed (Murray, 1956). Some information pertaining to such reactors follows:

The processes in a nuclear reactor are very complex. Roughly, it is the following reaction that delivers the power, radioactive materials, and neutrons to keep the chain reaction going:

$$\ce{^{235}_{92}U} + \ce{^{1}_{0}n} \rightarrow \ce{^{144}_{56}Ba} + \ce{^{90}_{36}Kr} + 2\,\ce{^{1}_{0}n} + 180 \quad \text{MeV},$$

where 180 MeV $= 2.88 \times 10^{-11}$ W-sec. (Instead of U^{235}, U^{233}, or Pu^{239} may be used.)

The neutrons (on the average somewhat more than 2 per fission) are of fairly high energy—about 2 MeV. The following things can happen to these neutrons:

(1) Leave the system through the surface. This gives rise to the neutron radiation of nuclear reactors.

To make this loss small enough the reactor surface/volume ratio has to be sufficiently small, or the reactor must not be "subcritical" (geometry, size). Using neutron reflectors, this loss of neutrons is reduced. (There are, strictly speaking, no neutron reflectors. In practice, a moderator-like substance, e.g., BeO, is provided that returns, by collision-scattering processes, part of the neutrons back to the reactor. For very large reactors, the neutron loss can be accepted, and no reflection is necessary. For a specific design, the critical mass of U^{235} with infinite reflector is 10.3 kg, and without reflector 25 kg. Weightwise, therefore, it can be advantageous to increase the uranium weight and save the heavy reflector. Varying the degree of reflection by movable reflectors can be used for reactor control purposes. (See Figs. 2.3 and 2.4 for some numerical information.)

(2) React with U^{238}, thus finally producing plutonium Pu^{239}. This is very probable for neutrons having an energy between 1 and 100 eV. It is utilized to "breed" plutonium (or U^{233} from Th^{232}).

(3) Captured by some other material within the reactor. To make this neutron loss small, the presence of such neutron captures must be carefully controlled. As cadmium captures neutrons, motion of cadmium rods sticking into the reactor can be utilized for reactor control.

(4) Produce another fission. Since only 0.7% of natural uranium is U^{235}, and, on the average, one fission for any two neutrons is needed to keep

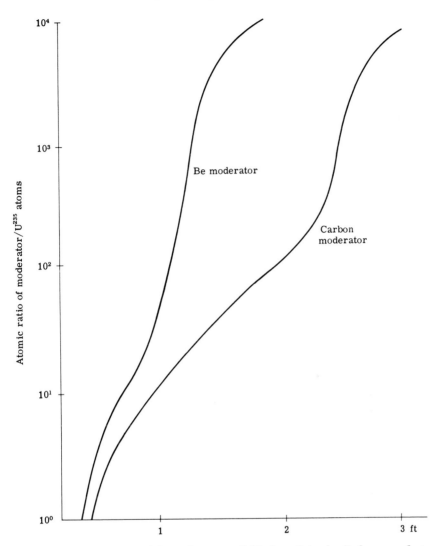

FIG. 2.3. Critical radius of thermal reactors. Critical equilateral cylinders; unreflect-ed; 20% void volume; density: $\varrho_U = 15.0$, $\varrho_C = 1.4$, $\varrho_{Be} = 1.42$. Critical radius for U^{233} ($\varrho = 15,0$) or Pu^{239} ($\varrho = 15.8$), about 0.2 ft less.

the chain reaction going, some means of increasing the probability of fission must be found. There are two ways to do this. The first one is to take advan-tage of the fact that, for thermal neutrons (energy below 0.1 eV), the cross section is favorable for fission (several hundred times as large for fission as for reaction with U^{238}). Therefore, in a "thermal reactor," the neutrons have to be slowed down. This is done by elastic scattering collisions. The U^{238} atoms are not suitable, since, for one thing, they are fairly heavy, leading to only a small transfer of energy from the neutron to the nucleus per collision, and secondly, they would capture the neutrons before they are sufficiently slowed down. Therefore, besides the "fuel elements," which contain, e.g., uranium carbide, another substance has to be introduced, which

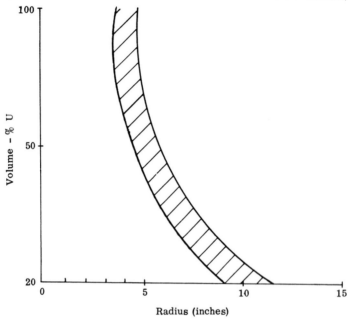

Fig. 2.4. Critical radius of fast reactors. Critical equilateral cylinders; 20% void volume; diluent: heavy metal (W, M_0, Zr, and others).

slows down the neutrons without capturing them: a moderator. In homogeneous reactors, fuel and moderator are intimately mixed, whereas in heterogeneous reactors they are not. Several materials are usable—e.g., heavy water D_2O, carbohydrates with hydrogen being replaced by heavy hydrogen D_2, graphite C, or a refractory compound or alloy of beryllium. Even with only 0.7% of the uranium being the isotope 235, because the cross section of fission is so great compared to that of capture by U^{238} a neutron entering uranium still has a better than 50% chance of producing a fission: therefore, thermal reactors may operate on natural uranium. But often U^{235} is enriched, up to a few per cent, or much higher, thus allowing smaller reactors to become critical. For a reactor to become critical means that the number of neutrons within the reactor is constant, independent of time. Most of the neutrons ("prompt") from fissions appear nearly instantaneously ($< 10^{-4}$ sec) after fission takes place, but a few ($\sim 0.75\%$) appear 10 sec ("delayed") after the fission process.[1] To keep the number of neutrons within the reactor constant, the controls act upon the delayed neutrons. But it is possible for a reactor to be critical even when all the delayed neutrons are captured: prompt critical. Because of the resulting loss of control and the rapid power increase (e.g., factor of 10 in 1.6 sec), this is a potentially dangerous situation, which should not be allowed to take place.

If the void volume in a reactor is filled with some substance, the neutrons may interact, and the velocity spectrum of the neutrons may be altered: it is possible that reactivity is so strongly increased that the reactor becomes prompt critical. This may indeed be the case, under certain circumstances, when liquid hydrogen fills the reactor.

A radiative environment (e.g., radiation in space, such as van Allen zone, or radiation from another reactor) may also make a reactor prompt critical.

The second method of increasing the probability of fission is to increase the concentration of U^{235} to practically 100% (up to about 12 gm/cm³ of U^{235}) in the core material, which is a convenient uranium compound, e.g., uranium carbide, or introduce core materials that do not interact with the neutrons, e.g., "metal cores" such as tungsten[2]/UO_2, so that without the moderator the chain reaction continues in spite of the fact that the cross section for fission is only a few pro mille of its value for thermal neutrons. This is the fast reactor.[3] Its control is not materially more difficult than that of the thermal reactor, as in both cases control occurs via the "delayed neutrons." The emerging neutron radiation is more energetic. Core sizes well below 100 kg can be critical, but more U^{235} is necessary than for a critical thermal reactor. The materials present in a reactor are active material (e.g., uranium), moderator [e.g., graphite (not in a fast one)], reflector (e.g., beryllium), and neutrals (e.g., tungsten). Neutral materials are those that show practically no interaction with the neutrons. They may be present for structural reasons. Some neutrals—e.g., tungsten—can be used in a fast, but not in a thermal, system.

A nuclear bomb is a special case of an uncontrolled very fast reactor (pure U^{235}, Pu^{239}, or U^{233}).

---

[1] Delayed neutrons are decay products from radioactive fission fragments.

[2] Chemical symbol W, wolfram.

[3] Intermediate reactor types do exist.

What performance can be expected? The energy of 1 MW-day equals 24×10^3 kWh, which equals 8.81×10^9 mkg, which corresponds (from Einstein's law $E = mc^2$) to a mass conversion of $\Delta m = 0.962 \times 10^{-3}$ gm. A mass loss of 10^{-3} gm corresponds to 1 gm of fissionable material which has been "used up." One gram of fissionable material may be contained within 50 gm of "enriched" uranium which demands, with moderator, etc., about 400 gm of total reactor. Therefore, 1 ton of this type of reactor can deliver a total energy of about 2500 MW-days.[1] (This leads, with 3 cents per kWh, to a price of 1.8×10^6 \$/ton.) For comparison to chemical energy sources, 2500 MW-days are contained in about 16,100 tons of H_2/O_2 mixture at 3200 kcal/kg. For a fast reactor, the figure of 2500 MW-days per ton can be ~ 300 times larger—750,000 MW-days per ton.[2] But the cost per ton of a fast reactor will be more than 300 times higher (or more than 5.4×10^8 \$/ton) than cost per ton of thermal reactor, because the former consists of the order of 50%, and the latter of about 0.25% U^{235}. Of course, the reactor can only deliver energy as long as it is critical—finally, "burn-up" (usage of U^{235}) or "poisoning" (production of neutron-capturing nuclei) will stop the energy production.

The Materials Test Reactor of the U.S. AEC (1952) has a core volume of $\frac{1}{6}$ m³, an average density of 2 gm/cm³ (thermal reactors can go up to 3.5, fast reactors might be around 13 gm/cm³), and a power output of 40 MW with a total weight of ~ 333 kg (unshielded). Let us assume that with both thermal and fast reactors very high specific powers of around 1 MW/kg core could be achieved. With a fast reactor of a total energy content of 750 MW-days/kg, the rate of 1 MW/kg can be maintained for 750 days, and with a thermal reactor only for 60 h. This is still much longer than the operational time of a nuclear high-thrust rocket engine during one firing. Therefore, a nuclear high-thrust rocket system will not exhaust the reactor during one firing application.

With a low-thrust system for 10^3 days of operation, and a thermal reactor, we can only use 2.5×10^{-3} MW/kg $= 2.5$ kW/kg, a fairly low power density. A fast reactor would increase this value to 750 kW/kg.

What about energy densities? With a density of 2 gm/cm³ and an arbitrary figure of 0.3 MW/kg, we get about 600 MW/m³. Assuming that, considering heat transfer, five times this figure can be handled, we get, for thermal reactors, 1.5 MW/kg or 3000 MW/m³, and for fast reactors, with

---

[1] To be exact, the fissionable material must be divided into "criticality fuel," which is not consumed, and "power fuel," which is consumed.

[2] Practical difficulties pose a limit of about 50,000, or 6.7% of above value.

3000 MW/m³, about 230 kW/kg, still quite below the, from the energy point of view, allowable 750 kW/kg for 10^3 operational days. What do such figures mean?

Power densities in chemical rocket engine thrust chambers are very high—let us estimate them. If V is the volume of the reaction chamber, F the throat area, L^* the characteristic length, an engineering parameter, defined from $V = FL^*$, c_F the thrust coefficient, p the chamber pressure, T the thrust, $\dot{w}$ the propellant weight flow rate, and I_{sp} the specific impulse, then the thrust is

$$T = c_F F p = \dot{w} I_{sp} \quad \text{or} \quad V = \frac{\dot{w} I_{sp}}{c_F p} L^*.$$

With an efficiency η, we can write, for the energy $\dot{E}$ released in the thrust chamber,

$$\dot{E}\eta = \tfrac{1}{2}\dot{w}g I_{sp}^2 ,$$

where g is the Earth's gravitational acceleration. So

$$V = \frac{2\eta \dot{E}}{g I_{sp} c_F p} L^*,$$

or finally, for the energy density,

$$\dot{e} = \frac{\dot{E}}{V} = \frac{g I_{sp} c_F p}{2\eta L^*} .$$

If $g \approx 9.8$ m/sec, $c_F = 1.75$, $L^* = 1.5$ m, $\eta = 0.6$, then $\dot{e}$ [MW/m³] $= 0.935p$ [atm] $\times I_{sp}$ [sec], or $\dot{e} \approx 200$–$20{,}000$ MW/m³.

This is the same order that we find in nuclear reactors. It indicates the tremendous magnitude of the problem of leading this energy away from the reactor before it can damage [melt] the reactor core. Indeed, the problems of heat transfer are so great that this can be a reason for the power density limit in a reactor, where the upper limit can be realized only for a short lifetime of a few minutes or, at most, a few hours. For comparison, some other $\dot{e}$-values are given in the accompanying tabulation:

Burning chambers	$\dot{e}$ (MW/m³)
Ramjet	10–1000
Piston engine Gas turbine	50–1000

What temperatures are obtainable within a solid-core reactor? This is determined by the structural materials, design of reactor, loads imposed, heat transfer and conduction rates, and chemical and physical interactions between the reactor surface and the coolant. Against the latter, coatings of the reactor elements or additions to the coolant can be developed. In the case of the nuclear high thrust rocket the coolant has to be pure hydrogen for all practical purposes. Additives would be permissible in traces only, as they would increase the average molecular weight, thus reducing specific impulse.

Uranium melts at 1150°K, uranium oxide at 2100°K, and the carbon moderator would undergo sublimation at about 3500°K. Thus it appears optimistic, but reasonable, to assume that the maximum reactor temperature within a fuel element is 3000°K. The surface temperature of a fuel element is, because of the finite heat conduction, somewhat lower. It may be possible to heat some gas within the reactor up to perhaps 2600°K, and have this gas expand through a rocket exhaust nozzle. As 2600°K is below the expected combustion temperature in high performance chemical rocket engines (up to 4000°K and possibly higher), an improved performance can result only for a mean molecular weight of the exhaust gases, which is noticeably reduced below its value for chemical engines. A survey of possible exhaust substances shows that only hydrogen is attractive.

The principle of a solid core nuclear reactor high acceleration rocket engine is shown in Fig. 2.5.

Initially, we will neglect the power for the pump and the energy lost from the reactor by radiation. This is only a small fraction of the energy delivered to the gas.

On page 522 of this book is a Mollier diagram for hydrogen, taken from Jordan (1958). From this is found, for a chamber pressure of $p_c = 60$ atm and a chamber temperature $T_c = 2600$°K, a hydrogen enthalpy $H_c = 20.05$ kcal/gm-mole. For a typical space engine, we may have the ratio

$$\frac{\text{chamber pressure}}{\text{nozzle exit pressure}} = \frac{p_c}{p_e} = 550.$$

Assuming the expansion in the nozzle is isentropic we read from the diagram, for $p_e = p_c/550 = 0.109$ atm, a value of

$$H_e = 3.5 \quad \text{kcal/gm-mole} \qquad (\text{and } T_e \approx 400\text{°K}).$$

The difference $H_c - H_e = 16.55$ kcal/gm-mole has been converted to kinetic energy of 1 gm-mole ≈ 2 gm of hydrogen. From the energy law

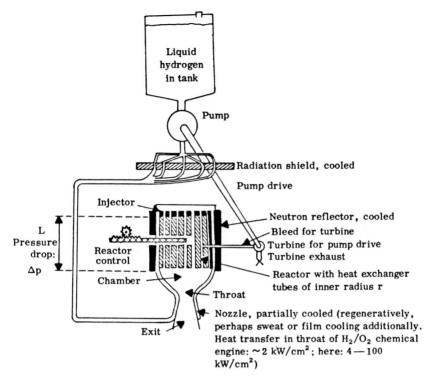

FIG. 2.5. Solid core nuclear rocket engine.

can be derived, for the specific impulse, $I_{\text{sp}} = 208(H_c - H_e)^{1/2} = 846$ sec. This still has to be corrected for thrust due to nozzle exit pressure, frictional losses, etc. With a nozzle throat area A_t the flow rate $\dot{w}$ follows approximately from Eq. (1.6) of Vol. 1, thrust $\approx 1.6 p_c A_t = \dot{w} I_{\text{sp}}$, or $\dot{w} \approx 1.6 p_c A_t / I_{\text{sp}}$. If the ambient pressure p_a is zero, then

$$\frac{(p_e - p_a)A_e}{\dot{w}} \approx 0.62 \, \frac{p_e}{p_c} \, \frac{A_e}{A_t} \, I_{\text{sp}} .$$

The value of A_e/A_t for a given ratio p_c/p_e can be read, e.g., from Figs. 3-7 and 3-8 of Sutton (1963), when the specific heat ratio k is known.[1] Assume $k = 1.35$. Then, for $p_c/p_e = 550$, we have $A_e/A_t = 30$. Now $0.62(p_e/p_c)(A_e/A_t)I_{\text{sp}} \approx 28.6$ sec. The total ideal specific impulse then is $846 + 29 = 875$ sec.

The same computation has been done for other chamber pressures p_c and

---

[1] At high temperature, for hydrogen $k = 1.292$.

chamber temperatures T_c, and the results are plotted in Fig. 2.6. Lowering the chamber pressure p_c to 0.1 atm, and leaving all other parameters unchanged, increases I_{sp} to 989 sec. The reason is to be found in the increased dissociation of the hydrogen with decreasing pressure. Indeed, $H_c=26.3$ and $H_e = 5.1$ kcal/gm-mole. So $208(21.2)^{1/2} = 957$ sec, and the correction due to nozzle exit pressure is 32 sec. Of course, the thrust would go down by a factor of approximately $0.1/60$, or acceleration from perhaps $2g$ to about $3 \times 10^{-3}g$. Generally, the increase in gravity loss will more than compensate for the increase in specific impulse from 875 to 989 sec; therefore, if gravity losses are significant, it will not be worthwhile to go to a very low chamber pressure.

Let us again return to $p_c = 60$ atm and $T_c = 2600°$K. But this time we will assume operation at ambient pressure of 1 atm with optimum nozzle exapansion, i.e., $p_e = p_a = 1$ atm, and $A_e/A_t \approx 6.4$. Again $H_c = 20.05$ kcal/gm-mole but $H_e = 6.6$ (and $T_e = 930°$K), thus $I_{sp} = 762$ sec. The same engine in vacuum would increase its specific impulse by the exit area pressure correction $0.62 \times 1/60 \times 6.4 \times 762 \approx 50$ sec to $I_{sp\ v} \approx 812$ sec.

Assuming that liquid hydrogen is converted to a hot gas by energy from the reactor,[1] the energy extracted per gram-mole of flowing medium is approximately $E' = H_c +$ molar heat of vaporization $= H_c + 0.225$ kcal/gm-mole, where 1 gm-mole hydrogen equals 2.016 gm. In kilowatts per gm/sec of flow rate, we have

$$E = 2.076H_c + 0.46 \quad \text{kW}/(\text{gm}/\text{sec}),$$
$$1 \text{ kWh} = 860.5 \text{ kcal} = 3.671 \times 10^5 \text{ mkg}.$$

The absolute maximum of the specific impulse ($H_e = 0$, and total energy input converted to kinetic energy of the jet) is therefore $I_{sp\,max} = 208 (H_c + 0.225)^{1/2}$, which for $H_c = 20.05$ is 937 sec. Possible practical effective values are given in the following tabulation (with estimated correction factors around 0.9):

Engine	$I_{sp\,max}$ (sec)
In an atmosphere of 1 atm pressure	$0.92 \times 762 = 701$
In vacuum	$0.92 \times 812 = 747$
With a vacuum engine	$0.9 \ \times 875 = 787$

[1] As mentioned, it is probable that liquid hydrogen should not enter the reactor for reactor control reasons. Therefore, the conversion to gaseous hydrogen takes place in the heat shield, neutron reflector, and engine cooling passages.

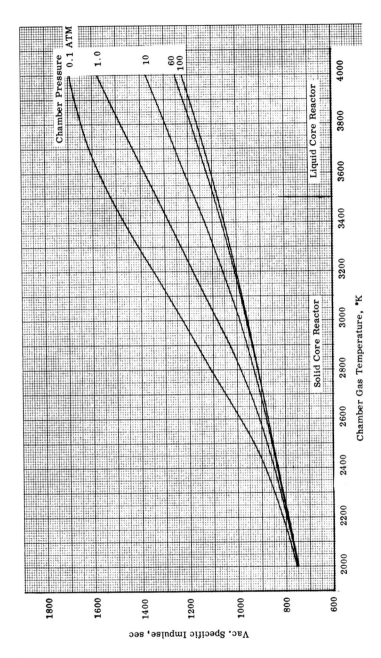

Fig. 2.6. Theoretical specific impulse of nuclear hydrogen rocket. Equilibrium expasion of hydrogen; nozzle area ratio 30 : 1.

The thermodynamic efficiency is then $\eta_{th} = (I_{sp}/I_{sp\,max})^2 = 56,\ 63.5,$ and 70.5%—quite attractive values.

Let us assume a thermal reactor with a thermal energy production of 1000 MW is available to heat hydrogen to 2600°K. To put this assumption in proper perspective: today's commercial reactors operate at much lower temperatures—1000°K is not considered to be very low. And the largest U.S. reactor—Dresden nuclear power station, Morris, Illinois—delivers "only" 626 thermal megawatts. The reactor for the nuclear ship Savannah has an output of a mere 69 thermal megawatts. Submarines (Nautilus) run about 70 MW at 250°C, whereas, for the nuclear aircraft, three reactors of about 250 MW each at 900–1100°C were envisioned. Thus it is understandable that most authorities put an operational nuclear rocket vehicle quite far into the future—to, say, the mid-seventies. It will be shown that the advanced assumptions made here lead to about the minimum useful vehicle. Since for $H_c = 20.05$ kcal/gm-mole the energy requirement is $E = 42.06$ kW/(gm sec), the mass flow rate is $1{,}000{,}000/(42.06) = 23{,}460$ gm/sec, and the thrust would be as given in the following tabulation:

Thrust	In kg
In an atmosphere of 1 atm pressure	$701 \times 23.46 = 16450$
With the same engine in vacuum	$747 \times 23.46 = 17500$
With a vacuum engine	$787 \times 23.46 = 18450$

The reactor may have a solid core weight of 3 tons and a mean (solid) density of 2 gm/cm³; this leads to a volume of 1.5 m³, a specific power of 333 kW/kg core, and a power density of 667 MW/m³. These are reasonable values.

The first American flyable nuclear engine (NERVA, Nuclear Engine Reactor for Vehicle Application) for "Project Rover" utilizes a KIWI-type reactor of a nominal power level of 1000 MW. This engine was the propulsion system of the RIFT (Reactor In Flight Test) vehicle, to be tested as an upper stage of the SATURN V launch vehicle. Project RIFT was canceled in Dec. 1963 for economy reasons. The first full power and temperature reactor test of one minute duration was accomplished successfully on May 13, 1964.

The first restart was demonstrated on August 28, 1964 (first run, 8 min) and September 10, 1964 (second run, more than 2 min). The specific impulse has been quoted to be "750 sec or higher when corrected for altitude."

The more advanced Phoebus engine class is reported to have a nominal power level of 5000 MW(th) and 250,000 lb thrust. During Fall of 1964 an estimate was published in *Aviation Week*, stating the theoretical limit of the specific impulse of a graphite reactor core rocket engine to be about 900 sec.

A detailed study performed in 1964 regarding graphite solid core nuclear engines resulted in the data given in Table 2.2.

TABLE 2.2

Thrust/weight ratio for 1000 MW thermal	3
Thrust/weight ratio for 10,000 MW thermal	7
Optimum expansion ratio for space usage	120–160
Optimum chamber pressure (atm)	25–30
Typical specific engine data:	
Thrust (tons)	102.5
I_{sp} (vacuum design and operation) (sec)	850
Weight (tons)	17
Expansion ratio	120
Thermal power (MW)	5099
Cooling channel diameter (mm)	2.5

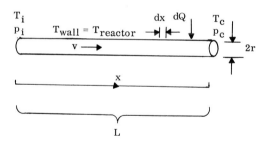

FIG. 2.7. Depiction of tube flow.

A very difficult question has to do with the heat transfer from the reactor to the gas. For turbulent hydrogen flow (see Fig. 2.7) through a tube we can say

$$\frac{p_i - p}{\varrho} = \lambda \frac{x}{2r} \frac{v^2}{2} \quad \text{and} \quad p = p_i - \frac{p_i - p_c}{L} x.$$

For the friction loss coefficient λ let us estimate the usual value 0.04. [Compare Sutton (1963), p. 200]. The relation between Stanton number S, $S = (\pi r^2 h)/(c_p \dot{w}) = \lambda/10$ and friction coefficient [Eckert (1950), p. 124], will be used later. Hence, $v^2 = 100[(p_i - p_c)/Lg\varrho]rg$ and, from the gas law,

$$g\varrho = \frac{pM}{RT} = \frac{p_i - (p_i - p_c)x/L}{(R/M)T} ,$$

where R is the universal gas constant[1] and M the molecular weight. With a wall temperature T_r and a heat transfer coefficient h, it follows, for the heat flow dQ to the gas in the time $dt = dx/v$, and a gas temperature T, that

$$dQ = h \times 2\pi r\, dx(T_r - T)\frac{dx}{v} = c_p \pi r^2\, dx\, g\varrho\, dT ,$$

or

$$(T_r - T)2h\frac{dx}{rv} = c_p g\varrho\, dT .$$

Inserting terminal values for the flow speed v and the gas density $g\varrho$ (because $g\varrho v = \text{const}$ within a tube), we obtain, after integration ($T_i = 0$),

$$2\frac{hL}{c_p r g\varrho_c v_c} = \ln \frac{T_r}{T_r - T} .$$

For $T_r = 3000°\text{K}$, $T_c = 2600°\text{K}$, and a cubical reactor, i.e., $L = (1.5)^{1/3} = 1.145$ m, we have

$$\frac{h}{c_p g\varrho_c v_c} = \frac{r[\text{m}]}{1.135} .$$

Now let us assume that a total of n such heat-exchanger tubes go through the reactor, and the total "void" volume is 25% of the core volume (perhaps 25% for thermal and 50% for fast reactors—larger "void" volumes are permissible with proper designs):

$$n\pi r^2 L = 0.25 \times 1.5 \text{ m}^3$$

or

$$nr^2 = 0.104 \text{ m}^2 .$$

The weight flow through all these tubes is

$$ng\varrho_c v_c \pi r^2 = \dot{W} = 23{,}460 \quad \text{gm/sec},$$

---

[1] 848 gm m/mole °K.

or

$$g\varrho_c v_c = 71{,}900 \quad \text{gm}/\text{m}^2 \text{ sec.}$$

Let us summarize the equations, using $p_i - p_c = \Delta p$ and with r expressed in meters:

$$v_c^2 = 100 \frac{\Delta p}{1.145 g\bar{\varrho}} rg \,,$$

$$\frac{h}{c_p g\varrho_c v_c} = 0.004 \,,$$

$$g\varrho_c = \frac{p_i - \Delta p}{11.02 \times 10^5} = \frac{p_c}{11.02 \times 10^5}$$

$$\frac{h}{c_p g\varrho_c v_c} = \frac{r}{1.135} \,,$$

$$nr^2 = 0.104,$$

and

$$g\varrho_c v_c = 71{,}900.$$

Assuming that for the average flow speed there is $\bar{v}^2 = \frac{1}{2}v_c^2$, and $\bar{\varrho}\bar{v} = \varrho_c v_c$, then

$$\bar{\varrho} = 2^{1/2}\varrho_c \,.$$

These are seven equations with the unknown quantities v_c, Δp, $\bar{\varrho}$, r, h/c_p, ϱ_c, and n. The solution gives $r = 4.54$ mm, $n = 0.504 \times 10^4$ (cross section of reactor $L^2 = 13.110$ cm^2; therefore, we have an area of 2.6 cm^2 per tube), and $h/c_p = 287$ (with $c_p = 3.45 \times 10^{-3}$ kcal/gm $^\circ$K comes $h = 0.99$ kcal/m^2 sec $^\circ$K). Assuming $p_c = 60$ atm $= 60 \times 10^7$ gm/m^2, we get $g\varrho_c = 544$ gm/m^3, $v_c = 132$ m/sec (sonic speed in chamber gas is about 3750 m/sec; so v_c is well subsonic), $\Delta p = 0.344$ atm, and $g\bar{\varrho} = 768$ gm/m^3. The total pressure losses in the reactor are pressure drop at tube inlet plus pressure drop along the tube (Δp) plus pressure drop at tube outlet. Such pressure drops can be estimated from hydraulics:

For the inlet: ~ 0.2 atm;
For the outlet: ~ 0.1 atm.

Total pressure drop across the reactor is ~ 1 atm. The mean Reynolds number of the flow in the tube will be computed:

$$\bar{\varrho} = 0.077 \quad \text{kg sec}^2/\text{m}^4,$$

$$2r = d = 0.00908 \quad \text{m},$$

$$\bar{v} = 94 \quad \text{m}/\text{sec},$$

$$\bar{\mu} = 2.58 \times 10^{-6} \quad \text{kg sec}/\text{m}^2 \quad \text{(viscosity of } H_2, \text{ for } T = 1500°\text{K)},$$

$$\text{Reynolds number} \approx 25{,}500.$$

From Sutton (1963, p. 201, curve 12) we have $\lambda = 0.039$, which is sufficiently close to the estimated value 0.04. Also, we verified the assumption of turbulent flow, since the flow is laminar for $\text{Re} \leq 2000$ and turbulent for $\text{Re} \geq 4000$.

For compressible flow, $\lambda' = \lambda + (2r/L) \ln(T_c/T_i)$ is a correction. This might here increase λ to 0.07, adding 0.26 atm to the pressure drop within a tube. The pressure drop across the reactor was estimated high to account for this correction.

The simple theory outlined resulted in seven equations, as given. For a significant improvement of two of these equations, we are indebted to Robert F. Nixon of the Propulsion and Vehicle Engineering Laboratory of NASA's G. C. Marshall Space Flight Center. One of the equations as derived reads:

$$\frac{h}{c_p g \varrho_c v_c} = \frac{r}{1.135} .$$

With the relationship between Stanton number and friction coefficient, this can be rewritten as

$$0.099\lambda = r/L .$$

We shall now develop an improved equation: Starting from

$$dQ = h \times 2\pi r \, dx \, (T_r - T) \frac{dx}{v} = c_p \pi r^2 \, dx \, g\varrho \, dT ,$$

we obtain, with the flow rate $\dot{w} = \pi r^2 v g \varrho$ and the heat transfer rate $q = h(T_r - T)$,

$$(q/\dot{w}) \, 2\pi r \, dx = c_p \, dT.$$

Let us prescribe q instead of constant wall temperature as was previously done.

$$q = \tfrac{1}{2}\pi \bar{q} \sin \pi(x/L).$$

This does describe the true situation in a nuclear reactor quite well. The average value of heat transfer rate is given by

$$\frac{1}{L} \int_0^L q \, dx = \bar{q} .$$

On substitution we get

$$dT = \frac{2\pi r L}{\dot{w}c_p} \left(\frac{\pi}{2}\, \bar{q}\right) \left(\sin \pi\, \frac{x}{L}\right) d\left(\frac{x}{L}\right).$$

By integrating between the limits T_c and T_i we get

$$T_c - T_i = \frac{2\pi r L}{\dot{w}c_p}\, \bar{q}\,.$$

The gas temperature follows by integration between the limits T and T_i,

$$\frac{T - T_i}{T_c - T_i} = \frac{1}{2}\left[1 - \cos \pi\, \frac{x}{L}\right].$$

Since $q = h(T_r - T) = \frac{1}{2}\pi\bar{q}\,\sin(\pi x/L)$, for the wall temperature T_r,

$$\frac{T_r - T_i}{T_c - T_i} = \frac{\pi r}{4L}\,\frac{1}{S}\,\sin \pi\, \frac{x}{L} + \frac{1}{2}\left[1 - \cos \pi\, \frac{x}{L}\right],$$

where S is the Stanton number. By differentiation, the maximum wall temperature occurs for $\tan(\pi x/L) = -\,(\pi r/2L)(1/S)$, and follows from

$$\frac{T_{r\,\max} - T_i}{T_c - T_i} = \frac{1}{2}\left\{1 + \left[\left(\frac{\pi r}{2L}\,\frac{1}{S}\right)^2 + 1\right]^{1/2}\right\} \approx 1 + \left(\frac{\pi r}{4L}\,\frac{1}{S}\right)^2.$$

Solving the above equation for r/L we have, with $S = 0.1\lambda$,

$$\frac{r}{L} = \frac{0.4\lambda}{\pi}\,\frac{T_{r\,\max}}{T_c - T_i}\left[\left(1 - \frac{T_i}{T_{r\,\max}}\right)\left(1 - \frac{T_c}{T_{r\,\max}}\right)\right]^{1/2}$$

$$\approx \frac{0.4\lambda}{\pi}\left[\frac{T_{r\,\max} - T_c}{T_c - T_i}\right]^{1/2}.$$

Substituting $T_{r\,\max} = 3000°\mathrm{K}$, $T_c = 2600°\mathrm{K}$, and $T_i = 200°\mathrm{K}$, we have $r/L = 0.0561\lambda$; or, with $\lambda = 0.04$ and $L = 1145$ mm we have $r = 2.57$ mm, considerably smaller than the simple value of 4.54 mm.

The pressure drop equation is

$$v_c^2 = 100\, \frac{\varDelta p}{1.145g\bar{\varrho}}\, rg\,.$$

An improved version has been developed by Fox (1960).

This equation is quite complicated. A greatly simplified version, tailored to the needs of this case, reads as follows:

$$\frac{\Delta p}{P_c} = \frac{3.05}{T_c} \left(\frac{v_c}{100}\right)^2 \left\{1 + 0.004 \frac{L}{r}\right\}.$$

Inserting $P_c = 60$, $T_c = 2600$, $v_c/100 = 1.32$, $L/r = 1145/4.54$, we obtain $\Delta p = 0.246$ atm, not far off from the value given previously.[1]

After these rough calculations, detail work must begin. This would mainly have to do with determination of realistic values for the friction loss coefficient λ and the heat transfer coefficient h. Is the thermal conductivity within the core material sufficiently high to prevent "hotspots"? Of course, our fast method of estimating a mean value for the gas density ϱ has to be replaced by more accurate integration. Deviations of hydrogen from the ideal-gas law have to be regarded. And investigation is necessary as to the influence of the hydrogen-filled void space in the nuclear reactor. (For example, hydrogen is an effective neutron reflector, or it can capture neutrons to become deuterium. Fortunately, the cross section for this reaction is low.) This can force us to use a different void fraction, or a different geometry. Transient phases (starting and stopping) require special investigations. Can the reactor mechanically withstand the forces due to pressure, flow, acceleration, vibration, thermal expansion? Is there any surface erosion to be expected? Can this erosion be avoided by surface coatings? Does the hydrogen destroy the coating? What about radioactivity of the jet? Finally, again optimization is necessary: size and design of reactor, pressure drop in reactor, reactor and gas temperature, chamber pressure and nozzle exit pressure are some of the variables. Obviously, the nuclear engine can only be optimized together with the vehicle it is intended for. The liquid hydrogen in the tank is heated by radiation from the nuclear reactor in the engine. Geometry of the tank bottom, engine-tank separation, thrust structure and shielding have to be chosen so that this effect is sufficiently reduced. But how does the hydrogen in the tank behave? Two extreme models are described by either stratification (i.e., each hydrogen layer is heated by the radiation it absorbs, but there is no mixing between the layers) or by complete mixing (i.e., the hydrogen in the tank has a uniform temperature); truth will be in between these models.

Hydrogen exists in two versions: orthohydrogen, where the spins of

---

[1] Because of nonuniform radial power distribution, the design pressure loss may be 1.5–3 times as large as the pressure loss computed assuming average radial power density.

the two atoms in the molecule are parallel, and parahydrogen having anti-parallel spin operation. The ortho form transforms itself slowly into the para form; this reaction is exothermic, releasing 168 kcal/kg, and this heat leads to a quite rapid evaporation of hydrogen. To avoid this, the liquid hydrogen as it is used for the nuclear rocket contains the two hydrogen forms in their equilibrium fractions to start out with; this can be perturbed, because neutron radiation leads to a para → ortho conversion.

Let us consider further our hypothetical 1000 MW engine. Boiling of the liquid hydrogen in the heat exchanger will not be a serious problem, as critical pressure of hydrogen is $p_{crit} = 12.8$ atm, and the pressure will always be greater than this. Before the hydrogen is injected into the reactor, it will be circulated through a regenerative cooling system of radiation shield, neutron reflector, thrust chamber, and nozzle. It will reach the reactor as a gas. The pressure drop in the cooling channel is 4 atm, and 1 atm in the feed line, giving a required pump outlet pressure of 66 atm. To round off the picture, we shall look at the hydrogen feed system.

The specific gravity of liquid hydrogen is only about 0.07 gm/cm³. Therefore, the flow rate $\dot{w} = 23,460$ gm/sec has a volume of 0.335×10^6 cm³/sec. The work done by the pump is

$$66 \, \frac{\text{kg}}{\text{cm}^2} \, \frac{0.335 \times 10^6}{100 \, \text{cm/m}} \, \frac{\text{cm}^3}{\text{sec}} = 0.221 \times 10^6 \, \frac{\text{mkg}}{\text{sec}} = 2.17 \, \text{MW} = 517 \, \frac{\text{kcal}}{\text{sec}} .$$

The pump could be driven by a turbine, which has a chemical energy source of its own. But we will assume that it runs on hydrogen coming from the reactor at 60 atm pressure and only 1400°K. The enthalpy is 10 kcal/gm-mole, and the turbine exit enthalpy shall be 5.5 kcal/gm-mole (15 atm, 800°K). The energy delivered to the turbine is 4.5 kcal/gm-mole, which requires, for a turbine power of 517/(0.77) = 670 kcal/sec, a turbine flow of 149 gm-mole/sec ≈ 299 gm/sec, or about 1.27% of the propulsive jet flow.[1] The reduction in effective specific impulse is thought to be taken care of by the factor 0.9 or 0.92, with which the theoretical values were multiplied to get effective values. Thus no further reduction takes place.

The following pump drive cycles are of interest:

Cold bleed. The hydrogen needed to drive the turbine is taken from the cooling system prior to entry of the gas into the reactor.

---

[1] For 60-atm, 800°K turbine inlet and 10-atm, 500°K outlet the energy delivered to the turbine is 2.2 kcal/gm-mole, requiring an increase of the turbine flow to 612 gm/sec, which is 2.6% of the propulsive jet flow.

Heated bleed. The hydrogen source is as in cold bleed, but prior to turbine entry it is heated to a higher temperature in cooling channels of the nozzle.

Hot bleed. The hydrogen stems from the chamber, at its maximum temperature. To obtain the desired turbine inlet temperature, colder hydrogen is added to the hot gas.

Pressure-fed systems have no turbine or pump. In this and all other cases where an available hydrogen cooling flow is not utilized to drive the turbine, one may expand the cooling flow—after it has done its job—through small nozzles parallel to the main nozzle; there is no loss involved in this procedure if the hydrogen temperature in the cooling system gets high enough—indeed, there can be a noticeable gain if this procedure is considered for a hydrogen-burning chemical engine.

Topping cycle. The hydrogen goes through a pump. Thereafter, it is heated up in cooling the nozzle and radiation shield; following this, it delivers energy to a turbine which drives the pump. The turbine exhaust pressure is so high that it feeds the injector to the reactor, where the gas is finally heated up to form the exhaust jet.

The energy taken from the reactor for the turbine is, in our example,

$$E_t = (2.076 \times 10 + 0.46)\, 299 \approx 6.4 \quad \text{MW}.$$

By radiation, reactors lose about 2% of the energy output. All these losses can be compensated by uprating the reactor from 1000 to about 1030 MW.

The turbine exhaust delivers some useful thrust too. Assume it is expanded through a nozzle of area ratio 6.4, resulting in a pressure ratio of 60, or a nozzle exit pressure of 0.25 atm. From the Mollier chart we have enthalpy, 1.9 kcal/gm-mole, and a temperature of about 300°K. For zero ambient pressure, we have the specific impulse $I_{sp} = 421$ sec, and a thrust of $421 \times 299 \times 10^{-3} = 126$ kg. This thrust not only augments the main engine, but it can be used for roll-control, attitude-control, and vernier purposes.

If the same flow goes through the reactor and leaves the vehicle through the main nozzle instead of through the turbine exhaust nozzle, its ideal specific impulse would go up to 875 sec, and the ideal thrust would be 261 kg. This is a gain of $261 - 126 = 135$ kg, or corrected with the standard correction factor of 0.9, only 121 out of 17,850 kg. This is an increase of 0.68%, or, expressed as an increase in effective specific impulse, it is $(0.68/100)787 \approx 5.3$ sec;[1] this is very small, considering that some disadvantages—e.g.,

---

[1] For the case discussed in the previous footnote: 12 sec.

loss of a simple method for roll control—result also. Therefore, the increase in effective specific impulse alone is no big incentive to develop the mentioned, improved "topping" hydrogen feed system.

A vehicle built with the described engine might have the characteristics (with the average effective specific impulse $= 701 + \frac{2}{3} \times 46 = 731$ sec) shown in Table 2.3. Using the values given in the table we have .

$$v_{\text{id}} = 731g_0 \ln \frac{13}{8} = 3.48 \quad \text{km/sec.}$$

TABLE 2.3

CHARACTERISTICS OF THE VEHICLE

Characteristics of vehicle	Weight (tons)
Sea level thrust	16.45
Vacuum thrust	17.5
Launch weight	13
Reactor weight	3
Engine, engine mounting, and pumps	1.5
Radiation shielding	1
Guidance, control, and instrumentation	1
Payload	1
Tankage and residuals	0.5
Usable hydrogen	5.0
Launch weight	13.0
Cutoff weight	8

This is not very impressive—it would be a missile of about 600 km range. It is indeed something like a minimum useful nuclear stage, as stated before. The poor mass ratio is the main reason for the insufficient performance. A larger vehicle with higher thrust is better, as most of the inert weight increases only slowly (engine) or not at all (guidance, control, instrumentation, perhaps payload) with thrust.

Here we must make some basic remarks: Having the assumed thermal reactor of 1000 MW thermal output, it does not take much more weight to increase the energy output, if energy density is increased. Finally, the energy density reaches the limit of heat transfer capability and further increases in thermal output are only possible by increasing the reactor volume (or weight) proportionally.

For a fast reactor, operation can always occur at the limit of heat transfer capabilities, since here the total core mass (order of 50 kg, at the high density of 13 gm/cm³) is so small. Then all increases in power output demand a proportional increase in core weight.[1] The small core leads to a small radiation shield mass (see Fig. 2.8.)

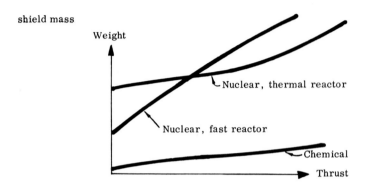

FIG. 2.8. Weight vs thrust trends of nuclear and chemical engines.

It can be seen that, under certain conditions, the fast reactor can be advantageous for this type of nuclear rocket. Additional benefits from the fast reactor are: higher temperature possible because of absence of moderator, and some high melting-point materials (e.g., hafnium carbide, zirconium carbide, tantalum carbide, tungsten, molybdenum) absorb no fast neutrons, but cannot be utilized in a thermal reactor.[2] Compared to graphite, the interaction of the reactor material with hydrogen appears to be reduced. With these remarks in mind the characteristics of a somewhat advanced vehicle, whose effective average specific impulse is 800 sec, are given in Table 2.4. This performance is obviously interesting. But less advanced vehicles can be attractive if properly used. If the previously described small engine of 18.5 tons thrust were utilized in an upper stage, we could tolerate perhaps $\frac{1}{3}g$ as initial acceleration, thus having an initial weight of $18.5 \times 3 = 55.5$ tons, of which 43.5 tons are usable hydrogen.

[1] Some remarks derived from Cooper (1961) are of interest in connection with Fig. 2.8. The fast reactor shall be tungsten-based, with a small (10–20 in.) core diameter. Then it can be shown, that the minimum engine weight is given by 1000 lb + 1 lb per MW of reactor power, whereas for a graphite reactor the minimum weight is given by 4500 lb + 1 lb per MW.

[2] An increase of T_c from 2600 to 2700°K increases the specific impulse from 787 to 802 sec.

TABLE 2.4

CHARACTERISTICS OF AN ADVANCED VEHICLE[a]

Characteristic of vehicle	Weight (tons)
Thrust	160
Reactor weight	20
Engine, etc.	5
Radiation shielding	4
Guidance, control, and instrumentation	1
Payload	1
Tankage and residuals	9
Usable hydrogen	90
Launch weight	130

[a] Here $v_{id} = 9.25$ km/sec.

With the vacuum value of the specific impulse (787 sec), we now have $v_{id} = 11.82$ km/sec. This shows clearly that even relatively small nuclear rocket vehicles will bring noticeable gains when they are employed as upper stages in connection with chemical boosters. A similar application is for the stage to leave a circular orbit around Earth.

Demanding from the described 55.5-ton vehicle $v_{id} = 3.5$ km/sec (sufficient to escape from orbit), the mass ratio is only 1.572, and the cutoff weight 35.3 tons, leaving a payload of 26.8 tons to be hurled to escape. A chemical stage with $I_{sp} = 430$ sec and 500 kg engine weight would require 31.3 tons of propellants and 3.1 tons of tankage for the same initial weight of 55.5 tons, which leaves, with 1 ton for guidance, etc., 19.6 tons for payload.

When $v_{id} = 11.15$ km/sec, the "burning time" for the 55.5-ton vehicle is rather long:

$$\frac{43.5 \times 10^3}{23.46} = 1854 \text{ sec} \approx 31 \text{ min} \approx 0.5 \text{ h}.$$

The total energy extracted from the reactor is

$$1030 \times \frac{0.5}{24} = 21.48 \quad \text{MW-days} \quad \text{or} \quad 7.15 \quad \text{MW-days/ton},$$

being only about 0.286% of the total energy content of the reactor. This immediately poses the question as to reuse of a reactor. One could think, e.g., of a flight from the Earth to a circular orbit around the Earth having a nuclear last stage, and taking the same vehicle to leave orbit after it has been resupplied with liquid hydrogen. Or one might think of a "shuttle service" between an Earth satellite orbit and a lunar satellite orbit, where after each round trip the shuttle has only to be refilled with hydrogen.

Opening up and closing down of a nuclear reactor is no simple thing. In starting, the procedure has to be slow for reasons of reactor control and to avoid thermal cracking—start-up time may be between $\frac{1}{2}$ and 1 min.[1] If this has to be shortened, it may be possible to run the reactor at highly reduced power, highly reduced flow rate, and nearly terminal temperature —then "full power" can be given faster.

When a reactor is closed down, the decaying radioactive products are still in it, which will cause it to melt in a few seconds unless the reactor is cooled. After T_0 days of operation at a constant power level P, the energy release at day number $T \geq T_0$ due to β-γ radiation from the radioactive products is approximately

$$\frac{\Delta P}{P} = \frac{5.9}{10^3} \left[\frac{1}{(T - T_0)^{0.2}} - \frac{1}{T^{0.2}} \right].$$

If a close and restart capability is desired, typically some 10^3 lb hydrogen (or some other medium) has to be provided for cooling during the "runout" phase. Perhaps the trapped hydrogen and hydrogen vapor from the tank can be utilized. Without reuse, the reactor would be separated from the vehicle and be allowed to melt.[2]

Some of the decay products building up within the reactor absorb thermal neutrons ("poisons"). The most severe of these is xenon, which forms and decays as follows:

$$\underset{\beta,2 \text{ min}}{_{52}\text{Te}^{135}} \rightarrow \underset{\beta,6.7 \text{ h}}{_{53}\text{I}^{135}} \rightarrow \underset{\beta,9.2 \text{ h}}{_{54}\text{Xe}^{135}} \rightarrow \underset{\beta,2.1\times10^6 \text{ yr}}{_{55}\text{Cs}^{135}} \rightarrow \underset{(\text{stable})}{_{56}\text{Ba}^{135}} .$$

Because of its large cross section for thermal neutrons, the xenon is continuously "burned out" by the neutron flux within the operating reactor, and an equilibrium concentration of xenon is reached.

---

[1] A warm-up time, possible with no hydrogen flow at all, of around 1 h may be required.

[2] Cycling of a carbide or metal core might be simpler than of a graphite core, because of reduced thermal stress effects.

When a reactor is shut down, the iodine, formed at its equilibrium concentration, continues to supply Xe^{135} poison, which is now not "burned out"; the Xe^{135} concentration rises above its equilibrium value. Finally, the general decay leads again to xenon reduction ("recovery" of the reactor). From these considerations it follows that a nuclear engine can be shut down for a brief time period (from $\frac{1}{2}$ to 6 h typically) and restarted. If shut down longer, the xenon poison prevents restart; but after a longer time (typically, 18–48 h) the reactor has recovered, and restart can be accomplished.

Clustering of nuclear rocket engines creates a special problem with regard to "cross-talk" between the reactors; there is a coupling of the reactors via the neutron radiation. But proper geometry, shielding, distance between the engines and reactor design make clustering possible. Of course, we are looking somewhat into the future: in 1964, the KIWI-reactor series—still in the form of nonflyable feasibility demonstration models of solid core nuclear reactor high acceleration rocket engines—was in the testing phase. We believe it is not too optimistic to assume that about 10 years later flyable hardware (NERVA, and more advanced types, like PHOEBUS) can be available as an outgrowth of the nuclear rocket project "Rover," in the form of an upper stage for large chemical boosters such as Saturn.

Most improvements on the thermodynamic scheme have to do with increases in gas temperature. There are several possibilities:

(1) *Solid core reactor.* In the "standard" nuclear rocket as described, some of the gas is extracted for the turbine to drive the pump. Let us change this and let us extract all the gas and duct it through a large turbine or through an MHD power generator. In either case, the large power output is converted to electric energy. The gas is not exhausted, but brought again through the reactor, and flows this time to the engine chamber, where it has the temperature T_c. This temperature is further increased by adding the electric energy generated before, e.g., by utilizing an electric arc (Goldsmith, 1959). Application of this "Ackeret cycle" could raise the specific impulse by about 100 to 200 sec (or more, when several Ackeret cycles are utilized). [See Fig. 2.9.] Of course, there are many problems having to do with complexity, strong pressure drops, heavy weight of the electric equipment, etc. Let us investigate an idealized situation:

Per mole of flowing gas, the electric energy produced by the first generator is given by

$$E_1 = \eta \frac{T_1 - T_2}{T_1} C_p T_1 ,$$

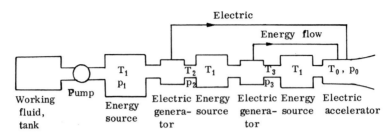

FIG. 2.9. Ackeret cycle. T is temperature and p pressure. Energy source: solid, liquid, or gaseous core fusion or fission reactor or reactors; or heat exchangers heated by nuclear or solar power, or a mixture of such devices. Electric generator: turbine and rotating machinery, or MHD generators, etc. Electric accelerator: the gas is heated from T_1 to T_0 by adding the energy, e.g., by an electric arc or the gas flows through an MHD accelerator.

where η is the efficiency and C_p the molar specific heat. We also have the relationship

$$\frac{p_1}{p_2} = \left(\frac{T_1}{T_2}\right)^{\varkappa/(\varkappa-1)},$$

where $\varkappa$ is the specific heat ratio. If we adjust p_3 so that $p_3/p_2 = p_2/p_1$, then $T_3 = T_2$, and the energy produced by the second generator is given by $E_2 = E_1$.

Generally, for n generators the electric energy follows from

$$E = n\eta \left(1 - \frac{T_2}{T_1}\right)C_p T_1,$$

$$\frac{T_2}{T_1} = \left(\frac{p_2}{p_1}\right)^{(\varkappa-1)/\varkappa},$$

and

$$\frac{p_0}{p_1} = \left(\frac{p_2}{p_1}\right)^{n}.$$

We add the energy E with an efficiency η_1 to the gas in the electric accelerator. The resultant enthalpy is

$$C_p T_0 = C_p T_1 + E\eta_1,$$

or

$$T_0 = T_1 \left\{1 + n\eta\eta_1 \left[1 - \left(\frac{p_0}{p_1}\right)^{(\varkappa-1)/n\varkappa}\right]\right\}.$$

We write $I_{\text{sp}\,0}$ for the specific impulse of this engine for the case of E being zero; then, approximately, for the general case

$$I_{\text{sp}} = I_{\text{sp}\,0} \left\{ 1 + n\eta\eta_1 \left[1 - \left(\frac{p_0}{p_1} \right)^{(\varkappa-1)/n\varkappa} \right] \right\}^{1/2} .$$

Example. Let $I_{\text{sp}\,0} = 700$ sec (atmosphere) or 850 sec (vacuum), $\eta = 0.9$, $\eta_1 = 0.75$, $p_1 = 200$ atm, $p_0 = 34$ atm; then the values of I_{sp} are as given in the following tabulation:

$\varkappa$	n	I_{sp}(atmosphere) (sec)	I_{sp}(vacuum) (sec)
1.4	1	845	1025
1.4	2	880	1068
1.67	1	868	1053
1.67	2	922	1120

If the propulsion system is sufficiently large, the acceleration of a vehicle driven by such a propulsion system may conceivably be larger than 10 m/sec².

The augmented Ackeret cycle as described by Rosa (1961) is a further improvement, usable within an atmosphere (see Fig. 2.10).

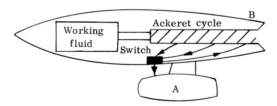

FIG. 2.10. Augmented Ackeret cycle.

The electric energy is lead to a switch, which may deliver it to an air-breathing engine operating on electric power (A) or to the electric accelerator (B). The switchover would occur at an optimum time, or—better, but more complicated—be gradually changed following an optimum program.

The "equivalent specific impulse" of such a scheme within an atmosphere might be several thousand seconds, and still only 1000 sec in space. Such a system might be ideally suited for Earth-to-orbit type transportation systems, rendering such flights a routine mission.

The Ackeret cycle is comparable to an arc jet system, but being an open loop system it does not require any radiator. On the other hand, its working fluid is identical with its exhaust mass, which may pose an operational disadvantage.

(2) *Liquid core reactor.* Higher reactor temperature leads to a higher gas temperature T_c. The reactor temperature might be between 4000 and 5000°K. With a gas temperature $T_c = 4800$°K, $p_c = 60$ atm, and $p_e = 0.109$ atm, we can read from the Mollier diagram $H_c = 74.5$ kcal/gm-mole and $H_e = 23$ kcal/gm-mole. Thus the theoretical value of $I_{sp} \approx 1492$ sec. To this we must add the correction due to exit-pressure thrust giving a total of 1542 sec, or, to be realistic, perhaps 1400 sec. Confinement of the liquid reactor might be by rotation as indicated in Fig. 2.11. The hydrogen could bubble through the reactor.

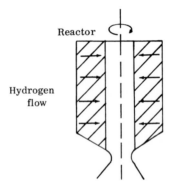

Reactor

Hydrogen
flow

FIG. 2.11. Principle of liquid reactor.

Loss of reactive material with the exhaust (due to its vapor pressure) can present economic or other problems.

A dust bed reactor may be simpler than a liquid core design and have a peformance which is halfway between solid and liquid core design (specific impulse being 1100 sec).

(3) *Gaseous core reactor.*[1] Confinement of the radioactive material appears to be difficult, but possible, by hydrodynamic and/or magnetohydrodynamic

---

[1] Stambler (1962) has mentioned that the Soviet Union in September, 1957 tested a reactor to produce a chain reaction with gaseous hexafluoride fuel, enriched to 90% of U^{235}. The power level was about 1.5 kW, the gas volume in core 213×10^3 cm³, and the critical mass 3.34 kg.

means or by transparent walls or by recirculation.[1] Many problems concerning a gaseous fission reactor are not yet solved. If it can be made to operate, it looks promising. But the minimum thrust is hardly below 500 tons; acceleration of greater than one Earth-gravity is possible.

The cavity containing the reactor will be surrounded by walls. It is usually estimated that 10% of the gas core reactor energy output is transferred to these walls, clearly necessitating cooling.

Let us assume that the total exhaust flow is used to cool the walls. After having done this, the exhaust flow cannot be hotter than that coming from a solid core reactor; i.e., if we were to vent it to space, we would have a specific impulse of about 800 sec. But, instead of venting it to space, we inject it into the gas core reactor, where nine times as much energy is added to what has been absorbed already. Therefore, the specific impulse of the gas core system is about $800(10)^{1/2} \approx 2500$ sec. More detailed considerations appear to limit the specific impulse even lower—about 1800 sec or so.

This limit can be circumvented, if higher heat transfer to the wall can be permitted; i.e., if the walls are cooled by other means. In a practical way, this can be accomplished by cooling loops, transferring energy to radiators and thus radiating the energy into space. Unfortunately, the thrust-to-weight ratio of the engine will now be well below one, but very high specific impulses (up to 5000 sec, at a gas temperature of 50,000°K) can be obtained.

The problems of fissionable material containment can be avoided, if we design a closed loop nuclear MHD generator electric energy producing system, which uses a separate exhaust mass for cooling of the wall, etc., and for the heat sink (i.e., no radiators are required). With the electric energy, the exhaust mass is "afterheated," before we expand it through a nozzle; this engine promises about the specific impulse of gas-core motors, at somewhat lower thrust-to-weight ratio.

Even more nebulous is the outlook of utilization of a (gaseous) fusion reaction. There appear to be two possibilities: either have parts of the gas of the fusion reaction directly form the jet and have low acceleration (thrust/weight $= 10^{-3}$), but specific impulse around 10^5–10^6 sec, or similar to a gas cavity reactor, use the reaction to heat some gas to form the jet and go possibly up to $1g$ in acceleration, but with a specific impulse reduced perhaps to about 2500 sec. The temperature within the fusion reactor is between 100×10^6 and 1000×10^6°K. Compared to fission, only little radiation is expected from a fusion reactor. Very clearly, all such really advanced

---

[1] The fraction λ of uranium atoms in the exhaust has to be less than 10^{-4} (Tumm, 1966). For $\lambda = 2 \times 10^{-7}$, the cost of U^{235} in the exhaust equals the cost of the hydrogen.

schemes are beyond our present technical capabilities. [Compare, e.g., Rosa (1961), Fowler and Post (1966), and Ehricke (1966).]

(4) *Isothermal expansion.* Assume that the nuclear reactor could be arranged around the exhaust nozzle, so that the gas flowing through the nozzle remains at constant temperature T_0.

If a gas expands adiabatically from a pressure p_1 to a pressure p_2 and k is the specific heat ratio, then for the temperatures we have

$$\frac{T_1}{T_2} = \left(\frac{p_1}{p_2} \right)^{(k-1)/k}.$$

It follows that, for $k = 1$, we have $T_1 = T_2$, i.e., isothermal expansion. Therefore, the isothermal case can be obtained from the adiabatic case, as the limit $k \to 1$.

The major results are

$$c^2 = 2 \, \frac{p_0}{\varrho_0} \ln \left(\frac{p_0}{p} \right),$$

where c is the gas speed, p_0 the pressure in the chamber, ϱ_0 the gas density in the chamber, p the gas pressure; and

$$\frac{p_0}{\varrho_0} = g_0 p_0 V_0 = g_0 \, \frac{\mathscr{R} T_0}{\mu} = a^2,$$

g_0 the gravitational acceleration, $\mathscr{R}$ the universal gas constant, V_0 the specific volume, μ the molecular weight, and a the speed of sound in the gas. With T_0 measured in degrees Kelvin and a measured in meters per second, we have

$$a^2 = 8316 \, \frac{T_0}{\mu}$$

and

$$c^2 = 16{,}632 \, \frac{T_0}{\mu} \ln \left(\frac{p_0}{p} \right) = 2a^2 \ln \left(\frac{p_0}{p} \right).$$

For the nozzle throat we obtain $T_t = T_0$ (isothermic process), $a_t = a$ (isothermic process), and $p_t = (1/e)^{1/2} p_0 = 0.607 p_0$. And the nozzle area ratio is given by

$$\frac{F}{F_t} = \frac{1}{e^{1/2}} \, \frac{1}{(p/p_0)[2 \ln(p_0/p)]^{1/2}} = 0.429 \, \frac{p_0/p}{[\ln(p_0/p)]^{1/2}}.$$

The mass flowing through the nozzle is given by

$$\frac{\dot{m}}{F_t} = \frac{p_0}{e^{1/2} a} = 0.607 \, \frac{p_0}{a}.$$

The thrust is

$$S = \dot{m}c = \left\{0.858 \left[\ln\left(\frac{p_0}{p}\right)\right]^{1/2}\right\}p_0 F_t \,.$$

Example. $T_0 = 2600°K$, $\mu = 2$, $a^2 = 10.81 \times 10^6$ (m/sec)^2, $a = 3288$ m/sec, $p_0/p = 600$ (or 78,000), $c = 11,770$ m/sec (or 15,600 m/sec), $F/F_t = 101.7$ (or 10^4), $S = 2.17 p_0 F_t$ (or $2.88 p_0 F_t$).

This performance improvement has been obtained without increasing the temperature. The difficulty, of course, is that we do not know how to get isothermal expansion within a practical system.

The energy efficiency of the isothermal engine is inferior to the energy efficiency of the adiabatic engine, since the exhaust gases of the isothermal engine are much hotter, i.e., carry a larger loss of thermal energy. This is not an important consideration, if energy is relatively freely available (as might be the case for nuclear heating or solar heating).

For area ratios between 10^2 and 10^4, the increase in exhaust speed obtained by isothermal expansion is 30 to 60%, compared to the adiabatic expansion for the same temperature and nozzle expansion ratio. Obviously, because of the heating of the gas during expansion, the isothermal engine will be heavier than the adiabatic one, especially for larger nozzle area ratios.

2.2 Problems of Radiation from a Solid-Core Nuclear Reactor

For a space vehicle, shielding of the payload against harmful radiation is very important—especially for manned vehicles. Transistors may be quite sensitive, but tubes are not. Man, of course, is very sensitive. For the present we will look only into problems of shielding against radiation coming from a nuclear reactor.

Within the atmosphere, this radiation can reach the payload compartment from all directions because of atmospheric scatter. Therefore, shielding is necessary all around the payload, thereby increasing its weight considerably. Outside of any atmosphere, "shadow shielding" will suffice[1]: here a shield (and cargo, propellants, etc.) is placed only between reactor and payload. Because of the often fairly heavy shield, we will look into this case only, or, in other words, operation of the nuclear propulsion system is not anticipated inside any scattering medium. In practice, this means that nuclear propulsion is used either on top of a chemical booster at sufficiently large altitude—for Earth, e.g., 60 km—or to leave from a satellite orbit.

---

[1] Some care has to be utilized regarding scatter radiation from parts of the vehicle itself and from the exhaust jet.

This avoids an additional problem: within the atmosphere, the hydrogen jet from the nuclear engine would have a long afterburning flame reacting with surrounding atmospheric oxygen. (But a similar problem is present with chemical H_2/O_2 engines, which operate hydrogen rich.) Some launch safety problems are eliminated too, because the reactor is not under power, or at least not at full power, during ground handling and launching of the vehicle.

A somewhat crude approximation of the radiation from a 1000-MW thermal reactor is as follows:

$$\text{Energy release per fission} = 2.88 \times 10^{-11} \text{ W sec.}$$

Therefore, the number of fissions is

$$N = \frac{1000 \times 10^6}{2.88 \times 10^{-11}} = 3.48 \times 10^{19} \quad \frac{\text{fissions}}{\text{sec}}.$$

About 3γ-quanta of 1 MeV may escape per fission. And about $\frac{1}{2}$ neutron, n, per fission may escape, of which half may have high and the other half have thermal energy. So the total radiated energy for $1 \times 10^{20}\,\gamma$/sec, 0.9×10^{19} n/sec (fast), and 0.9×10^{19} n/sec (thermal) is

$$1.2 \times 10^{20} \text{ MeV} \approx 19.2 \text{ MW} \approx 2\% \text{ of } 1000 \text{ MW.}$$

(For a fast reactor, some more γ-quanta may escape, and all the neutrons may be fast ones.) The flux at the crew compartment—assuming no shield—can be reduced by merely having a large distance d between reactor and compartment. With $d = 1$ m, the flux to be expected is

$$\varphi_\gamma = 8 \times 10^{14}\,\gamma/\text{sec cm}^2,$$

and

$$\varphi_{n_f} = \varphi_{n_{th}} = 7 \times 10^{13} \, n/\text{sec cm}^2.$$

For γ radiation, the absorption (= change in intensity J) per path length dx can be described by $dJ/dx = -J\mu$, where μ is a material constant. With ϱ being the specific gravity, very roughly (for γ-radiation) $\mu = 0.03\,\varrho[1/\text{cm}]$. The incident energies are

$$
\begin{aligned}
J_\gamma &= \quad 8 \times 10^{14} \text{ MeV/cm}^2 \text{ sec} = \ \sim 30 \text{ cal/cm}^2 \text{ sec} \\
J_{n_f} &= 1.4 \times 10^{14} \text{ MeV/cm}^2 \text{ sec} = \ \sim 5 \text{ cal/cm}^2 \text{ sec} \\
J_{n_{th}} &= \quad 7 \times 10^6 \ \text{ MeV/cm}^2 \text{ sec} = \ \sim \frac{3}{10^7} \text{ cal/cm}^2 \text{ sec}
\end{aligned}
$$

$$\text{Total} \qquad\qquad\qquad\qquad 35 \text{ cal/cm}^2 \text{ sec}$$

For aluminum, $\varrho \approx 2.7$ gm/cm³, $\mu = 0.08$ and the maximum absorption $\mu \times 35 = 2.8$ cal/cm³ sec ≈ 1 cal/gm sec. As the specific heat is about 0.214 cal/gm degree, this would suffice for a temperature rise of 5°C/sec.

Approximately, an absorbed energy (in air at standard conditions) of 83 erg/cm³ is the equivalent to a radiation intensity of 1 roentgen (r).[1] Therefore, 1 r $= 5.18 \times 10^7$ MeV/cm³, and 0.0075 r/h $= 7.5$ mr/h ≈ 100 MeV/cm³ sec. With $\varrho = 1$ (human tissue) and $\mu = 0.03$/cm this corresponds to an incident radiation of $J_0 = 3.333 \times 10^3$ MeV/cm² sec of γ-radiation, or $J_\gamma = 8 \times 10^{14}$ MeV/cm² sec corresponds to $2.4 \times 10^{11} \times 7.5 \times 10^{-3} = 1.8 \times 10^9$ r/h. This has to be multiplied with an empirical factor ("relative biological effectiveness") to be converted to "roentgen equivalent man" (rem). Approximately, there may be (with RBE of $n_f = 10$, $n_{th} = 5$, and $\mu_{n_f} = 0.3\varrho$, $\mu_{n_{th}} = 1.5\varrho$):

From γ-radiation:	γ	$= 1.8 \times 10^9$ rem/h
From fast neutrons:	n_f	$= 30 \times 10^9$ rem/h
From thermal neutrons:	$n_{th} =$	3×10^3 rem/h

These are only very coarse data. For example, the fact that bone structure will absorb differently from tissue structure has not been taken into account.

Equally approximate, a table of radiation damage for man is:

Continuous exposure
- 0.007 r/week average dosage rate any human receives
- 0.03 r/week not dangerous
- 0.3 r/week slight harm possible
- 10 r per space expedition allowable
- 50 r per first 35 yr of life, doubling spontaneous rate of mutation

(AEC rule, since Jan. 1, 1961: exposure limit is 5 rem/yr, with not more than 3 rem in any one quarter.)

Single exposure
- > 500 r — death results
- 300–500 r — might escape death
- 100–250 r — survival probable; nausea
- 25–100 r — always curable with no remaining harm

It is hoped that drugs will be developed to heal radiation damage, or prevent

---

[1] More precisely, this is the definition of one physical roentgen equivalent, called rep.

it from occurring. Such drugs could increase the allowable dosage in the future. Furthermore, partial shielding (e.g., for the eyes) may alleviate the situation, and there is some evidence that by complete shielding of one part of the body (e.g., an arm) the total permissible radiation dose can be increased markedly.

The total radiation rate from the reactor is about 32×10^9 rem/h $= 5.4 \times 10^{12}$ rem/week, at a distance of 1 m. At 14,000 km distance it is 0.03 r/week; evidently, the crew compartment cannot be protected by distance alone when crew compartment and reactor are in the same vehicle.

For a high-acceleration vehicle, the design may be as sketched in Fig. 2.12 (see Shepherd and Cleaver, 1948–1949).

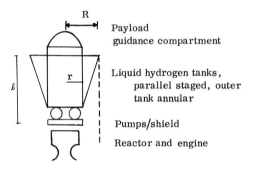

FIG. 2.12. Shadow shield.

In this design much of the structure can be utilized for radiation shielding. Unfortunately, a shadow shield is still necessary—if for nothing else than to protect the liquid hydrogen from overheating. (As shown, the heating rate can be quite significant.) The hydrogen flow to the engine can be utilized to cool the radiation shield if necessary.

If the shield thickness is x, then the radiation behind the shield is about

$$\gamma\text{-radiation:} \qquad J_r = 1.8 \times 10^9 \exp(-0.03\varrho x) \text{ rem/h}$$
$$\text{Fast neutrons:} \qquad J_{n_f} = 30 \times 10^9 \exp(-0.3\varrho x) \text{ rem/h}$$
$$\text{Thermal neutrons:} \qquad J_{n_{th}} = 3 \times 10^3 \exp(-1.5\varrho x) \text{ rem/h}$$

Here ϱx is just the weight per square centimeter of the shield—let us call this w. With the assumption that none of the radiation intensity shall be more than 1000 r/h (with a high-acceleration system, total nuclear propulsion period per space expedition may be 2 h; the distance between shield and cabin may be 30 m, resulting in about 1 r/h at the crew cabin, or 2 r for the whole expedition due to the reactor), we have

For γ-radiation: $\qquad w = 500$ gm/cm^2

For fast neutrons: $\qquad w = 60$ gm/cm^2

For thermal neutrons: $\qquad w = 0.7$ gm/cm^2.

Therefore, with about 5 tons/m^2, adequate shielding can be provided, with γ-radiation being the most demanding one. Fortunately, the rule does not hold that absorption is strictly a function of weight per area only. More effective, laminated shielding can be provided. Assuming that an improvement by a factor of five is obtainable, we finally require a shield with a weight of 1 ton/m^2 (or 100 gm/cm^2). Some further improvement is possible when the hydrogen and the structure are effectively utilized for reduction of the radiation after the shield.

Let us go back to the upper stage vehicle described, with the initial acceleration of only $0.3g$. There were 41.5 tons ≈ 593 m^3 of liquid hydrogen. This could be accommodated in tankage of (see Fig. 2.12) $R = 6.5$ m and $l = 11.8$ m. The radius of the inner tank is $r = 0.85$, slightly more than the radius of the nuclear reactor. The volume of the inner tank is 26.8 m^3, or 4.5% of the total volume of 593 m^3. This means that the benefit of the shielding due to the hydrogen in the inner tank can be had for 95.5% of the operational time, when the hydrogen from the outer tank is used up first. From the inner tank alone, the hydrogen area density is 82.6 gm/cm^2. During the time duration T of usage of the hydrogen from the "inner" tank, the length of the hydrogen-filled part of the tank can be written $l(1 - t/T)$, where t is the time. The radiation "leaked" through can be given as

$$\bar{J}T = J_0 \int_0^T \exp[- \mu l(1 - t/T)] \, dt = J_0 \frac{T}{\mu l} [1 - \exp(- \mu l)].$$

From $J = J_0 \exp(- \mu \bar{l})$ we have, for the effective length,

$$\bar{l} = \frac{1}{\mu} \ln \left[\frac{\mu l}{1 - \exp(- \mu l)} \right].$$

Here, for γ-radiation, $\mu l = 0.03 \times 82.6 = 2.48$, $\mu = 0.03 \times 0.07 = 21 \times 10^{-4}$, and hence $\bar{l} = 4.75$ m or about 40% of the $l = 11.8$ m. This 40% effective shielding acts only over 4.5% of the total operational time, as stated before. Therefore, the total effective hydrogen shielding length $\bar{\bar{l}}$ can be estimated to be $0.995 \exp(- \mu l) + 0.045 \exp(- \mu \bar{l}) = \exp(- \mu \bar{\bar{l}})$ or

$\bar{l} = 11.1$ m, or 76.8 gm/cm². This can replace about $77/5 \approx 15.5$ gm/cm² of the radiation shield assuming that 5 gm/cm² of H_2 are equivalent to 1 gm/cm² of radiation shield. With the assumption that structure, non-sensitive equipment, and nonsensitive parts of the payload are utilized for additional protection of the crew, a total "shielding equivalent" of 25 gm/cm² appears to be reasonable. This reduces the shield to 75 gm/cm², or a total shield weight of $13,110 \times 75 \times 10^{-3} = 985$ kg or about 1 ton, as previously assumed.

Details that have to be studied include: What about scatter radiation from the outer tank and from vehicle structure, or direct radiation from spreading rocket exhaust gases? How to design the radiation shield, especially how to cool it? Fortunately, the radiation absorbed by the hydrogen behind the shield will not pose much of a problem as to heating the hydrogen. Before the shield, we have 35 cal/cm² sec energy flux and behind, about 5×10^{-4} cal/cm² sec, or during half an hour 0.9 cal/cm². Assuming this is completely absorbed by 75 gm/cm² of hydrogen, we have 0.012 cal/gm absorbed energy. This is harmless. (Specific heat ~ 3 cal/gm °K, heat of melting 14 cal/gm, and heat of evaporation 112 cal/gm.)

The shield absorbs about 35 cal/cm² sec, or 0.466 cal/gm sec, or during half an hour 840 cal/gm. (This is, of course, a mean value; absorption would be higher toward and lower away from the reactor.) Cooling may be necessary, as remarked before.

Two methods of reducing the radiation flux from the reactor at the crew compartment have been applied: one is putting a distance between those two items—but structure weight increases with this distance. The other is to put a shield between them. As shield weight decreases with increasing distance, there is clearly an optimum distance which minimizes the sum of structure weight plus shield weight. To have mentioned this "optimum separation distance" may suffice here. (It goes without saying that this optimum distance will be very large and the shield weight correspondingly small or zero, if the "boom structure" is very light: a limiting case would be to separate "reactor vehicle" and "crew vehicle" and have wireless energy transmission between them. The "reactor vehicle" could be a convenient celestial body, too, if the transmission problem were solved.)

For a fast reactor of 6 MW power production per kilogram core, but the same 1030 MW total power output, more radiation can be expected, as the internal self-absorption is smaller and the percentage of fast neutrons is higher. This requires a shield of somewhat higher area density: let us estimate, 10% higher. But the volume of this fast reactor with a density of 15 gm/cm³ is smaller by a factor of 135. Then the cross section is smaller by a factor $135^{2/3} \approx 26$. The total shadow shield weight is only $100(1.1/26)$ $\approx 4.3\%$ of the value for the thermal reactor. Problems of heat transfer (both within the reactor to the working medium and outside the reactor to the shield) are much more severe than they are for the thermal reactor. The thermal and the fast reactors would behave very similarly, when both are operated at the same power output per cm³. The main difference of the fast reactor under that condition is its higher total energy content (factor 20), its higher weight (factor 7.5), and its much higher cost due to the higher uranium investment.

The exhaust jet can become radioactive only by contamination with radioactive substances, which might occur within the heat exchanger. This can be prevented by proper design and coating of the heat-exchanger tubes. For nuclear upper stages, a slight contamination of the jet may be of no significance—this might make the design of the heat exchanger easier.

In case of an accident, a reactor can melt when the cooling becomes insufficient to carry the developed energy away. This can result in local radioactive contamination. In other accidents even a small inefficient nuclear explosion cannot be completely ruled out, at least for fast reactors. For thermal reactors, this is nearly impossible. A pressure vessel explosion is possible with all types of reactors. In any case, by error or design, the reactor may impact on Earth or water, or burn up in the atmosphere. The amount of radioactivity contained within a reactor depends on whether it has been fired, for what time, and how long ago. In all cases, some hazards are involved which make flight testing of nuclear rockets very difficult. Indeed, there were careful investigations required as to whether such tests should be made in ground-launch vehicles, on top of chemical boosters, or from an orbit around Earth, before a decision in favor of the second method was reached. So testing of nuclear rockets will be by no means a simple operation. On the other hand, the hazards may be comparable to those of nuclear submarines, nuclear ships, nuclear aircraft, or aircraft carrying nuclear weapons: some hazard is the price to be paid for progress. The hazard is easily estimated: A 20-kt nuclear bomb releases 84×10^{12} W sec, or delivers about 300×10^{22} fissions resulting in about 6×10^{24} unstable nuclei, or 10 moles of radioactive material. A 10,000-MW reactor delivers in 10^3 sec only 10×10^{12} W sec, and contains, therefore, only about 1.2 moles of active material, only 12% of the value released by a moderate nuclear explosion. On the other hand, after long operating times, a large quantity of radioactive material has accumulated in the reactor. In trying to shut down a nuclear rocket, these active products are the reason for the necessity of a cool-down period.

To finish the considerations on radiation hazards due to nuclear reactors, let us look at nuclear-propelled low-acceleration vehicles. Here the operational time may be 1000 days. With a total energy content of 2500 MW-days/ton, a thermal reactor can only deliver 2.5 MW/ton = 2.5 kW/kg, an uncomfortably low value. With a fast reactor this can be increased to 750 kW/kg. Let us utilize only 50 kW/kg—this then is smaller, by a factor 6.67, than the energy output per kg core in the thermal reactor of the example of the high acceleration system. For the lower total power output of 100 MW (thermal) the core weighs 2 tons. Per cubic centimeter, the power output has slightly decreased (factor 0.9), as the total volume of the 2-ton reactor with an average specific gravity of 12 gm/cm³ is 167 liters. Therefore, heat transfer problems are somewhat simplified. Even more so, when it is considered that now hydrogen no longer has to be taken to transport the energy: the coolant will be chosen for its thermodynamical and chemical behavior, and for its property not to interfere with the reactor operation and not to become radioactive—the liquid metal isotope Li⁷ looks promising.

Total power radiated from the reactor is higher, because it is a fast reactor (no more than factor 2) and lower, because the power output is only 100 MW (factor 10). For the 1000-MW thermal reactor, the γ-radiation intensity 1 m away was 1.8×10^9 rem/h. Thus, here we expect 4×10^8 rem/h.

Let the crew compartment be 100 m away, and the intensity be 0.03 r/week. At point A (Fig. 2.13), we can allow $(0.03 \times 10^4)/(7 \times 24)$ r/h. Thus we need a shield so that $4 \times 10^8 \exp(- 0.03W) = 1.79$, or $W \approx 640$ gm/cm². This is about the same value as in the case of the nuclear high-thrust system shield. As the reactor itself is much smaller (volume about $\frac{1}{3}$, cross section about 0.233 of the 1000-MW thermal reactor), total shield weight will be hardly more than 30% of the case of the high-acceleration system. (With a thermal reactor in place of the fast one, this is not true

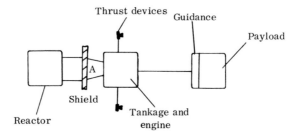

Fig. 2.13. Possible arrangement of nuclear-electric rocket.

since for 100 MW at 2.5 kW/kg we would need a core of 40 tons weight or a volume of 20 m³ with a cross section of about 7.4 m². The shield might weigh about 7 tons. From this figure, all-around shielding might weight 50 tons. In comparison, the shielding weight for the 70-MW submarine reactor is 500 tons, and for the 200-MW aircraft reactor it is hoped to be not more than 70 tons.) The machinery for power conversion is placed so that it assumes the equivalent protection role of the hydrogen in the central tank in the high-acceleration design. In passing it may be remarked that power production, hence radiation, from a nuclear reactor can be modulated; this could result in a direct means of communication, without electric generator, radio, and antenna.

Shielding may be required not only against radiation from the reactor but also against radiation from the natural environment. As for Earth escape missions the stay time of a low-acceleration vehicle in the van Allen radiation zone is long compared to the stay time of a high-acceleration vehicle, the "environmental radiation shield" will be heavier for the low-acceleration vehicle. The action of the radiation belt is in addition to other effects—e.g., solar flares—which are the same in both cases. This topic is taken up again in the next chapter.

2.3 Low-Acceleration Propulsion Systems (Sutherland, 1959)

2.3,1 Introduction

Increase in specific impulse (or exhaust speed) is the main field of rocket improvement. Drastic increases in specific impulse force us to go to low thrusts and thereby, low accelerations, as treated in deriving Eq. (1.5) of Vol. 1. Low accelerations have long times of operation as a consequence. Then the powered trajectory forms a major fraction or all of the total trajectory. The trajectory analysis becomes markedly different from the case of high-acceleration systems, where the length of the powered part usually is negligible compared to the length of the free-flight part. Furthermore, the propulsion system can only fight forces which are not larger than the propulsive force; this then rules out launch from Earth surface, or from the surface of any major celestial body. Instead, launch has to occur from an orbit around the celestial body (or from an escape trajectory), and the target is either another orbit around the same body, or another celestial body, or the vehicle is going out into space, or it hits a celestial object. In case reuse is contemplated, another orbit[1] is the only practical target possibility.

---

[1] Or the same orbit, after a round-trip.

To reach higher specific impulses than about 1000 sec, which appears to be the limit of "conventional" nuclear rockets, fundamentally four ways have to be investigated:

(1) *Mechanical engines.* There appears to be no way to get very high speeds of an "impulse carrier" by mechanical means, such as springs, etc.

(2) *Thermodynamic engines.* A gas of low molecular weight has to be heated to a high temperature, and the internal gas enthalpy is converted to kinetic energy in a nozzle. Some possibilities (gaseous core reactor and others) have been described previously. We will consider only two more, namely, the nuclear-energy arc-heated plasma jet, and the solar-heated hydrogen rocket.

(3) *Electromagnetic engines* (Moeckel and Rayle, 1959; Camac, 1960). Very high speeds can be reached by electrically charged particles moving in an electric field. This is the fundamental principle of the ion engine, which shall be examined in some detail later.[1]

The utilization of the phenomenon of the "electric wind" for propulsion has been proposed by Oberth (1929 and 1954). Some ions accelerated by an electric field drag nonionized particles from a vapor or gas along. Jet speed could be lower than for a pure ion-propulsion system (around 10–100 km/sec) with correspondingly higher thrust and acceleration. Some problems might be simplified (e.g., less ionization, simpler beam neutralization, more choice for jet materials) while others more complicated (e.g., velocity homogenization within the jet, jet formation, electrode erosion).

Plasma acceleration can be accomplished apart from thermodynamic processes by the interaction of electric and magnetic fields, or by "magnetic pressure." An example of the first type is the "crossed field accelerator," in which use is made of the Lorentz force [$\mathbf{j}\ \mathbf{B}$]—the plasma is a conductor carrying a current $\mathbf{j}$ across a magnetic field, and in doing so the Lorentz force acts upon it (see Fig. 2.14).

If the density of the plasma is sufficiently low, so that the free path length becomes large, the charged particles will try to spiral around the magnetic field lines, which is prevented by the electric field (at high plasma densities, it is prevented by collisions); the resulting motion is cycloidal.

In this latter engine, no current flows over the gap. Of course, the exhaust still represents a current I and its velocity corresponds to a voltage U, and

---

[1] Neglecting the ion current, these engines are frequently referred to as "electrostatic engines."

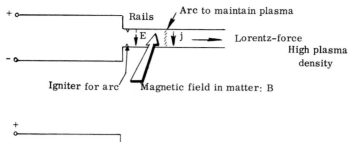

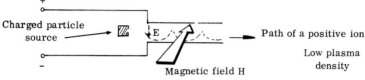

Fɪɢ. 2.14. Principle of crossed-field accelerator

the energy IU has to be supplied as electric energy. The term j being zero, this device might be called an [**E H**] accelerator.[1]

An accelerating "magnetic mirror" (an inhomogeneous, as seen from the arriving particle, strongly converging magnetic field) will serve to accelerate a plasma or a singly charged particle. This is an example of utilization of "magnetic pressure." Another example is the interaction of a current loop with its own magnetic field (Fig. 2.15).

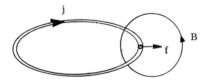

Fɪɢ. 2.15. Interaction of a current loop with its magnetic field.

The field within the loop is stronger than that on the outside. Thus a net outward force results from [**j B**]. A practical machine could look like a rail accelerator without its external magnetic field. Large currents are required: exploding of a wire across the rails permits the establishment of an initially dense plasma. Electric discharges, shock waves, and intense electromagnetic radiation can also provide plasmas.

These examples of MHD propulsive engines may suffice here. What are the motives in persuing such devices against ion engines? First, there

[1] Because of their different charge-to-mass ratios, ions and electrons can be acted upon differently. This might require compensatory fields.

exists the possibility that something better may be found—after all, nature appears to favor the plasma state, when we look around in the universe. Furthermore, from a fusion reactor, a plasma may be available anyway. The efficiency of conversion of electric energy to kinetic energy of the jet will be smaller than for the ion engine, because of the need to create a plasma.[1] Nevertheless, high efficiencies appear possible.[2] The jet density might be higher than it is possible to obtain with an ion engine, as there is no equivalent for the space charge, which limits the ion current. There are no problems of jet neutralization, as the plasma is electrically neutral anyway. A plasma contains, by definition, an equal amount of positive and negative charge. As there may be fewer problems in focusing the plasma jet, a plasma engine may have a more easily varied specific impulse than an ion engine. And in the lower specific impulse area (down to 1000 sec), it may be easier to develop a plasma than in an ion engine (which, without colloidal particles, may not get below 2000 sec). However, the ion engine has one definite advantage: its operation and its technique appear to be much better understood today than those of the MHD propulsion devices. A good survey on the latter systems is given by Demetriades (1962).

A novel electric thrustor principle called *thermionic propulsion* has been under development by the Giannini Scientific Corporation. The device shows combined factors of arc and MHD jets, without using any external magnetic field. There is a wide choice of working fluids.

Specific impulse values of the order of 10,000 sec have been obtained during 1963–1964. It is expected that this value could be doubled, at good energy conversion efficiency (up to 80%). A simple analytical explanation is given by Peters (1965).

Other engine types having "hybrid" arc jet with MHD features are under investigation, e.g., the Hall current accelerator (" Harcjet").

If correct and if the required lifetime can be demonstrated, these developments might constitute a breakthrough in the electric thrustor field.

The general scheme of electric propulsion systems is shown in Fig. 2.16.

Whenever possible, it will be of advantage to generate the electric power in its required form or forms, thus being able to do away with the power conditioning equipment. This action will not only reduce the weight (by typically 1 lb/kW) but will also increase the reliability and avoid an energy

---

[1] This is not true under all conditions, since creating the ions for an ion engine requires energy also.

[2] It is reported in *Aviation Week* (Sept. 5, 1966) that a pulsed plasma engine with a specific impulse of 5000 sec and an efficiency of 67% has been demonstrated.

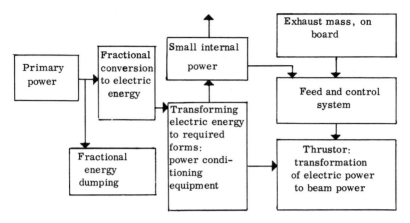

Fɪɢ. 2.16. General outline of electric propulsion systems.

conversion loss. If an available power source has to be utilized, its output will rarely be in the desired form, losing the advantage of elimination of the power conditioning system. On the other hand, it does not appear to be practical to have a special generator for every application.

(4) *Optic/quantum mechanic engines.* The photon propulsion system has been described sufficiently at the beginning of this chapter.

2.3,2 Production of Electric Energy for Propulsion

2.3,2,1 Fᴀsᴛ Soʟɪᴅ-Coʀᴇ Nᴜᴄʟᴇᴀʀ Fɪssɪᴏɴ Rᴇᴀᴄᴛᴏʀ

Today, only the solid-core nuclear fission reactor or utilization of solar energy appears adequate to cover the energy demand for low-acceleration long duration space-propulsion systems. As shown before, neglecting cost, the fast reactor appears to be more promising than the thermal one, without posing more severe heat-transfer problems than the thermal reactor does in connection with a high-thrust thermodynamic rocket engine. Other suitable energy sources may become available later; one thinks immediately of a fusion reactor.

In principle, the source of electric energy is built as shown in Fig. 2.17. The first system might be a one-phase (gaseous) or a two-phase (vapor-liquid) flow arrangement. In the second system, the flow of potentially radioactive liquid is strongly reduced, and more design freedom can be gained by employing two fluids. But both complexity and weight are higher. The same is true for the third system; here, the two other loops could be all liquid, the inner loop all gaseous, thus simplifying some difficult design aspects.

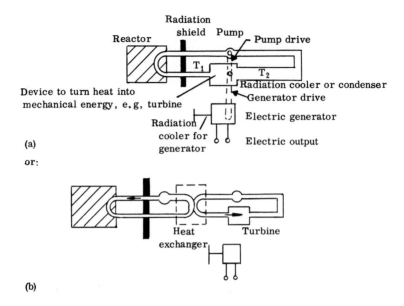

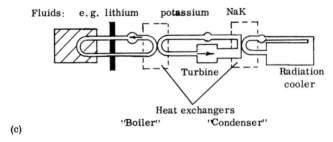

Fig. 2.17. General outlines of electric energy sources.

At the present time other systems appear to be less suitable for high energy outputs, though finally one would hope for a power source without moving parts, for example, as shown in Fig. 2.18.

Between the hot and cold areas, thermocouples or, even better, thermionic converters are placed.[1] (In reality, the hot side would be not only the outside, but also the surface of tubes inside the reactor. The cold side is then supplied by a cooled surface which is cooled via a flowing coolant and a radiation cooler.)

---

[1] A single thermionic converter unit may have a power output of 100 W; thus a 1-MW (e) system will contain 10,000 units; power conditioning will be difficult, but reliability will be high if the redundancy is utilized properly and if a single failure does not induce further failures.

In practical cases, it is difficult to place components within a reactor, for two reasons: the radiation interaction with the component, and the component's interaction with reactor nucleonics.

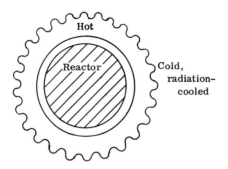

FIG. 2.18. Possible energy source with no moving parts.

In NASA contract NASW-741, three promising design cases have been investigated for nuclear-thermionic electric generators of 100 kW (e, short for "electric") output, representing about 1968 state of technology, as shown in the following tabulation:

Design No.	No. of fluid loops	No. of heat exchangers	Placement of thermionic generator	Reactor thermal power (MW)	Weight	
					With shield, power conditioning equipment, etc. (lb)	Without shield power conditioner equipment, etc. (lb)
1	1	0	Reactor	1.92	10,800	4200
2	2	1	Radiator	1.92	11,300	5400
3	2	1	Heat exchanger	1.80	10,100	4200

For electric propulsion requirements, these power-to-weight ratios are impractically low. But in the future such generators may well become available with sufficiently high power/weight ratios; ultimately, they may reach 0.5 kg/kW. The reliability of such devices should surpass anything we can design today. And obviously, for the long operation times needed, this is a very important consideration. The fluid here is truly only a coolant as it is at the low side of the temperature only. This allows high-temperature "hot sides."

A generator consists fundamentally of an electric conductor, moving through a magnetic field. The conductor may be a plasma; thus, MHD generators are possible. They appear to be attractive for large power outputs (order of 10 to 100 MW or more) and when a plasma (possibly created by "seeding" a "cold gas" or utilizing some other method to convert it to a cold plasma, instead of a hot plasma) is already present or can be obtained sufficiently easily. MHD generators can be expected to play an important role in the future.[1] Now let us return to the first system sketched in Fig. 2.17.

The pump is necessary to keep the circulation up in the gravity-free state. Besides mechanical pumps, induction pumps, or pumping by rotating magnetic fields, might find application. With the latter pumps, electric energy (from the electric main output) could be utilized. The lack of moving parts will improve reliability, but total weight is higher.

The fast solid-core reactor may produce $E = 100$ MW of thermal energy; its core weight is about 2 tons, the shield weight 0.25 tons. Let us guess a total weight (including pump, plumbing, and structure) of 3 tons, or generally the weight $W_1 = \frac{3}{100} E$, where W_1 is expressed in kilograms and E in kilowatts.

The temperature at the turbine (assuming that the thermal-mechanical energy converter is a turbine) is T_1, and the radiator temperature is T_2. The energy converted to mechanical energy is, in a Carnot engine, $E_{id} = E(T_1 - T_2)/T_1$. In reality, we can expect only $E_m = \eta E(T_1 - T_2)/T_1$, with $\eta < 1$. The rest, $E_r = E - E_m = E[1 - \eta(T_1 - T_2)/T_1)]$, has to be radiated away from the condenser, or radiator. (A radiator "looking" at free space "sees" an infinite energy sink of only about 3.5°K temperature; therefore, it receives virtually no radiative energy.) Per unit area, we can radiate $\varepsilon \sigma T_2^4$. Therefore, the radiator area is

$$A = \frac{E[1 - \eta(T_1 - T_2)/T_1]}{\varepsilon \sigma T_2^4}.$$

With r being the weight of the radiator per unit area, the radiator weight is

$$W_r = r \frac{E[1 - \eta(T_1 - T_2)/T_1]}{\sigma \varepsilon T_2^4}.$$

[1] Electrohydrodynamic systems are feasible too, but efficiencies obtained so far have been only about 1%.

The weight of the turbine is estimated to be

$$W_t = \alpha_1 E_m = \alpha_1 \eta E(T_1 - T_2)/T_1 .$$

Let us assume that 95% of E_m is converted to electric energy, and 5% is again radiated away (mainly friction and electric losses). The weight of this small radiation system is absorbed in the generator weight

$$W = \alpha_2 E_m = \alpha_2 \eta E(T_1 - T_2)T_1 .$$

Therefore, we can write for the total weight

$$W \text{ [kg]} = \left[\frac{3}{100} + r \frac{1 - \eta(T_1 - T_2)/T_1}{\varepsilon\sigma T_2{}^4} + (\alpha_1 + \alpha_2)\eta \frac{T_1 - T_2}{T_1} \right] E \text{ [kW]},$$

where r is the area weight of radiator in kg/m^2, η the efficiency of the turbine, T_1 and T_2 [°K] the upper and lower temperatures of working cycle, respectively, in °K, α_1 the specific weight of turbine in kg/kW, α_2 the specific weight of electric generator in kg/kW, ε the emissivity of radiator surface, and σ the Stefan-Boltzmann constant in kW/m^2 °K^4. The electric energy produced is $E_e = 0.95\eta[(T_1 - T_2)/T_1]E$. Of greatest interest is the overall quotient

$$\alpha \left[\frac{\text{kg}}{\text{kW}} \right] = \frac{W}{E_e} = 1.05 \left(\frac{0.03 + r/\varepsilon\sigma T_2{}^4}{\eta(T_1 - T_2)/T_1} - \frac{r}{\varepsilon\sigma T_2{}^4} + \alpha_1 + \alpha_2 \right).$$

Introducing $\alpha_3 = r/(\varepsilon\sigma T_1{}^4)$ and $T_2/T_1 = x$ this can be written as

$$\alpha = 1.05 \left(\frac{0.03}{\eta(1 - x)} + \alpha_3 \frac{1/\eta - 1 + x}{x^4(1 - x)} + \alpha_1 + \alpha_2 \right). \tag{2.1}$$

Optimization of the power plant demands that α be as small as possible. Optimization of the thermodynamic efficiency would call for $x \to 0$, which would be far from minimization of α; for space power plants, optimization of thermodynamic efficiency is no valid criterion.

Now let us ascribe some numerical figures to the constants. The efficiency η appears twice in the form of $1/\eta$ as factor; we want η as large as possible to minimize α. Therefore $\eta = 0.9$ will be optimistic, and $\eta = 0.5$ quite pessimistic.

The temperature T_1 appears (apart from the independent variable x) only in $\alpha_3 r/(\varepsilon\sigma T_1{}^4)$ (under the assumption made, that the 0.03 does not depend on T_1). To minimize α_3, T_1 should be as large as possible. Experience with turbines demands that we not exceed $T_1 = 1400$°K, which we will use. (For gas-cooled reactors, 1300°K could be realized in 1966.)

The constant ε is a function of the radiator material, its surface treatment, and its surface temperature. From experience, $\varepsilon = 0.95$ is certainly possible. The Stefan-Boltzmann constant is $\sigma = 5.67 \times 10^{-11}$ kW/m² °K⁴.

The value r is mainly a function of radiator design, pressure, type of material, working fluid, and temperature T_2. Let us take $r = 5$ kg/m² of useful radiator area.[1] Then follows $\alpha_3 = 0.0242$ kg/kW.

The specific weight of the turbine may be $\alpha_1 = 1$ kg/kW, and for the generator we also assume $\alpha_2 = 1$ kg/kW. Aircraft generators run about 2 kg/kW, but larger units should be better, and we have some design freedom—for the large power, transformation after the production should be avoided, as described previously. Therefore, for an ion engine, output from the generator should be direct current at the correct voltage of usually a few kilovolts. This may allow the use of a permanent magnetic or an electromagnetic or an electrostatic generator. Above a voltage of 50 kV, an electrostatic generator may be lighter than an electromagnetic one. For charged colloidal particles, such high voltages are interesting.[2] Of course, there is also some power requirement at lower voltage, e.g., for the ion source, for control, and for internal power purposes, etc. So, perhaps two generator types should be carried. We obtain

$$\alpha = 1.05 \left(2 + \frac{0.03}{\eta(1-x)} + 0.0242 \frac{1/\eta - 1 + x}{x^4(1-x)} \right).$$

It is useful to introduce $y = 1/x = T_1/T_2 > 1$:

$$\alpha = 1.05 \left[2 + 0.0242 \frac{1.24y + \eta y^4 + (1-\eta)y^5}{\eta y - \eta} \right].$$

To compute $y = y_{\text{opt}}$ we differentiate and set $da/dy = 0$:

$$1.24 + 4\eta y_{\text{opt}}^3 + (5 - 8\eta)\, y_{\text{opt}}^4 - 4(1-\eta)\, y_{\text{opt}}^5 = 0 .$$

[1] According to Welsh et al. (1959), $r = 0.5$ kg/m² for $T_2 = 325$°K, and $r = 5$ kg/m² for $T_2 = 700$°K. (For present designs, including realistic meteoroid protection, these figures may have to be doubled.) If in the following analysis r is regarded as a function of T_2, the optimum would shift towards smaller T_2 values. This effect is neglected here. Up to about 900°K, the radiator material could be beryllium; for higher temperatures, because of the vapor pressure of beryllium, some other material—e.g., columbium— has to be used, leading to an unfavorable weight increase.

[2] From a Goodrich-High Voltage Astronautics publication: "With sufficient effort, a compact (electrostatic) generator could be available by 1963, which would develop 1 kW per pound of mass with an efficiency greater than 98%."

Rearranging,

$$\eta = \frac{y_{\text{opt}}^2 - 1.25 y_{\text{opt}} - 0.31/y_{\text{opt}}^3}{(y_{\text{opt}} - 1)^2}.$$

Now a simple graph of y_{opt}(or x_{opt}) vs η can easily be drawn (see Fig. 2.19).

It is interesting to regard α_1 as a function of η. For an extreme case, put $\alpha_1 = \eta$. The new value of (weight)/(electric power) $= \hat{\alpha} = \alpha - (1 - \eta)$ is indicated in Fig. 2.19, too. Several conclusions can be drawn:

(1) The reactor will be the lightest element in the power production plant, among the subsystems considered here.

(2) The radiator weight (and therefore area, as we chose r to be a constant) depends very little on η, but radiator temperature T_2 does. It will be easier to meet the condition of $r = 5$ kg/m² for the radiator with the lower temperature.

(3) The Carnot efficiency is only 29.7 and 30.4%, respectively. This is fairly small. As pointed out before, maximizing the Carnot efficiency is not a valid criterion. The influence of η on the optimum Carnot efficiency is relatively small.

(4) The main weight is in the turbine and generator. Improvements in these fields would pay off most.

(5) The result α is remarkably insensitive to η. This would only change when turbine and generator weights could be reduced markedly. A value of $\alpha = 3$ kg/kW certainly does not look wildly optimistic.[1] With a weight of 60 tons, electric output could be 20 MW. The reactor would suffice for about 40 yr continuous operation. The reactor lifetime was calculated under the assumption that all fissionable material actually can be utilized. But as fission products accumulate, they might capture neutrons, until finally the reaction is no longer sustained: reactor self-poisoning. For fast reactors, this is insignificant, and nearly the full amount of the fissionable material can be utilized, until the reactor becomes subcritical. But even if one would carry along a second reactor, $\alpha = 3$ kg/kW might be realized.

---

[1] It should be clear that we consider a highly developed system, which may be realized only well after 1980. For the mid-seventies, the practical outlook for a rotating generator in the electric megawatt range is as follows (the number giving the mass in kilograms per electric kilowatt): Radiator 4, turbine/generator 3, reactor 1, pumps 1, redundancy/spares 2, shieldings (manned) 5, power conversion 2, electric engine (thrustor) 1; giving us a total of 19 kg/kW. Assuming that 80% of the electric power is converted to jet power, we have 23.7 kg/kW jet power. This is too large, by a factor of approximately 2, to render electric propulsion really attractive for many missions.

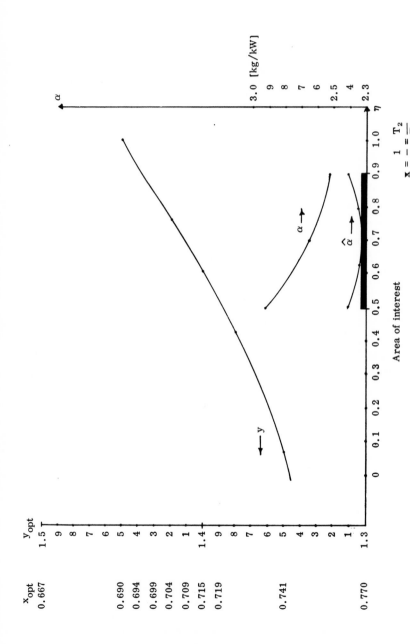

FIG. 2.19. Graph of optimum temperature ratio and weight to power ratio vs turbine efficiency.

(6) For $\alpha_1 = \eta$, we find that $\eta \approx 0.7$ results in a flat optimum. The $\hat{\alpha}$-curve is very flat. Overall efficiency is then $\eta_{\text{overall opt}} = 0.7 \times (1 - 0.769) \approx 0.22$.

How could the "ultimate" thermionic/nuclear device perform? Assuming optimistically the "hot" end has a temperature $T_1 = 3500°$K, and an advanced reactor weight of only $\frac{2}{100}$ kg/kW of thermal energy, and an advanced radiator of only 4 kg weight per square meter, we get (with $T_2/T_1 = T_2/3500 = x$): thermal energy production, E kW; delivered to "hot" end, $0.95E$; converted to electric energy, $0.95E\eta(1 - x)$; advanced thermionic system, $\eta = 0.9$; radiated away, $E[1 - 0.95\eta(1 - x)]$; radiated per square meter of radiator, $0.95\sigma T_1^4 x^4$. Therefore, the weight is

$$W = \frac{2}{100} E + 0.5 \times 0.95 \, E \, 0.9(1 - x) + 4 \frac{1 - 0.95 \times 0.9(1 - x)}{0.95\sigma T_1^4 x^4} E \, ;$$

and for electric output we have $E_e = 0.9 \times 0.95 \, (1 - x)E$. Hence,

$$\frac{W}{E_e} = \alpha = 0.5 + \frac{1}{10^4} \left\{ \frac{234}{1 - x} + \frac{5.78}{x^4(1 - x)} - \frac{4.94}{x^4} \right\}.$$

The ratio α has a minimum for $x = 0.446$ and is $\alpha_{\text{opt}} \approx 0.556$ kg/kW.

It should be mentioned again that, for very large power outputs, MHD generators can look attractive.[1] (In them, a plasma moving in a magnetic field acts much like a conventional generator.) We will not look into this subject.

2.3,2,2 SOLAR POWER PLANT

A power plant scheme for high electric energy outputs is shown in Fig. 2.20. Photovoltaic systems—usually associated with lower power levels, but recently considered up to the order of megawatts—are discussed in the next chapter.

Let us again consider an overall performance analysis. If e is the energy density of solar radiation [kW/m²], then the intercepted energy is $E_1 = e\pi R^2$. Of this 95% is reflected upon the boiler, which partly reradiates, partly reflects, and partly gives the energy to the working fluid. The energy given to the working fluid is

$$E = \varepsilon_1 \, 0.95 e\pi R^2 - \varepsilon_2 \sigma T_1'^4 a \, ,$$

[1] It is estimated (Lindley, 1963) that ultimately α is between 0.1 and 2. A 1966 design study for a closed loop MHD/reactor power plant of 500 kW(e) output resulted in $\alpha = 8$ kg/kW.

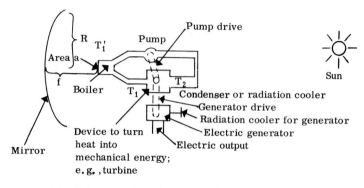

FIG. 2.20. Schematic for solar power plant; T is temperature.

where ε_1 is the boiler absorptivity for solar radiation and ε_2 the boiler emissivity for radiation of the temperature T_1'. The turbine converts the fraction $E_m = \eta[(T_1 - T_2)/T_1]E$ to mechanical energy, and 95% of this may be transformed to electric energy

$$E_e = 0.95\eta \, \frac{T_1 - T_2}{T_1} \{\varepsilon_1 \, 0.95e\pi R^2 - \varepsilon_2\sigma T_1'^4 a\} \,,$$

where $T_1' > T_1$. Let assume that $T_1' = T_1(1 + 0.1)$, or $T_1'^4 \approx 1.4 \, T_1^4$. The weights are

Mirror weight $= \alpha_4 \pi R^2$, where α_4 is in kg/m²;

Boiler weight $= \alpha_5 a$, where α_5 is in kg/m²;

Radiator/condenser weight $= \dfrac{r(\varepsilon_1 \, 0.95e\pi R^2 - \varepsilon_2\sigma T_1'^4 a) \, [1 - \eta(T_1 - T_2)/T_1]}{\varepsilon\sigma T_2^4}$;

Turbine weight $= \alpha_1 \eta \, \dfrac{T_1 - T_2}{T_1} \{\varepsilon_1 \, 0.95e\pi R^2 - \varepsilon_2\sigma T_1'^4 a\}$;

Generator weight $= \alpha_2 \eta \, \dfrac{T_1 - T_2}{T_1} \{\varepsilon_1 \, 0.95e\pi R^2 - \varepsilon_2\sigma T_1'^4 a\}$.

For the ratio,

$$\frac{\text{total weight}}{\text{electric energy output}} = \frac{W}{E_e} = \alpha \,.$$

Then, with the abbreviations $r/\varepsilon\sigma(1400)^4 = \alpha_3$, $x = T_2/T_1$, $T_1/1400$

$= \tau$, $\beta = a/\pi R^2$, and $\gamma = (321/e)(\varepsilon_2/\varepsilon_1)\beta$, we have

$$\alpha \left[\frac{\text{kg}}{\text{kW}} \right]$$

$$= 1.05 \left\{ \frac{\alpha_4 + \beta\alpha_5}{0.95\varepsilon_1 e\eta(1 - x)\,(1 - \gamma\tau^4)} + \frac{\alpha_3}{\tau^4}\frac{1/\eta - 1 + x}{x^4(1 - x)} + \alpha_1 + \alpha_2 \right\}.$$
(2.2)

This equation is more complicated than Eq. (2.1), mainly because of the boiler reradiation term $\gamma\tau^4$. If $\gamma = 0$, we would simply pick τ as large as possible, which means $\tau = 1$ (or $T_1 = 1400°\text{K}$). In the preceding equation we have to demand $\tau \leq 1$, because $T_1 \leq 1400°\text{K}$ for turbine-endurance reasons. Obviously, $T_1 = 1400/\gamma^{1/4}$ is another upper limit for T_1.

The constants α_1, α_2 are the same as in the reactor system. The radiator is a place to lose energy; therefore, it should take in as little solar energy as possible. This can be provided by one or several means:

(1) *Orientation.* No part of the radiator surface should see the Sun, or another hot object.

(2) *Surface.* The surface of the radiator should have a good emissivity for the radiator temperature T_2, but a poor absorptivity for solar and other incident radiation.

(3) *Temperature.* The radiator temperature T_2 should be high above its equilibrium temperature in solar light.

The radiator could be "double-sided," i.e., its design like a thin sheet, with two radiating sides; or it might have only one radiating side, which could be utilized structurally—e.g., the back side of the mirror would be a radiator, which could structurally support the mirror, and would fulfill the above "orientation condition" ideally.

We have to look into some possible mirror boiler designs to ascribe numerical values to α_4, α_5, and β. Then γ can be found immediately.

Mirror-Boiler: Design Example One, the Ehricke Sphere. A thin-walled Mylar sphere (Mylar is a transparent polyester that promises to withstand space conditions; specific gravity is 1.4 gm/cm³, and tensile strength at elevated temperature is 700 kg/cm²) is pressurized in space. (Internal pressure, p, kg/cm², radius R—then the wall thickness δ comes from $\delta/R = p/1400$; δ below 5×10^{-6} m cannot be satisfactorily produced today. We will take 5×10^{-4} atm, and hydrogen gas for pressurization.) Half of it is silvered, and serves as a spherical mirror. With $R = 50$ m we get $\delta = 50 \times (5 \times 10^{-4}/1400) \approx 2 \times 10^{-5}$ m. The Mylar weight is 0.88 tons, the pressurization gas weight (at a gas temperature of °C) about 25 kg. The complete mirror is 1 ton, or $\alpha_4 = 0.1272$ kg/m².

In Earth vicinity, $e = 1.4$ kW/m². Because of absorption in the sphere before the mirror is reached, only $e = 0.95 \times 1.4 = 1.33$ kW/m² will be used.

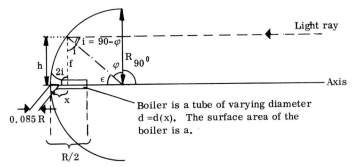

Fig. 2.21. Diagram of a spherical mirror.

Figure 2.21 shows some simple geometric optical considerations for a spherical mirror. We have

$$\frac{h}{R} = \cos \varphi , \qquad \frac{h}{f} = \sin 2i ,$$

$$\frac{f}{R} = \frac{\cos \varphi}{\sin 2i} = \frac{\cos \varphi}{\sin 2\varphi} = \frac{1}{2 \sin \varphi},$$

$$x = R - R \sin \varphi + f \cos 2i$$

$$= R - R \sin \varphi - f \cos 2\varphi = R \left(1 - \sin \varphi - \frac{\cos^2 \varphi - \sin^2 \varphi}{2 \sin \varphi} \right)$$

$$= R \left(1 - \frac{1}{2 \sin \varphi} \right) = R \left(1 - \frac{1}{2 \cos \varepsilon} \right) = R \left(\frac{1}{2} - \frac{\varepsilon^2}{4} \cdots \right).$$

For small ε, we can talk of a "focal point" at $x = \frac{1}{2}R$. For $x = 0$, we have $\sin \varphi = \frac{1}{2}$ or $\varphi = 30°$. Between $\varphi = 0°$ and $30°$, multiple reflections occur. This is fairly complicated and will not be considered here. It increases the energy flux over the indicated inner part ($0.085R$) of the axis.

The energy reaching the mirror is either absorbed (and, for equilibrium, again emitted[1]), or transmitted, or reflected: $\varepsilon + \tau + \varrho = 1$, where ε is the emissivity, etc. Because $\tau = 0$ we have $\varepsilon = 1 - \varrho$. Lambert's law

[1] From this balance, the mirror temperature can be computed.

says[1] that $\varepsilon = \varepsilon_n \cos i = \varepsilon_n \sin \varphi$. Thus for the mirror $\varrho = 1 - \varepsilon_n \sin \varphi$, or with $\varrho_n = 1 - \varepsilon_n$ it follows that $\varrho = 1 - (1 - \varrho_n) \sin \varphi$. For simplicity, we assume $\varrho = \text{constant} = 0.95$.

As seen from Earth vicinity, the solar diameter is equal to 32 min of arc $= 0.0093$ rad. The boiler is as shown in Fig. 2.21, its diameter at the place x equals $d(x)$, where

$$d = 0.0093f = \frac{0.0093R}{2} \frac{1}{\sin \varphi} = 0.0093(R - x) .$$

(Only for x/R between 0.085 and 0 do we deviate from this result; for $x/R = 0.085$, we use it and go linearly to $d = \frac{1}{2}\pi R \times 0.0093$ for $x/R = 0$. The reason is to intercept the multiple-reflection radiation.) The area a follows from

$$a = \int_0^{R/2} \pi d \, dx \approx 0.0042\pi R^2.$$

To compensate for imperfections, let us take $\beta = 7 \times 10^{-3}$. With $\varepsilon_1 = 0.9$ and $\varepsilon_2 = 0.3$, we have $\gamma = 0.561$. An estimate is $\alpha_5 = 10 \ \text{kg/m}^2$. Then finally

$$\alpha = 1.05 \left\{ 2 + \frac{0.0242}{\tau^4} \frac{1/\eta - 1 + x}{x^4(1 - x)} + \frac{0.1736}{\eta(1 - x)(1 - 0.561\tau^4)} \right\} .$$

To be more general,

$$\alpha = 1.05 \left\{ 2 + a \left[\frac{1}{\eta\tau^4 x^4(1 - x)} - \frac{1}{\tau^4 x^4} + \frac{b}{\eta(1 - x)(1 - \gamma\tau^4)} \right] \right\} ,$$

or with $y = 1/x$, $z = 1/\tau^4$, we get

$$\frac{[\alpha/(1.05) - 2]\eta}{a} = \left[(1 - \eta)y^4 + \eta y^3 + \frac{1}{z/b - \gamma/b} \right] z \frac{y}{y - 1} .$$

Letting $z/b = u$ and $\gamma/b = c$, we have

$$\frac{[\alpha/(1.05) - 2]\eta}{ab} = \left[(1 - \eta)y^4 + \eta y^3 + \frac{1}{u - c} \right] \frac{y}{y - 1} u = \Lambda .$$

To maximize α as a function of x and τ it suffices to maximize $\Lambda = \Lambda(y, u)$; a, b, and c are constants and η is a parameter.

---

[1] The index n stands for "normal direction."

By setting $\partial \Lambda / \partial y = 0$ and $\partial \Lambda / \partial u = 0$ we obtain (with the abbreviation $A = u - c$):

$$\text{from } \frac{\partial \Lambda}{\partial y} = 0, \qquad \eta = \frac{4y^5 - 5y^4 - 1/A}{4y^3(y-1)^2};$$

$$\text{from } \frac{\partial \Lambda}{\partial u} = 0, \qquad \eta = \frac{y^4 - c/A^2}{y^3(y-1)}.$$

Equating these two and solving for A, we have

$$A = u - c = \left[4c \frac{y-1}{y^4} + \frac{1}{(2y^4)^2} \right]^{1/2} - \frac{1}{2y^4}.$$

The solution proceeds as follows: Estimate a value for $x = T_2/T_1$; $y = 1/x$. Then compute A; $u = A + c$; and $\tau = (1/bu)^{1/4} = T_1/1400°K$. Compute η and α.

The results are plotted in Fig. 2.22 for the case of design example one. Again the case $\hat{\alpha}$ corresponding to $\alpha_1 = \eta$ is included. It is interesting to note that

(1) $\tau_{opt} < 1$ always.
(2) x_{opt} is smaller than in the nuclear case (Fig. 2.19).
(3) α is more sensitive to η than in the nuclear case (Fig. 2.19).
(4) α is about 1.5 times as large as it was in the nuclear case (Fig. 2.19). ($\alpha = 4.5$ does not look too optimistic here.)
(5) $\hat{\alpha}$ behaves similar to α.

A modification of the Ehricke sphere should be mentioned; namely, the sphere is completely covered with a 50% reflective layer (realized, e.g., by reflecting "polka-dots"). Now only about 25% of the intercepted energy reaches the collector, but the system does not require attitude control, if the collector also is omnidirectional. For an interesting application see Stewart and Swale (1963).

Mirror-Boiler: Design Example Two, The High-Quality Parabolic Mirror (Fig. 2.23). We have just considered one extreme case, namely, the light-weight spherical (therefore, optically quite poor) mirror. Now, at the other extreme, we have the not-so-light weight but highest quality parabolic mirror.

The equation of a parabola is

$$y = (2px)^{1/2}.$$

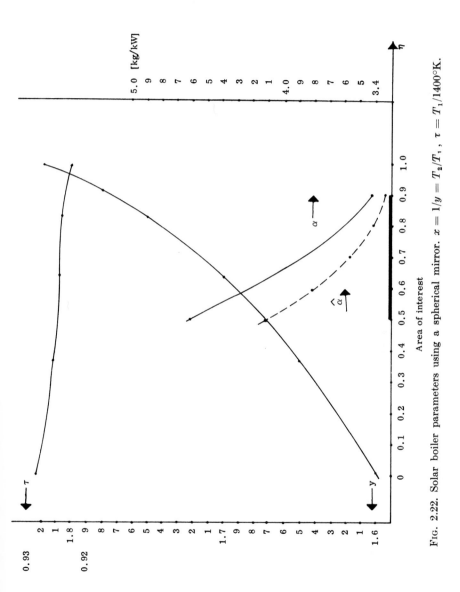

FIG. 2.22. Solar boiler parameters using a spherical mirror. $x = 1/y = T_2/T_1$, $\tau = T_1/1400°\text{K}$.

Differentiating,

$$\frac{dy}{dx} = \frac{p}{(2px)^{1/2}} \; .$$

Hence,

$$ds = dx \left[1 + \left(\frac{dy}{dx} \right)^2 \right]^{1/2} = dx \left(\frac{2x + p}{2x} \right)^{1/2} .$$

Surface area is

$$F = \int_{x-0}^{x} 2\pi y \; ds = \frac{2}{3}\pi p^{1/2}[(2x + p)^{3/2} - p^{3/2}] \; .$$

Introducing $p = 2f$ and $x/f = z$, we have

$$F = \frac{8}{3}\pi f^2[(z + 1)^{3/2} - 1] \; .$$

For the mirror weight we have $\alpha_4 F$. Let us assume that $\alpha_4 = 1.5 \; \text{kg/m}^2$. (Electro-Optical Systems, Inc. announced on May 2, 1960 that they have parabolic mirrors weighing less than $1.4 \; \text{kg/m}^2$; thus with some auxiliary equipment, the above choice for α_4 appears to be reasonable.)

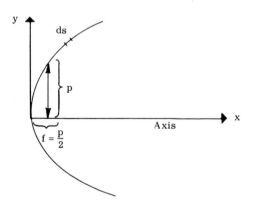

FIG. 2.23. Diagram of a parabolic mirror.

The solar picture formed at the focus will have, at Earth vicinity, a diameter of $d = 0.0093f$; the area of the solar picture is $a = \frac{1}{4}\pi(0.0093)^2 f^2$. To cut down on reradiation, we will use a cavity boiler (Stephens et al., 1961). (See Fig. 2.24.)

Let us take $3a$ for the hole area. For the boiler weight we guess that since the hole area is $3a$ (because of the near-rim rays, which have a path length $l \approx p = 2f$; see Fig. 2.24), the front wall area is $50a$. With 10 kg/m^2 the weight can be estimated to be $4000a$ kg.

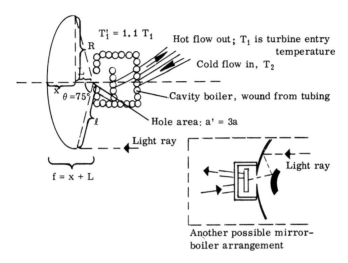

FIG. 2.24. Diagram showing two possible methods of using a cavity boiler.

For geometrical and structural reasons, $\theta = 75°$ appears reasonable ($\theta = 90°$ may be a maximum choice).

Thus $l = 2f/(1 + \cos 75°) = 1.591f$, $R = 1.54f$, and the cross-sectional area of the mirror $S = \pi R^2 = \pi \times 2.37f^2$. We have $L = 0.412f$ and $x = 0.588f$, therefore, $z = x/f = 0.588$, and the mirror weight is $4\pi f^2$ kg.

With 95% reflectivity and the energy density e in the solar radiation it follows, for the energy given to the working fluid (again putting the fluid temperature at T_1, and the surface temperature in the boiler at $T_1' = 1.1T_1$),

$$E = 0.95 \, e \times 2.37\pi f^2 - 3\frac{\pi}{4}(0.0093)^2 f^2 \sigma \times 1.4T_1^4 .$$

The fraction $E_m = \eta(T_1 - T_2)/T_1$ is converted to mechanical energy, and the electric output is

$$E_e = 0.95\eta \frac{T_1 - T_2}{T_1}\left\{2.25 \, e - \frac{9.1}{10^5}\sigma T_1^4\right\} \pi f^2 .$$

Now the weights are

Mirror	$= 4\pi f^2$ kg;
Boiler	$= \dfrac{8.7}{10^2}\pi f^2$ kg;
Radiation cooler	$= \dfrac{r\{2.25e - 9.1\times10^{-5}\sigma T_1{}^4\}\,\pi f^2\,\{1 - \eta(T_1 - T_2)/T_1\}}{\varepsilon\sigma T_2{}^4};$
Turbine	$= \alpha_1\eta\,\dfrac{T_1 - T_2}{T_1}\left\{2.25e - \dfrac{9.1}{10^5}\sigma T_1{}^4\right\}\pi f^2;$
Generator	$= \alpha_2\eta\,\dfrac{T_1 - T_2}{T_1}\left\{2.25e - \dfrac{9.1}{10^5}\sigma T_1{}^4\right\}\pi f^2.$

Again for the ratio (total weight)/(electric power output) $= \alpha$, we have

$$\alpha = 1.05\left\{\frac{1.915}{e\eta(1 - x)\,(1 - \gamma\tau^4)} + \frac{\alpha^3}{\tau^4}\,\frac{1/\eta - 1 + x}{x^4(1 - x)} + \alpha_1 + \alpha_2\right\},$$

where, again, in Earth vicinity $e = 1.4$ kW/m², $x = T_2/T_1$, $\tau = T_1/1400°$K,

$$\gamma = 4.04 \times 10^{-5}\sigma(1400)^4/e \approx 6.3 \times 10^{-3},$$

is the emissivity of the radiator $\varepsilon = 0.95$, $\alpha_3 = r/(\varepsilon\sigma 1400^4) = 0.0242$ kg/kW, and $\alpha_1 + \alpha_2 = 2$ kg/kW. So, finally,

$$\alpha = 1.05\left\{2 + \frac{0.0242}{\tau^4}\,\frac{1/\eta - 1 + x}{x^4(1 - x)} + \frac{1.37}{\eta(1 - x)\,(1 - 6.3 \times 10^{-3}\tau^4)}\right\}.$$

This is of the same form as for the simple spherical mirror. Optimization would, because of the small value

$$\gamma = \frac{6.3}{10^3 \times 1.37} < \frac{1}{100},$$

result in $\tau > 1$, which we cannot allow. Therefore, we have to choose $\tau = 1$, and optimize for x only:

$$\alpha = 1.05\left\{2 + 0.0242\,\frac{1/\eta - 1 + x}{x^4(1 - x)} + \frac{1.38}{\eta(1 - x)}\right\}.$$

This is of the same simple nature as Eq. (2.1). Optimization proceeds as described for the nuclear reactor-power system, with the result shown in Fig. 2.25. Again, $\hat{\alpha}$ stands for the case of $\hat{\alpha}_1 = \eta$. Hence the conclusions are:

(1) The heavy mirror forces us to high Carnot efficiency in order to reduce mirror weight.

(2) The value of α may be about 9 kg/kW—double the value obtainable with the simple Ehricke sphere collector.

(3) For practical purposes, $\hat{\alpha} \approx \alpha$; the mirror weight is the governing factor.

(4) α is fairly sensitive to η.

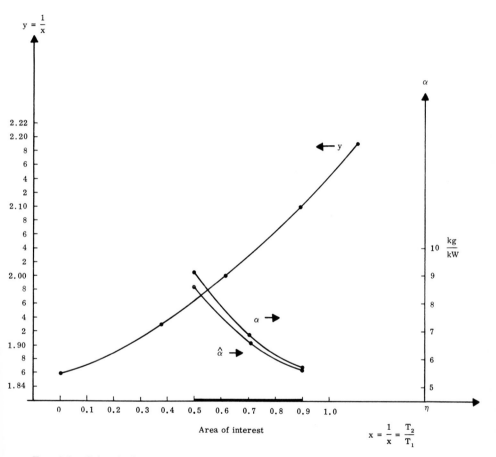

FIG. 2.25. Solar boiler parameters using a parabolic mirror. $y = 1/x = T_2/T_1$.

To complete the comparison between nuclear and solar power plants, some weights [kg] and sizes [m²] shall be summarized as they follow from the described optimization procedure. It should be borne in mind that the solar power plants were optimized for solar radiation in Earth vicinity. In all

TABLE 2.5

	$\eta = 0.5$	$\eta = 0.9$
Fast nuclear reactor:		
Thermal output (kW)	$7.25\ E_e$	$3.85\ E_e$
Weight (kg)	$0.22\ E_e$	$0.12\ E_e$
Radiator:		
Area (m²)	$0.12\ E_e$	$0.06\ E_e$
Weight (kg)	$0.60\ E_e$	$0.30\ E_e$
Working fluid upper temperature $T_1(°K)$	1400	1400
Working fluid lower temperature $T_2(°K)$	1010	975
Turbine weight (kg)	$1.05\ E_e$	$1.05\ E_e$
Generator weight (kg)	$1.05\ E_e$	$1.05\ E_e$
Total weight (kg)	$2.9\ E_e$	$2.5\ E_e$

cases, we are considering advanced systems, which could be realized only with considerable development effort.[1]

The electrical output is E_e kW, at least several hundred kilowatts. Then the results are:

(1) *Fast nuclear reactor-turbine generator* (see Table 2.5). Lifetime: about 40 yr continuous operation for 100% reactor utilization, or determined by mechanical lifetime, or radiator breakdown due to meteor hits, etc. Area of main improvement: reduce weight of turbine/generator. Main advantage: small radiator, no mirror; little hazard from environment; light system. Main disadvantage: usage of fuel; radiation.

[1] For comparison, let us look at an example of an Earth-surface based air transportable nuclear power plant, viz., Martin-Marietta Corporation's PM-3A:

Location: Antartica.
Modules: 14 basic modules.
Weight: ~ 200 tons.
Shielding: local aggregate.
Reactor: Total weight ~ 2000 lb. Loading: 29.2 kg U^{235} (741 tubes at 40.13 gm each). Working fluid: water; temperature: 239°C. Thermal output: 9.37 MW. Nominal lifetime: 2 yr.
Electric power: Turboelectric: turbine/generator speed: 3600 rpm. Condenser: air-cooled. Voltage: 4160 V, 3 phase, 60 cycle. Electric energy output: 1500 kW (1964).

Overall weight/power ratio, approximately 400 lb/kW. (Note that we desire, for electric propulsion, about 10 lb/kW and ten times the power, and for stationary use on the lunar or Martian surface, about 40 lb/kW and a twentieth of the power.)

TABLE 2.6

	$\eta = 0.9$
Fast nuclear reactor:	
Thermal output (kW)	2.005 E_e
Weight (kg)	0.042 E_e
Radiator:	
Area (m²)	0.0035 E_e
Weight (kg)	0.014 E_e
Working fluid upper temperature $T_1(°K)$	3500
Working fluid lower temperature $T_2(°K)$	1561
Thermionic converter weight (kg)	0.5 E_e
Total weight (kg)	0.556 E_e

(2) *Fast nuclear reactor-thermionic converter*: "*ultimate design*" (see Table 2.6). This is the most advanced of the systems described so far. Lifetime considerations are similar to the previous case, but the small radiator area makes meteor hits more improbable. The reliability should be very good, in view of the lack of moving parts. It appears as if this "ultimate system" is worth the strong development effort it would require.

Thermionic converters are space-charge limited. To overcome this, either very close spacing of the electrodes, or filling of the gap between the electrodes with cesium vapor can be applied.

It is of interest to mention that it was believed in May 1963 that a 5-MW electric power supply system could be realized eventually for 5.5–9 kg/kW using rotating machinery, and for 4.5–9 kg/kW using thermionic devices. Such realistic figures are considerably worse than the 0.6 kg/kW shown in the above table.

If a gas core reactor is used (gas temperature 3500°K, radiator temperature 1000°K) then a MHD generator is the natural choice. According to R.J. Rosa of AVCO Everett Research Laboratory, such a system might obtain a specific mass of 1 kg/kW, for large power outputs (tens of megawatts electric). For higher gas temperatures and higher powers, even lower mass-to-power ratios appear obtainable. But we believe such operational devices to be quite far in the future—maybe 25 years or more.

(3) *Solar power-Ehricke sphere* (see Table 2.7). Lifetime: determined by mechanical lifetime, mirror or radiator breakdown due to the environment (radiation, meteors). Area of main improvement: (1) reduce weight of

TABLE 2.7

	$\eta = 0.5$	$\eta = 0.9$
Mirror:		
Total intercepted solar energy (kW)	9.1 E_e	4.8 E_e
Weight (kg)	0.83 E_e	0.43 E_e
Cross-sectional area (m²)	6.5 E_e	3.4 E_e
Boiler:		
Weight (kg)	0.55 E_e	0.29 E_e
Surface area (m²)	0.05 E_e	0.03 E_e
Working fluid upper temperature $T_1(°K)$	1295	1293
Working fluid lower temperature $T_2(°K)$	774	729
Radiator:		
Weight (kg)	1.10 E_e	0.57 E_e
Area (m²)	0.22 E_e	0.11 E_e
Turbine weight (kg)	1.05 E_e	1.05 E_e
Generator weight (kg)	1.05 E_e	1.05 E_e
Total weight (kg)	4.6 E_e	3.4 E_e

radiator/turbine/generator; (2) by choosing proper surfaces for the boiler, ε_2 may be chosen such that T_{opt} will be 1400°K. This should result in a slight improvement. Main advantage: use of solar energy; simple mirror. Main disadvantage: with larger radiation, and large, extremely nonrigid mirror there are great environmental hazards. Therefore, this system is attractive perhaps only in the lower power range.

(4) *Solar power high-quality parabolic mirror* (see Table 2.8). Lifetime is limited by considerations similar to previous cases. Area of main improvement: reduce weight of mirror. Main advantage: use of solar energy; mirror area reduced.

The main disadvantage is that a foldable mirror is complicated, but still has environmental hazards; it is the heaviest system. Again, most interest in this system lies perhaps in the lower power output area, where mirror and radiator are not too large.

Let us repeat that the values obtained here are valid only for large power outputs of the order of several hundred kilowatt (electric) or higher. For smaller power outputs, the weight/power ratio goes up. In the next chapter some methods of production of auxiliary power for lower total outputs and their weight/power ratios are described.

TABLE 2.8

	$\eta = 0.5$	$\eta = 0.9$
Mirror:		
Total intercepted energy (kW)	4.4 E_e	2.2 E_e
Weight (kg)	5.77 E_e	2.93 E_e
Cross-sectional area (m²)	3.13 E_e	1.6 E_e
Boiler:		
Weight (kg)	0.13 E_e	0.07 E_e
Surface area (m²)	0.013 E_e	0.007 E_e
Working fluid upper temperature $T_1(°K)$	1400	1400
Working fluid lower temperature $T_2(°K)$	713	665
Radiator:		
Weight (kg)	1.13 E_e	0.57 E_e
Area (m²)	0.23 E_e	0.11 E_e
Turbine weight (kg)	1.05 E_e	1.05 E_e
Generator weight (kg)	1.05 E_e	1.05 E_e
Total weight (kg)	9.1 E_e	5.7 E_e

2.3,2,3 SOLAR MIRRORS: ADDITIONAL DISCUSSION

What can be achieved by mirrors with regard to concentration of solar flux? For the parabolic case, the cross-sectional area of the mirror may be πR^2, and that of the solar picture is about $\frac{1}{4}\pi(R \times 0.0093)^2$, R being the path length of near-rim rays from the mirror to the focus and 0.0093 the angular diameter of the Sun. The maximum concentration ratio then is about 46,000. Because of some small effects, such as limb darkening of the Sun, about 47,000 is the absolute maximum. For the Ehricke sphere, the boiler area is $a = 0.007\pi R^2$; therefore, the average concentration ratio is 143. With the "ideal value" of $a = 0.004\pi R^2$, we have an average concentration ratio of 250. Let us use this value from now on.

Cylindrical parabolic mirrors are comparable to circular spherical mirrors in their performance, and cylindrical circular mirrors are very poor. For the latter, the average concentration ratio is only 2 (see Fig. 2.26).

What is the maximum temperature T_m which we can hope to achieve in the focus of a good parabolic mirror? With a solar constant of 1.4 kW/m² and a concentration ratio of 47,000, the flux is 65,800 kW/m². The equilibrium temperature of a specimen exposed to this flux is, with ε_1 being the absorptivity for solar radiation and ε_2 the emissivity for its own thermal radiation, from Stefan-Boltzmann's law, $T_m = 5850(\varepsilon_1/\varepsilon_2)^{1/4}$°K. From the same law, what is the surface temperature T_0 of the Sun, assuming the Sun radiates as a black body? With the Earth-Sun distance being 149.5×10^6 km, and the solar radius being 0.696×10^6 km it follows that $T_0 \approx 5800$°K. As $T_m \approx T_0$, we have to assume $\varepsilon_1 = \varepsilon_2$, and get the simple result $T_m = T_0$.

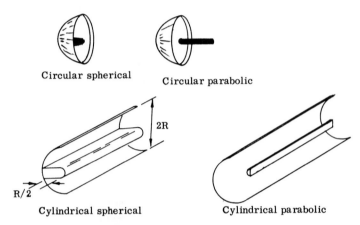

Circular spherical   Circular parabolic

2R

R/2

Cylindrical spherical   Cylindrical parabolic

Fig. 2.26. Some mirror/boiler shapes.

For a spherical mirror, the average concentration ratio was only 250 or 143. For $\varepsilon_1/\varepsilon_2 = 3$ we get $T_m = 2070$ (or 1800) °K only. As this is much lower than T_0, $\varepsilon_1/\varepsilon_2 = 3$ can be realized. From such considerations of maximum obtainable temperatures it is sometimes concluded that the spherical mirror should not be used in connection with a solar power plant; this conclusion is erroneous, as in the form of the Ehricke sphere such a mirror is so light that, in spite of the low efficiency, such power plants have a favorable energy output/weight ratio, as has been shown.

With the circular cylindrical mirror and the assumption as in the previous case it follows that $T_m = 600$°K only.

Let us refer back to Fig. 2.21. For a small angle $d\varphi$ around φ, the collected energy equals $e \times 2\pi hR \, d\varphi \sin \varphi = e \times 2\pi R^2 \cos \varphi \sin \varphi \, d\varphi$. With ϱ_n the reflectivity for normal incidence we get, as previously shown, for the reflectivity $\varrho = 1 - (1 - \varrho_n) \sin \varphi$; therefore, the reflected energy flux is

$$dq = 2\pi e R^2 \cos \varphi \sin \varphi \left[1 - (1 - \varrho_n) \sin \varphi \right] d\varphi .$$

This is thrown on a piece of the boiler tube of length $dx = \frac{1}{2}R(\cos \varphi \, d\varphi / \sin^2 \varphi)$, and diameter $d = (0.0093/2)R/\sin \varphi$, the surface of which is

$df = 0.002325 \cos \varphi (\pi R^2 / \sin^3 \varphi) d\varphi$. The radiation absorbed by df is $\varepsilon \, dq = \varepsilon_n \sin 2\varphi \, dq$. Finally,

$$\frac{\varepsilon \, dq}{df} = 1720 e \varepsilon_n [1 - (1 - \varrho_n) \sin \varphi] \cos \varphi \sin^5 \varphi \, .$$

For $\varrho_n = 1$, this has a maximum for $\sin^2 \varphi = 5/6$ or $\varphi = 66°$. The maximum[1] is $445 \varepsilon_n e$. This is quite different from the estimated average concentration ratio of 143.

For a spherical mirror of rim angle φ_0 the energy collected can be written as $E = e \pi R^2 \cos^2 \varphi_0$. The weight per square meter surface is w; then for the mirror weight we have

$$W = w \times 2\pi R^2 (1 - \sin \varphi_0),$$

and

$$\frac{E}{W} = \frac{e}{2w} \frac{\cos^2 \varphi_0}{1 - \sin \varphi_0} = \frac{e}{2w} (1 + \sin \varphi_0).$$

$\varphi_0 = 90°$ would be the best choice, but is clearly impractical. The minimum value for φ_0 is zero—a good, practical solution seems to be $\varphi_0 = 30°$. Obviously, this does not apply to the Ehricke sphere, as there the weight W does not depend upon φ_0 at all. In this case, it is best to maximize E, i.e., choose $\varphi_0 = 0$.

The total absorbed radiator flux is, for $\varphi_0 = 0$,

$$Q = \int \varepsilon \, dq = 4\pi e R \varepsilon_n \int_0^{\pi/2} \sin \varphi^2 \cos^2 \varphi \, [1 - (1 - \varrho_n) \sin \varphi] \, d\varphi \, .$$

For $\varrho_n = 1$, $Q = (\frac{1}{4}\pi \varepsilon_n) e \pi R^2$. By proper shaping of the boiler, ε_n may stand instead of $\frac{1}{4}\pi \varepsilon_n$. But this appears to be complicated, and hardly worthwhile.

2.3,2,4 RADIOISOTOPE POWER SOURCE

Usually, one thinks of radioisotope power sources to be applicable in the low power regions; but in the recent literature (Michelsen and Low, 1963) a system delivering several kilowatts has been described. It consists of two concentric spherical shells (ratio of radii is 2, total diameter is 1 m, output is 5 kW at 700 kV, dc), where the inner shell consists of Mo (25.9 mg/cm²) carrying 70 mg/cm² of radioisotope material (Ce^{144}), and the outer

---

[1] As the incoming radiation is not parallel, light is also reflected to dx from other mirror sections. This increases the concentration ratio, perhaps by a factor 2.

shell consists of Al (5 mg/cm²). Typical temperatures are between 300 and 600°C, where the inner shell is at the higher and the outer shell at the lower temperature. The weight-to-power ratio is—without shielding—initially 0.29 kg/kW, but the power decreases according to the equation E/E_0 = exp($-t$ days/411). Problems—apart from engineering ones—involve (1) availability of radioisotopes; (2) γ-radiation; (3) ground handling, especially during launch preparation and launch; (4) decay of power source.

2.3,3 Solar Thermal Propulsion (Ehricke, 1956a, b)

This engine is the solar-energy powered counterpart to the nuclear heat-exchanger type engine. But it will not be possible to reach high accelerations. Therefore, the application—if any—can be only in the low-acceleration class of vehicles.

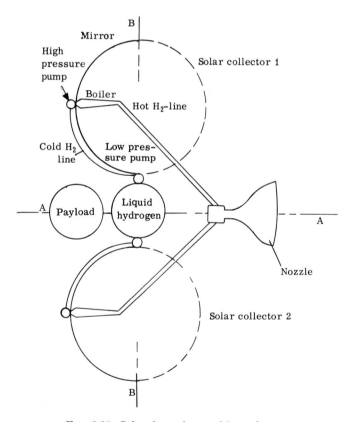

FIG. 2.27. Solar-thermal propulsion scheme.

The fundamental principle of this engine is to use solar energy without any conversion to heat up hydrogen,[1] which then is expanded through a nozzle thus providing thrust. For universal application, the design has to provide independence of the thrust direction from the direction to the Sun. A solution is as sketched in Fig. 2.27.

The orientation is as follows: Line up axis $A - A$ in the desired thrust direction and rotate around $A - A$ until axis $B - B$ is vertical on the direction to the Sun. Then rotate the mirrors only around $B - B$, until they face the Sun.

The "hot" pipe lines are heavy (high pressure, hot gas, with only a little heat loss allowed). Therefore, to minimize weight they should be as short as possible. A better construction, in this respect, is as shown in Fig. 2.28.

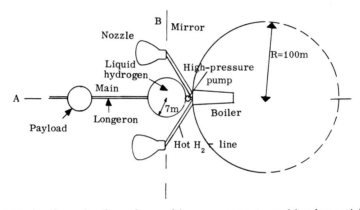

FIG. 2.28. Another solar-thermal propulsion arrangement requiring less weight.

The axis $A - A$ is first aligned toward the Sun; then the vehicle rotates around $A - A$, until $B - B$ is vertical on the direction of the desired thrust, and then the nozzles only rotate around $B - B$ until the thrust direction is as desired. But there is a limitation: the jet must not hit the mirror. So there is not complete independence of thrust direction and direction to the Sun. But this limitation does not appear to be very severe. To assure that the thrust always goes through the center of gravity, it might be necessary to move the payload along the main longeron.

The mirror shall be designed as an Ehricke sphere with the very large size of 100 m radius. The weight of the complete mirror is 4 tons. The boiler weight might be 2.5 tons. Let us assume furthermore that we have weights

[1] Other methods of heating—e.g., by radioisotopes—may find application. For details, see Romero (1966).

of 8.5 tons of hydrogen lines, pumps, nozzles, etc., 5 tons of payload, 5 tons of hydrogen-tankage, and 100 tons of usable hydrogen.

The assumptions are fairly optimistic, as is evident. They lead to an all-up weight of 125 tons and a cutoff weight of only 25 tons. With an estimated 30 kg of thrust the initial acceleration is $2.4 \times 10^{-4}g$, the final acceleration is $1.2 \times 10^{-3}g$. These figures bring the vehicle to the borderline of the, for Earth-to-Moon flights, attractive and not extremely low acceleration group.

As computed, the maximum average boiler temperature to be expected for a spherical mirror will be about 2070°K. Since at this temperature all of the incoming energy is reradiated, nothing could be given on to the hydrogen. This, therefore, is the upper limiting case of temperature for zero hydrogen flow.

Let us assume we succeed in heating the hydrogen to 1900°K in the boiler and get it to the nozzle at 1860°K at a pressure of 100 atm. The hydrogen enthalpy is 13.3 kcal/gm-mole. At an exit pressure of 0.1 atm, we read 2 kcal/gm-mole, and a gas temperature of about 300°K. The area ratio is about 45. Thus the uncorrected specific impulse is about $208(13.3 - 2)^{1/2}$ = 695 sec. The correction due to exit pressure is $0.62 \times 10^{-3} \times 45 \times 695$ ≈ 19 sec, or the total ideal specific impulse is 714 sec. With a corrective factor of 0.9, the true specific impulse then could be 642 sec. The characteristic velocity of the vehicle follows:

$$v_{\text{id}} = 642 \times 9.8 \ln(125/25) = 10130 \quad \text{m/sec.}$$

This would suffice to make an escape from a low circular Earth orbit, but it would not suffice to make a trip from such an orbit around the Moon and return to the orbit. We have to conclude that this type of vehicle does not look promising. The average boiler temperature is $\bar{T} = 1900$°K. At $\bar{T}$ = 2070°K, all of the incident energy is reradiated from the boiler. So, at 1900°K, the reradiated energy fraction is $(1900/2070)^4 = 0.712$. The mirror intercepts an energy $E = 1.4\pi R^2 = 44{,}000$ kW. Of this, 71.2% is reradiated from the boiler, and 28.8% or 12,700 kW (which is equal to 303 kcal/sec) is utilized to heat up the hydrogen.

The energy requirement is about 13.6 kcal/gm-mole per mole hydrogen; so the flow rate is $(303/13.6) \times 2.01 = 44.8$ gm-sec, and the thrust becomes $44.8 \times 642 \times 10^{-3} = 28.8$ kg. This is sufficiently close to the previously "estimated" value of 30 kg.

For near-zero hydrogen flow, the maximum hydrogen temperature in the boiler may be 2200°K and in the nozzle 2150°K, resulting in a specific impulse of 716 sec. This would be about the maximum for the described system.

With a parabolic high-quality mirror, the mirror-boiler weight would go up by perhaps a factor of 10, and the specific impulse to not more than 900 sec in view of the discussion under the nuclear heat-exchanger rocket engine. This results in a characteristic speed of $v_{id} = 900 \times 9.8 \ln(175/75) = 7460$ m/sec. Again, the high-quality mirror gives a less favorable result.

Auxiliary power, and power to drive the pumps, etc., can stem from a small solar power plant, or is taken with the help of a turbine from the hot hydrogen.

2.3,4 Solar-Chemical Propulsion (Ehricke, 1956)

There are basically three ways to improve on the unfavorable result of the previous section:

(1) *To reduce the mission requirement.* In practice, this can be done for a given mission only by going to high accelerations above about 0.3 Earth gravities.

(2) *To improve on vehicle performance via mass ratio.* As a mass ratio of about five is already very good for a single-stage vehicle of this type, the only practical way would be to stage—perhaps, tank staging. Without further investigation, the prospects do not appear promising.

(3) *To improve on vehicle performance via specific impulse.* This can be done by either going to higher temperatures with the exhaust gas, or by using nonthermodynamic methods to expel the gas. Generally, this appears to be the most promising method.

Let us briefly consider method (1). Here it is proposed to carry water into an Earth orbit, and there decompose it into H_2 and O_2 by electric (solar) power. From this, liquid H_2 and liquid O_2 can be produced, which is used to refuel a final stage, possibly with the additional feature of tank staging. Advantages of this scheme have to do with the cheapness of water, the high density of water, and the (hopefully) availability of final stages in orbit, utilizing H_2/O_2 for propellants anyway.

One cubic meter of water weighs one ton. By adding 3.47×10^6 kcal/ton, this can be split into 111 kg gaseous hydrogen and 889 kg gaseous oxygen. In reality, there may be some small loss of gases—let us assume, all in all, 5%. Thus, finally, we have 105 kg liquid hydrogen (energy for lique-faction is 18×10^3 kcal/kg) with a volume requirement of 1.5 m³, and 844 kg liquid oxygen (energy for liquefaction is 740 kcal/kg) requiring a volume of 0.74 m³. With the optimum (maximum specific impulse for a ratio of chamber to exit pressure being 25) mixture ratio of about 3.7, we need only 388 kg of LOX to burn with the 105 kg of liquid H_2: therefore, 456 kg of LOX (or gaseous O_2, if it is not liquefied)[1] should find other uses—perhaps for cleaning/disinfecting and breathing. The total volume of the usable propellants[2] is about 1.84 m³, which required only 1 m³ of transport volume. This may be attractive in view of the large volume requirements to supply an H_2/O_2 rocket system. On the other hand, for 1 ton water we get only 493 kg propellants.[3] The energy used equals $(3.47 + 2.19) \times 10^6$ kcal/ton of water. Therefore, this system can be economical only if (1) the residual oxygen is also utilized; (2) transport cost to orbit is cheap; and (3) electric energy is freely available.

The electric plant to convert the water to LOX/liquid H_2 may be of the solar power-Ehricke sphere type and have an output of 1000 kW with a weight of 4 tons. Because of shadow times, servicing, and other uses (refrigeration, communication, etc.) only 600 kW $= 4.86 \times 10^5$ kcal/h will be available for the electrolytic process. So about 2 tons of water could be processed per day, giving above 1 ton of propellant mixture.

The system water + (solar, nuclear) electric energy $\rightarrow H_2 + O_2 \rightarrow$ thrust could be applicable for special cases, such as attitude control of 24-h communication satellites.

By going to a high acceleration, the velocity requirement for an Earth escape from an orbit can be reduced to about 45% of the requirement for accomplishing the same mission with low acceleration. Therefore, the "reduced specific impulse" of the solar-thermal propulsion (Sec. 2.3,3) system is about $0.45 \times 642 = 289$ sec. With the O_2/H_2 system, we may have about 430 sec or an improvement by a factor of 1.5.[4]

At the same time, we have a crude yardstick to compare low-acceleration to high-acceleration chemical vehicles; only when the specific impulse is markedly larger than $(420)/(0.45) = 956$ sec, can attractiveness be expected. Indeed, since the mass ratio of the chemical vehicle is superior, the break-even point is even higher at 1200 sec or so. [Compared to high-acceleration nuclear rockets, "the break even" may occur at 2200 sec or higher. According to Fimple and Edelbaum (1965) it occurs at 3000 sec.]

---

[1] At a mixture ratio of 5 (optimum for a pressure ratio of about 600), about 319 kg of O_2 remain.

[2] At a mixture ratio of 5, it is 1.96 m³.

[3] At a mixture ratio of 5, we get 630 kg.

[4] Only if the residual oxygen is utilized.

2.3,5 Arc-Heated Plasma Jet Propulsion (Heller, 1959)

This is an attempt to improve the vehicle by going to higher specific impulse. Electric energy (from a nuclear or solar power plant) is generated and used to heat up some convenient material (to be practical, only hydrogen appears attractive with values of the specific impulse up to 1500–2000 sec; ammonia—much more easily stored—might permit 1000 sec) via an electric arc (or other convenient method—e.g., resistance heating via a solid electric heating element, or high-frequency heating) thus creating a plasma. This expands through a nozzle forming the propulsive jet.[1]

At 4000°K and 0.1 atm chamber pressure the enthalpy of the over 90% dissociated hydrogen is 135 kcal/gm-mole, going, for an expansion to 10^{-4} atm, to 67 kcal/gm-mole, 2300°K and 45% dissociation with a nozzle area ratio $A_{exit}/A_{throat} \approx 45$. (Perhaps heat transfer considerations will force us to go to a higher chamber pressure of about 1 atm. We will neglect this here.) The specific impulse, uncorrected for nozzle exit pressure, is 1715 sec. The correction for exit pressure is about 48 sec, giving a "realizable total" of $0.9(1715 + 48) = 1588$ sec.[2]

According to John *et al.* (1963), the following values have been obtained with radiation-cooled arc jet engines, operating in steady state condition:

Power (kW)		30	30	215
Working fluid		H_2	NH_3	H_2
Arc current (amp)		150	280	1350
Arc voltage (volt)		200	107	160
Mass flow rate (gm/sec)		0.1	0.25	0.33
Overall efficiency (%)		38	40	35
Specific impulse (sec)		1550	1000	2200
Arc temperature (°K)	$\sim 50{,}000$			
Average H_2 temperature (°K)	$\sim 10{,}000$			
Maximum H_2 temperature (°K) $[I_{sp} \approx 5000 \text{ sec}]$	$\sim 25{,}000$			

Let us assume that electric energy of 1 MW is available. The power plant weight (including nozzle, pumps for hydrogen, piping, controls,

[1] Detail problems have been neglected: hot vs cold chamber wall, frozen vs shifting gas flow, gas ionization, velocity profile losses (see under ion engine; production of ions), arc stabilization without external resistor, ac vs dc arc, etc.

[2] According to Page (1962), arc jets may reach up to 2500 sec, and resistojets up to 1000 sec.

etc.) shall be 10 tons. Of the 1 MW, 90% shall be available for propulsion, of which again 90% is transferred to the hydrogen; this gives, for the hydrogen, an energy flow rate of 810 kW = 193.8 kcal/sec. Therefore, the hydrogen flow per second can be about $(193.8)/(135) = 1.435$ gm-mole $= 2.87$ gm, and the thrust is only 4.55 kg. The efficiency in the sense of (jet power)/(electrical input power) will not be greater than 60%, under favorable circumstances. Accepting the low initial acceleration of $5 \times 10^{-5}g$ the launch weight comes out to be about 91 tons. With 10 tons for payload, 6 tons for tankage, 1 ton for structure, and 64 tons for liquid hydrogen, we have a characteristic speed of 18.9 km/sec. This is sufficient for a trip from a low circular Earth orbit around the Moon back to the orbit. The total trip time would be rather long, between 200 and 250 days. For comparison, a high-thrust vehicle could carry out the trip Earth orbit–around the Moon–landing on Earth at about 5 km/sec in 10 days.

A weight breakdown for a 91-ton all-chemical vehicle could be as follows:

Part	Weight (tons)
Propellants	64
Tankage	6
Structure	2
Engine[a]	1
Payload	18
Total	91

[a] Engine thrust is 30 tons.

The 18-ton entry vehicle could be equivalent to the 10-ton payload carried by the electric vehicle. So, for one flight, the same 91 tons have to be carried from Earth surface to orbit. But when the flight is to be repeated, the arc-jet vehicle requires only about 65 tons (instead of 91 tons for the complete chemical vehicle) of liquid hydrogen to be brought to orbit. Therefore, in the long run the arc-heated craft would have an advantage over the chemical vehicle. But when we compare it to a nuclear high-thrust rocket system, things look different again, as can be seen in the following tabulation with $v_{id} = 10$ km/sec,[1] $I_{sp} = 800$ sec:

[1] This is twice the value for the chemical vehicle, since this nuclear vehicle shall return to the initial Earth orbit, to be reused.

Part	Weight (tons)
Hydrogen	66
Tankage	6
Structure	2
Engine/shielding[a]	8
Payload	9
Total	91

[a] The thrust is 30 tons.

The weight-carrying capability is about the same as that of the arc-heated machine, when it is considered that two men during 150 days require a total supply of at least 1.5 tons. The important difference is that the mission time is only that of a high-acceleration vehicle, i.e., about 10 days. So the high-thrust nuclear system would be preferable on this circumlunar mission to both the chemical and the arc-heated system, when repeated flights are planned.

But there are other missions. If we think, e.g., of the 24-h communication satellite with its difficult position-keeping problem, it is desirable that this satellite have a propulsive engine to correct deviations from the desired position. Some special requirements for this engine are: (1) small accelerations—very sensitive control; (2) high specific impulse—long lifetime; (3) multistart capability; (4) light engine weight.

As electric energy is available anyway for the mission of this satellite, electric energy should be used to create the propulsive jet. Arc heating of hydrogen[1] must be carefully considered for this application. Generally, application of the arc-jet propulsion system looks promising for low powers (up to perhaps 30 kW) and unmanned scientific missions, if the velocity requirement is not high, e.g., mapping of the van Allen radiation zone by slowly spiraling throught it. All of the electrically propelled vehicles have a large amount of electric energy available, after the flight mission is performed. The utilization of this energy deserves further study.

As in all low-acceleration systems, the arc-jet system has to operate continuously for a long time, generally. (An exception might be the described satellite position correction.) To fulfill and prove reliability demands becomes a severe problem, which is increased by the high temperature electric

[1] Or some other working fluid.

arc and electrode erosion. An "electrodeless arc"—e.g., a radio-frequency field[1]—could be substituted. To test a high-thrust system over about 10 times its operational lifetime requires only of the order of 5 h. But it takes more than 10 yr to test a low-thrust interplanetary vehicle over the same tenfold increased operational lifetime. This a severe problem for all low-thrust systems, which in practice can probably be solved only by simple, fail-safe, and reliable design and self-healing features, or provision for in-flight repair.

2.3,6 Ion Propulsion (Stuhlinger and Seitz, 1960; Michelsen, 1960)

The numerical results of this section are approximately valid for all electric or electromagnetic systems which reach very high specific impulses: in practice, these are, besides the ion-engine (including Oberth's "electric wind" system), the MHD devices only.

2.3,6,1 THE THRUST CHAMBER

The power source—nuclear or solar—has been sufficiently described.

Let us consider the "thrust chamber" now. An ion of mass $m = A\mu$ [where A is the atomic weight, μ the mass per unit atomic weight $= 1.008/(6.026 \times 10^{23})$ gm] and a charge ne (where e is the elementary charge $= 1.6021 \times 10^{-19}A$ sec, $n = 1, 2, \cdots$) has a speed c after falling through a voltage V given by

$$c = 13840 \left(\frac{nV}{A}\right)^{1/2} \frac{m}{sec}. \tag{2.3}$$

An electric current density j flowing through a condenser (Fig. 2.29) can be limited by two effects:

(1) The number of available ions can be limited; we will assume this is not the case.

(2) Space charge influences limit the maximum current density. Numerically, the Child-Schottky-Langmuir equation describes this effect:

$$j_{max} = 5.45 \times 10^{-8} \left(\frac{n}{A}\right)^{1/2} \frac{V^{3/2}}{d^2} \frac{amp}{cm^2}. \tag{2.4}$$

In practice, only some fraction ε of this can be reached, i.e.,

$$j = \varepsilon \times 5.45 \times 10^{-8} \left(\frac{n}{A}\right)^{1/2} \frac{V^{3/2}}{d^2} \frac{amp}{cm^2}. \tag{2.5}$$

---

[1] Or a resistance heater.

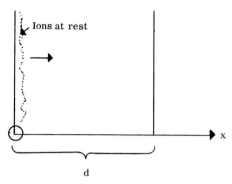

FIG. 2.29. Electric current flow through a condenser.

The weight flow rate per square centimeter is, of course,

$$\dot{w} = \frac{j}{ne} A\mu = \varepsilon \times 5.68 \times 10^{-13} \left(\frac{A}{n}\right)^{1/2} \frac{V^{3/2}}{d^2} \quad \left[\frac{gm}{cm^2 \ sec}\right]. \quad (2.6)$$

This is connected to the particle number per second per square centimeter by the equation

$$N = \frac{\dot{w}}{A\mu} = \varepsilon \times 3.4 \times 10^{11} \frac{1}{(An)^{1/2}} \frac{V^{3/2}}{d^2}. \quad (2.7)$$

Assuming that the jet is parallel, we have a thrust density

$$f = \frac{\dot{w}c}{g} = \varepsilon \times 8.01 \times 10^{-10} \frac{V^2}{d^2} \quad \frac{gm}{cm^2}. \quad (2.8)$$

(A slight modification results when $V^2 = (A/n)^2 c^4 \times (13840)^{-4}$ is inserted.) The ratio V/d is the field strength; to avoid arcing, a rule is[1] to keep V/d below 50–1000 kV/cm, resulting in $f \leq 8$ gm/cm². In practice, hardly more than 1 gm/cm² can be realized. Plasma jets can go more than one order of magnitude higher. The total energy in the jet is, with C the cross-sectional area,

$$E = Cj V = C\varepsilon \times 5.45 \times 10^{-8} \times \left(\frac{n}{A}\right)^{1/2} \frac{V^{5/2}}{d^2} \quad \frac{W}{cm^2}. \quad (2.9)$$

Thus,

$$\frac{f}{E} \sim \left(\frac{A}{n}\right)^{1/2}. \quad (2.10)$$

---

[1] Breakdown voltage in vacuum: U is in kilovolts and d in cm. Then, approximately, $U = 290 \, d^{1/2}$, or the maximum field strength is $U/d = 290/d^{1/2}$ kV/cm.

If f/E is to be high, then A/n should be large; from the second form of Eq. (2.8) is seen that $f \sim (A/n)^2$ for a given jet speed c. But for a given V/d the thrust f is independent of A/n. Therefore, we can only say that for some conditions (namely, for relatively small c values) large A/n can be of advantage: the maximum A/n might be realized utilizing colloidal particles with a ratio $A/n \approx 10^6/1$.

Because of its fundamental importance, Eq. (2.4) shall be derived. Let $\mathbf{E}$ be the electric field strength; then let us call E_n the component of $\mathbf{E}$ which is normal to an element df of an area f. Let f be a closed area, and $\varphi = \oint_f E_n \, df$. If we take f to be a sphere of radius r, the center of which contains electric charge Q, then $E_n = Q/r^2$ and $\varphi = 4\pi Q$. Generally, if ΣQ_i is the electric charge within any closed area f, then $\varphi = \oint_f E_n \, df = 4\pi \, \Sigma Q_i$. Allowing the closed area f to contract until only the small volume $d\tau$ is enclosed, and calling the quotient of (electric charge within the volume $d\tau$)/(volume $d\tau$) the "electric charge density" ϱ_e, this equation can be written in vector notation

$$\text{div } \mathbf{E} = 4\pi\varrho_e .$$

Obviously, by moving a small electric charge along any closed path S in an electric field, energy cannot be gained, or a perpetual motion machine could be built. Thus,

$$\oint_S \mathbf{E} \, d\mathbf{S} = 0,$$

or by choosing S to include a small area df and going to vector notation: rot $\mathbf{E} = 0$, or there exists a potential function U such that $\mathbf{E} = - \text{grad } U$.

Together with the previous vector equation, we obtain Poisson's equation immediately:

$$\varDelta U = - 4\pi\varrho_e .$$

If l particles per cm^3, with the charge ne_0 each, move parallel with a speed v, then a current density $j = ne_0 lv$ exists. In the stationary case, j may not vary locally, because the space charge does not vary in time at any place (condition of continuity, or div $\mathbf{j} = 0$).

If v is due to a potential difference U, then from the energy law $\frac{1}{2} m_0 v^2 = ne_0 U$, where m_0 is the mass of the particle with the charge ne_0.

Now in a simple one-dimensional case (with the dimension being along the x axis), introducing $V = U_0 - U$, we have

$$- \frac{d^2 V}{dx^2} = - 4\pi\varrho_e = - 4\pi n l e_0 = - 4\pi \frac{j}{v} = - 4\pi \frac{j}{(2ne_0 V/m_0)^{1/2}} .$$

Writing $m_0 = A\mu$, multiplying with dV/dx and integrating between $x = 0$ and x:

$$\left(\frac{dV}{dx}\right)^2 - \left(\frac{dV}{dx}\right)_0^2 = \frac{16\pi j(A\mu)^{1/2}}{(2ne_0)^{1/2}}\,[V^{1/2} - V_0^{1/2}].$$

When $(dV/dx) = 0$, no further increase of j can occur. We put $V_0 = 0$ and get

$$\frac{dV}{dx} = \left[\frac{16\pi j_{\max}(A\mu)^{1/2}}{(2ne_0)^{1/2}}\right]^{1/2}(V)^{1/4}.$$

Integrating again between $x = 0$ and $x = d$, and calling $V_d = V$:

$$\frac{4}{3}V^{3/4} = (8\pi j_{\max})^{1/2}\left(\frac{2\mu A}{e_0 n}\right)^{1/2}d$$

or

$$j_{\max} = \frac{1}{9\pi}\left(\frac{2e_0}{\mu}\right)^{1/2}\left(\frac{n}{A}\right)^{1/2}\frac{V^{3/2}}{d^2}.$$

Specific charge of a proton is 2.87×10^{14} electrostatic cgs units, and $1\ V = 1/300$ electrostatic cgs units, and $1\ \text{amp} = 3 \times 10^9$ electrostatic cgs units.

Thus, if V is inserted in volts and d in centimeters, we have

$$j_{\max} = 6.2 \times 10^{-8}\left(\frac{n}{A}\right)^{1/2}\frac{V^{3/2}}{d^2}\frac{\text{amp}}{\text{cm}^2}.$$

This agrees sufficiently well with Eq. (2.4). At the same time, we have a physical understanding of why the current density is limited: the ion density (or space charge) in the area $x \approx 0$ becomes so high that $(dU/dx)_0 = E_0 = 0$. So no new ions leave the electrode, even if they are avaliable. The quantity p is defined as

$$p = \frac{(\text{total current})\ \text{amp}}{(\text{voltage})^{3/2}} = \frac{jC}{V^{3/2}} = 6.2 \times 10^{-8}\left(\frac{n}{A}\right)^{1/2}\frac{C}{d^2},$$

and, writing $C = \frac{1}{4}\pi D^2$, we obtain

$$p = \frac{jC}{V^{3/2}} = 4.87 \times 10^{-8}\left(\frac{n}{A}\right)^{1/2}\left(\frac{D}{d}\right)^2.$$

The quantity p is called "permeance" and $R = D/d$ the "aspect ratio."

Most of the ion and electron beam experience of today is for $R < 1$, but ion engines will operate at $R \gg 1$. The beam neutralization, to be discussed later, is not much of a problem below about $R = 1$, where, in vacuum, the beam just diverges. But for $R \gg 1$, conditions are more unfavorable. We will return to this topic later on.

Now to a conceptual design of an ion engine:

(1) *Production of ions.* A supply of ions has to be created before they are accelerated in the acceleration voltage. The following three conditions should be fulfilled:

(a) All ions should have the same (A/n) value to result in a defined exhaust speed, and to ease some electron-optical considerations. This condition may be difficult for the colloidal system. A constant exhaust speed will result in minimum energy consumption for a given thrust. Let m_i be some mass elements, which are jettisoned per second with a speed v_i; then the energy is

$$E = \Sigma \tfrac{1}{2} m_i v_i^2 \,,$$

and the thrust is

$$T = \sum_1^i m_i v_i \,.$$

To minimize E at constant T, consider

$$\frac{\partial}{\partial v_K} (E - \lambda T) = 0$$

for all K, which gives $v_K = \lambda$, or all v_K are equal. As the second derivative is always positive, we have indeed a minimum of E. (A numerical example shows at once that $m_1 = m_2 = 1$, $v_1 = v_2 = 1$, $T = 2$, $E = 1$, and $m_1 = m_2 = 1$, $v_1 = 0$, $v_2 = 2$, $T = 2$, $E = 2 > 1$.)

(b) All of the efflux material should be ionized in order to avoid a loss of nonionized jet material and to avoid scatter of ionized particles.

(c) Obviously, ionization should take as little energy as possible.

There are some possibilities for such ion sources: we could, e.g., think of electrons which are oscillating within a potential well which contains them, thus ionizing a gas or an electric arc might be used. Of promise is contact ionization[1] of alkaline vapors on a hot platimun or tungsten surface

---

[1] Recently, methods of volume ionization have caught up with methods of surface ionization. The SERT test described later utilized one ion engine of the type described above, and one utilizing mercury for working fluid and ion production by electron bombardment of mercury vapor.

(work function 5.2 or 4.5 eV, respectively). Cesium appears to be the best choice. (Price $ 540, may go down to $ 25/lb; density 1.9 g/cm³; ionization energy 3.86 eV; melting temperature 29°C and boiling point at 1/760 atm pressure, 277°C, and at 1 atm, 690°C; atomic No. 55; atomic weight $A = 132.91$). The temperature of the ionizing metal surface has to be somewhat above a critical temperature (about 1200–1500°K), which increases with increasing current density. The ionization efficiency can be considerably above 99% if no atoms can go through the ionizer without striking the hot surface. As the ions should leave the ion source with zero velocity to give well-defined initial conditions for the accelerator, a hot porous tungsten wall (melting point of platinum 1760°C, and tungsten 3400°C) with a pore diameter of about 0.4×10^{-4} cm looks promising. The cesium atoms should go through the tungsten wall, and after they emerge from this as ions they should enter the accelerating field.

The energy efficiency of ion sources is poor; whereas the ideal energy requirement for the formation of one ion-electron pair is low (3.86 eV for Cs, 10.4 eV for Hg), actual sources use several hundred electron volts per pair. For example a well-designed surface ionization source has a radiation loss of, typically, 150 eV per pair (1 W-sec $= 6.24 \times 10^{18}$ eV; 1 mamp/cm² corresponds to a flow of 6.24×10^{15} ions/cm² $=$ sec). Therefore, in spite of the simplicity of electric heating of the ionizer, in order to avoid the losses in the heat-electricity-heat conversion, this energy should be directly derived from the primary thermal source, or be derived from an independent thermal energy source (e.g., reactor, radioisotope, solar power).

(2) *The acceleration system.* The ions enter an electric field. After acceleration they should pass the electrode and leave the vehicle. They must not hit the accelerating electrode for two reasons: first, they would be lost to the case of thrust production, and secondly, high-energy particles hitting the electrode would lead to sputtering. Assuming one hitting cesium ion removes ten atoms from the electrode, we can make a coarse estimate: the total vehicle may have 500 tons initial weight, propellant (cesium) may be 250 tons, the ion engine about 10 tons with 1 ton for the accelerating electrodes, of which not more than 250 kg may be removed by sputtering. Thus, about 25 kg of cesium is allowed to hit, which is a maximum of 1 atom out of 10^4. To fulfill this, n/A and the accelerating voltage probably have to be accurately constant. Otherwise, provision for electrode renewal in flight has to be made. (It is interesting to remark that some types of plasma propulsion use just this sputtering to provide the jet material.) Besides sputtering, secondary electron emission resulting from ions hitting an electrode can increase

the current without increasing the thrust, thereby lowering the thrust/energy ratio.

With the proper ion source, the operation will be space-charge limited. To get a high current density, a high accelerating voltage is required. This may result in too high a jet velocity—it will be shown that an optimum value exists. This suggests the placing of a decelerating electrode system after the acceleration system in order to adjust the jet velocity towards its optimum value. From the physical understanding of Schottky-Langmuir's equation it can be seen that this decelerating system will not limit the current density. Indeed, the current density of the acceleration system can be maintained in proper designs. This is a great advantage of so-called accel-decel systems. The energy requirement is, of course, determined only by the final speed and current strength. The power requirement in the ion source is mainly due to radiation from the hot surface. Generally, this will be about 5–10% of the total power. As the energy consumption in the ion source is mainly a function of current strength, but total power is the product of current strength and accelerating voltage, we expect a rise of ion source power for lower voltages. Indeed, the ion source power may be 40–50% of the total power at about 1000 V acceleration. (It is for this reason that the tapping of some primary thermal power source is far superior to using electric power, because of the low efficiency of thermal-electric-thermal conversion.)

(3) *Beam neutralization.* After the ions have passed the last electrode, the jet has to be neutralized as soon as possible: the reason is that the emerging ions have to move against an increasing space charge, if the beam is not neutralized, which would even lead to reversal of the beam. Roughly, neutralization has to be accomplished at a distance about equal to the acceleration gap in front of the final electrode. This is only true—as mentioned—for aspect ratios of $R \gg 1$; for $R < 1$, the beam just diverges by action of internal ion-ion forces. For $R \approx 1$, current neutralization, i.e., ion current equal to electron current, suffices. For $R \gg 1$, charge neutralization is required.[1]

As the production of convenient negative ions is quite difficult, neutralization should be done by injecting electrons into the jet. This, at the same time, will keep the vehicle electrically neutral.

For an electron, $A/n \approx 1/1840$. So it is quite capable of reaching high jet speeds [see Eq. (2.3)]—but it will be shown that such very high jet speeds are not favorable. And as the electrons are very inefficient producers

---

[1] For electrons, permeance $p = 1.83 \times 10^{-6}R^2$; and for Cs ions, $p = 0.37 \times 10^{-8}R^2$.

of thrust for a given energy [see Eq. (2.10)], they should not take part in the thrust. Besides, for proper beam neutralization (current and charge neutralization), the electron speed should be about equal to the ion speed, which demands from Eq. (2.3) that nV/A should be a constant for both the ions and the electrons, or about

$$\frac{V_{electron}}{V_{ion}} = \left(\frac{A}{n}\right)_{electron} \left(\frac{n}{A}\right)_{ion} = \frac{A_{electron}}{A_{ion}} = \frac{1}{1840 \times 133},$$

or with $V_{ion} \approx 10^4$ V, we have

$$V_{electron} \approx 0.04 \text{ V}.$$

These are just thermal electrons which can be "boiled off" from hot filaments. Their energy and thrust contributions are negligible. On the other hand they are difficult to beam.

The ion density in the outgoing jet is very low: With $V = 10^4$ V and $A = 133$ we have, from Eq. (2.3), $c = 120$ km/sec, and with $\varepsilon = \frac{1}{3}$, $d = 1$ cm, from Eq. (2.7), we obtain $N \approx 10^{16}$ ions/cm^2 sec. So within the jet the density is only $N/c \approx 10^9$ ions/cm^3. (Air at normal pressure and temperature contains about 3×10^{19} particles/cm^3.) It cannot be expected that ions and electrons will recombine at such low particle densities. Therefore, the jet can at best be a neutral plasma. In the laboratory, beam neutralization presents no severe problem. Both theoretical and empirical results obtained during 1961–1963 indicate that the difficulties of beam neutralization in space appear to have been overestimated. No serious problems are expected in this area.

After having described the elements of an ion engine the conceptual design is quite straightforward (see Fig. 2.30). We can consider the "thrust chamber" to consist of a large "cluster" of elemental thrust chambers—about 10^4/m^2. The electrons are injected at the rim of the ion jet which should leave the accelerator as a nearly paralled jet to get maximum thrust, similar to the corresponding requirement in chemical rocket engines. Later, it might diverge due to internal forces, without influencing performance. The electrons start oscillating through this jet because of the forces from the ions to the electrons. In this oscillation, the electrons move fastest in the middle and slowest at the rim of the ion jet (see Fig. 2.31). Therefore, the jet plasma may be overall neutral, but has "zones" of surplus positive and other zones of surplus negative charge.

These electron oscillations are a source of electromagnetic noise, which can interfere with communication or experiments, or which, with proper

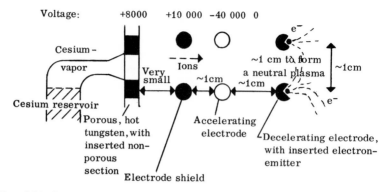

Fig. 2.30. Ion engine concept. Controls: measure ion current and cesium-vapor current; adjust tungsten temperature for complete ionization and cesium resevoir temperature for desired ion current. Measure electrode sputtering: adjust focusing voltage; measure neutralization in beam; adjust electron emitter temperature; measure accelerating voltage; adjust as required.

modulation, perhaps can be used as a transmitter antenna. Much research is still necessary to prove that this beam type of plasma arrangement is stable—or to find another solution in case it is not. [For example, the Pierce gun (Seitz and Raether, 1959), which is an ion-optical device to get an ion beam.] Laboratory simulation is very difficult because of the long path

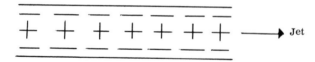

Fig. 2.31. General location of positive and negative charges in ion jet.

lengths involved, because of the vacuum required, and because of undesirable jet-wall interaction. (The latter ones are not present during a brief initial time interval.) Therefore, experimentation in space is required; a simple test might be to use a short lifetime battery-powered low-acceleration engine to change the spin of a ballistic vehicle.[1]

[1] Project SERT (Space Electric Rocket Test) consists of a 375-lb (of which 73 lb are chemical batteries) Scout launched, spin stabilized, RCA built capsule, testing two ion engines (Lewis: electron bombardment; Hg; I_{sp} = 4900 sec; thrust 0.00637 lb; weight 11.6 lb; diameter 7.5 in. Hughes: contact ionization; Cs; 8050 sec; 0.0011 lb) in a free ballistic flight of about 45 min duration. In the first flight test on July 20, 1964, the Lewis engine worked fine, proving beam neutralization, etc. The Hughes engine failed. The U. S. Air Force launched a similar experiment successfully in August 1964,

In the accel-decel system as sketched, electrons cannot reach an electrode; this is an advantage, since such electrons would increase the current strength without contributing to the thrust.

From Eq. (2.9) we have, for the cross-sectional area of the beam,

$$C = \frac{E}{jV} = \frac{E \times 10^8 d^2}{\varepsilon \times 5.45 \, V^{5/2}(n/A)^{1/2}} \, .$$

Expressing the electric energy E in kilowatts, it follows that, for $\varepsilon = \frac{1}{3}$, $d = 1$ cm, $V = 10{,}000$ V, $A/n = 133$: $C = 63.5E$ cm². With electrodes, etc., the total cross section of the engine may be twice as great[1]: $C_{tot} \approx 125E$ cm², and the weight, with 10 gm/cm², about $W = 1250E$ gm. The total engine weight (including controls, feed system, support, etc.) may be two to three times as high—as an estimate the total ion engine weight,[2] where E is the electric energy in kilowatts:

$$W_{engine} = 3E \quad \text{kg.} \tag{2.11}$$

It is interesting to remark that this weight is not negligible in comparison to the weight of the electric power supply.

2.3,6,2 VEHICLES UTILIZING ION PROPULSION: DESCRIPTION AND BASIC OPTIMIZATION

The power plant of an ion-propelled space vehicle consists of an energy source, the conversion system to electric energy, and the ion thrust chamber. For the nuclear reactor-generator system we found a weight of 3 kg/electric kW. Assuming that 10% of the electric energy is used in the ionization system, 10% in the vehicle for communication, etc., and 5% is lost, only 75% is actually available for the jet, resulting in a specific weight of 4 kg/kW. Adding the 3 kg/kW for the ion engine and 1 kg/kW for wiring and contin-

---

testing an Electro-Optical Systems cesium ion contact engine (thrust larger than 2×10^{-3} lb; $I_{sp} = 6000$–8000 sec).

On April 13, 1965 an Atlas-Agena launched the first nuclear reactor power supply system (SNAP 10A; thermoelectric generator, 600 W electric, 970 lb weight) into a long lifetime (3000 yr) polar orbit. One of the experiments is an EOS cesium ionic engine ($I_{sp} = 6000$–8000 sec; porous tungsten surface ionizer, 1200°C hot; thrust 2×10^{-3} lb). The engine appeared to operate properly; but there was electric interference with the telemetry system.

[1] In 1963, the value of 93 cm²/kW was obtained.

[2] In 1963, it appears as if from 0.9 to 2.3 kg/kW are practical figures for the thrustors.

gencies we get for the overall power plant $\alpha_0 = 8$ kg/kW jet power. The total ionization losses, etc., may be 20% instead of 10%, giving $\alpha_0 = 9$ kg/kW jet power. The "conversion efficiency" of a plasma jet is probably about 25% less.

A corresponding consideration for the " ultimate" reactor—thermionic system may result in the "ultimate system" of $\alpha_0 = 2.5$ kg/kW jet power.[1] Optimistically, for the reactor—converter system we assumed 0.6 kg/useful electric kW and 1.4 kg/kW for the ion thrust system, and 0.5 kg/kW contingencies.

In the long run, even our optimistic figure might turn out to be conservative, and energy sources other than nuclear reactor or solar sources may be applicable for propulsive purposes: in Sec. 2.3,2,4 a radioisotope-type battery was described in which the isotope is on a plate of a two-plate consender, and the other plate intercepts the charged decay particles (see Fig. 2.32). The energy user (an ion engine) could be connected to the plates directly.

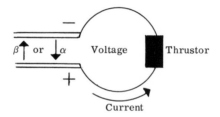

FIG. 2.32. Diagram of a radioisotope-type battery.

There are many difficulties connected with such a system. It has been proposed by Shepherd and Cleaver (1948–1949) and it has been investigated in some detail also by Low and Michelsen (1962) and Ruppe (1956). It shall suffice here just to mention the existence of such optimistic considerations.

With solar power and the Ehricke sphere, about $\alpha_0 = 10$ kg/kW jet power can be realized. With the described parabolic mirror system, this value goes up to $\alpha_0 = 14$ kg/kW jet power.

Summarizing, it can be said that α_0 will be between 2 and 20 kg/kW jet power for all systems considered. A jet power of $\alpha_0 = 10$ kg/kW appears to be a reasonable goal right now, both for reactor-powered and solar-powered vehicles. In all cases, these figures are only applicable for large powers—a few hundred electric kilowatts or more. Smaller engines will

---

[1] In early 1964 the outlook for the early eighties was as follows: $\alpha_0 = 18$ for rotating generator; $\alpha_0 = 11$ for out-of-reactor thermionic generator; $\alpha_0 = 9$ for best foreseeable in-reactor thermionic generator.

have less favorable parameters. Some data for two small ion engines presently under active considerations are given in Table 2.9. (Power supply:
SNAP 8 system; see Chap. 3.) These engines may find application for satellite attitude control or satellite orbit correction. The larger might be
used to propel a space probe. Mainly, the engines should be considered
as test items.

TABLE 2.9

Parameter	Smaller engine	Larger engine
Weight (kg)	68	680
Thrust (gm)	0.495	57.6
Weight flow rate (gm/sec)	0.867×10^{-4}	1.01×10^{-2}
Jet speed (m/sec)	49.65×10^3	56×10^3
Jet power (W)	107	15.9×10^3
Total electric power (W)	300	35×10^3

The efficiency of the electric engine[1] is defined as $\eta = \frac{1}{2}\dot{m}c^2/E_e'$, where $\dot{m}$
is the jet mass flow rate, c the jet speed, E_e' the electric energy, used by the
propulsion system. So far η has been treated as a constant, which is a rough
approximation. A better one, which we will only mention, is given by

$$\eta = \frac{\varepsilon}{1 + C^2/\varepsilon c^2} ,$$

where C is a constant of the dimension of a speed, characteristic for ionization losses; and ε is the ratio of mass of propellant, which is accelerated,
to total mass flow of propellant.

Typical 1963 data are given in the following tabulation:

Bombardment ion engine (Hg)		Electrically heated ionizer,[2] contact ion engine (Cs)
ε (—)	0.80	0.95
C (km/sec)	20	40

[1] Excluding the power supply system.
[2] Direct heating might give $C = 20$.

Thus the efficiency for typical values of the exhaust speed, as we will require them, is given in the following tabulation[1]:

c (km/sec)	Bombardment engine	Contact engine
50	0.67	0.57
76	0.736	0.736
100	0.76	0.81
200	0.79	0.91

The thrust F can be written as

$$F = \dot{m}c = \frac{2\eta E_e{}'}{c} .$$

Inserting η, we obtain

$$F = \frac{2\varepsilon E_e{}'}{c + C^2/\varepsilon c} .$$

Regarding F as a function of c only, we find that a maximum occurs,

$$F_{max} = \frac{\varepsilon^{3/2}}{C} E_e{}' ,$$

for $c = c_m = C/\varepsilon^{1/2}$ and $\eta = \eta_m = \frac{1}{2}\varepsilon$.

We would always choose $c \geq c_m$, because for all values of $c < c_m$ there exists another value $c > c_m$ so that the thrust is unaltered. Therefore, for all practical cases, $\eta \geq \eta_m$. The limiting case of maximum thrust is given in the following tabulation:

	Bombardment engine	Contact engine
F_{max}(gm)	3.65 $E_e{}'$ kW	2.36 $E_e{}'$ kW
c_{min}(km/sec)	22.37	41.05
$\eta_{min}{}^a$	0.4	0.475

[a] For arc jet engines, typically, $\eta = 0.3$–0.5.

[1] Compare a relevant footnote in Section 2.3,1, for plasma engines.

Therefore, ion engines are unsuited for operation at low jet speed and high thrust, which would not violate the energy law, but which does not agree with the behavior of engine efficiency.

This efficiency will be treated as a constant in the following portion of this chapter for the sake of simplicity.

There are several possibilities for optimization of low-acceleration vehicles. Because of its logic and clearness, the procedure of Stuhlinger and Seitz (1960) shall be followed:

For a required velocity v and constant jet speed c, the rocket equation gives

$$M_0/M_e = \exp(v/c) \,,$$

where M_0 is mass at ignition and M_e is the mass at cutoff. Let M_p be the mass of powerplant, M_L the mass of payload (including guidance and control, etc.), M_c the mass of cesium (or generally, exhaust material mass), and M_s the mass of structure. Then

$$M_0 = M_p + M_L + M_c + M_s \,.$$

Furthermore,

$$M_p = \frac{\alpha_0}{g_0} E \,,$$

where E is the jet power in kilowatts and $g_0 = 9.8 \text{ m/sec}^2$. It is valid that $\frac{1}{2} M_c c^2 = E\tau \times 3.671 \times 10^5$, where τ is the time of engine operation or powered flight time in hours. (Total flight time can be longer because of free-flight periods.[1]) The factor 3.671×10^5 converts kilowatt-hours to meter-kilograms; the exhaust speed c has to be measured in meters per second, $g_0 M$ in kilogram. Then

$$M_c = \frac{2E\tau}{c^2} \times 3.671 \times 10^5 \,.$$

Let us assume that $M_s = (2/100)M_e$. (Because of the low accelerations, only a little structure is necessary.) Again

$$M_e = M_p + M_L + M_s \,,$$

---

[1] From Pinkel *et al.* (1964) we have that, for constant thrust low-acceleration transfers, a good choice is to spend $\frac{1}{3}$ of the total transfer time in free flight and $\frac{2}{3}$ thrusting; whereas for optimum variable thrust and specific impulse no free-flight periods occur but the "middle period" has very high specific impulse (typically, an order of magnitude above average) and correspondingly very low thrust, i.e., is nearly a free-flight phase.

or

$$M_L = M_e - M_p - M_s = M_e - \frac{\alpha_0}{g_0} \frac{M_c c^2}{2\tau \times 3.671 \times 10^5} - \frac{2}{100} M_e .$$

Of course,

$$\frac{M_0}{M_e} = \frac{M_e + M_c}{M_e} = 1 + \frac{M_c}{M_e} = \exp(v/c)$$

or

$$M_L = M_e \left[0.98 - \frac{\alpha_0 c^2}{2g_0\tau \times 3.671 \times 10^5} [\exp(v/c) - 1] \right].$$

So, finally,

$$\frac{M_0}{M_L} = \frac{\exp(v/c)}{0.98 - [\alpha_0 c^2/(2g_0\tau \times 3.671 \times 10^5)] [\exp(v/c) - 1]} . \qquad (2.12)$$

The special case of absolute maximum performance follows for $M_L = 0$, or

$$\exp(v/c) = 1 + 0.98 \frac{2g_0\tau \times 3.671 \times 10^5}{\alpha_0 c^2} .$$

Optimistic figures are[1] $\tau = 3$ yr $= 26{,}300$ h, $\alpha_0 = 2.5$ kg/kW, and, hence,

$$\exp(v/c) = 1 + \frac{7.4 \times 10^{10}}{c^2} .$$

The velocity v becomes a maximum for

$$\frac{7.4 \times 10^{10}}{c^2} \approx 4,$$

or $c \approx 136$ km/sec: $v_{\text{max abs}} = 217$ km/sec. Since the low acceleration pays a penalty in the form of high gravity loss, this might correspond to the performance of a high-acceleration vehicle of about $v_{\text{id}} = 100$ km/sec. In Chapter 6 of Vol. 1 this value has been chosen to estimate the possibility of reaching a close fixed star.

Now back to the general case of $M_L \neq 0$; M_0/M_L is the growth factor G, and letting

$$A = \frac{\alpha_0 v^2}{0.98 \times 2g_0\tau \times 3.671 \times 10^5} ,$$

---

[1] τ is a free parameter, limited only by practical considerations about mission duration. Important consequences of this free choice of τ will be mentioned in Sec. 2.4,6.

where A can be considered to be a known constant, and where v/τ can be replaced by the average acceleration, we get, by introducing $x = v/c$,

$$0.98G = \frac{\exp(x)}{1 - (A/x^2)[\exp(x) - 1]}. \tag{2.13}$$

The value x should be chosen such that G is a minimum. Differentiating to determine $x = x_{opt}$, we get

$$2 \exp(x) = 2 + x + \frac{x^3}{A}. \tag{2.14}$$

Power series development (for $x \le 1$) gives

$$2\left(1 + x + \frac{x^2}{2} + \frac{x^3}{6}\right) = 2 + x + \frac{x^3}{A};$$

and from this, for $A \le 0.43$,

$$x_{opt} = \left(\frac{v}{c}\right)_{opt} \approx \frac{3A}{2(3 - A)}\left\{\left(\frac{12 - A}{3A}\right)^{1/2} + 1\right\}. \tag{2.15}$$

For $A < 0.3$, we have

$$\left(\frac{v}{c}\right)_{opt} \approx A^{1/2} + \frac{A}{2} \qquad \text{[from Eq. 2.15)]};$$

and, for $A < 4/100$,

$$\left(\frac{v}{c}\right)_{opt} \approx A^{1/2};$$

and

$$G_{opt} \approx \frac{1 + A^{1/2}}{0.98(1 - A^{1/2})}.$$

This optimum is quite flat up to $A \le 0.2$, but becomes more pronounced for larger A values.

It is easy to plot, from Eq. (2.14), $x_{opt} = (v/c)_{opt}$ vs A, and from this M_0/M_e, M_L/M_0, and M_p/M_0 can be found. This has been done in Fig. 2.33.[1]

---

[1] It is very interesting to note that $100M_p/M_0 = 0.24 \pm 0.02$ for a large span of A values, viz., for $0.1 \le A \le 0.6$. This constitutes a simple "rule of thumb" for optimization purposes. Also, only for $A < 0.64$ can missions be performed. Staging can increase performance; but it may become more important to increase reliability (Edelbaum, 1962a; Martelly, 1961).

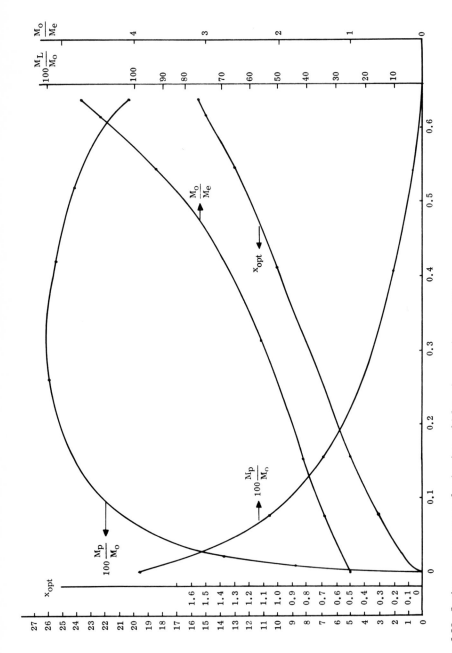

Fig. 2.33. Optimum parameters for ion-jet vehicles. $A = \alpha_0 v^2/(\tau \cdot 61{,}431)$ where α_0 is in kilograms per kilowatt, v in kilometers per second, and τ in years.

What about the acceleration? The mass flow rate is simply M_c/τ, and the thrust

$$F = \frac{M_c}{\tau} c = \frac{M_0}{\tau} \left(\frac{M_0 - M_e}{M_0} \right) c = \frac{M_0}{\tau} \left(1 - \frac{M_e}{M_0} \right) c$$

or

$$a_0 = \frac{F}{M_0 g_0} = \frac{1}{g_0 \tau} \left(1 - \frac{M_e}{M_0} \right) c \, ,$$

and

$$a_e = \frac{F}{M_e g_0} = \frac{M_0}{M_e} a_0 \, .$$

Writing τ in seconds,

$$A = \frac{a_0 v^2 3.6}{0.98 \times 2g_0 \tau \times 3.671 \times 10^2}$$

or

$$\frac{v}{g_0 \tau} = 200 \frac{A}{a_0 v} \, ;$$

from which

$$a_0 v a_0 = 200 A \frac{1 - M_e/M_0}{x_{\text{opt}}} \, . \tag{2.16}$$

Here a_0 is expressed in kg/kW jet power, v in m/sec, and a_0 in units of Earth gravitational acceleration. Figure 2.34 is a plot of this relation.

Now there is one main problem left, namely, to correlate the "required velocity v" with missions. In the last chapter of Vol. 1, such computations have been carried out with the assumption that gravity losses are small (or, accelerations higher than approximately 0.3 of the acceleration of gravity at the location of the vehicle). This problem will be taken up later in this chapter.

Example. Let $v = 45$ km/sec and $\tau = 1.5$ yr. (These values are approximately applicable for a flight Earth orbit–Mars orbit–return to Earth orbit. Total time in transit about 30% longer than for high-acceleration vehicle and Hohmann transfer.)

The evaluations corresponding to the different values of a_0 are given in Table 2.10.

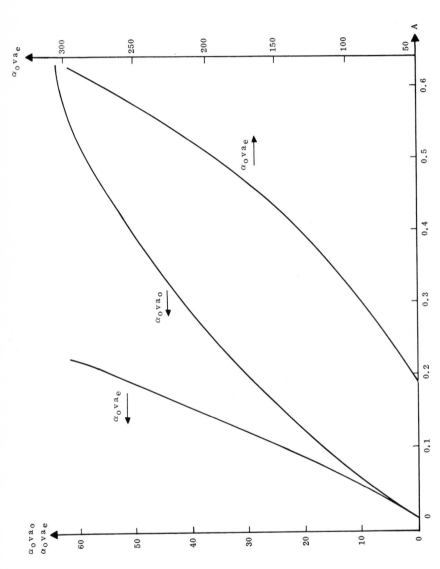

FIG. 2.34. Initial and final accelerations. Units: α_0 in kilograms per kilowatt, v in meters per second, and $a = 9.8$ m/sec².

TABLE 2.10

$\frac{\alpha_0}{\text{kg/kW}}$	A^a	$x_{\text{opt}}^{b,f}$	c_{opt}^b (km/sec)	$\frac{M_0^b}{M_e}$	$100\frac{M_p^b}{M_0}$	$100\frac{M_L^b}{M_0}$	$\alpha_0 v a_0^c$	$\alpha_0 v a_e^c$	a_0^d ($\times 10^{-4}$)	a_e^e ($\times 10^{-4}$)
2	0.044	0.2	225	1.2	17.5	66	8	9.5	0.89	1.06
10	0.22	0.62	72.6	1.88	25.5	25	32.7	61	0.726	1.355
20	0.44	1.06	42.5	2.86	25.2	8	54	155	0.6	1.722

[a] Calculated.
[b] From Fig. 2.33.
[c] From Fig. 2.34.
[d] With v in m/sec and the values of a_0 are in Earth-surface g.
[e] With v in m/sec and the values of a_e are in Earth-surface g.
[f] x_{opt} could be evaluated using $x_{\text{opt}} = (v/c)_{\text{opt}}$.

Conclusions from this table are:

(1) The accelerations are so low[1] that the data from the high-thrust transfers will not even be an approximation. (Indeed, for an Earth orbit–Mars orbit–return flight with a high-acceleration system the required speed was about 16 km/sec, instead of 45 km/sec, as outlined in the previous chapter.)

(2) Payload fractions appear very attractive for about $\alpha \le 10$, but not for $\alpha \ge 20$.

(3) The optimum jet speeds are high—indeed, the specific impulses are of the order of 10^4 sec. About 3×10^3 sec might be necessary to break even with the nuclear heat-exchanger vehicle. (This has $I_{\text{sp}} \approx 10^3$ sec, but a required speed by a factor ~ 2.5 lower, and lower engine weight.) Therefore an improvement over the nuclear high-acceleration vehicle can be expected as long as the low-acceleration vehicle has a specific impulse above $\sim 3 \times 10^3$ sec.

(4) Jet-accelerating voltages for the three cases, from Eq. (2.33), are 35,100, 3660, and 1253 V, respectively. These voltages are not unreasonable.

(5) Total electric power in the jet, per ton of M_0, is given by $100(M_p/M_0) \times 10(1/\alpha_0)$ and, hence, for the three cases it is 87.5, 25.5, and 12.6 kW/ton of M_0, respectively.

---

[1] Inertial measurement of such a low acceleration acting for a long time is a difficult task. The low acceleration vehicles will require new technical developments in the guidance field.

(6) This then means ion currents (in the three cases) of 2.49, 6.96, and 10.05 amp/ton of M_0.

(7) With the estimated ion engine cross section of $125E$ we obtain, for the ion engine cross sections (for the three cases): 1.095, 0.319, and 0.1576 m²/ton of M_0.

(8) For a payload $M_L = 100$ tons, we obtain the data given in Table 2.11.

TABLE 2.11

α_0	M_0 (tons)	M_e (tons)	M_c (tons)	I^a (amp)	F^b (kg)	C^c (m²)	I/C (amp/m²)	E^d (MW)	$E_e{}^e$ (MW)	E'_{th} (MW)
2	152	126.5	25.5	379	13.53	167	2.26	13.3	17.8	89
10	400	212.5	187.5	2790	29.05	128	21.7	10.2	13.6	68
20	1250	437	813	12580	75	197	63.8	15.76	21	105

[a] Total current.
[b] Thrust.
[c] Total ion engine cross section.
[d] Total electric power in the jet.
[e] Total electric power produced. It is about 4/3 times E. (For comparison, 777×10^9 kWh of electricity was sold to the U.S. public in 1962, resulting in an average power of 88.6×10^3 MW.)
[f] Thermal power production (20% efficiency).

(9) From Eq. (2.5) we estimate, with $\varepsilon = \frac{1}{5}$, $V \approx 50 \times 10^3$ V, that $j_{max} \approx 10 \times 10^{-3}$ amp/cm². This then would require only a much smaller ion engine cross section, as can be seen from the tabulation:

α_0	C' (m²)	I/C' (amp/m²)
2	3.8	100
10	27.9	100
20	125.8	100

The reason for the discrepancy between C and C' is due to the derivation for C, where a constant accelerating voltage of 10 kV and a "safety factor" of α was provided. About $2C'$ might be a good estimate for the actual ion engine cross section of the type shown in Fig. 2.30. According to Stuhlinger, $I/C \approx 200$ amp/m² were realized in 1965.[1] A Pierce gun cross section would be considerably larger.

Low acceleration vehicles look promising if values of $\alpha_0 \leq 10$ kg/kW beam power can be realized. One simple method of optimization has been described, which maximizes the ratio (payload)/(initial weight). It has been possible to reduce the problem to only one important parameter A, and to present graphs showing the optimized solution.

Optimizations other than those outlined are possible—e.g., instead of maximizing the payload ratio a different criterion can be used (e.g., minimizing flight time), or the ground rules can be changed (e.g., optimum variation of jet speed instead of constant jet speed; for the mentioned reason of ion beam–electrode interaction, and because, with a variable jet speed but constant total energy, the ion engine cross section and weight are governed by the most unfavorable condition in the variable jet-speed program, and because of the reliability of the added hardware, such a variation may not be practical or not be even desirable). It is interesting to note that the following three cases lead to the same result:

(1) Maximize M_L for specified values of M_0, α_0, τ, v, M_s.
(2) Maximize v for specified values of M_0, α_0, τ, M_L, M_s.
(3) Minimize τ for specified values of M_0, α_0, v, M_L, M_s.

A good survey on various optimization criteria is given by Stuhlinger *et al.* in Simkin-Szego (1961). Let us look into a quite simple case:

$$\text{thrust } F = \frac{M_c c}{\tau} = (7.342 \times 10^5 g_0)^{1/2} \left(\frac{M_p M_c}{\alpha_0 \tau} \right)^{1/2}.$$

So

$$a_0 = \frac{F}{M_0} = \left(\frac{7.342 \times 10^5 g_0}{\alpha_0 \tau} \right)^{1/2} \frac{(M_p M_c)^{1/2}}{(M_p + M_L + M_c + M_s)}.$$

For given values of α_0, τ, M_0, M_L, and M_s it follows that a_0 has a maximum if $M_p = M_c = \frac{1}{2}(M_0 - M_L - M_s)$.

This simple solution—leading to maximum initial acceleration—describes the distribution of mass between the propulsion system and the exhaust mass.

---

[1] Goodrich, High Voltage Astronautics, report to have measured current densities in excess of 3000 amp/m² in the beams from a duoplasmatron ion source, at useful extraction voltages. The first generation of ion engines (1962) does go up to 120 amp/m² current density.

We shall now investigate an idealized case of the problem of minimization of flight time.

The mass flow rate is $\dot{m}$, c the constant jet speed, and $\eta\dot{E}$ the available energy rate such that $\frac{1}{2}\dot{m}c^2 = \eta\dot{E}$, and $\dot{m} = 2\eta\dot{E}/c^2 = $ constant, and for the vehicle mass $m = m_0 - \dot{m}t$, or, if T is the total operational time,

$$m_e = m_0 - \dot{m}T.$$

The total exhaust mass is

$$m_T = \dot{m}T.$$

For the speed in field- and resistance-free space, $v = c\ln(m_0/m)$ when the initial speed is zero, and, of course,

$$v_{max} = c\ln\left(\frac{m_0}{m_e}\right) = c\ln\left(\frac{m_e + m_T}{m_e}\right) = c\ln(1 + x),$$

where $x = m_T/m_e$ and the mass ratio is $m_0/m_e = 1 + x$. The path length covered is

$$s = \int_0^t v\,dt = c\left[t - \left(\frac{m_0}{\dot{m}} - t\right)\ln\left(\frac{m_0}{m}\right)\right],$$

or the total path length

$$S = cT\left[1 - \frac{1}{x}\ln(1 + x)\right].$$

The mass m_e consists of the payload and an energy generation device. Let us assume that we will always choose their masses to be equal. Then we can say that $L = \eta\dot{E}/m_e$ is a given constant: the power plant alone may have an output to be transferred to the jet of $1/10$ kW/kg; including the payload this is $\frac{1}{20}$ kW/kg, or L may be

$$L = \frac{1}{20}\left[\frac{kW}{kg}\right] \times 100\left[\frac{mkg}{kW\ sec}\right] \times 9.8\left[\frac{m}{sec^2}\right] = 50\ \frac{m^2}{sec^3}.$$

We write

$$c^2 = \frac{2\eta\dot{E}}{\dot{m}} = \frac{2Lm_eT}{m_T} = 2L\frac{T}{x},$$

then we have

$$\frac{S}{(2L)^{1/2}} = \frac{T^{3/2}}{x^{1/2}}\left[1 - \frac{1}{x}\ln(1 + x)\right].$$

Question. Is there a value $x = x_{opt}$ such that, for given T and L, the quantity S becomes a maximum? Or—the same question—minimize T for given S and L.

Answer.

$$\frac{\partial}{\partial x} \left[\frac{x - \ln(1 + x)}{x^{3/2}} \right] = 0 \rightarrow 3 \ln(1 + x) = x \frac{3 + x}{1 + x},$$

from which

$$x_{opt} = 1.79.$$

For $x = x_{opt}$, we have

$$TL^{1/3} = 1.7 S^{2/3}.$$

The thrust is

$$f = \dot{m}c = \frac{m_T}{T} \left(2L \frac{T}{x} \right)^{1/2} = m_e \left(2L \frac{x}{T} \right)^{1/2},$$

or the initial acceleration is

$$a_0 = \frac{f}{m_0} = \left[\frac{L}{T} \frac{2x}{(1 + x)^2} \right]^{1/2}.$$

Inserting $x = x_{opt}$,

$$a_{0\,opt} = 0.519 \left(\frac{L^2}{S} \right)^{1/3}.$$

For an interplanetary transfer, $S = 300 \times 10^9$ m; with $L = 50$ m²/sec³ we have $T = 240$ days, and

$$a_{0\,opt} = \frac{1.05}{10^3} \frac{\text{m}}{\text{sec}^2} = \frac{1.07}{10^4} g_0 .$$

The jet speed is

$$c_{opt} = \left[2L \frac{T}{x_{opt}} \right]^{1/2} = 33.8 \times 10^3 \quad \text{m/sec}.$$

These are, again, data which are typical for low-acceleration vehicles. The jet speed c was kept constant. What if we ask for the optimum jet speed program?

$$S = - \int_0^T dt \int_0^t \frac{c}{m} dt;$$

again

$$\tfrac{1}{2}\dot{m}c^2 = -\,L\,m_e = \text{const}$$

or

$$c = \frac{(2Lm_e)^{1/2}}{(-\,\dot{m})^{1/2}}\,.$$

So

$$S = -\,(2Lm_e)^{1/2} \int_0^T dt \int_{m_0}^{m(t)} \frac{dm}{m(-\,\dot{m})^{1/2}}\,.$$

To maximize S (for given m_0, m_e, L, T) is a problem of the calculus of variations. A complete solution is given by Leitmann (1961). We are greatly
indebted to T. Edelbaum for drawing this reference to our attention, correcting an error in the original manuscript.

We will give a more elementary solution to the problem at hand, assuming
that the optimum acceleration is an analytical function of time t. Thus we
write, with constants A, B, C_i, for the acceleration

$$a = A + Bt + \sum_{i=2}^{\infty} C_i t^i\,;$$

and for the speed

$$v = \int_0^t a\,dt = At + \frac{B}{2}\,t^2 + \sum_{i=2}^{\infty} \frac{C_i}{i+1}\,t^{i+1}\,;$$

and for the path length

$$S = \int_0^T v\,dt = \frac{A}{2}\,T^2 + \frac{B}{6}\,T^3 + \sum_{i=2}^{\infty} \frac{C_i}{(i+1)\,(i+2)}\,T^{i+2}\,.$$

We write again $(-\,\dot{m})c^2 = 2Lm_e = \text{const} = 2K$ and

$$(-\,\dot{m})c = ma = m(A + Bt + \sum_{i=2}^{\infty} C_i t^i)\,.$$

Inserting c from the second equation into the first one and rearranging,
we obtain

$$-\,\dot{m}/m^2 = a^2/2K\,,$$

or by integration

$$2K(1/m_e - 1/m_0) = \int_0^T a^2\,dt\,.$$

Let us call the integral U and perform the integration:

$$U = \int_0^T a^2\, dt = A^2 T + ABT^2 + \left(\frac{B^2}{3} + \frac{2}{3} AC_2\right)T^3 + \frac{1}{2}(AC_3 + BC_2)T^4$$

$$+ \sum_{n=4}^{\infty} \frac{2AC_n + 2BC_{n-1} + \sum\limits_{i=2}^{n-2} C_i C_{n-i}}{n+1}\, T^{n+1}.$$

The problem can be restated quite simply: Determine A, B, C_i so that S is a maximum, keeping U constant.

The solution follows from the set of equations

$$\frac{\partial}{\partial A}(S + \lambda U) = 0,$$

$$\frac{\partial}{\partial B}(S + \lambda U) = 0,$$

$$\frac{\partial}{\partial C_i}(S + \lambda U) = 0, \qquad \text{for} \quad 2 \le i \le \infty.$$

Together with $U = 2K(1/m_e - 1/m_0)$ there are a sufficient number of equations to determine A, B, C_2, C_3, ..., C_∞, and the Lagrangian multiplier λ. We find that $C_2 = 0$, $C_3 = 0$, ..., $C_\infty = 0$; $A = -T/2\lambda$; $B = 1/2\lambda$. Therefore, $a = -(1/2\lambda)(T - t)$, from which we see that $\lambda < 0$. Inserting the result for the acceleration a, we have

$$U = \frac{1}{12\lambda^2}\, T^3 \qquad \text{and} \qquad S = -\frac{1}{6\lambda}\, T^3.$$

From these we easily obtain, introducing again $m_0/m_e = 1 + x$,

$$S = \left[\frac{2}{3} L \frac{x}{1+x}\right]^{1/2} T^{3/2},$$

or rearranging

$$T^3 L^{1/2} = \left(1.5 \frac{1+x}{x}\right)^{1/3} S^{2/3}.$$

Interestingly, now we have $x_{\text{opt}} = \infty$. For $x = \infty$, we have $TL^{1/3} = 1.144 S^{2/3}$, and for $x = 1.79$, $TL^{1/3} = 1.328 S^{2/3}$.

In both cases, the time T for the same S and L values comes out to be considerably shorter (32.7 and 21.8%, respectively) than for the optimum constant jet speed case. Taking the same time T, then x is only 0.44 instead of 1.79, or the required mass ratio is only 1.44 instead of 2.79, or the cutoff mass m_e equals $m_0/2.79$ in one and $m_0/1.44$ in the other case—an increase of 94%.

This represents an upper limit for the increase in payload carried by the rigorously optimized vehicle. In practice, the more complicated engine (variable exhaust speed!) and the more complicated control system will diminish the gain in payload, may decrease reliability, or may be otherwise disadvantageous, to such a degree that the potential 94% payload increase is not sufficient to render the "optimum vehicle" attractive.

The optimum exhaust speed program follows:

$$c = \frac{2Lm_e}{ma} = \frac{2Lm_e}{m_0}\frac{m_0}{m}\frac{(-2\lambda)}{T-t};$$

inserting λ we obtain

$$c = \left(\frac{2LT}{x}\right)^{1/2}\frac{1}{[3(1+x)]^{1/2}}\frac{m_0/m}{1-t/T}.$$

For the case of constant exhaust speed, the best choice is

$$c = \left(\frac{2LT}{x}\right)^{1/2}.$$

Thus we have in the case of variable exhaust speed a considerably smaller value initially, and $c \to \infty$ as $t \to T$. Since for an ion engine $c \sim V^{1/2}$, where V is the ion acceleration voltage, the variation of the voltage is even greater than that of the exhaust speed. Transformation at the high electric energy levels required is, from weight considerations, disadvantageous. A better possibility might be to have a number of smaller generators, which are connected in a controllable manner in series or in parallel. Still, this does not solve the ion-optical problem, and the weight of the system would be determined by the most unfavorable working condition encountered.

The simpler case of optimizing the acceleration a for maximum speed at cutoff shall be left to the interested reader. The result is $a = $ constant. It might be mentioned that the case of optimized constant acceleration is quite a good solution—but not optimum—to maximize S, leading to

$$S = \left(\frac{L}{2}\frac{x}{1+x}\right)^{1/2}T^{3/2}.$$

Let us now turn to some questions of flight mechanics of low-acceleration vehicles in order to find required velocities for some missions, flight times, etc.

2.4 Flight Mechanics of Low Acceleration Vehicles

2.4,1 Introduction (Fox, 1961)

In Sec. 5 of the last chapter of Vol. 1 it was shown that if a vehicle is in a circular orbit with the local gravitational acceleration equal to g, and if the vehicle goes from circular speed to about parabolic speed under the influence of rocket thrust, with constant acceleration a, then the approximation of high thrust systems is, in terms of energy, applicable for $a/g \geq 0.4$.

The question as to what acceleration is to be called low can be answered similarly: when in the case just described of an escape from a circular orbit, several—perhaps 5—revolutions around the central body are necessary to reach escape conditions, we will call the acceleration low. The circular speed is $V_K = (gr)^{1/2}$. The period is $T = 2\pi r/V_K = 2\pi(r/g)^{1/2}$. Thus, the condition of low acceleration can be written as

$$aT = a\, 2\pi(r/g)^{1/2} \leq \tfrac{1}{5}(2^{1/2} - 1)(gr)^{1/2},$$

or, approximately, $a/g \leq 10^{-2}$. Intermediate accelerations between the "high" and "low" limits are difficult to treat analytically. The solar gravitational acceleration in Earth vicinity is only 5.92×10^{-3} m/sec², or expressed in units of Earth-surface gravitational acceleration, about 6.05×10^{-4}. Therefore, accelerations of $a > 2.4 \times 10^{-4}g_0$ have to be considered as "high" during interplanetary flights, and only $a < 6 \times 10^{-6}g_0$ is "low." The actual accelerations of the outlined ion-propelled vehicles were about $10^{-4}g_0$, which is definitely low in near-Earth space. For the interplanetary phase, this acceleration is intermediate between high and low. Fortunately, these complications will not increase the difficulty of estimating required speed.

2.4,2 Two-Body Problem—Powered Trajectory from Circular Orbit to Escape

Only the planar case shall be investigated. (See Fig. 2.35.) Rewriting Eq. (4.14) of Vol. 1,

$$\ddot{r} - r\dot{\varphi}^2 + \gamma\frac{M}{r^2} = \frac{f}{m}\cos\beta\,,$$

$$r\ddot{\varphi} + 2\dot{r}\dot{\varphi} = \frac{1}{r}\frac{d}{dt}(r^2\dot{\varphi}) = \frac{f}{m}\sin\beta\,. \tag{2.17}$$

The term $\gamma(M/r^2)$ can be written as $g_0(r_0/r)^2$, where the index zero marks some reference condition (often initial condition).

The problem is to reach escape condition from an initial circular orbit. Four different cases of choices for β will be described.

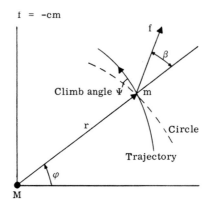

FIG. 2.35. Trajectory parameters for escape from circular orbit. f, thrust; β, thrust direction; r, radius vector; m, vehicle mass; c, exhaust speed; M, central mass; γ, constant in Newton's gravitational law.

2.4,2,1 Circumferential Thrust, or $\beta = \frac{1}{2}\pi$ (Tsien, 1953)

The free variable angle β is chosen so that $\beta = \frac{1}{2}\pi$. Furthermore, introducing the new variables $\varrho = r/r_0$, $\tau = (g_0/r_0)^{1/2}t$, $f/m = ag_0$, we have

$$\varrho'' = \varrho\varphi'^2 - \frac{1}{\varrho^2}$$

$$\frac{d}{d\tau}(\varrho^2\varphi') = a\varrho \qquad (2.18)$$

$$a = -\frac{c}{(g_0r_0)^{1/2}}\frac{d}{d\tau}(\ln m).$$

In Eq. (2.18), φ' stands for $(d\varphi/d\tau)$, etc. Let us treat a as a constant. This could be realized by varying $\dot{m}$ accordingly. If c is variable, this analysis is no longer valid.

If both $\dot{m}$ and c are kept constant, a is nearly constant, as shown by the numerical examples previously given.

If index 0 marks the initial and index f the final condition, then from the last equation of Eq. (2.18):

$$a\tau\Big|_0^f = \frac{c}{g_0r_0}\ln\left(\frac{m_0}{m_f}\right)$$

or

$$a(t_f - t_0) = \Delta v = c \ln \left(\frac{m_0}{m_f} \right).$$

We have again the familiar basic rocket equation.

For the remaining equations, the initial conditions are

$$\varrho_0 = 1, \qquad \tau_0 = 0, \qquad (\varphi')_0 = \frac{2\pi}{T} \left(\frac{r_0}{g_0} \right)^{1/2} = 1, \qquad (\varrho')_0 = 0.$$

From the first of Eq. (2.18),

$$(\varrho'')_0 = 0.$$

Elimination of φ' between the two equations gives

$$\frac{d}{d\tau} (\varrho^3 \varrho'' + \varrho)^{1/2} = a\varrho. \tag{2.19}$$

Solution for high acceleration. Presumably, $\varrho \approx 1$ will be an acceptable first approximation. The differential equation is simply

$$\frac{d}{d\tau} (\varrho'' + 1)^{1/2} = a,$$

or, with C as a constant of integration,

$$\varrho'' + 1 = C^2 + 2Ca\tau + a^2\tau^2.$$

From $(\varrho'')_0 = 0$, we obtain $C = \pm 1$, and

$$\varrho'' = \pm 2a\tau + a^2\tau^2$$

or

$$\varrho = C_2 + C_1\tau \pm \frac{a}{3} \tau^3 + \frac{a^2}{12} \tau^4,$$

$$\varrho_0 = 1 \to C_2 = 1 \qquad \text{and} \qquad (\varrho')_0 = 0 \to C_1 = 0.$$

For acceleration, ϱ will increase. Thus, finally,

$$\varrho = 1 + \frac{a}{3} \tau^3 + \frac{a^2}{12} \tau^4 + \cdots.$$

By substitution in the differential equation, higher terms can be determined:

$$\varrho = 1 + \frac{a}{3} \tau^3 + \frac{a^2}{12} \tau^4 - \frac{a^3}{160} \tau^5 - \cdots \tag{2.20}$$

The cutoff condition (for parabolic speed) is

$$\text{Energy } E = \frac{v^2}{2} - g_0 \frac{r_0{}^2}{r} = 0$$

or

$$\varrho \frac{v^2}{g_0 r_0} = 2 .$$

Thus,

$$v^2 = \dot{r}^2 + (r\dot{\varphi})^2$$

$$= r_0{}^2 \dot{\varrho}^2 + r_0{}^2 (\varrho \dot{\varphi})^2$$

$$= r_0{}^2 \varrho'^2 \frac{g_0}{r_0} + r_0{}^2 (\varrho \varphi')^2 \frac{g_0}{r_0} ,$$

or

$$\frac{v^2}{g_0 r_0} = \varrho'^2 + \varrho^2 \varphi'^2 .$$

Since

$$\varrho^2 \varphi'^2 = \varrho \varrho'' + \frac{1}{\varrho} ,$$

we have

$$\frac{v^2}{g_0 r_0} = \varrho'^2 + \varrho \varrho'' + \frac{1}{\varrho} ,$$

and the cutoff condition is

$$\varrho^2 \varrho'' + \varrho \varrho'^2 = 1 . \tag{2.21}$$

Putting Eq. (2.20) in (2.21) and solving gives approximately

$$a\tau_f = (\sqrt{2} - 1) + \frac{0.002349}{a^2} - \frac{0.00004791}{a^4} + \cdots . \tag{2.22}$$

The expression $a\tau_f = [a g_0 / (g_0 r_0)^{1/2}] t_f$ is nothing but the required speed, expressed in units of initial circular speed. It is, indeed, slightly larger than the ideal value of $2^{1/2} - 1$, and this excess represents the gravity loss for this maneuver. The climb angle follows from $\tan \Psi = \dot{r}/r\dot{\varphi} = \varrho' / (\varrho \varrho'' + 1/\varrho)^{1/2}$, and $\tan \Psi_f \approx 0.19/a$.

Solution for low acceleration. Equation (2.19) is approximated by

$$\frac{d}{d\tau} \varrho^{1/2} = a\varrho$$

or

$$\frac{1}{2} \frac{d\varrho}{\varrho^{3/2}} = a\, d\tau$$

$$\varrho = \frac{1}{(1 - a\tau)^2} \; .$$

From this equation

$$\varrho' = \frac{2a}{(1 - a\tau)^3} \quad \text{and} \quad \varrho'' = \frac{6a^2}{(1 - a\tau)^4} \; .$$

This does not fulfill $\varrho_0' = 0$, $\varrho_0'' = 0$. But we can take

$$\varrho = \frac{1}{(1 - a\tau)^2} - 2a\tau - 3a^2\tau^2 \; . \tag{2.23}$$

This fulfills the initial conditions, and Eq. (1.19) was only solved approximately anyhow. This improvement has little practical significance, since towards the end $a\tau \to 1$. Inserting the simpler solution in Eq. (2.21) we obtain

$$a\tau_f = 1 - 10^{1/8}a^{1/4} = 1 - (3.16a)^{1/4} = 1 - 1.33a^{1/4}. \tag{2.24}$$

Inserting in Eq. (2.23),

$$\varrho_f \approx \frac{1}{(3.16a)^{1/2}} \; .$$

Except towards the end, ϱ' is small. Therefore, the speed is approximately always horizontal, and its square has a magnitude

$$(r\dot\varphi)^2 = g_0 r_0 \varrho^2 \varphi'^2$$

$$= g_0 r_0 \left(\varrho\varrho'' + \frac{1}{\varrho} \right)$$

$$= g_0 r_0 \left[\frac{6a^2}{(1 - a\tau)^6} + 1 + a^2\tau^2 - 2a\tau \right]$$

$$\approx g_0 r_0 [1 - 2a\tau]$$

$$\approx g_0 r_0 \left(\frac{1}{\varrho} \right)$$

$$= \frac{g_0 r_0^2}{r} \; ,$$

for small a, τ.

This shows that the vehicle stays approximately in a circular orbit with approximately circular speed. This is certainly a very simple result. The climb angle Ψ can be estimated

$$\tan \Psi = \frac{\dot{r}}{r\dot{\varphi}} = \frac{\varrho'}{(\varrho\varrho'' + 1/\varrho)^{1/2}} \approx 2a \ ,$$

or Ψ is usually less than a few minutes of arc. Assuming the climb angle is constant, the trajectory follows from $dr/r \, d\varphi = \tan \Psi$ to be $r/r_0 = \exp(\tan \Psi)\varphi$.

Thus, crudely, with $\varrho_f = 1/(3.16a)^{1/2}$,

$$\frac{1}{2} \ln \left(\frac{1}{3.16a} \right) = \varphi_f \, 2a \ ,$$

or the total number of revolutions is

$$n_f \approx \frac{\varphi_f}{2\pi} = \frac{\ln(1/3.16a)}{8\pi a} \ . \tag{2.25}$$

This estimate will give a high value, because the trajectory steepens toward the end.

2.4,2,2 Radial Thrust, or $\beta = 0$ (Copeland, 1959)

The equivalent of Eq. (2.18) is

$$\varrho'' = \varrho\varphi'^2 - \frac{1}{\varrho^2} + a \ ,$$
$$\frac{d}{d\tau}(\varrho^2\varphi') = 0 \ . \tag{2.26}$$

Immediately $\varrho^2\varphi' = \text{const} = (\varrho^2\varphi')_0 = 1$; thus

$$\varrho'' - \frac{1}{\varrho^3} + \frac{1}{\varrho^2} = a \ .$$

Let us write for the moment $a = a'/\varrho^2$; then

$$\varrho'' - \frac{1}{\varrho^3} + \frac{1-a'}{\varrho^2} = 0 \ ,$$

which can be integrated to give

$$\varrho'^2 = 2\,\frac{1-a'}{\varrho} - \frac{1}{\varrho^2} + (2a' - 1), \tag{2.27}$$

fulfilling the above differential equation and the initial condition that $(\varrho')_0 = 0$ for $\varrho_0 = 1$. Equation (2.27) will be used later.

The above differential equation can be integrated also for $a = $ constant, and gives, observing the initial condition $\varrho_0' = 0$,

$$\varrho'^2 = \frac{2}{\varrho} - \frac{1}{\varrho^2} + 2a(\varrho - 1) - 1 . \tag{2.28}$$

For a parabolic speed the cutoff equation is again

$$\varrho(\varrho'^2 + \varrho^2\varphi'^2) = 2 ,$$

or here

$$\varrho\left(\varrho'^2 + \frac{1}{\varrho^2}\right) = 2 ,$$

or

$$\varrho_{f \text{ par}} = 1 + \frac{1}{2a} \quad \text{and} \quad \varrho_f{}'_{\text{ par}} = \frac{1 + 1/a}{(1 + 1/2a)^2} . \tag{2.29}$$

Generally,

$$\frac{v^2}{g_0 r_0} = \varrho'^2 + \varrho^2\varphi'^2$$

$$= \varrho'^2 + \frac{1}{\varrho^2}$$

$$= \frac{2}{\varrho} + 2a(\varrho - 1) - 1 ,$$

and

$$\left(\frac{v^2}{g_0 r_0}\right)_{f \text{ par}} = \frac{4a}{2a + 1} = \frac{2}{\varrho_{f \text{ par}}} . \tag{2.30}$$

From Eq. (2.28), we calculate the altitude ϱ_{crit} for which $\varrho' = 0$. It follows that

$$\varrho_{\text{crit } 1} = 1 \quad \text{and} \quad \varrho_{\text{crit } 2,3} = \frac{1 \pm (1 - 8a)^{1/2}}{4a} .$$

The symbol $\varrho_{\text{crit } 1}$ indicates only the initial condition. The symbol $\varrho_{2,3}$ indicates that, for the outgoing case $a > 0$ only for $a \leq 1/8$, and for the ingoing case $a < 0$, always at least one positive real "critical radius" exists. Only for $8a > 1$ is there no real radius $\varrho > 1$, for which $\varrho' = 0$; in other words, the outward motion is then definitely not bounded, since nowhere is $\varrho' = 0$.

To understand the critical radii $\varrho_{\text{crit }2,3}$, let us plot ϱ'^2 or, because it is simpler,

$$A = \frac{\varrho^2 \varrho'^2}{\varrho - 1} = 2a\varrho^2 - (\varrho - 1).$$

In order to have a possible case of motion, we have to demand that, for the outgoing case, $a > 0$, $\varrho > 1$, so that $\varrho^2\varrho'^2/(\varrho - 1) > 0$, and similarly

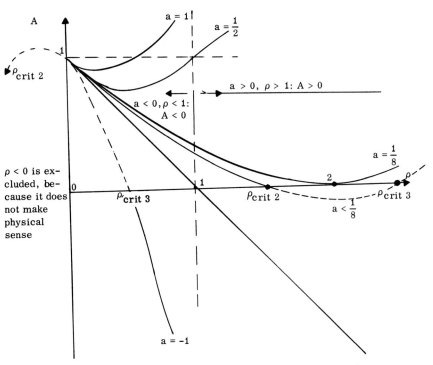

FIG. 2.36. Plots of a, ϱ, and A for low acceleration motion.

for the ingoing case, $a < 0$, $\varrho < 1$, so that $\varrho^2\varrho'^2/(\varrho - 1) < 0$. (See Fig. 2.36.) Now it is evident that:

(1) For large outward accelerations, e.g., $a = 1$, there is an $A > 0$ for all $\varrho > 1$, or in other words, no limit exists for the motion.

(2) For small outward acceleration, e.g., $a = \frac{1}{16}$, for $\varrho > 1$ we find $A < 0$ for $\varrho_{\text{crit }2} < \varrho < \varrho_{\text{crit }3}$, or, a vehicle starting at $\varrho = 1$ cannot get beyond $\varrho_{\text{crit }2}$. The motion is bounded. Evidently, the case $a = \frac{1}{8}$ is the limit between "high" and "low" accelerations. The question of whether or not for

$a = \frac{1}{8}$ the value $\varrho = 2$ is a boundary requires more study. This follows later—see Eq. (2.33).

(3) For vehicles going inward $(a < 0)$ from $\varrho = 1$, the value $\varrho_{\text{crit 3}}$ is a boundary, as $A > 0$ for $0 \leq \varrho < \varrho_{\text{crit 3}}$.

This is very peculiar behavior since, in spite of a constant continuous radial acceleration, the vehicle cannot get beyond $\varrho_{\text{crit 2}}$ (outward, $a < \frac{1}{8}$) or $\varrho_{\text{crit 3}}$ (inward). How can this be understood? The behavior of ϱ' gives the clue: the vehicle starts to go in an ellipse-like orbit with ϱ' being in the direction of the acceleration, say, outward as is shown in Fig. 2.37. The thrust acceleration a is split into two components a_v parallel to the velocity, and a_n normal to the velocity. It can be seen that a_v tends to increase the speed and thus the energy. After some time, $\varrho' = 0$; that is, a kind of apocenter is reached.

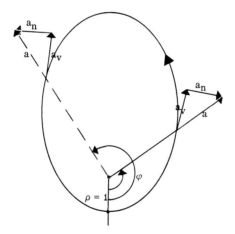

Fig. 2.37. Diagram showing low radial acceleration parameters.

Thereafter, a_v is antiparallel to the velocity, i.e., the thrust actually brakes. Thus it can be understood that in this case the vehicle cannot go further than a certain limiting value, because the changing accelerating and braking periods prevent the transfer of more than a certain limited amount of energy to the vehicle.

With the physical understanding of the phenomenon it is not difficult to show how the limitation can be bypassed: we need only go from $+ a$ to zero, or to $- a$ at the apocenter (and correspondingly from $- a$ to zero or $+ a$ at the pericenter for the inward-going case), thus avoiding the braking phase, or converting it to an accelerating phase. In doing this, we require that the vehicle does not impact on the central body.

From Eq. (2.28), we have

$$\tau = \int_1^\varrho \frac{\varrho \, d\varrho}{[(\varrho - 1)(2a\varrho^2 - \varrho + 1)]^{1/2}}, \qquad (2.31)$$

and an approximate solution for $\varrho - 1$ that is small compared to one, and to $2a$, and $a \geq 0$, proceeds as follows:

$$\tau = \frac{1}{(2a)^{1/2}} \int_0^{\varrho-1} \frac{dx}{x^{1/2}[1 - x/2a(x+1)^2]^{1/2}}$$

$$\approx \frac{1}{(2a)^{1/2}} \int_0^{\varrho-1} \frac{dx}{x^{1/2}[1 - x/2a(1+2x)]^{1/2}}$$

$$\approx \frac{1}{(2a)^{1/2}} \left[\int_0^{\varrho-1} \frac{dx \, \{1 + [x/4a(1+2x)] \cdots\}}{x^{1/2}} \right]$$

$$\approx \frac{1}{(2a)^{1/2}} \left[\int_0^{\varrho-1} dx \left\{ \frac{1}{x^{1/2}} + \frac{1}{4a}(x^{1/2} - 2x^{3/2}) + \cdots \right\} \right].$$

The integrals can be easily evaluated and give the result

$$a\tau = [2a(\varrho-1)]^{1/2} + \frac{[2a(\varrho-1)]^{3/2}}{24a^2} - \frac{[2a(\varrho-1)]^{5/2}}{40a^3} + \cdots . \quad (2.32)$$

For escape, we have, from Eq. (2.29), $(\varrho_{f \text{ par}} - 1) \, 2a = 1$; thus[1]

$$(a\tau)_{\text{esc}} = \frac{\text{velocity requirement for escape}}{\text{circular speed in initial orbit}} = 1 + \frac{1}{24a^2} - \frac{1}{40a^3} \cdots .$$

For a radial kick to reach the escape condition, it follows at once (from the simple consideration that $v_{\text{esc}} = 2^{1/2}v_{\text{circ}}$, regardless of direction) that the required speed for kick is $\Delta/v_{\text{circ}} = 1$. The angles are indicated in Fig. 2.38.

Now back to the special case $a = \frac{1}{8}$ that separates the "high" from "low" accelerations; here Eq. (2.31) becomes

$$\tau = \int_1^\varrho \frac{\varrho \, d\varrho}{[(\varrho - 1)(\frac{1}{4}\varrho^2 - \varrho + 1)]^{1/2}} = \int_1^\varrho \frac{\varrho \, d\varrho}{(\varrho - 1)^{1/2}(1 - \frac{1}{2}\varrho)}.$$

Introducing $\varrho - 1 = x^2$ we get

$$\tau = 4 \int_0^{(\varrho-1)^{1/2}} \frac{1 + x^2}{1 - x^2} \, dx ,$$

[1] Valid for sufficiently large a, possibly $a > 0.5$–1.

which can be integrated in closed form to give

$$\tau = 4 \ln \left[\frac{1 + (\varrho - 1)^{1/2}}{1 - (\varrho - 1)^{1/2}} \right] - 4(\varrho - 1)^{1/2} . \qquad (2.33)$$

Looking at $\varrho \rightarrow 2$ it is seen that $\tau \rightarrow \infty$; it takes an infinite time before the vehicle could pass the "limiting radius" $\varrho_{crit} = 2$, which can be understood considering that for $a = \frac{1}{8}$ and $\varrho = 2$ not only is $\varrho' = 0$, but also $\varrho'' = 0$.

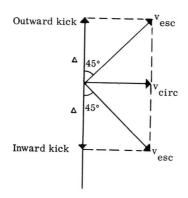

FIG. 2.38. Diagram of conditions for escape.

Thus, we expect an asymptotic approach to ϱ_{crit}. Escape would occur for $\varrho_{f\,par} = 5$, but this distance is not reached in a finite time, for practical purposes, for a constant radial acceleration of $a = \frac{1}{8}$, escape is not possible.

Now consider a special case of radial acceleration, viz, radiation pressure.

What is the radiation pressure upon a reflecting sphere (reflectivity ε)? Per unit area and unit time, the radiation will transport an energy e. (See Fig. 2.39.) Then writing $e = mc^2$ we get, for the impulse $I = mc = e/c$,

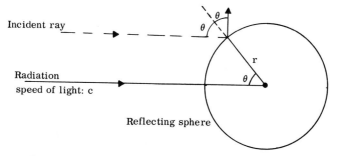

FIG. 2.39. Radiation incident upon reflecting sphere.

and for the impulse change (equal to force per unit area, or pressure) in the direction of the radiation:

$$\text{pressure} = I + \varepsilon I \cos 2\theta;$$

thus, for the radiation force upon the sphere,

$$f = \int_0^{2\pi} (I + \varepsilon I \cos 2\theta) \, 2\pi r (\sin \theta) r \, d\theta \cos \theta.$$

Integrating, $f = \pi r^2 I$, independent of ε! This is a surprising result, but we will not investigate it any further here. The pressure due to solar radiation (with a solar constant of 2 cal/cm² min = 142 mkg/m² sec) is, in Earth vicinity,

$$I = \frac{142}{3 \times 10^8} \frac{\text{m kg sec}}{\text{m}^2 \text{ sec m}} = 4.7 \times 10^{-7} \frac{\text{kg}}{\text{m}^2},$$

or measuring the distance ϱ from the Sun in astronomical units:

$$I = \frac{4.7}{\varrho^2} \times 10^{-7} \frac{\text{kg}}{\text{m}^2}.$$

The weight of an Ehricke sphere (with a radius of r meters) is $0.1272\pi r^2$ kg. Let us assume an extremely light weight sphere, which has no purpose other than to be seen, with a weight of $0.047\pi r^2$ kg. The solar radiation pressure could lead to an acceleration (in Earth's gravitational accelerations) of $(4.7 \times 10^{-7})/(\varrho^2 \times 0.047) = 10^{-5}/\varrho^2$. The gravitational acceleration due to the Sun in Earth vicinity was about 6.05×10^{-4} (Sec. 2.4,1), leading to a "radiation sphere" acceleration expressed in this unit of solar gravitational acceleration of

$$a = \frac{10^{-5}}{6.05 \times 10^4} \frac{1}{\varrho^2} = \frac{1.65}{100} \frac{1}{\varrho^2} = \frac{a'}{\varrho^2}.$$

When this sphere is brought, by some vehicle, into the Earth orbit and released there, Eq. (2.27) describes the sphere under the influence of the solar radiation pressure.[1] (This is a simple example of "solar sailing.") To find how far out the visibility sphere would go, we put $\varrho' = 0$ in Eq. (2.27) and solve for ϱ. (This is the same procedure which gave us $\varrho_{\text{crit 2,3}}$ in the case of constant radial acceleration.) It is found that

----

[1] The motion can be understood as a simple two-body problem, with properly reduced central mass.

$$\varrho_{\text{crit } 1} = 1 \qquad \text{(initial condition)},$$

$$\varrho_{\text{crit } 2} = \frac{1}{1 - 2a'} \ .$$

Therefore, escape from the solar system is possible[1] only for $a' \geq \frac{1}{2}$. To go from Earth to Mars, or from 1 to 1.524 a.u., a value $a' = 0.172$ is required. With the already optimistic value $a' = 1.65/100$, the sphere goes out only to $\varrho_{\text{crit } 1} \approx 1.033$ a.u., which is about 5×10^6 km—quite insignificant in interplanetary space.

2.4,2,3 TANGENTIAL THRUST (Benney, 1958; Perkins, 1959; Shi and Eckstein, 1967)

From Eq. (2.17) follow the equations of motion:

$$\varrho'' + \frac{1}{\varrho^2} - \varrho\varphi'^2 = a \frac{\varrho'}{(\varrho'^2 + \varrho^2\varphi'^2)^{1/2}} \ ,$$

and

$$\frac{d}{d\tau}(\varrho^2\varphi') = \varrho a \frac{\varrho\varphi'}{(\varrho'^2 + \varrho^2\varphi'^2)^{1/2}} \ .$$

From Eq. (3.3) of Vol. 1,

$$\dot{v} = -g\cos\beta + \frac{F'}{m} \ ,$$

or here

$$\dot{v} = -g_0\left(\frac{r_0}{r}\right)^2 \frac{\dot{r}}{v} + ag_0 \ .$$

This can be written, measuring v in units of $(g_0 r_0)^{1/2}$,

$$v' = -\frac{\varrho'}{v\varrho^2} + a, \tag{2.34}$$

and the first equation of this section, with $v^2 = \varrho'^2 + \varrho^2\varphi'^2$:

$$\varrho'' = \frac{v^2}{\varrho} - \frac{\varrho'^2}{\varrho} - \frac{1}{\varrho^2} + a\frac{\varrho'}{v} \ .$$

Assuming that ϱ'^2 and $a\,\varrho'$ are negligibly small,

$$\varrho'' \approx \frac{v^2}{\varrho} - \frac{1}{\varrho^2} \ ,$$

[1] For $a' = \frac{1}{2}$, the time to reach escape condition is infinitely long.

we get, by expansion around the reference condition given below,

$$\varrho_0{}'' + \Delta\varrho'' = \left(\frac{v_0{}^2}{\varrho_0} - \frac{1}{\varrho_0{}^2}\right) + \frac{2v_0}{\varrho_0}\,\Delta v - \frac{v_0{}^2}{\varrho_0{}^2}\,\Delta\varrho + \frac{2\,\Delta\varrho}{\varrho_0{}^3}\,.$$

The reference condition is the initial condition:

$$v_0 = \varrho_0 = 1, \qquad \varrho_0{}'' = \frac{v_0{}^2}{\varrho_0} - \frac{1}{\varrho_0{}^2} = 0, \qquad \Delta\varrho'' = 2\,\Delta v + \Delta\varrho\,.$$

Similarly,

$$\Delta v = a\,\Delta\tau - \Delta\varrho\;;$$

inserting $\Delta\tau$ and requiring that it be the independent variable,

$$\Delta\varrho'' = \frac{d^2(\Delta\varrho)}{d(\Delta\tau)^2} = 2a\,\Delta\tau - \Delta\varrho\,.$$

Integrated,

$$\Delta\varrho = C_1 \sin \Delta\tau + C_2 \cos \Delta\tau + 2a\,\Delta\tau\,.$$

Initial conditions are

$$(\Delta\varrho)_0 = 0 \rightarrow C_2 = 0\,,$$

$$\left(\frac{d(\Delta\varrho)}{d(\Delta\tau)}\right)_0 = 0 \rightarrow C_1 = -2a\,.$$

So, finally,

$$\Delta\varrho = 2a(\Delta\tau - \sin \Delta\tau). \qquad (2.35)$$

In this equation, the meaning of $\Delta\tau$ is very simple: we had

$$\Delta\tau = \left(\frac{g_0}{r_0}\right)^{1/2} \Delta t = \frac{(g_0 r_0)^{1/2}}{r_0}\,\Delta t = \frac{v_0\,\Delta t}{r_0}\,,$$

which equals, for circular orbits, the true anomaly φ. Inserting this result in the previous equation, $\Delta v = a\,\Delta\tau - \Delta\varrho$, we have

$$\Delta v = -a(\Delta\tau - 2 \sin \Delta\tau). \qquad (2.36)$$

Equations (2.35) and (2.36) show that, besides the "mean" path, some oscillations occur. Neglecting them, let us turn to the secular parts only:

$$\Delta\varrho = 2a\,\Delta\tau \qquad \text{and} \qquad \Delta v = -a\,\Delta\tau = -\frac{\Delta\varrho}{2}\,.$$

Using the definition,

$$\Delta v_{id} = a \, \Delta \tau = - \, \Delta v ,$$

or the speed requirement is

$$v_{id} = v_{initial} - v_{final} .$$

The initial conditions are $\varrho_0 = 1$ and $v_0 = 1$; circular speed can be written as

$$v_k = \frac{1}{\varrho^{1/2}} ,$$

or

$$dv_k = - \frac{1}{2\varrho^{3/2}} \, d\varrho = - \frac{d\varrho}{2} \quad \text{for} \quad \varrho_0 = 1 .$$

Therefore, the new orbit

$$\varrho_1 = \varrho_0 + \Delta\varrho, \qquad v_1 = v_0 + \Delta v$$

will again be a circular one, and thus can be utilized to start again, putting the new initial conditions $\varrho_1 = 1$, $v_1 = 1$, going to the new circular orbit ϱ_2, v_2, etc. Thus, the vehicle moves in a near-circular orbit forever:

$$v^2\varrho = 1 . \tag{2.37}$$

We have the following simple results:

(1) The vehicle starting with a constant low tangential acceleration to leave a circular orbit spirals out, staying—disregarding some oscillations—approximately in a circular orbit, as long as the acceleration measured in local accelerations of gravity is low (smaller than a few percent).

(2) The velocity requirement is equal to the difference between the circular speeds at the initial and the final positions, with the requirement that the acceleration be low.

(3) Duration of the low-acceleration maneuver can be found by dividing the velocity requirement by the acceleration.

These approximations become poor when the acceleration is no longer low in comparison to the local acceleration of gravity, in spiraling out from a central mass; even a "low-acceleration system" will finally assume the character of a high-acceleration system, when the local gravitational acceleration becomes sufficiently small.

A simple verification preceeds as follows: potential energy in a circular orbit is given by

$$- E_{\text{pot}} = \gamma \frac{M}{r}, \qquad \frac{dE_{\text{pot}}}{dr} = \gamma \frac{M}{r^2};$$

and the equation for the kinetic energy in a circular orbit is

$$E_{\text{kin}} = \tfrac{1}{2} v_k{}^2 = \frac{1}{2} \gamma \frac{M}{r}, \qquad \frac{dE_{\text{kin}}}{dr} = - \frac{1}{2} \gamma \frac{M}{r^2}.$$

In words, if a motion proceeds such that the vehicle remains in a circular orbit, then the change in total energy is just equal to the negative of the change of kinetic energy, or if v_k stands for actual speed and v_{id} for ideal speed, then the total energy is $\tfrac{1}{2} v_{\text{id}}^2$, and $dv_{\text{id}} = - dv_k$.

Equation (2.34) can be rewritten as

$$v \, dv + \frac{d\varrho}{\varrho^2} - av \, d\tau = 0 ,$$

or integrated with s being the flight path lengths

$$\frac{1}{2} v^2 = \frac{1}{\varrho} + as + \text{const,}$$

or, since for $v = 1$, $\varrho = 1$, we have $s = 0$,

$$v^2 = \frac{2}{\varrho} + 2as - 1 . \qquad (2.38)$$

Writing $v_{\text{esc}}^2 = 2/\varrho$ we get simply

$$2as_{\text{esc}} = 1.$$

Knowing that the vehicle always has circular speed,

$$v^2 \approx \frac{1}{\varrho} ,$$

$$2as \approx 1 - \frac{1}{\varrho} ,$$

$$\frac{d\varrho}{ds} = \varrho^2 \, 2a \approx 2a .$$

For the logarithmic spiral resulting from circumferential thrust,

$$\varrho \approx \exp(2a\varphi),$$

or, for n revolutions,

$$s = \int_0^{n\,2\pi} \varrho \, d\varphi \approx \frac{1}{2a} \left[\exp(4\pi n a) - 1 \right],$$

or putting $n = n_f$ for escape

$$4\pi n_f a \approx \ln 2 \qquad \text{or} \qquad n_f \approx \frac{\ln 2}{4\pi a} \, ;$$

hence

$$\frac{n_f}{2} = \frac{\ln 2}{8\pi a}, \qquad \varrho_{n_f/2} = \exp[2a \times (2\pi \ln 2)/8\pi a] = 2^{1/2},$$

$$\varrho_{n_f/2}^2 = 2.$$

Thus, as a better approximation,

$$\frac{d\varrho}{ds} \approx 4a,$$

and using this result we find

$$n_f \approx \frac{\ln 3}{8\pi a}. \tag{2.39}$$

What is the speed requirement for escape? We know that it is approximately 1, but a somewhat better approximation [similar to Eq. (2.34)] can be found.

Let us introduce the radius vector $r = r(s)$ to describe the flight path. What is the radius of curvature R? Some geometric relations (see Fig. 2.40) which will be useful follow:

$$\Psi = \varphi + \beta \qquad \text{or} \qquad d\Psi = d\varphi + d\beta,$$

$$ds = R \, d\Psi,$$

$$\cos \beta = \frac{dr}{ds}, \qquad \sin \beta = \frac{r \, d\varphi}{ds}.$$

A dynamic equation puts centrifugal force equal to the proper gravitational component:

$$\frac{v^2}{R} = \frac{\gamma M}{r^2} \sin \beta.$$

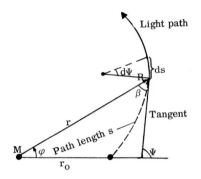

Fɪɢ. 2.40. Low acceleration flight path.

By measuring again the speeds in units of $(g_0 r_0)^{1/2}$ and lengths in units of r_0 we get

$$\frac{v^2}{R} = \frac{1}{\varrho} \frac{d\varphi}{ds} ,$$

or, with $R = ds/d\Psi$,

$$v^2 = \frac{1}{\varrho} \left(\frac{d\Psi}{d\varphi} \right)^{-1} ,$$

$$d\Psi = d\varphi + d\beta \to v^2 = \frac{1}{\varrho} \left(1 + \frac{d\beta}{d\varphi} \right)^{-1} ,$$

$$\beta = \cos^{-1} \left(\frac{d\varrho}{ds} \right) ,$$

$$\frac{d}{d\varphi} \beta = \frac{d}{ds} \left[\cos^{-1} \left(\frac{d\varrho}{ds} \right) \right] \frac{ds}{d\varphi} = - \frac{\varrho (d^2 \varrho/ds^2)}{1 - (d\varrho/ds)^2} .$$

So

$$v^2 = \frac{1 - \varrho'^2}{\varrho (1 - \varrho'^2 - \varrho \varrho'')} ,$$

where ϱ' denotes $d\varrho/ds$, etc. Inserting v^2 from Eq. (2.38),

$$[(2as - 1)\varrho + 1] [1 - \varrho'^2] = [(2as - 1)\varrho + 2] \varrho \varrho'' . \qquad (2.40)$$

Assume we solve this and find $\varrho = \varrho(s)$. From Eq. (2.38) then, by integration,

$$v^2 = \left(\frac{ds}{d\tau} \right)^2 = \frac{2}{\varrho} + 2 as - 1 ,$$

from which follows $s = s(\tau)$. Hence $\varrho(\tau)$ can be determined. The escape condition was $2as_{esc} = 1$; knowing s_{esc} we can get the escape time τ_f from $s = s(\tau)$.

The required speed for escape is, as before, $a\tau_f$, since a constant acceleration a was assumed.

Solution for high acceleration. Introducing a new variable $x = 2as$, the differential equations assume a form that suggests we assume a series solution

$$\varrho = 1 + \sum_{n=1}^{\infty} \frac{\varrho_n}{a^{2n}} \, ,$$

where the ϱ_n are functions of x. Determining the solution and going through lengthy calculations, we get

$$a\tau_f = (2^{1/2} - 1) + \frac{0.001615}{a^2} + \frac{0.000064}{a^4} + \cdots . \qquad (2.41)$$

Comparing Eqs. (2.41) and (2.22), it is found that tangential thrust is somewhat more favorable than circumferential thrust, the gravity loss being about 30% (of the loss in the circumferential case) smaller here.

Solution for low acceleration. Putting $\varrho'' = \varrho' = 0$ in Eq. (2.40),

$$\varrho \approx \frac{1}{1 - 2as} \, .$$

Putting the escape condition $2as_{esc} = 1$ in Eq. (2.40) gives

$$1 - \varrho_f'^2 = 2 \, \varrho_f \, \varrho_f'' \, .$$

We have that

$$\varrho' = + \frac{2a}{(1 - 2as)^2} \quad \text{and} \quad \varrho'' = \frac{8a^2}{(1 - 2as)^3} \, ,$$

or, for escape,

$$1 - \frac{4a^2}{(1 - 2as)^4} = \frac{16a^2}{(1 - 2as)^4}$$

or

$$1 = 20a^2 \varrho_f^4 \, .$$

Thus,

$$\varrho_f = \frac{1}{4(20)^{1/2}} \frac{1}{a^{1/2}} = \frac{1}{(4.47a)^{1/2}}, \qquad (2.42)$$

$$\left(\frac{ds}{d\tau}\right)^2 = \frac{2}{\varrho} + 2as - 1 \approx 1 - 2as,$$

or

$$\left\{\frac{1}{a} - \frac{1}{a}(1 - 2as)^{1/2}\right\}_{\text{esc}} = \tau_f,$$

$$(1 - 2as)_{\text{esc}} = \frac{1}{\varrho_f} = (20)^{1/4} a^{1/2},$$

$$a\tau_f = 1 - 20^{1/8}a^{1/4} = 1 - 1.455a^{1/4}. \qquad (2.43)$$

Comparing with Eq. (2.24), it is seen that again tangential thrust is somewhat more economical than circumferential thrust. By "low acceleration" we always mean "low compared to the local acceleration of gravity." Since, in spiraling out from a circular orbit, the local gravitational acceleration gets smaller in the same manner as $1/\varrho^2$, a low acceleration system will finally become a high acceleration system. From Eq. (2.42), $\varrho_f^{-2} = 4.47a$. Therefore, at cutoff,

$$\frac{\text{vehicle acceleration}}{\text{local gravitational acceleration}} = \frac{1}{4.47} = 0.224,$$

which is just becoming a "high" acceleration. During the "initial low" phase, speed is always circular, i.e., decreases with time; in the final phase, speed goes up again. Thus a minimum is expected. Let us investigate the asymptotic behavior. From Eq. (2.34) we have

$$v' = a - \frac{\varrho'}{v\varrho^2}, \qquad \text{where} \quad v' = \frac{dv}{d\tau}, \text{ etc.,}$$

and

$$\varrho'' = \frac{v^2}{\varrho} - \frac{\varrho'^2}{\varrho} - \frac{1}{\varrho^2} + a\frac{\varrho'}{v}.$$

Introducing the new variables $H = \varrho a^{1/2}$, $W = v/a^{1/4}$, $T = a^{3/4}\tau$, we have

$$\frac{dW}{dT} = 1 - \frac{dH/dT}{WH^2},$$

or, simplifying,

$$\dot{W} = 1 - \frac{\dot{H}}{WH^2} \; ; \tag{2.44a}$$

correspondingly,

$$\ddot{H} = \frac{W^2}{H} - \frac{\dot{H}^2}{H} - \frac{1}{H^2} + \frac{\dot{H}}{W} \; . \tag{2.44b}$$

For a circular orbit, using the old variables, it was valid that $v^2 \varrho = 1$; here, similarly, $W^2 H = 1$.

The differential equations for $\dot{W}$ and $\ddot{H}$ are independant of a. Therefore, all conclusions from them are true for all systems using tangential constant acceleration under the gravitational influence of one mass center, independent of whether the acceleration is "high" or "low."

Now we will turn to the initial circular phase of flight. For low acceleration, we have the relations

$$W^2 H = 1 \; ,$$

$$2\dot{W}WH + W^2\dot{H} = 0 \; ,$$

$$\frac{\dot{H}}{W} = -2\frac{\dot{W}H}{W^2} = -2\dot{W}H^2 = -2\left(H^2 - \frac{\dot{H}}{W}\right) = -2H^2 + 2\frac{\dot{H}}{W} \; ,$$

$$\frac{\dot{H}}{W} = 2H^2 \; .$$

On the other hand,

$$\frac{\dot{H}}{W} = \frac{\varrho'}{v} = \sin\theta \; ,$$

where θ denotes the flight path angle $= \frac{1}{2}\pi$ minus the angle between velocity vector and local vertical. Thus,

$$\sin\theta = \frac{\dot{H}}{W} = 2H^2 = \frac{2}{W^4} \; .$$

Inserting these results in Eq. (2.44), we obtain

$$\dot{W} = 1 - \frac{\dot{H}}{WH^2} = -1 \; .$$

The speed decreases linearly with time. Since $\dot{H} = 2/W^3$, we have

$$\frac{\dot{H}}{\dot{W}} = \frac{-2}{W^3} \; .$$

In a circular orbit, $H = 1/W^2$, or $dH/dW = -2/W^3$. As shown, this is fulfilled. No contradiction develops when we assume that the vehicle stays in a circular orbit.

Let us look at the final (or high acceleration) phase. As $\varrho' \leq v$ always, $\varrho'/v\varrho^2 \leq 1/\varrho^2$; therefore, finally, it is valid that, for large ϱ, $v' \approx a$. From the second equation $\varrho'' \approx a\varrho'/v$. Inserting v and integrating yields

$$\varrho' = v = A + a\tau_1 \quad \text{and} \quad \varrho'' = v'.$$

In the transformed equations[1]:

$$\dot{W} = 1, \qquad \ddot{H} = \frac{\dot{H}}{W} = 1, \qquad W\dot{W} = \dot{H},$$

$$\frac{W^2}{H} = 2,$$

$$\frac{dH}{dW} = \frac{\dot{H}}{\dot{W}} = W,$$

and flight path angle, $\sin\theta = \dot{H}/W = \dot{W} = 1$ for vertical flight.

Whereas in the circular phase for positive dH the corresponding dW was negative, here it is positive. This shows that a minimum of the speed will occur. From numerical analysis, the following tabulation has been found (for $a > 10^{-2}$), with H as the altitude parameter, W as the speed parameter, θ as the flight path angle, and the time (or speed requirement) parameter is $Ta^{1/4}$:

	Condition of end of circular phase	Condition of minimum speed	Escape condition
H	0.30	0.741	0.879
W	1.85	1.494	1.509
Θ	9.4°	33.3°	39.2°
$Ta^{1/4}$	$1-1.85a^{1/4}$	$1-0.960a^{1/4}$	$1-0.809a^{1/4}$

[1] Note that from the equation

$$\ddot{H} = \frac{\ddot{H}}{W} - \frac{\dot{H}}{W^2}\dot{W} = \frac{\dot{H}}{W^2}(1 - \dot{W}) = 0$$

we obtain $\ddot{H} = \text{constant}$. That the constant is 1 follows from physical reasoning.

Let us estimate the speed requirement to obtain a given hyperbolic excess speed v_∞. Naively, we spiral at first from the initial circular orbit to a high-altitude orbit of zero speed, requiring $(Ta^{1/4})_1' = 1$. To this value v_∞ has to be added. Thus, the total speed requirement is simply $v_{req}' = 1 + v_\infty$.

A somewhat more sophisticated escape requirement follows for $(Ta^{1/4})_1 = 1 - 0.809a^{1/4}$, and for the following phase (if $v_\infty \geq 1.509a^{1/4}$) we need $v_\infty - 1.509a^{1/4}$, giving a total requirement of $v_{req} = 1 + v_\infty - 2.318a^{1/4}$, or $v_{req} = v_{req}' - 2.318a^{1/4}$. The reduction of v_{req}' results from a not being infinitely small. The approximation as developed here overestimates the reduction of v_{req}', because the speed $1.509a^{1/4}$ occurs at a finite altitude, and not at infinity. Therefore, only part of this speed can be realized as a contribution to v_∞. From Perkins' analysis follows from the asymptotic behavior of v_∞, approximately valid for $v_\infty > 0$,

$$v_{req} = 1 + v_\infty - 1.746\, a^{1/4} + \frac{0.937\, a^{1/4}}{(1 + v_\infty/a^{1/4})^{2.5}} ,$$

where $v_{req}' = 1 + v_\infty$. The last term can be neglected for $v_\infty \geq 1.75a^{1/4}$. Typical numerical values for launch from a low Earth satellite orbit and $a = 10^{-4}$ are

$$1.746a^{1/4}\, v_{circ} = 1.36 \quad \text{km/sec,}$$

reducing the power flight time by $1360/10^{-4}g_0 = 1.38 \times 10^6$ sec or 16.05 days, out of a total of possibly 12 km/sec and 141.3 days.

2.4,2,4 Optimum Thrust Direction (Lawden, 1958; Long, 1959)

The problem is to escape from a circular orbit with constant acceleration. We looked into three cases of thrust direction programming (circumferential, radial, tangential) and found solutions for either high or low acceleration.

We pose a much more difficult question now: what thrust direction programming will minimize required speed (and—because of constant acceleration—time) and thereby, usually, maximize payload? This problem was answered by Lawden and later extended to the practical problem of reaching higher than parabolic speed by Long. Because of the length of the derivation we will give just the results here. The interested reader should refer to the original literature. (See Fig. 2.41.)

It is easy to visualize that the optimum direction will be near-tangential, because, considering kinetic energy only, $E = \frac{1}{2}v^2$, $\partial E = \mathbf{v}\, d\mathbf{v}$, which is a maximum for $\mathbf{v}$ paralled to $d\mathbf{v}$. This argument does not always hold,

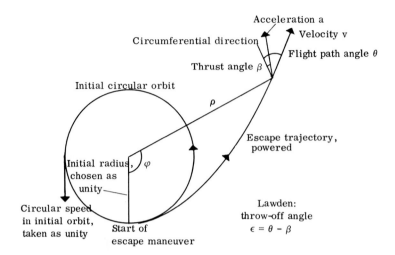

FIG. 2.41. Diagram to show nomenclature for minimizing required speed.

since the potential energy cannot be neglected. It optimizes $\dot{E}$ at every instant, but not over the total propulsive period. [In the restricted three-body problem, Chap. 4 of Vol. 1, Jacobi's constant was $C = E - \omega L$, where E is the total energy, L the angular momentum, and ω the angular speed of the main bodies. It appears to be quite useful to choose β so that $\dot{C} = \dot{E} - \omega \dot{L} = v\dot{v}\cos(\theta - \beta) - \omega\varrho\dot{v}\cos\beta$ is a maximum. This leads to

$$\tan \beta = \frac{\tan \theta}{1 - \omega\varrho/(v\cos\theta)}.$$

Putting $\omega = 0$ we have $\beta = 0$, or tangential thrust. Again, only optimization for every instant, and not over the total propulsive time, has been achieved.]

We know from previous considerations that "burning at altitude" increases gravity losses: so we expect that the optimum thrust direction will be that which will reduce altitude gain somewhat over the tangential case, or we expect $\beta < 0$. Since we found numerically that the tangential program was better than the circumferential one, we conclude that $0 < \beta_{opt} < 0$.

Toward the terminal phase, the motion is described by high-acceleration considerations, as shown before. In the final instant of rocket action, the altitude is immaterial, and we can optimize only by gaining as much energy as possible. Thus, we expect that, in the limit toward the end of the propulsive period, $\beta_{opt} \to 0$.

The actual solution shows this reasoning to be correct. Furthermore, in all cases tangential thrust turns out to be close to the optimum. [It has been shown (Edelbaum, 1961b) that this is also true for escape from an elliptic satellite orbit; for optimized variable exhaust speed and low acceleration, the speed requirement is given by $(\gamma m/a)^{1/2}$.]

Solution for high acceleration. Introducing the symbol w for required speed i.e., $w = a\tau$, and for the final condition $W = a\tau_f$, it can be written for the case of parabolic cutoff condition:

$$\beta = \tfrac{1}{2}\{\tfrac{1}{2}(w+1)^2 - \tfrac{1}{2}2^{1/2}(w+1) + \tfrac{1}{4}(2-2^{1/2})\} \tag{2.45}$$

$$\varrho' = \frac{1}{a}\left\{\frac{1}{2}(w+1)^3 - \frac{1}{4}2^{1/2}(w+1)^2 - \frac{1}{4}(2+2^{1/2})(w+1) + \frac{1}{2}2^{1/2}\right\},$$

$$v\cos\theta = w+1, \qquad \varrho = 1, \qquad \varphi = \frac{1}{a}(w+1),$$

$$\theta = \frac{1}{a}\left\{\frac{1}{2}(w+1)^2 - \frac{1}{4}2^{1/2}(w+1) - \frac{1}{4}(2+2^{1/2}) + \frac{2^{1/2}}{2}(w+1)^{-1}\right\},$$

$$\varepsilon = \frac{2^{1/2}}{4a}\frac{(w+1-2^{1/2})^2}{w+1},$$

$$W = 2^{1/2} - 1 + \frac{1}{a^2}\frac{5\times 2^{1/2}-7}{48} = 0.414214 + \frac{0.001481}{a^2}.$$

Long extended the computations for the case where the cutoff condition is not just parabolic, but hyperbolic. He kept the result $\varrho = 1$ or, in other words, the acceleration is so large that no noticeable altitude is gained during the propulsive period.

The cutoff speed is v_c, parabolic speed v_p, hence the speed remaining at infinity is $v_\infty = (v_c^2 - v_p^2)^{1/2}$ or $v_c = (v_p^2 + v_\infty^2)^{1/2}$. In units of circular speed in the initial orbit, Long introduced $\alpha = (2 + V_\infty^2)^{1/2}$ as a new parameter. Then we have the following results for the optimum thrust program:

$$\varepsilon = \frac{1}{a}\frac{(w+1-\alpha)^2}{2\alpha(w+1)},$$

$$W = (\alpha - 1) + \frac{1}{a^2}\frac{(\alpha-1)^4(\alpha+1)}{24\alpha^2}. \tag{2.46}$$

Correspondingly, for the tangential thrust program we have

$$W = (\alpha - 1) + \frac{1}{a^2}\frac{\alpha^3 + 12\alpha - 16 + 3/\alpha - 12\alpha\ln\alpha}{24};$$

and for the circumferential thrust program we have

$$W = (\alpha - 1) + \frac{1}{a^2} \frac{(\alpha - 1)^4 (2\alpha^2 + 8\alpha + 5)}{180\alpha}.$$

These formulas have been evaluated in Table 2.12, by introducing

$$W = W_0(\alpha) + \frac{1}{a^2} W_1(\alpha) + \cdots,$$

where

$$\alpha = (2 + V_\infty^2)^{1/3}.$$

TABLE 2.12

Speed Requirement Coefficients

| V_∞ | W_0 | W_1 | | |
		Optimum	Tangential	Circumferential
0	0.4142	0.001418	0.001615	0.002349
1	0.7321	0.010897	0.012321	0.022897
$2^{1/2}$	1.0000	0.031250	0.036019	0.080556
$3^{1/2}$	1.2361	0.062951	0.073413	0.190746
2	1.4495	0.105744	0.124258	0.366391

In Eq. (6.16) of Vol. 1, an approximate result $W_1 = 0.00207$ was found for $V_\infty \approx 0$, which is the right order of magnitude. The approximate relationship $W_1 \approx 0.0015 + 0.013 V_\infty^3$ shows that for $V_\infty > \frac{1}{2}$ the acceleration a has to increase in proportion to $V_\infty^{3/2}$ if the gravity loss is to be a given constant value. The symbol a stands for a constant acceleration. We will assume, for the case of nonconstant acceleration, that the symbol a means the average acceleration.

For constant thrust it can be derived that

$$a = a_0 \frac{W/C}{1 - \exp(-W/C)},$$

where a_0 is the initial acceleration and C the exhaust speed in units of initial circular speed. From Table 2.12, we have, approximately,

$$W = W_0 + \frac{0.0015 + 0.013 V_\infty^3}{a^2}.$$

A minimum acceleration may be defined by permitting the gravity losses to be not larger than 10% of the minimum speed requirement, or

$$\frac{0.0015 + 0.013 V_\infty^3}{a^2} < 0.1 W_0 \approx 0.1 (0.42 + 0.35 V_\infty^{3/2}) .$$

From these equations can be derived, putting $W = 1.05 W_0$ in the above equation for a,

$$a_0 > C \left[1 - \exp\left(-\frac{0.44 + 0.37 V_\infty^{3/2}}{C} \right) \right] \frac{(0.0136 + 0.118 V_\infty^3)^{1/2}}{(0.42 + 0.35 V_\infty^{3/2})^{3/2}} .$$

The results for the initial acceleration $a_{0\ min}$ are shown in the following tabulation:

V_∞	$C = 1$	$C = \frac{1}{2}$
0	0.153	0.125
1	0.298	0.215
2	0.451	0.282

Approximate interpolation formula is

$$a_{0\ min} \approx 0.14 + C \times 0.16 V_\infty .$$

From numerical investigations published in NASA TR R–53 it follows that, for $C = 1$, $a_{0\ min} = (0.1 \pm 0.1) + (0.2 \pm 0.08) V_\infty$, which is in good agreement with the equation derived here. Additional information is contained in Figs 2.42 to 2.45 (Stafford and Catelfamo, 1963; Stafford and Harlin, 1963).

Solution for low acceleration. We have

$$\varrho' \approx \frac{2a}{(1 - w)^3} , \qquad V \cos \theta = 1 - w ,$$

$$\varrho = \frac{1}{(1 - w)^2} , \qquad \varphi = \frac{1}{4a} \{ 1 - (1 - w)^4 \} ,$$

or the number of revolutions is

$$n \approx \frac{1}{8\pi a} \{ 1 - (1 - w)^4 \} .$$

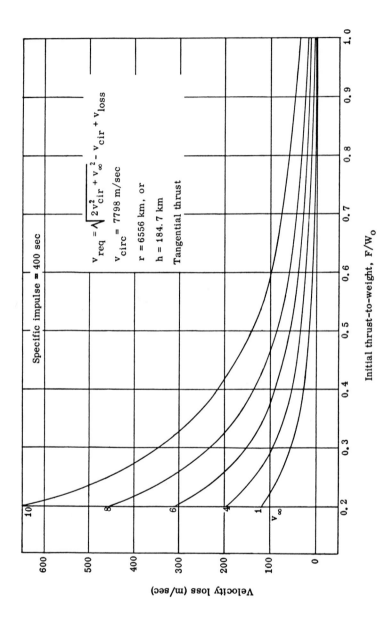

Fig. 2.42. Velocity loss (m/sec) due to gravity vs thrust-to-weight ratio with hyperbolic excess velocity v_∞ (km/sec) as a parameter.

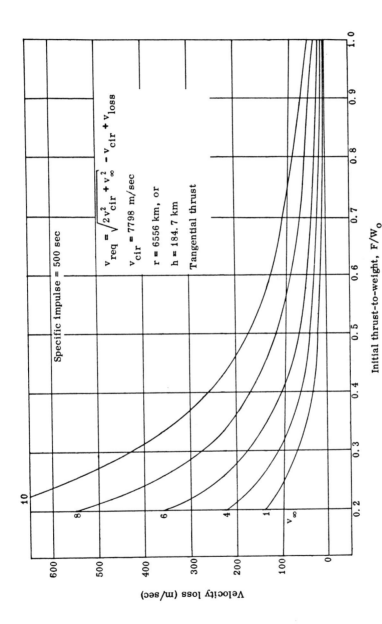

FIG. 2.43. Velocity loss (m/sec) due to gravity vs thrust-to-weight ratio with hyperbolic excess velocity v_∞ (km/sec) as a parameter.

For escape we have $W = 1$ and

$$\beta_{\text{opt}} \approx \tfrac{1}{2}\theta \qquad \text{or} \qquad \varepsilon_{\text{opt}} \approx \tfrac{1}{2}\theta. \tag{2.47}$$

During the final phase, ε_{opt} will go toward zero.

2.4,3 Some Low Acceleration Maneuvers Other Than Escape from a Circular Orbit by Continuous Thrust

2.4,3,1 Inclination Change

This has already been discussed in Sec. 1.4,7. We state the main results:

Problem. Being in a circular orbit, the inclination is to be changed by an angle α. With a high acceleration system, this can be done by one kick $\varDelta v$ of magnitude $\varDelta v / v_c = 2 \sin \tfrac{1}{2}\alpha$. For a continuous low acceleration system the speed requirement for constant altitude is [Eq. (1.32)]

$$\frac{\varDelta v}{v_c} = \pi \frac{\alpha}{2}.$$

The thrust is distributed over the whole trajectory. If time is of no importance, the inclination change can be effected by many (say, n) small nodal kicks of angular change $\varDelta \alpha = \alpha / n$ each:

$$\frac{\varDelta v}{v_c} = 2 \sum_{i=1}^{n} \sin \frac{\varDelta \alpha_i}{2} = 2n \sin \frac{\varDelta \alpha}{2} \to \alpha, \tag{2.48}$$

for large n. This requirement is between the one-kick transfer and the continuous low thrust transfer.

It was shown for the high-acceleration case that when several maneuvers can be lumped together (e.g., circularization and inclination change), usually an advantage occurs insofar as the resultant speed requirement is smaller than the sum of the speed requirements for the single maneuvers. Corresponding advantages can be realized in a low acceleration system by combining maneuvers.

2.4,3,2 Change of Eccentricity (Planar Problem) (Edelbaum and Oickle, 1959; Edelbaum, 1961a)

A vehicle is in a circular orbit [radius r_0, circular speed $v_0 = (g_0 R^2 / r_0)^{1/2}$] around a mass center (radius R, surface gravity g_0). Adding a small radial speed $\varDelta v_r = A(g_0/r_0)^{1/2}(R/r_0)$ results, at a true anomaly of $\tfrac{1}{2}\pi$ later, in an elevation of $\varDelta r = A$, and $\tfrac{3}{2}\pi$ later in a depression of $\varDelta r = A$, compared to the original circular orbit, as derived on p. 76. This corresponds to a small eccentricity $\Delta\varepsilon_r$ such that

$$r_{\max} = r_0 + \Delta r = p(1 + \Delta\varepsilon_r)$$

and

$$r_{\min} = r_0 - \Delta r = p(1 - \Delta\varepsilon_r),$$

where

$$\Delta\varepsilon_r = \frac{\Delta r}{r_0} = \frac{A}{r_0} = \frac{\Delta v_r}{[(g_0/r_0)R^2]^{1/2}} = \frac{\Delta v_r}{v_0} .$$

As seen from the new elliptic orbit, the radial kick has been applied at a true anomaly of $\varphi = \frac{1}{2}\pi$. Therefore, assuming an initial slightly elliptic orbit, $\varphi = \frac{1}{2}\pi$ is the most effective location to change eccentricity by a radial kick. Furthermore, if a_r is a radial acceleration [in units of (length)/(time^2)]

$$\Delta v_r = a_r \, \Delta t ,$$

thus

$$\frac{\Delta\varepsilon_r}{\Delta t} = \frac{a_r}{v_0} \sin\varphi .$$

Likewise, applying, instead of Δv_r, a tangential kick

$$\Delta v_t = A \left(\frac{g_0}{r_0}\right)^{1/2} \frac{R}{r_0}$$

results in an elevation at $\varphi = \pi$ later of $\Delta r = 4A$ (Fig. 1.16):

$$r_{\max} = r_0 + 4A = p\,(1 + \Delta\varepsilon_t) ,$$
$$r_{\min} = r_0 = p\,(1 - \Delta\varepsilon_t) ,$$

from which, in a similar manner as for $\Delta\varepsilon_r/\Delta t$, is found

$$\frac{\Delta\varepsilon_t}{\Delta t} = 2\,\frac{a_t}{v_0}\cos\varphi .$$

Hence,

$$\frac{d\varepsilon}{dt} = \frac{a_r}{v_0}\sin\varphi + 2\,\frac{a_t}{v_0}\cos\varphi . \tag{2.49}$$

The derivation was only approximate. To be exact, assume an elliptic orbit, add a speed $\Delta \mathbf{v} = \mathbf{v}_r + \mathbf{v}_t = (\mathbf{a}_r + \mathbf{a}_t)\Delta t$ at an anomaly φ, compute the change in eccentricity $\Delta \varepsilon$ and get

$$\lim_{\Delta t \to 0} \frac{\Delta \varepsilon}{\Delta t} = \dot{\varepsilon} \ .$$

Equation (2.49) is the result when the initial eccentricity is small.

Introducing the thrust angle β (see Fig. 2.41), we have

$$\dot{\varepsilon} = \frac{a}{v_0} (2 \cos \varphi \cos \beta + \sin \varphi \sin \beta).$$

For an approximate optimization β can be chosen such that $\dot{\varepsilon}(\beta)$ is a maximum, which leads to

$$\tan \beta_{\text{opt}} = \tfrac{1}{2} \tan \varphi. \tag{2.50}$$

This allows, after trigonometric transformations, Eq. (2.49) to be rewritten as

$$\dot{\varepsilon}_{\text{opt}} = 2 \frac{a}{v_0} \left(1 - \frac{3}{4} \sin^2 \varphi\right)^{1/2}. \tag{2.51}$$

So, for an impulsive maneuver, $\dot{\varepsilon}_{\text{opt}} = 2a/v_0$ or $\Delta v/v_0 = 0.5 \, \Delta \varepsilon$, $\varphi = 0$, and $\beta_{\text{opt}} = 0$ is the best possibility. If time is of no concern, a number n of small impulses $\Delta v_{\text{low}} = \Delta v/n$ will give the same result, but the time required is equal to $(n-1)$ periods, which can be very long.

For continuous low thrust, introducing $r_0 \, d\varphi = v_0 \, dt$ we have, with $v_0^2 = g_0 R^2 / r_0 = g_r r_0$, where g_r is the gravitational acceleration at the distance r_0, for the maximum change in eccentricity per revolution:

$$\Delta \varepsilon_{\text{max}} = 8 \left(\frac{a}{g_r}\right) \int_0^{\pi/2} \left(1 - \frac{3}{4} \sin^2 \varphi\right)^{1/2} d\varphi \ .$$

The integral is a complete elliptic integral of the second kind; a crude approximation is to insert $\tfrac{1}{2}$ for $\sin^2 \varphi$ giving

$$\int_0^{\pi/2} \left(\frac{5}{8}\right)^{1/2} d\varphi = 1.24 \ .$$

The exact solution is 1.2111, giving

$$\Delta \varepsilon_{\text{max}} = 9.6888 a/g_r, \tag{2.52}$$

or, with the time of one revolution $T = 2\pi(r/g_r)^{1/2}$, we have

$$\left(\frac{\Delta v}{v_0}\right)_{\min} = 0.65\,\Delta\varepsilon\;;$$

or the ratio of velocity requirements to perform a given small eccentricity change $\Delta\varepsilon$ is

$$\frac{\text{velocity requirement for continuous low thrust}}{\text{velocity requirement for kick}} = 1.3\;.$$

From Edelbaum (1962b) stems the following information:

A transfer is to be made from a circular to a coplanar elliptic orbit, using low acceleration without free-flight periods. Assuming variable thrust and thrust direction, the characteristics of the minimum energy (= minimum time of flight, for constant acceleration) solution are:

(1) Average thrust acceleration during orbit No. i is a_i; then the best choice is to have $a_1 = a_2 = \cdots = a_n$; i.e., constant acceleration.

(2) Transfering between circular orbits, tangential thrust is to be applied; $\Delta v = v_{\text{circ init}} - v_{\text{circ fin}}$.

(3) To obtain an eccentricity of 1, the optimum condition is

$$\frac{\text{semimaior axis final}}{\text{initial circular orbit radius}} \approx 2.4\;,$$

$$\frac{\text{speed requirement}}{\text{initial circular speed}} \approx 0.80\;.$$

(Leaving the first value at 1, the latter is about 0.85, noticeably higher than 0.65, which is valid for small changes in eccentricity.)

2.4,3,3 Escape by Many Small Pericenter Kicks (Camac, 1958; Roberson, 1959).

The velocity requirement for escape from a circular orbit of speed v_0 is, ideally, for one kick $\Delta v_k = (2^{1/2} - 1)v_0$, and for a continuous low acceleration system $\Delta v_L = v_0$. This large loss is due to burning at altitude, and can be avoided:

(1) Operate the low thrust system for a short time, thus putting the vehicle in an ellipse.

(2) At every pericenter passage, give a small kick. This places the apocenter further and further out without materially affecting the pericenter. (The situation is similar to the case of a satellite being braked by at-

mospheric resistance. We find the main drag around pericenter, and the main effect is a reduction in apocenter altitude.) Finally, escape condition is attained.

The penalty connected with this plan has to do with the long time involved, and the possible difficulty of repeated starts and stops of the engine. Two ways of improvement are:

(1) Extend the "ideal pericenter pulse" to burning around pericenter. Ehricke (1956) found that only a small additional loss is incurred when the propulsive period is extended from being at a true anomaly of zero to a true anomaly between $-50°$ and $50°$. This is a total length of $100°$, or about 28% of a full circle, or 28% of one period T_0 can be useful time for propulsion. For elliptic orbits, this ratio gets worse.

About 100 days may be the longest time we want to devote to reach escape condition from a low circular orbit around Earth. This calls for a continuous low acceleration system having an average acceleration (in Earth gravities) of

$$a \approx \frac{8000 \text{ m/sec}}{100 \times 24 \times 3600 \times 9.8} \approx 10^{-4}g .$$

To reach escape condition in the same time with the propulsive periods being at a true anomaly between $-50°$ and $50°$ only, it will be shown after Eq. (2.53) that the acceleration has to be about 40 times as high and the engine system has to allow for an order of a hundred starts and stops, and the speed requirement would drop by about 50%. With the same acceleration of $10^{-4}g$, the number of starts and stops is several thousand, and the time to escape 50 yr.

Therefore, it must be concluded that this scheme does not look promising.[1]

(2) Another possibility would be to have the energy generating system of the engine in continuous operation, and provide for storage (e.g., in batteries) of this energy. Only near pericenter is the total energy utilized in the thrust-producing part of the engine. With no losses in the energy storage system, the same ideal speed aT_0, as provided during one period with the continuous thrust operation, is now provided in the pericenter kick. Therefore, the pulsed operation would ideally cut both speed requirement and time to escape to about 41.4% of the values of continuous low accelera-

---

[1] This conclusion does not hold for propulsive accelerations between 0.01 and 0.2g, which might be of importance for nuclear heat-exchanger type propulsion systems, viz., if relatively low-thrust engines are used to launch relatively large vehicles from orbit (Johnson and Rom, 1962).

tion. Practical difficulties have to do with design and losses in the energy storage system, weight of the energy storage system (this weight prevents the vehicle with energy storage from reaching the same acceleration as the nonstorage vehicle), weight of the thrust-generating system (which is heavier in the energy-storage vehicle since the thrust is about by an order of magnitude higher over a shorter time), and with, of the order of 10^2, starts and stops, for the thrust system. Generally, this system does not appear to be very promising either.

Now to be more precise on the time requirement to reach escape speed from a circular orbit by using pericenter kicks:

Initially, the vehicle is in a circular orbit (radius r, gravitational attraction $g \approx \gamma M/r^2$, circular speed $v_0 = (gr)^{1/2}$, period T_0) around a mass center M. Per revolution, the small speed $\Delta v = \delta v_0$ is added at the pericenter. When a is the major half-axis, and v_p the pericenter speed, then from Eq. (1.16),

$$\frac{v_p{}^2}{2} - \frac{\gamma M}{r} = -\frac{\gamma M}{2a},$$

or rearranging and observing that $v_0{}^2 = gr = \gamma M/r$, we have

$$\frac{r}{a} = 2 - \left(\frac{v_p}{v_0}\right)^2.$$

From Kepler's third law we have $T^2 \sim a^3$; thus the period, in an ellipse of given v_p/v_0 ratio, is

$$\frac{T}{T_0} = \left\{2 - \left(\frac{v_p}{v_0}\right)^2\right\}^{-3/2}.$$

After i pericenter kicks, the speed is $v_p = v_0 + i\,\Delta v = v_0(1 + i\delta)$. Therefore, the period in the orbit after kick No. i has been fired is

$$\frac{T_i}{T_0} = \{1 - i^2\delta^2 - 2i\delta\}^{-3/2}.$$

The total number N of kicks is, ideally,

$$N = \frac{2^{1/2} - 1}{\delta};$$

thus,

$$T_i = T_0 \left\{1 - 2\frac{2^{1/2} - 1}{N} i - \left(\frac{2^{1/2} - 1}{N}\right)^2 i^2\right\}^{-3/2}$$

The time T_E to escape is approximated as an integral:

$$T_E = \sum_{i=1}^{N-1} T_i \approx \int_{\frac{1}{2}}^{N-\frac{1}{2}} T_i \, di = NT_0 \int_{1/2N}^{1-1/2N} \frac{dx}{[1 - 2(2^{1/2} - 1)x - (2^{1/2} - 1)^2 x^2]^{3/2}} \cdot$$

If $X = a + bx + cx^2$, then

$$\int \frac{dx}{X^{3/2}} = \frac{2(2cx + b)}{(4ac - b^2)X^{1/2}} \cdot$$

Evaluating the integral, we get

$$T_E \approx T_0 N \left(1 + \frac{2^{1/2}}{2}\right)^{3/2} N^{1/2} = 2.23 N^{1/2} N T_0 \,. \tag{2.53}$$

Assuming a continuous system operates with $10^{-4}g$'s, or 10^{-3} m/sec² acceleration, the time to escape from a low circular orbit around Earth is approximately

$$T_{E \text{ con}} \approx \frac{8000}{10^{-3}} = 8 \times 10^6 \text{ sec} \approx 80 \text{ days} \,,$$

or, if $T_0 \approx 6 \times 10^3$ sec,

$$T_E = 1.3 \times 10^3 T_0 \,.$$

To do the same with the pulsed system, Eq. (2.53) demands $N \approx 70$, or $\delta v_k = 0.414 \times 8000/70 = 47$ m/sec. The time available to do this is about 20% of T_0 or 1.2×10^3 sec, which demands an acceleration of 39×10^{-3} m/sec², or about 39 times more than for the case of continuous acceleration. If, on the other hand, the pulsed system has an acceleration of only 10^{-3} m/sec², then $\delta v_0 = 1.3$ m/sec or $N = 2700$ and $T_E \approx 50$ yr.

2.4,4 Some Guidance Considerations

2.4,4,1 INTRODUCTION

Since, for all low-acceleration missions, the vehicle is for a long time under propulsion, and since trajectories are different from free-flight trajectories, there are some differences compared to the guidance aspects of high-acceleration vehicles.

A fundamental difficulty is that big errors take very long times to be corrected, e.g., from Eq. (2.52) it follows that, with $a = 10^{-4}g$, the maximum eccentricity to be brought to zero in one revolution is only about 10^{-3}. Thus, if by error any large eccentricity builds up, it takes a long time to correct. Therefore, continuous guidance should be applied, possibly by an inertial system[1] controlled by a celestial guidance system. Should large guidance maneuvers become necessary, then low-acceleration vehicles might be equipped with a short-time medium acceleration capability, perhaps typically 1 m/sec² over 100 sec.

There are several possibilities of doing this, e.g., an ionic propulsion system might be shut off and the electric power might be used in an arc jet system instead. We found in Sec. 2.2,5 that with hydrogen a value of I_{sp} = 1588 sec may be realized, and the thrust for 0.900 MW electric energy equals 4.55 kg.

Another possibility is to stop the electric power generation system, and use the thermal energy output in a high-thrust heat exchanger type engine. The temperature in the power reactor may be assumed to be 1000°K, and the hydrogen may be assumed to be heated to 900°K. For such a corrective system, a pressure-fed engine can be assumed. The specific impulse will be about 485 sec. The thrust then will be, per megawatt thermal output (see Sec. 2.1,3), 17.85(761/485) = 28 kg.

With this information and referring back to the sample data generated in Sec. 2.3,6,2, we obtain the values listed in Table 2.13.

TABLE 2.13

HIGH ACCELERATION CORRECTIVE SYSTEM

Weight/power (kg/kW)	α	2	10	20
Average vehicle mass (tons)	M	140	310	850
Thermal power available for thrust generation (MW)	E_{th}	66	51	79
Thermal power, actually transferred to thrustor (MW)	P_{th}	60	46	72
Electric power available for propulsion (MW)	E_e	13.2	10.2	15.76
Thrust				
Ionic system (kg)		13.53	29.05	75
Arc jet (I_{sp} = 1588 sec) (kg)		67.2	51.5	79.5
Heat exchanger (I_{sp} = 485 sec) (kg)		1680	1290	2020

[1] Attention should be drawn again to the problem of measuring such low accelerations inertially with sufficient accuracy.

Superconducting accelerometers may be capable of measurement to an accuracy of $10^{-10}g$, according to several Master of Science theses, 1964, Experimental Astronomy Laboratory of Massachusetts Institute of Technology. This is of direct interest also for gravity gradient determination (see Sec. 1.4,6,1 of this volume).

It can be seen that the arc jet system might find application for the case of $\alpha = 2$. But the much higher thrust may make the latter system more desirable, in spite of its complication relative to the arc jet system.

Only thorough system studies can show whether such a dual thrust capability is really desirable, and—if it is—whether this dual thrust capability is not better provided by addition of a chemical propulsion system.

Thanks to their continuous thrust capability, the low-acceleration vehicles can move in a circular orbit with both under—or over—circular speed balancing the difference in centrifugal acceleration by thrust acceleration:

$$\frac{(v_0 + \Delta v)^2}{r} = g_r \pm a = g_r \left(1 \pm \frac{a}{g_r} \right) = \frac{v_0^2}{r} \left(1 \pm \frac{a}{g_r} \right),$$

where v_0 is the circular speed at distance r. From this

$$\left(\frac{\Delta v}{v_0} \right)^2 + 2 \frac{\Delta v}{v_0} = \pm \frac{a}{g_r} \qquad \text{or} \qquad \frac{\Delta v}{v_0} \approx \pm \frac{1}{2} \frac{a}{g_r}.$$

With R being the radius of the central body and g_0 the surface gravity,

$$\Delta v = \frac{(g_0 R)^{1/2}}{2} \frac{a}{g_0} \left(\frac{r}{R} \right)^{3/2}$$

With $a = 10^{-3}$ m/sec² we obtain the values of Δv shown in the following tabulation:

Orbit	Δv (m/sec)	v_0 (m/sec)
Close Earth satellite orbit	0.4	7850
Circular orbit around Earth in lunar distance	180	1000
Circular orbit around the Sun, at 1 a.u., disregarding Earth	2.6×10^3	29×10^3

This capability can be used as a correction maneuver in orbital, lunar, or interplanetary transfers.

2.4.4.2 Transfer between Circular Orbits (Coplanar Problem)

To go from one circular orbit to another coplanar one of different radius appears to be simple, since just in spiraling out (or in), the low-acceleration vehicle stays nearly in a circular orbit. And in the previous section was shown how to correct for the small eccentricity that accrues (because, after all, the vehicle stays only approximately in a circular orbit).

For historic interest, a different method will now be developed. This method is due to Rodriguez (1958):

Energy E and moment h (= constant in Kepler's second law) are characteristic for the motion. In a circular orbit (index 0), around the central mass m,

$$E = -\frac{\gamma m}{2r_0} \quad \text{and} \quad h = |[\mathbf{r}_0 \mathbf{v}_0]| = (\gamma m r_0)^{1/2}$$

or

$$-E = \frac{(\gamma m)^2}{2} \frac{1}{h^2},$$

$$\frac{dE}{d(h^2)} = \frac{(\gamma m)^2}{2h^4} = \frac{1}{2r_0^2}.$$

The equation of the tangent in a point $P_1(E_{01}, h_{01}^2)$ at the $E = E(h^2)$ curve has the form

$$\bar{E} = +E_{01} + \frac{1}{2r_0^2}(\bar{h}^2 - h_{01}^2),$$

where $\bar{E}\,\bar{h}^2$ are variables. Let us give a tangential kick Δv to the orbiting vehicle, then $\bar{E}$ goes to $\hat{E}$ given by

$$\hat{E} = +E_{01} + \tfrac{1}{2}(v_{01} + \Delta v)^2 - \tfrac{1}{2}v_0^2 = +E_{01} + \tfrac{1}{2}\Delta v^2 + v_{01}\Delta v,$$

and

$$\hat{h} = |[\mathbf{r}_0, \mathbf{v}_{01} + \Delta \mathbf{v}]| = h_{01} + r_0\Delta v,$$

or

$$\hat{h}^2 - h_{01}^2 = r_0^2\Delta v^2 + 2h_{01}r_0\Delta v$$

$$= 2r_0^2\left(\frac{\Delta v^2}{2} + v_{01}\Delta v\right);$$

thus,

$$\hat{E} = +E_{01} + \frac{1}{2r_{01}^2}(\hat{h}^2 - h_{01}^2).$$

Therefore, it is seen that the point $\hat{E}, \hat{h}^2$ is exactly on the tangent $\bar{E}, \bar{h}^2$. This is shown in Fig. 2.46.

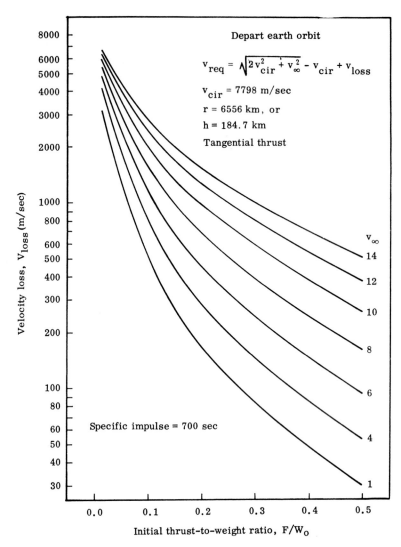

Fig. 2.44. Velocity loss (m/sec) due to gravity vs thrust-to-weight ratio with hyperbolic excess velocity v_∞ (km/sec) as a parameter.

If we now draw a tangent to the curve of circular orbits from the point $\hat{P} = (\hat{E}, \hat{h}^2)$ in Fig. 2.46, we find a point P_2. A second kick (tangential to the flight path in P_2) can get the vehicle from $\hat{E}, \hat{h}^2$ to P_2. We have a simple method to complete the transfer by tangential kicks between coplanar circular orbits; this is nothing but a Hohmann transfer, and the point $\hat{P}$ represents the transfer ellipse.

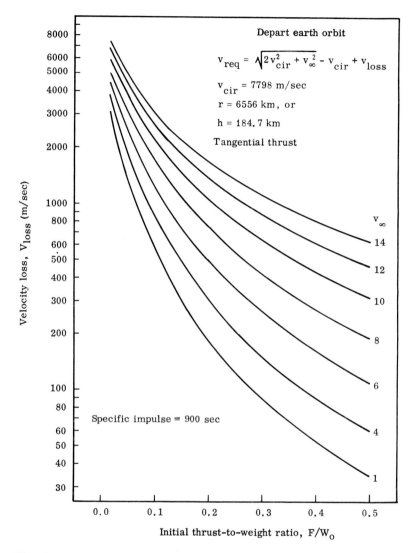

Fɪɢ. 2.45. Velocity loss (m/sec) due to gravity vs thrust-to-weight ratio with hyperbolic excess velocity v_∞ (km/sec) as a parameter.

For low-acceleration transfers, we shall look into four simple thrust direction programs, which we have already investigated:

(1) $h^2 = $ const, or $\dot{h} = 0$. We have the relationships

$$\mathbf{h} = [\mathbf{r}\ \mathbf{v}] \quad \text{and} \quad \dot{\mathbf{h}} = [\dot{\mathbf{r}}\ \mathbf{v}] + [\mathbf{r}\ \dot{\mathbf{v}}] = [\mathbf{r}\ \mathbf{a}_r],$$

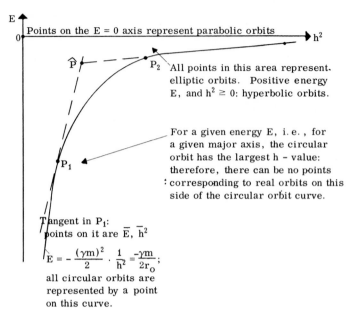

FIG. 2.46. Diagram of conic section orbits.

or for $\dot h = 0$ the acceleration $\mathbf{a}_r$ has to be parallel to $\mathbf{r}$, or we have to apply radial thrust. Due to an acceleration $\mathbf{a}$ the energy changes:

$$\dot E = \mathbf{v}\,\mathbf{a} = va\,\cos(\mathbf{v}, \mathbf{a}).$$

When $\mathbf{a}$ is parallel to $\mathbf{r}$, then, obviously,

$$v\cos(\mathbf{v}, \mathbf{a}) = \dot r\,,$$

and $dE = a_r\,dr$, or integrated from an arbitrary point P_0 to the point P_2, keeping a_r as constant:

$$a_r = \frac{E_2 - E_0}{r_2 - r_0}\,.$$

(2) The second thrust program required has $\dot E = 0$, or the acceleration a_p is vertical upon $\mathbf{v}$:

$$E = \text{const} = \frac{v^2}{2} - \frac{\gamma m}{r} = -\frac{\gamma m}{2r_2}\,,$$

if P_2 is on the line where $E = \text{constant}$. Therefore,

$$v^2 = \frac{2\gamma m}{r} - \frac{\gamma m}{r_2} = \frac{2\gamma m}{r}\left(1 - \frac{r}{2r_2}\right).$$

On the other hand,

$$(\dot{h}^2) = 2h \,|\,[\mathbf{r}\,\dot{\mathbf{v}}]\,| = 2hra_p \cos(r, a_p).$$

From simple geometric considerations,

$$(\dot{h}^2) = 2(h^2)^{1/2}ra_p\frac{\dot{r}}{v} = 2(h^2)^{1/2}a_p\frac{r^{3/2}\dot{r}}{[2\gamma m(1 - r/2r_2)]^{1/2}}\,,$$

$$\left(\frac{2\gamma m}{r_2}\right)^{1/2}\int_{h_0}^{h_2}\frac{dh^2}{2(h^2)^{1/2}} = r_2{}^2a_p\int_{r_0}^{r_2}\frac{(r/r_2)^{3/2}(dr/r_2)}{(1 - r/2r_2)^{1/2}}\,.$$

It will be shown later that $r_0 < r_2$ can always be obtained. Then

$$\left(\frac{2\gamma m}{r_2}\right)^{1/2}\{(h_2{}^2)^{1/2} - (h_0{}^2)^{1/2}\} = 4a_pr_2{}^2\int_{r_0/2r_2}^{1/2}\frac{y^{3/2}\,dy}{(1 - y)^{1/2}}\,;$$

$$4\int\frac{y^{3/2}\,dy}{(1 - y)^{1/2}} = -\{(2y + 3)[y(1 - y)]^{1/2} + \tfrac{3}{2}\arcsin(1 - 2y)\}\,.$$

(3) Tangential thrust:

$$\dot{E} = va_t\,,$$

$$\dot{h} = ra_t\sin(\mathbf{r}, \mathbf{a}_t)\,,$$

$$\frac{dE}{dh} = \frac{v}{r\sin(\mathbf{r}, \mathbf{a}_t)} \approx \frac{v}{r}\,.$$

(4) Circumferential thrust:

$$\dot{E} = va_c\cos(\mathbf{v}, \mathbf{a}_c)\,,$$

$$\dot{h} = ra_c\,,$$

$$\frac{dE}{dh} = \frac{v\cos(\mathbf{v}, \mathbf{a}_c)}{r} \approx \frac{v}{r}\,.$$

Thus, in both (3) and (4),

$$\frac{dE}{dh} \approx \frac{h}{r^2}\,,$$

or

$$\frac{1}{2h}\frac{dE}{dh} = \frac{dE}{d(h^2)} = \frac{1}{2r^2}\,,$$

and integrate from the point P_1 to an arbitrary point P_0:

$$E_0 - E_1 \approx \frac{(h_0{}^2 - h_1{}^2)}{(r_0{}^2 + r_1{}^2)} \, .$$

By comparison we see that E_0, h_0 will again be approximately on the tangent in P_1 to the $E(h^2)$ curve for circular orbits.

To go from P_1 to P_2 (in Fig. 2.46) via low-acceleration transfers, the procedure is as follows:

Step 1. Go via tangential or circumferential acceleration from P_1 (along the tangent), until *either* $h = h_2$ or $E = E_2$ is reached, which may define the point P_0. Compute h_0, E_0, r_0. Approximately at cutoff, $r_0 \approx r_1$ for high, and $r_0 \approx r_2$ for low-thrust, but r_0 can be varied by coasting between $r_{0\,\min} = (1 - \varepsilon)a$ and $r_{0\,\max} = (1 + \varepsilon)a$.

It can be seen that at cutoff, for $E_0 = E_2$, there will be $r_0 < r_2$, as the vehicle has above-circular energy during the transfer phase. For $E_0 = E_2$, of course, the major axis is $a = r_2$.

Step 2(a). For $E = E_0$, go via $E = $ constant (thrust normal on **v**) from P_0 to P_2; a_p was computed before.

Step 2(b). For $h = h_2$, go via $h = $ constant (radial thrust) from P_0 to P_2; a_r was computed before.

Since Step 1 is independent of the magnitude of the acceleration, we may use $|\mathbf{a}_r|$ or $|\mathbf{a}_p|$ during this step.

For many interplanetary transfers, a_r and a_p come out to be just in the interesting area around 10^{-4} Earth-gravities.

The main disadvantage of this method is that a large fraction of the transfer time is spent in Step 2, which is a very inefficient thrust program. Therefore, total required speeds are very high when this method is utilized.[1]

It will be more favorable to go via Step 1 to the point $\hat{P}$ (Fig. 2.46), stay there for the correct length of time and go again via a Step 1 type thrust program from $\hat{P}$ to P_2. This is possible for interplanetary type transfers, because even the low-acceleration systems behave similarly to high-acceleration systems because of the relatively low value of the local solar gravitational acceleration, as shown before. The speed requirement will be between the value for a Hohmann transfer and the simple difference of the circular speeds.

Going to a higher speed requirement, the transfer time can be shortened.

---

[1] An improvement results from using tangential thrust to go from E_1 to E_2; then remove the eccentricity, keeping E_2 constant.

To shorten mission durations which include return to Earth, proper trajectory choices have to be made. This is the same behavior as was found for high-acceleration vehicles going along "fast" transfers.

It should be mentioned that optimum low thrust transfers between circular orbits demand quite complicated thrust direction and possibly on-off programs, or programs of specific impulse variation.

2.4,5 Speed Requirements for Some Missions

Many missions will be performed to advantage utilizing electric propulsion systems. Let us mention a few:

Unmanned systems. Mapping of van Allen radiation zone; out of ecliptic probe; solar probe; Mercury probe; Jupiter probe[1]; other scientific missions.

Manned or unmanned systems. Attitude control; lunar ferry; planetary transportation.

It appears as if all unmanned missions can be performed with an electric power level between 1 kW and 1 MW, whereas the manned missions—with the exception of attitude control—seem to require between 1 and 50 MW.

For large unmanned space probes, a very useful design can be based upon the Saturn V launch vehicle delivering the probe to parabolic energy. Initial mass of the probe is about 90,000 lb, power 1 MW, power plant specific weight 30 lb/kW, propulsion time from 0.3 yr (inner solar system) to 5 yr (extreme outer solar system), mission time 0.3–7 yr, specific impulse (constant for each mission) 2500–11,000 sec, speed capability 15–70 km/sec, and

Power plant fraction	30%
Cesium	47%
Structure	8%
Payload	15%
Total	100% = 90,000 lb

Some specific remarks are

(1) *Attitude control.* Extremely low accelerations down to 10^{-6} Earth-g's can be useful because of the small perturbations. The speed requirement is obviously proportional to the required lifetime, and dependent upon required accuracy and prevailing perturbations.

---

[1] For probes to Jupiter and beyond, low-acceleration vehicles promise to be fast compared to Hohmann flight times.

(2) *Satellite orbit control.* Change in the orbital elements can be performed. This subject has been treated for the elements, with the exception of argument of pericenter.

(3) *Satellite ferry.* Low thrust vehicles can be useful for providing transportation between satellites.

(4) *Lunar ferry* (Stuhlinger, 1959). The vehicle starts in a circular orbit of speed v_c. To reach the lunar orbit, where circular speed with respect to Earth is about 1 km/sec, the speed requirement v_{r1} is about $v_{r1} = v_c - 1$ km/sec, and the time T_1 for continuous thrust flight is, with a mean acceleration a, of course, $T_1 = (v_c - 1)/a$.

If, for example, $a = 0.76 \times 10^{-4}g$, and launch is from a 300-km altitude orbit, then $v_{r1} \approx 6.75$ km/sec and $T_1 \approx 9.06 \times 10^6$ sec.

If the ferry returns to the 300-km orbit immediately after passing the Moon, having dropped a heavy chemical landing vehicle, there may be

$$a = 3.6 \times 10^{-4}g, \qquad \text{and} \qquad v_{r2} = v_{r1}, \qquad T_2 = 1.92 \times 10^6 \text{ sec.}$$

The chemical landing vehicle has to brake the velocity of about lunar escape speed (2.375 km/sec plus losses, etc.), when arriving on the lunar surface. When, instead of from the passage, the lunar lander is dropped from a lunar satellite, the required braking is only approximately 72% of escape speed. Thus, about 28% or about 0.7 km/sec speed requirement can be saved in the lander when the ferry, instead of just passing the Moon, spirals towards a low lunar satellite orbit; the additional requirement on the ferry is about 1.7 km/sec or, for a two-way trip, 3.4 km/sec. The additional time requirement is to spiral in $T_3 = 2.28 \times 10^6$ sec, and to spiral out $T_4 = 0.48 \times 10^6$ sec.

Tentatively, the "ultimate" system of Earth-lunar transportation may be outlined as given in Table 2.14.

The long flight time and the long stay time in the van Allen radiation belt may make the outlined "lunar ferry" attractive only for cargo transportation. High-thrust vehicles (e.g., nuclear for launch, chemical for landing, or reuse of the nuclear stage) can make the Earth-to-Moon flight economically in two to three days, and may be, therefore, preferable to transport men. In any case, a fast transportation system is required for emergency situations. Since the low-thrust flight time in our example is about 50 times longer than the high-thrust flight time, we can expect with a low-thrust system capable of an acceleration of $a = 5 \times 10^{-3}g$ to have the same flight time as a high-acceleration vehicle; and $a = 10^{-2}g$ acting continuously to the Moon will result in a fast transfer.

TABLE 2.14

	One-way Earth-Moon travel	Two-way Earth-Moon travel
Earth ground to Earth orbit	High-thrust chemical/nuclear or nuclear vehicle; first stage possibly air breathing; much or all of the vehicle recoverable and reusable. Flight time is of the order of 1 h.	
Earth orbit to lunar vicinity	Low acceleration ferry. The ferry just passes the Moon. Flight time is of the order of 100 days.	Low acceleration ferry. The ferry spirals to an orbit around the Moon. Flight time is of the order of 125 days.
Lunar vicinity to lunar surface	A chemical (or nuclear) one-stage rocket vehicle is released from the ferry and lands on the lunar surface. The flight time is again of the order of 1 h.	
Lunar surface to ferry		Either a chemical or a nuclear rocket, or if high accelerations are tolerable, some type of gun is used. Flight time is again of the order of 1 h.
Return	The ferry returns from lunar vicinity to the starting orbit around Earth. The flight time:	
	Will be only 20 days, because of the weight reduction due to the lander.	Is perhaps 60 days, because the ferry is lighter on the return leg than on the outward-bound leg.
Landing on Earth		Aerodynamic braking from orbit in special landing vehicle.[a] Time required is of the order of 1 h.

[a] Earth orbital ferry.

The utility of low-acceleration vehicles in an Earth-lunar transportation system has to be studied carefully before valid conclusions can be drawn. The time is clearly not yet ripe for an answer—but the question can be seen clearly.

(5) *Interplanetary flight*. The low-acceleration vehicles cannot depart from the surface of a celestial body having a gravitational acceleration at its surface larger than the thrust acceleration of the vehicle. Regarding such bodies, only passages (reconnaissance) or orbits around them (ferry) can be realized. With this restriction, all of the missions discussed for high-acceleration vehicles can also be flown by low-acceleration vehicles.

Let us look at an Earth-to-Mars transfer, demanding flight from a close Earth orbit to a close Mars orbit (Stuhlinger, 1957).

Phase One. To perform the escape from Earth, the velocity requirement equals the circular speed in the original orbit: $v_{r1} = v_{KE}$. The duration of this escape maneuver is $T_1 = v_{KE}/a_1$, where a_1 denotes the average thrust acceleration. To simplify the guidance problem, the escape maneuver should be planned such that no close approach to our Moon is made, therefore avoiding strong lunar perturbations.

Phase Two. During phase two, the vehicle transfers from Earth's orbit to Mars's orbit. For a Hohmann transfer, the speed requirement is (Fig. 6.45, Vol. 1) $v_{r2} = 5.64$ km/sec, whereas, for continuous acceleration, the difference in circular speeds is $v'_{r2} = 5.66$ km/sec, about the same as for a Hohmann transfer.

The Hohmann free-flight time was found to be 259 days; here we estimate $T_2 \approx 280$ days. Now we know that the relative inclination of the orbit of Mars has no important influence upon payload capability, but its eccentricity has a larger—still not drastic—effect (Melbourne, 1961).

Phase Three. The Martian capture maneuver demands, again, a required speed equal to the circular speed in the final orbit, $v_{r3} = v_{KM}$, and correspondingly a maneuver time $T_3 = v_{KM}/a_3$.

About 10 days and 2 km/sec should be added for maneuvering, plane change, etc.

To sum up, the total speed requirement is

$$v_r = v_{KE} + 7.66 + v_{KM} \quad \text{km/sec},$$

and the total time is

$$T = \frac{v_{KE}}{a_1} + \frac{v_{KM}}{a_3} + 290 \quad \text{days}.$$

Thus, with $v_{KE} = 7.75$ km/sec and $v_{KM} = 3.43$ km/sec, $v_r = 18.84$ or approximately 20 km/sec. For a high acceleration Hohmann transfer, only 7.5 km/sec is necessary for the same mission. London (1960) investigates and justifies the treatment of a three-body problem as a series of two-body problems as we did also in the impulsive case. Assuming that a nuclear high-thrust system can develop a specific impulse of 10^3 sec, and the low-thrust system 10^4 sec, then taking the heavy propulsion system of the low-acceleration vehicle into account by a factor of 2, for

$$v_r = \tfrac{1}{2}(10) \times 7.5 = 37.5 \quad \text{km/sec},$$

the low-thrust vehicle should carry about the same payload as the high-thrust system for 7.5 km/sec. Since 20 km/sec is considerably smaller than 37.5 km/sec, a clear payload advantage for the low-acceleration vehicle over the high-acceleration vehicle should result. But flight time will be considerably longer: about 260 days for the high-thrust vehicle and, for $a = 10^{-4}g$, about 434 days.

From Faulders (1961) we obtain for minimum time (i.e., no coast) transfer from Earth orbit to Mars orbit, neglecting planetary masses (i.e., phase two), for a constant acceleration of $10^{-4}g_0$, that the total time required for the transfer is only 174 days (instead of 280), but the speed requirement is 14.7 km/sec (instead of 5.6). If, additionally, the acceleration can be increased to $2 \times 10^{-4}g$, then the complete transfer of the low-acceleration vehicle can beat the Hohmann transfer time.

Because of this, about $10^{-4}g$ are considered to be the lowest useful acceleration for flight within the inner solar system. Similarly, $10^{-5}g$ suffices for flights to the outer solar system. The data found here verify the assumption on page 267 that a round trip can be carried out for $v_r = 45$ km/sec in 1.5 yr of powered and about 2.14 yr total flight time. The stay time—for Hohmann flights, about 450 days—should not be made too short. After all, the reason for the whole mission is to do planetary research, for which sufficient time must be made available.

An interesting question has to do with shortening the total mission duration over the minimum energy type solutions. This is of practical importance, especially for manned operations. For high-acceleration chemical propulsion systems, the increase in launch weight for a given payload will make drastic decreases in mission duration impractical. For nuclear high-acceleration systems, this is not necessarily the case.[1] How do the low-acceleration systems score on this point? First let us consider one-way probe-type missions. Since spiraling away from Earth and spiraling down to the target occur under constant propulsive power, the time required for phases one and three are already minimum. Only phase two, the heliocentric flight, has the traditional form of power-coast-power.

---

[1] See Sec. 6.10,7 of Vol. 1.

If one total heliocentric transfer duration is T_h and the corresponding speed requirement is $\varDelta v_h$, then, approximately, for another pair T and $\varDelta v$:

$$T_h \, \varDelta v_h = T \, \varDelta v \ .$$

From this relationship, fast transfers can be estimated; care must be used, because T is bounded by $T_{\max} \approx T_{\text{Hohmann}}$ and $T_{\min} = T_{\text{powered all the way}}$. Some numbers for heliocentric transfers are shown in Table 2.15.

TABLE 2.15

From Earth to	$T_h \, \varDelta v_h$ ($\times 10^9$ km)	Typical T_h (yr)
Jupiter	1.41	1.4
Saturn	2.97	2.3
Uranus	6.70	3.9
Neptune	11.30	5.5
Pluto	15	5.5

For manned missions, the optimization is considerably more difficult because the return flight is part of the mission profile.

Moeckel (1960) has performed a preliminary study, using besides other simplifications a simple type of interplanetary transfer trajectory, where the circumferential component of the velocity is equal to local circular speed at all times. In order to achieve short mission duration, both "direct" and "indirect" orbits have to be used, one for the outgoing and the other for the return portion. (See Fig. 2.47.) During powered flight, thrust (or specific impulse) is not constant, but power consumption is (variation in I_{sp}:

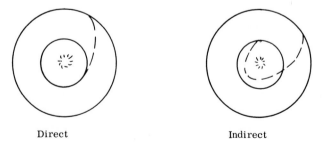

Direct   Indirect

Fig. 2.47. Earth-Mars trajectory profiles.

2500–3700 sec). The waiting time has been chosen to be about 30 days. Further data are[1]:

Circular orbit around Earth: 4020 km altitude.
Circular orbit around Mars: 4020 km altitude.
No free-flight portion for the low acceleration vehicle.
Mission: Earth orbit–Mars orbit–Earth orbit, always using rocket braking:

$$\frac{\text{power plant weight}}{\text{initial plant weight}} = 0.2.$$

The main result is shown in Figs. 2.48 and 2.49, where the additional constants for the manned mission are:

Crew: 8 men.
Daily used mass: 80 lb.
Exploration equipment to be left at Mars: 40,000 lb.
Return payload: 50,000 lb.

From this it might be concluded that low acceleration vehicles are attractive for fast missions also. With optimized trajectories, results are even better.[2] On the other hand, the realization of variable specific impulse may not prove to be practical; fairly optimistic α-values have been assumed, and the transportation requirement to orbit and the possible inability to take advantage of aerodynamic braking methods may turn out to be decisive disadvantages for low-acceleration systems. The orbits have been chosen impractically high—if low orbits are used instead, then the following disadvantages have to be added:

For low-acceleration systems. The mission duration increases by ~ 50 days (or v_r increases by 5720 m/sec, which gives 50 days of propulsion time with a mean acceleration of $1.35 \times 10^{-4}g$). The growth factor increases by a factor of about 1.2.

For high-acceleration systems. The growth factor increases approximately[3]

---

[1] For these terminal conditions, we get, for a one-way trip with a constant thrust acceleration of $10^{-4}g_0$: *Minimum time (no coast)*: transfer time, 250 days; propulsive time, 250 days; speed requirement, 21.2 km/sec (without steering, etc.). *Minimum energy*: transfer time, 375 days; propulsive time, 125 days; speed requirement, 10.6 km/sec (without steering, etc.).

[2] For manned Mars missions of about 500 days duration, ion propulsion leads to lower initial mass in Earth orbit than nuclear heat exchangers for $\alpha \leq 9$ kg/kW, if trajectories are optimized (Moeckel, 1963).

[3] For small hyperbolic excess speeds; for large ones the increases are smaller.

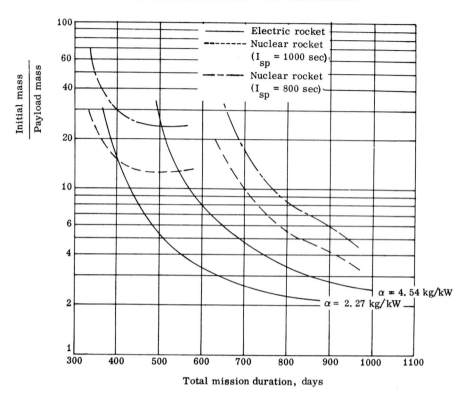

Fig. 2.48. Mass-ratio comparison for an unmanned Mars round trip. (Stay time at Mars: 30 days.)

by a factor of 3 (or v_r increases by 8140 m/sec, which requires, for $I_{sp} = 900$ sec, a mass ratio of 2.3), whereas mission duration is not influenced.

From Zola and MacKay (1963) we quote results of great interest for the planning of manned interplanetary missions. Let us give a simple example:

For power plant let $\alpha = 3$ kg/kW or 333 W/kg, and let the power plant weight fraction be 0.3 of initial mass. Thus $P/M_0 \approx 100$ W/kg.

Then from Fig. 2.50 we have

M_f/M_0	$= 0.40$
minus power plant	0.30
minus structures	0.02
payload fraction	0.08 or
growth factor	12.5

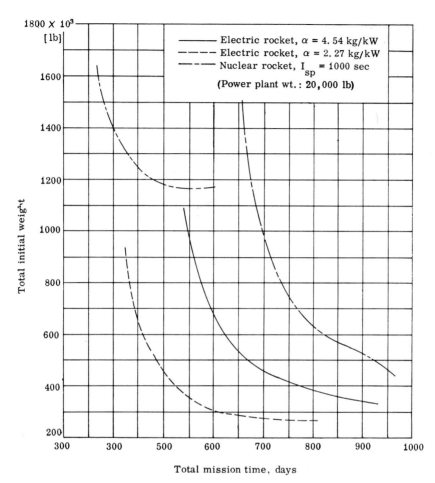

Fig. 2.49. Comparison of initial weights required for 8-man Mars mission as a function of total mission duration.

Again, from Fig. 2.50, we have for initial acceleration 2.2–2.7×10^{-4}, flat optimum at 2.5×10^{-4}, giving an optimum exhaust speed of 80 km/sec. The total speed requirement follows to be 73.2 km/sec. (An equally fast impulsive mission requires, typically, 30–40% of this.)

For $\alpha = 2$ kg/kW and other values as given above we obtain a growth factor of 5.55; the initial acceleration is between 2.4 and 2.8×10^{-4}, with a flat optimum at 2.8×10^{-4}, corresponding to an exhaust speed of 107 km/sec. The total speed requirement is 74.1 km/sec, not changed very much.

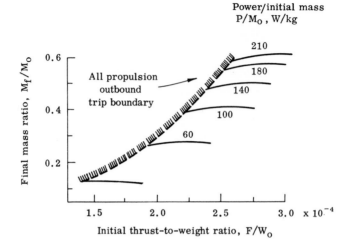

Fig. 2.50. Typical chart of variational round trip solutions. Low Earth orbit to low Mars orbit and return; mission time: 380 days, wait time: 10 days (short trip out, long trip home; constant power; constant exhaust speed; circular, coplanar planetary orbits).

The homebound trajectory involves a coast period in all cases. The total propulsive time is in both examples about 220 days, implying a total coast of about 150 days.

From Sauer and Melbourne (1963), the following data shall be quoted for fast low-acceleration Mars missions:

Mission profile.

Phase 1. Escape from circular satellite orbit (300 km altitude) around Earth; no dogleg, etc; tangential thrust; constant thrust acceleration.

Phase 2. Transfer between coplanar circular Earth/Mars orbits; optimum variable specific impulse.

Phase 3. Entry into Mars satellite orbit of parabolic energy.

Phase 4. Wait at Mars, T_w .

Phase 5. Reverse 3.

Phase 6. Reverse 2.

Phase 7. Reverse 1.

Optimized time distribution between maneuvers and optimized time of launch gives the following tabulation:

α (kg/kW)	Mission duration when $T_w = 48$ days (days)	Mission duration when $T_w = 144$ days (days)
0.1	157	282
1	326	440
10	738	884

Total mission duration is for the ratio

$$\frac{\text{payload mass}}{\text{orbital launch mass}} = 0.3 .$$

By comparison to high-acceleration nuclear capabilities, we find, for the minimum desirable fast mission, $\alpha = 8$ kg/kW; $T_w = 48$ days; mission duration is 560 days; (payload mass)/(orbital launch mass) = 0.18. Thus, from the electric propulsion point of view, only $\alpha \leq 8$ kg/kW (or 17.7 lb/kW) has to be achieved; this is an easier condition than was indicated by the studies using nonoptimized trajectories.

(6) *Interstellar flight.* It has been shown in the last chapter of Vol. 1 that even advanced vehicles within our technology are not adequate to perform interestellar flights within a reasonably short transfer time.

2.4,6 Performance Comparison of High and Low Acceleration Vehicles

For a trip from Earth orbit to Mars orbit and back, with a low-acceleration vehicle (requiring $v_{req} = 45$ km/sec), we have computed payload percentages in a previous section of this chapter. Let us—slightly extended—repeat the results in the following tabulation:

α_0 (kg/kW)	2	10	20
$100\,M_L/M_0$ for $v_{req} = 40$ km/sec $\tau = 1.33$ yr	68	28	11
$100\,M_L/M_0$ for $v_{req} = 45$ km/sec, $\tau = 1.5$ yr	66	25	8
$100\,M_L/M_0$ for $v_{req} = 55$ km/sec, $\tau = 1.83$ yr	60	20	3

A high acceleration vehicle would have a speed requirement of about[1] 14 km/sec for the same mission assuming no atmospheric braking is used. Let us check into 3 different cases of exhaust speed: 4.3 km/sec (high performance chemical), 7.5 km/sec (nuclear), and 10 km/sec (nuclear optimistic). For the chemical vehicle, $\varepsilon = 0.1$, and for the nuclear $\varepsilon = 0.15$. Then we have

$$v_r = 14 \text{ km/sec}, \qquad c = 4.3 \text{ km/sec}, \qquad \varepsilon = 0.1.$$

Hence the optimum step number $n_{\text{opt}} = 4$ and v_r per stage is $14/4 = 3.50$ km/sec; the mass ratio per stage $r = 2.258$ and $1/r = 0.443$, and $\lambda = 0.343$. Hence payload percentage is given by

$$100 \frac{M_L}{M_0} = 100(0.343)^4 = 1.382 .$$

If we consider the same mission, but with $c = 7.5$ km/sec (or 10 km/sec), $\varepsilon = 0.15$, we obtain $n_{\text{opt}} = 2$ and mass ratio per stage

$$r = 2.542 \quad (\text{or } 2.013),$$

$$\frac{1}{r} = 0.393 \quad (\text{or } 0.497),$$

$$\lambda = 0.243 \quad (\text{or } 0.347).$$

Payload percentage is given by

$$100 \frac{M_L}{M_0} = 5.91 \quad (\text{or } 12.03).$$

With the assumption that in the case of the low-acceleration vehicle 50% of M_L, for the high-acceleration vehicle (nuclear) 67% of M_L, and for the chemical rocket 80% of M_L represent "useful payload" (the "useless payload" shall account for radiation shielding, and life essentials for the longer mission duration), then the results for useful payload for a slow Earth-orbit to Mars-orbit and return flight, in percentage of initial launch weight, are as given in Table 2.16.

This shows that the chemical propulsion systems will not be able to compete economically with the advanced forthcoming space-propulsion systems. But a clear answer as to high-acceleration versus low-acceleration systems cannot be given. It all depends on the α_0-values and what c-values will finally be reached (Irving, 1959). And as the performance of both sys-

---

[1] This includes 3% performance reserve.

TABLE 2.16

LOW ACCELERATION VEHICLE			
α_0 (kg/kW)	2	10	20
Useful payload (%)	33	12	4
HIGH ACCELERATION VEHICLE			
c (km/sec)	4.3	7.5	10
Useful payload (%)	1.1	4	8

tems may come out to be reasonably close,[1] other considerations may well have the decisive influence as to which system will be adopted: flight time (see Figs. 2.48 and 2.49; flight time is so important because increases require also increased environmental protection systems; it is because of that effect that the results of Himmel *et al.* (1961) lead to an orbital launch weight of 1.3×10^6 lb for 460 days mission duration and 1.5×10^6 lb for the Hohmann case, both for nuclear high-thrust systems), guidance and control considerations, hazards, reliability, other operational aspects (e.g., aerodynamic braking capability), status of development and availability, growth potential, recovery and reuse of vehicles or major components (e.g., propulsion system), etc. Conceivably, both systems will ultimately be used, as today both ship and aircraft complement each other.

There is one fundamental difference between high-acceleration and low-acceleration vehicles which must be mentioned explicitly. If, for a given mission, growth factor is considered for high acceleration vehicles, an optimum occurs for a definite mission duration, and longer mission durations lead to worse growth factors. In contrast, low-acceleration systems lead to optimum growth factor (of approximately one) under the condition of infinitely long duration of the propulsive period τ. Therefore, for any given required speed v_{req} and α_0, a propulsive period τ can be found[2] so that a

[1] From Fig. 2.49 and the initial remarks, it can be deduced that for $I_{sp} = 1000$ sec the orbital launch weight is, for a mission duration of 540 days, about $3 \times 1160 \times 10^3 = 3.48 \times 10^6$ lb, whereas for $\alpha = 4.54$ kg/kW and 600 days duration, the orbital launch weight is only 1.15×10^6 lb. The factor 3 appears to be significant, but the α-value is quite optimistic. Therefore, the above conclusion as to the lack of a clear-cut decision appears to be correct.

[2] These durations can be long, as shown early in Section 2.4,5, especially for poor α values. It is for that reason that for electric propulsion purposes it can be more important to improve the lifetime than the α value of a given power supply system, once α is "not too poor."

given arbitrarily good growth factor results. In real cases, the required mission duration, or the required exhaust speed, may turn out to be impractical.[1]

Besides the discussed propulsion systems, there are some other competitors: the "upper-atmosphere-scooper" may make all systems more economical, and different nuclear or other systems may be developed, as discussed briefly in Chap. 1 of Vol. 1. Final answers cannot be expected for a long time, if ever; it can be hoped that there will always be the exotic system promising further improvements over whatsoever is available and operational.

For some more recent data and further literature, mainly on nuclear heat-exchanger type propulsion systems, see Ruppe (1963).

2.4,7 Some "Ingenious Solutions"

Every now and then an "ingenious solution" can be found in the literature. Let us consider some of these solutions:

(1) *Trajectory optimization for low acceleration vehicles.* Irving (1959) proceeds as follows: Let $P(t)$ be the power available at time t to be transferred to the exhaust jet. Then $P = -\frac{1}{2}\dot{m}c^2$, where c is the exhaust speed and $\dot{m}$ is the mass flow rate. For the acceleration $a = \dot{m}c/m$, where m is the instantaneous mass. Thus

$$\frac{a^2}{2P} = -\frac{\dot{m}}{m^2} = \frac{d}{dt}\frac{1}{m}$$

or

$$\frac{1}{m} = \frac{1}{M_0} + \int_0^t \frac{a^2}{2P}\,dt\,.$$

With τ as the time of operation and M_e the cutoff mass, we get

$$\frac{1}{M_e} = \frac{1}{M_0} + \int_0^\tau \frac{a^2}{2P}\,dt\,.$$

Obviously, $\int_0^\tau (a^2/2P)dt$ should be as small as possible. This leads us to demand that P be as large as possible. Let us take $P = \text{constant} = P_{\max} = E$, and as before $M_p = (\alpha_0/g_0)E$, where M_p is the mass of the

---

[1] Considerations of reliability and environmental effects lead to a finite optimum mission duration.

power plant. So

$$\frac{M_0}{M_e} = 1 + \frac{\alpha_0 M_0}{2g_0 M_p} \int_0^\tau a^2 \, dt \,.$$

Let us introduce

$$\gamma = \left(\alpha_0 \int_0^\tau a^2 \, dt \right) / 2g_0 \,;$$

this is—neglecting some numerical factors—for constant acceleration a identical with the parameter A, which we introduced before Eq. (2.13). Then we obtain

$$\frac{M_0}{M_e} = 1 + \frac{M_0}{M_p} \gamma \,.$$

With M_L as the payload and M_s as the structure mass:

$$\frac{M_L + M_s}{M_0} = \frac{M_e}{M_0} - \frac{M_p}{M_0} = \frac{1}{1 + (M_0/M_p)\gamma} - \frac{M_p}{M_0}$$

$$= \frac{M_p}{M_0} \left(\frac{1}{(M_p/M_0) + \gamma} - 1 \right) .$$

Since

$$0 \le \frac{M_p}{M_0} \le 1 \qquad \text{and} \qquad 0 \le \frac{M_L + M_s}{M_0} \le 1,$$

we obtain

$$0 \le \gamma \le 1 - M_p/M_0 \,.$$

With

$$M_s = \beta M_0 \qquad \text{and} \qquad M_p/M_0 = x \,,$$

we obtain

$$\frac{M_L}{M_0} = x \left(\frac{1}{x + \gamma} - 1 \right) - \beta \,,$$

or to optimize

$$\frac{\partial (M_L/M_0)}{\partial x} = \frac{1}{x + \gamma} - 1 - \frac{x}{(x + \gamma)^2} = 0 \; \rightarrow$$

$$x_{\text{opt}} = \left(\frac{M_p}{M_0} \right)_{\text{opt}} = \gamma^{1/2} - \gamma = \gamma^{1/2}(1 - \gamma^{1/2}),$$

$$\left(\frac{M_L}{M_0} \right)_{\text{opt}} = (1 - \gamma^{1/2})^2 - \beta \,,$$

and, for the jet mass expelled,

$$\left(\frac{M_c}{M_0}\right)_{\text{opt}} = 1 - \left(\frac{M_e}{M_0}\right)_{\text{opt}} = \gamma^{1/2} \,.$$

Quite obviously, the condition for optimum is now simply $\gamma \to$ minimum.[1]

With $\beta = \frac{1}{100}$, for $(M_L/M_0)_{\text{opt}} \geq 0$ the condition $\gamma \leq 0.81$ has to be fulfilled. This is the same behavior as depicted in Fig. 2.33, where $A \leq 0.64$. The approach presented here is more general, since $c = $ constant has not been required. Thus, a more rigorous optimization is possible.

What is an optimum choice for the acceleration $a(t)$? Let us write $v = \int_0^\tau a \, dt$, and let us introduce a mean constant acceleration such that

$$v = \int_0^\tau a \, dt = \int_0^\tau (\bar{a} + \varDelta a) \, dt = \int_0^\tau \bar{a} \, dt \,,$$

or

$$\int_0^\tau \varDelta a \, dt = 0 \,.$$

It follows that

$$\int_0^\tau a^2 \, dt = \int_0^\tau [\bar{a}^2 + 2\bar{a} \, \varDelta a + (\varDelta a^2)] \, dt$$

$$= \int_0^\tau \bar{a}^2 \, dt + \int_0^\tau (\varDelta a)^2 dt \,.$$

Obviously, for a minimum of

$$\gamma \sim \int_0^\tau a^2 \, dt \,,$$

we have to demand

$$\varDelta a \equiv 0 \,.$$

In words: constant acceleration will be the optimum thrust program. This leads, because of the demand for $P = $ constant $= P_{\text{max}} = E$, to a variable exhaust speed, which may, in practical cases, more than offset the advantage of a constant acceleration, making, probably, constant thrust the best practical program. This has been discussed earlier in this chapter.

---

[1] Criterion for trajectory optimization; a useful restriction for a given mission is $\int_0^\tau a \, dt = $ constant. This excludes—for finite τ—the trivial solution $a = 0$.

The conclusion a_{opt} = constant has been derived for motion in field- and resistance-free space. For spiraling out in a central gravitational field it is only an approximation, with the true optimum condition being rather involved. For practical cases stepwise constant or zero thrust will be a good program. For more details the paper by Irving (1959) should be consulted.

(2) *Solar sailing.* The use of radiation pressure as a propulsive force has been discussed. With a "sail" made up from plastic 10^{-4} cm thick, we get, with a specific weight of 2 gm/cm³, a weight of 2 gm/m², or a sail with the shape of a half-sphere of 100 m radius will have a weight of 125 kg; adding 20% for lines, etc., we have 150 kg for the sail. Assuming the vehicle proper to weigh another 150 kg yields an all-up weight of 300 kg with a cross-sectional area of 3.14×10^4 m², or ratio of (weight)/(area) $= 0.95 \times 10^{-2}$ kg/m². Solar radiation pressure for normal incidence on a perfect reflector[1] is, in Earth vicinity, about 0.94×10^{-6} kg/m², sufficing for an acceleration[2]

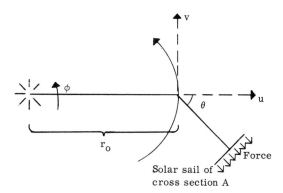

FIG. 2.51. Diagram of solar sail in space. $u = \dot{r}$; $v = \dot{r}\varphi$.

of about $10^{-4}g$. (See Fig. 2.51.) This is about a factor of ten better than was found for the visibility sphere, which was used as an example of motion under the influence of a low radial acceleration in Sec. 2.4,2,2 of this chapter. What is the optimum sail setting angle θ? Let the solar radiation pressure on a reflecting area at distance r_0 for $\theta = 0$ be called p_0. Then per

---

[1] Even if the half-sphere is a perfect reflector, the pressure P_R is $0.47 \times 10^{-6} < P_R < 0.94 \times 10^{-6}$; see Sec. 2.4,2,2 of this chapter for details. A practical value may be $P_R = 0.7 \times 10^{-6}$.

[2] Solar wind, to be described in the next chapter, leads to a maximum pressure between 10^{-12} and 10^{-4} kg/m², in Earth vicinity.

unit of A, generally $p = p_0 \cos^2\theta \ (r_0/r)^2$, and $p_0 = 0.94 \times 10^{-6}$ km/m², for $r_0 = 1$ a.u.

The equations of motion are (m is the vehicle mass, F_g the gravitational force, and F_r the radiation force):

$$\frac{-F_g + F_r \cos\theta}{m} = \dot{u} - \frac{v^2}{r},$$

$$-\frac{F_r \sin\theta}{m} = \dot{v} + \frac{uv}{r} = \frac{1}{r}\frac{d}{dt}(r^2\varphi).$$

Let us write

$$\frac{F_g}{m} = a_0 \left(\frac{r_0}{r}\right)^2.$$

where $a_0 \approx 0.59$ cm/sec², due to the Sun in Earth vicinity, and

$$\frac{F_r}{m} = \frac{Ap_0 \cos^2\theta}{m}\left(\frac{r_0}{r}\right)^2 = \alpha \cos^2\theta \left(\frac{r_0}{r}\right)^2,$$

where $\alpha = 0.1$ cm/sec² may be possible. So

$$(-a_0 + \alpha \cos^3\theta)\left(\frac{r_0}{r}\right)^2 = \dot{u} - \frac{v^2}{r}$$

$$-\alpha \sin\theta \cos^2\theta \left(\frac{r_0}{r}\right)^2 = \dot{v} + \frac{uv}{r}.$$

The value $\dot{u}$ will be small; so, approximately,

$$v = \frac{r_0}{r^{1/2}}(a_0 - \alpha \cos^3\theta)^{1/2}$$

and, for $v \sim r^{-1/2}$,

$$\dot{v} + \frac{uv}{r} = \frac{dv}{dr}\dot{r} + \frac{uv}{r} = \left(\frac{dv}{dr} + \frac{v}{r}\right)u \approx \frac{1}{2}\frac{v}{r}u;$$

so

$$u = -\frac{r_0}{r^{1/2}}\frac{2\alpha \sin\theta \cos^2\theta}{(a_0 - \alpha \cos^3\theta)^{1/2}} = \dot{r}.$$

Integrating the second equation, we obtain

$$t = \frac{1}{3}\frac{r^{3/2} - r_0^{3/2}}{r_0 \alpha^{1/2}}\frac{(a_0/\alpha - \cos^3\theta)^{1/2}}{\sin\theta \cos^2\theta}.$$

With Ψ being the path angle of the motion, as measured against the horizontal, we have

$$\tan \Psi = \left| \frac{u}{v} \right| \approx \frac{2 \sin \theta \cos^2\theta}{(a_0/\alpha) - \cos^3\theta} .$$

So it follows that Ψ is a constant for constant θ, or the flight path is a logarithmic spiral for the method considered here.

The total flight time between radii r_0 and r_1 is

$$T^2 = \frac{1}{9} \left[\left(\frac{r_1}{r_0} \right)^{3/2} - 1 \right] \frac{r_0}{\alpha} \frac{(a_0/\alpha) - \cos^3\theta}{\sin^2\theta \cos^4\theta} ,$$

or

$$T^2 \sim \frac{A - x^3}{(1 - x^2)x^4} ,$$

where $A = a_0/\alpha$, and $x = \cos \theta$. To minimize the flight time

$$\frac{\partial(T^2)}{\partial x} = -(x^4 - x^6) 3x^2 - (A - x^3)(4x^3 - 6x^5) = 0$$

$$\rightarrow 4A - 6Ax^2 - x^3 + 3x^5 = 0 .$$

Table 2.17 can now be easily computed:

TABLE 2.17

θ (deg)	35.3	34	33	31.5	29	20	10	0
$A = a_0/\alpha$	∞	5.9	2.95	1.96	Approximation of		1.001	1
α(cm/sec^2)	0	0.1	0.2	0.3	$\dot{u} = 0$ breaks down at		0.589	59
Ψ(deg)	0	8	17.5	29	such steep path angles			90

Clearly,

$$w^2 = u^2 + v^2 = \frac{r_0{}^2 a_0}{r} \left[1 - \frac{\alpha}{a_0} \cos^3\theta + 4 \left(\frac{\alpha}{a_0} \right)^2 \frac{\sin^2\theta \cos^4\theta}{1 - (\alpha/a_0) \cos^3\theta} \right] .$$

Thus, the speed is smaller by a few percent than local circular speed[1] v_c, where

$$v_c{}^2 = \frac{r_0{}^2 a_0}{r} .$$

---

[1] For $\cos \theta > 0$, i.e., inward-going motion.

Assuming the Earth orbital speed to be 30 km/sec, the vehicle speed may be 29 km/sec and 8° inclined against the Earth's motion, resulting in a relative speed between and Earth vehicle of about 4.1 km/sec. For a Hohmann transfer, the relative speed at large distance between vehicle and Earth for a Venus trip was only about 2.5 km/sec.

Obviously, the solar sailing vehicle cannot realize this initial condition. If the initial condition were fulfilled with the help of some booster, a direct ballistic (Hohmann-type) transfer to Venus would require less energy.

The flight time to Venus comes out favorably short. This is a fallacy, since the times for both escape from the launch planet and spiral to the final orbit around the target planet are not included.

Conclusion: Solar sailing does not appear to be promising. For special cases (e.g., attitude control, motion of a visibility sphere, small payload having parabolic speed) it will be applicable.[1]

The case of escape from a satellite orbit using solar sailing has been investigated (Fimple, 1960). The initial orbit is to be around Earth, circular, and have 805-km altitude, and its orbital plane is to be perpendicular to the Sun-planet line.[2] For the sail we assume: flat surface, not deforming, perfect reflector. The steering program maximizes the time rate of energy increase. Results for the escape time (in days) (approximately) are given in Table 2.18.

TABLE 2.18

Payload weight	Escape time in days for Sail weight (gm/m²)	
Total weight	2.93	1.465
0	63	30
0.2	79	40
0.4	107	54
0.5	129	65
0.6	161	81
0.8	327	158
0.9	650	350

[1] For example, a solar probe which spirals into the Sun after being launched with a hyperbolic excess of 4.1 km/sec is very favorable.

[2] Results are not too different if the Sun-planet line falls completely within the orbital plane.

These data indicate a possibility of application; but we have not yet looked at the difficult problems of handling the fragile "sail," stabilizing it (e.g., by stiffness or by proper force fields such as centrifugal force), transferring the weak forces, environmental interaction with the "sail," etc. The overall picture is not very promising.

(3) *Simple guidance program.* The vehicle guidance keeps the vehicle always on the radius vector Sun target. (See Fig. 2.52.) The angular speed

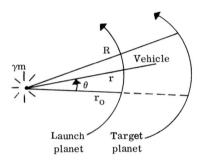

FIG. 2.52. Diagram of a simple method of guidance.

of the target is $\dot{\theta}$, then $R\dot{\theta}^2 = \gamma m/R^2$, and for the vehicle, the angular speed $\dot{\theta} = $ constant. Assuming zero radial acceleration due to thrust, we have

$$\ddot{r} = r\dot{\theta}^2 - \frac{\gamma m}{r^2} = \dot{\theta}^2 \left(r - \frac{R^3}{r^2} \right) ,$$

$$\ddot{r}\dot{r} = \dot{\theta}^2 \left(\dot{r}r - \frac{R^3}{r^2}\dot{r} \right) .$$

Performing the integration, we obtain

$$\frac{\dot{r}^2}{2} = \dot{\theta}^2 \left(\frac{r^2}{2} + \frac{R^3}{r} \right) + \text{const} ;$$

and $\dot{r} = 0$ for $r = R$ gives

$$\dot{r} = \dot{\theta} \left(r^2 + 2\frac{R^3}{r} - 3R^2 \right)^{1/2} .$$

Putting $r = R - x$, assuming $x/R < 1$, and developing in a power series to x^2 we get

$$\dot{r} \approx \dot{\theta} \, 3^{1/2}(R - r) .$$

The required transverse acceleration is

$$a_t = \frac{1}{r}\frac{d}{dt}(r^2\dot\theta) = 2\dot r\dot\theta \approx 2\ 3^{1/2}(R-r)\dot\theta^2 = 2\ 3^{1/2}\left(1-\frac{r}{R}\right)\frac{\gamma m}{R^2},$$

and the radial acceleration is zero. But here we have used instead of the exact solution an approximate one. Let us introduce a radial acceleration a_r, which makes the approximate solution exact:

$$\dot r = 3^{1/2}\dot\theta\ (R-r),$$

$$\ddot r = -\ 3\dot\theta^2\ (R-r).$$

Inserting this in

$$\ddot r - \dot\theta^2\left(r - \frac{R^3}{r^2}\right) = a_r,$$

we get

$$a_r = R\dot\theta^2\left[\left(\frac{R}{r}+1\right)^2 - 4\right].$$

The total acceleration is

$$a = (a_t^2 + a_r^2)^{1/2} = \frac{\gamma m}{R^2}\left[\left(\frac{R}{r}\right)^4 + 4\left(\frac{R}{r}\right)^3 - 2\left(\frac{R}{r}\right)^2 - 12\frac{R}{r}\right.$$

$$\left. + 21 - \frac{24}{R/r} + \frac{12}{(R/r)^2}\right]^{1/2}.$$

Introducing $r/R = 1 + y$, and developing to y^2, assuming $|y| < 1$, yields

$$a \approx \frac{\gamma m}{R^2}2\left(\frac{R-r}{R}\right)7^{1/2}.$$

For the required speed it follows that

$$v_r = \int_0^T a\ dt = \int_{r_0}^R a\ \frac{dr}{\dot r} \approx \left(\frac{14}{3}\right)^{1/2}\left(\frac{2\gamma m}{R}\right)^{1/2}\left(1 - \frac{r_0}{R}\right).$$

The flight time is

$$T = \int_{r_0}^R \frac{dr}{\dot r} \approx \frac{1}{3^{1/2}\dot\theta}\int_{r_0}^R \frac{dr}{R-r} = \frac{1}{\dot\theta 3^{1/2}}\ln(R-r)\Big|_R^{r_0} \to \infty,$$

the final approach is infinitely slow. Hence the conclusions are:

(a) The acceleration a is—measured in Earth-g's—low for interplanetary flights, but variable with r.

(b) The establishment of the initial condition with respect to angular speed is beyond the capability of a low acceleration system.

(c) The total required speed is very high.

(d) A modification is necessary to get a finite flight time.

The described program does not appear to be promising, in spite of its simplicity with respect to its guidance aspects.

(4) *Simple low-acceleration vehicle optimization.* The initial acceleration of a low-acceleration vehicle was written [for symbols, see Eq. 2.16]

$$g_0 a_0 = \frac{F}{M_0} = \frac{M_c}{M_0 \tau} \left(\frac{2E\tau}{M_c} \right)^{1/2} = \frac{1}{M_0} \left(\frac{2EM_c}{\tau} \right)^{1/2},$$

or

$$(a_0 g_0) = \frac{[2E/\tau)M_c]^{1/2}}{M_c + M_L + M_s + (\alpha_0/g_0)E}.$$

Characteristic speed of the vehicle is

$$v_{id} = g_0 \int_0^\tau a \, dt = a_0 g_0 \int_0^\tau \frac{M_0}{M} \, dt = - a_0 g_0 \int_{M_0}^{M_e} \frac{M_0}{M} \frac{\tau}{M_c} \, dM$$

$$= a_0 g_0 \frac{M_0}{M_c} \tau \ln \frac{M_0}{M_e} = g_0 \left\{ a_0 \frac{M_0}{M_c} \tau \ln \left[1 + \frac{M_c}{M_L + M_s + (\alpha_0/g_0)E} \right] \right\} \tau.$$

Inserting $g_0 a_0 M_0$ we have, of course, the rocket equation

$$v_{id} = \left(\frac{2E\tau}{M_c} \right)^{1/2} \ln \frac{M_0}{M_e}.$$

Let us consider in the expression for $a_0 g_0$, only M_c as a variable, and everything else as constant. Then $a_0 g_0$ is of the form

$$a_0 g_0 \sim \frac{M_c^{1/2}}{M_c + M_e},$$

and in order to maximize a_0 (which should lead to the shortest, or at least a short, total flight time):

$$\frac{\partial a_0 g_0}{\partial M_c} = \frac{(M_c + M_e)\frac{1}{2}(1/M_0^{1/2}) - M_c^{1/2}}{(M_c + M_e)^2} = 0 \rightarrow M_c = \tfrac{1}{2} M_0,$$

or

$$\left(\frac{M_0}{M_e}\right)_{\text{opt}} = 2 \, .$$

This procedure is not allowed, because the assumption of having only M_c variable and everything else constant is not justified.[1] One should rather keep v_{id} constant, which is not possible to achieve by changing M_c only.

From $v_{\text{id}} = $ constant comes,

$$\frac{(2E\tau)^{1/2}}{v_{\text{id}}} = \frac{M_c^{1/2}}{\ln(M_0/M_e)} = \frac{M_e^{1/2}(M_c/M_e)^{1/2}}{\ln(1 + M_c/M_e)} = -\frac{M_0^{1/2}(M_c/M_0)^{1/2}}{\ln(1 - M_c/M_0)} \, .$$

For given E, v_{id}, M_e it follows that τ is a minimum for

$$\left(\frac{M_c}{M_e}\right)_{\text{opt}} = 3.93 \qquad \text{or} \qquad \left(\frac{M_0}{M_e}\right)_{\text{opt}} = 4.93 \, .$$

Now we can derive:

$$\left(\frac{v_{\text{id}}}{c}\right)_{\text{opt}} = 1.595 \, ,$$

and

$$\tau_{\min}[\text{yr}] = \frac{M_e[\text{kg sec}^2/\text{m}] \, v_{\text{id}}^2 \, [\text{km}/\text{sec}]}{E\,[\text{kW}]\,2618} \, .$$

An example is given in Table 2.19.

It can be seen that the optimization with respect to M_L/M_0 appears to be more significant. Optimizing for τ results in poor M_L/M_0 ratios, whereas M_L/M_e is but little affected. A relatively small decrease in τ is shown to be expensive in M_L/M_0. Besides, one has to show whether really minimum τ leads to minimum mission time. But this investigation hardly appears to be worthwhile.

What will be the result if we minimize τ, keeping E, v_{id}, and M_0 constant? Roughly, keeping v_{id} constant means keeping $M_c c$ constant, and $2E = (M_c/\tau)c^2$. So $\tau/c \approx$ constant, or $\tau/(E\tau)^{1/2}M_c^{1/2} = $ constant, or $M_c\tau = $ constant. To minimize τ simply means to maximize M_c, and for a given M_0, $M_c = M_0$ is the maximum value of M_c. This is a completely impractical solution. Besides, c becomes small, thus defeating the whole purpose for using an energy-limited system in the first place. (These results as

---

[1] Because it leads to v_{id} variable.

TABLE 2.19

	Optimization for $\tau_{\min}$; first 4 values assumed to be given[a]		Optimization for M_L/M_0, as described in Fig. 2.33		Again optimization for $\tau_{\min}$
v_{id} (km/sec)	45	$\longrightarrow$	45	$\longrightarrow$	45
$g_0 M_e$(tons)	30.6		76	$\longrightarrow$	76
E (kW)	1500		4000	$\longrightarrow$	4000
α_0(kg/kW)	10	$\longrightarrow$	10	$\longrightarrow$	10
$g_0 M_s$(tons)	0.6		2		2
$g_0 M_p$(tons)	15		40		40
$g_0 M_L$(tons)	15		34		34
$g_0 M_0$(tons)	151	$\longrightarrow$	151		374
$g_0 M_c$(tons)	120.4		75		298
c(km/sec)	28.2		66.1		28.2
τ(yr)	1.61	$\longrightarrow$	1.61		1.5
$100 M_L/M_0$(%)	10		22		9
$100 M_L/M_e$(%)	49		44		44

[a] The arrows indicates transfer of number to next column.

approximated here follow exactly, when τ is minimized keeping E, v_{id}, and M_0 constant. The simple proof is left to the reader.)

(5) *Mixed high-low acceleration for orbital departure.* This subject is treated in sufficient detail in connection with Problem 2.8.

What should be the lesson of all these ingenious solutions?

(a) If a simple and ingenious solution is found, be sceptical. Over years of research the simple facts have been studied quite thoroughly, and the probability of new discoveries is declining, but not zero (Example 1 of this section).

(b) Specifically, are the boundary conditions fulfilled, or can the system be forced to fulfill them? If the system is forced to fulfill them, does the solution really still apply? (Examples 2, 3.)

(c) Are the imposed conditions physically sensible? If not: can they be altered so that they will be? (Example 4.)

(d) Compare the results always with those of the "orthodox" approach to find whether something really worthwhile has been introduced. (Example 4.)

Problems

2.1. In the equation for Λ on p. 229, what happens for $c \to 0$?

2.2. A rocket vehicle moves in field- and resistance-free space; the initial speed is zero, linear motion only is considered. Total energy[1] $P = \eta E/m_e = \frac{1}{2} m_T c^2/m_e$ is constant and given.
The objective is to move through a path length S in the least possible time.

(1) What is the best duration of thrust in comparison to free-flight time?
(2) Is there a best mass ratio?
(3) What is the improvement for variable c?

2.3. See Eq. (2.50): Is constant direction of thrust a usable approximation?

2.4. Explain why chemical rockets maximize $\int_0^t a \, dt$ and not $\int_0^t a^2 \, dt$.

2.5. Compute the mean acceleration $\bar{a}$ of a rocket flying with constant thrust F.

2.6. A simple method of optimization for a low-acceleration vehicle proceeds as follows: Let $\dot{m}$ be the mass flow rate, c the exhaust speed $=$ constant, τ the propulsion time duration, g the acceleration of gravity at Earth's surface, M_L the vehicle payload mass, M_s the vehicle structure mass, M_p the vehicle power-plant mass, M_c the vehicle propellant mass, and M_0 the initial vehicle mass. Then

$$M_0 = M_L + M_s + M_p + M_c$$

$$\Delta v = c \ln \frac{M_0}{M_L + M_s + M_p}$$

$$= c \ln \left[\frac{1 + M_p/M_c}{M_p/M_c + (M_L + M_s)/M_0} \right].$$

We have $M_c = \dot{m}\tau$, and

$$M_p = \frac{\alpha}{g} \frac{\dot{m} c^2}{2};$$

thus

$$\frac{M_p}{M_c} = \frac{c^2}{2\tau g/\alpha}.$$

---

[1] Then, $L = \eta \dot{E}/m_e$ is not a given constant for the vehicles to be compared.

Introducing a "characteristic speed" $U = (2\tau g/\alpha)^{1/2}$ or

$$U \,[\text{m/sec}] = \left(\frac{2\tau \,[\text{sec}]}{\alpha \,[\text{kg/kW}]} \times 10^3 \right)^{1/2}$$

yields, finally,

$$\frac{\Delta v}{U} = \frac{c}{U} \ln \left[\frac{1 + (c/U)^2}{(M_L + M_s)/M_0 + (c/U)^2} \right].$$

For a given U and $(M_L + M_s/M_0)$ (or Δv) there exists a value $c = c_{\text{opt}}$ so that Δv [or $(M_L + M_s)/M_0$] is a maximum. This value c_{opt} can be read from the included graph immediately (Fig. 2.53). It is seen that $c = U$ is a good solution always.

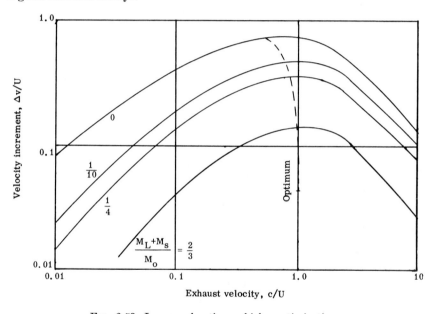

Fig. 2.53. Low acceleration vehicle, optimization.

Find an approximate solution c_{opt} for the special case $(M_L + M_s)/M_0 = 0$; investigate this case using the graph and compare the solution to the corresponding case treated in Chap. 2.

2.7. For a low-acceleration system, let F be the thrust, t the time of engine operation, v the required speed, c the exhaust speed, g the acceleration of gravity at the Earth surface, m_e the mass of energy source, generator, radiator, ion source, ion accelerator, feed system, etc., L the energy rate from source, L_e the electric energy rate, m_p the mass of payload, m_b the mass of exhaust material, m_s the mass of tankage (structure); $m_0 = m_p + m_e + m_b + m_s$ the initial mass, and $m_f = m_p + m_e + m_s$ final mass.

We have the relations

$$I = \frac{Ft}{m_0 g} , \qquad L_e = \eta L , \qquad F = \frac{m_b}{t} c ,$$

$$m_e = \alpha L , \qquad m_s = \beta m_b , \qquad \frac{m_0}{m_0 - m_b} = \exp(v/c) .$$

If t, g, m_p, m_0, α, β, η are given constants, find c so that v is a maximum.

2.8. *Mixed high-low thrust.* T. N. Edelbaum of United Aircraft Corporation drew our attention to the fact that, under certain conditions, a mixture between high and low acceleration systems can give optimum results.

For example, for an escape maneuver from an orbit the optimum appears to be [1]:

Phase one: little altitude gain → high I_{sp}, consequently low thrust.

Phase two: rapid altitude gain → high thrust, consequently low I_{sp}.

Phase three: altitude is what it is → high I_{sp}, consequently low thrust.

Of course, the low thrust system need not be switched off during the high-thrust system operation.

A simpler case is to proceed in two phases for an escape mission:

Phase 1: high acceleration to a speed v_1;

Phase 2: low acceleration from v_1 to the final speed v_c.

Written this way, all low acceleration missions from Earth surface follow this pattern; often we choose v_1 to be circular speed for many valid reasons (e.g., operational ones). But from the flight mechanics optimization point of view, the crossover from high to low acceleration does not necessarily occur at this speed. It can be shown that $v_1 \neq v_p$, where v_p is the parabolic speed, for positive values of the hyperbolic excess speed v'_∞; the v_∞ value

---

[1] Some results are (Edelbaum, 1962c):

(1) The series low-high-low acceleration will generally maximize payload fraction to be delivered from a satellite orbit to a given hyperbolic excess speed.

(2) A major gain in payload (20%) can result for relatively fast missions by going to mixed propulsion.

(3) High thrust should not be used to establish a high circular orbit; this should be done with the low-acceleration system. If the high-thrust system is used first, it should rather be utilized to established an elliptic orbit. See also Fimple (1963).

at the end of the high acceleration phase follows from $v_\infty = (v_1{}^2 - v_p{}^2)^{1/2}$, from which $dv_\infty/dv_1 = [1(- (v_p/v_1)^2]^{-1/2} \to \infty$ for $v_1 \to v_p$; therefore, a relatively large v_∞ increase will result from a small increase in cutoff speed. In other words, if $v_1 = v_p$ then we should have increased the transition speed into the hyperbolic regime. Thus the choice $v_p = v_\infty$ is definitely non-optimum. It can be expected that the optimum crossover depends, for a given mission, upon the relative qualities of the high-acceleration and the low-acceleration systems; it may—as shown—not occur at parabolic speed and, practically speaking, not below low-altitude circular condition.

MacKay (1964) wrote the first paper in which an optimized mode of mixed acceleration for a complete manned planetary mission was utilized. He chose the following mission profile: Starting from a polar circular orbit around Earth (altitude 0.1 Earth radius), a first impulsive velocity increment Δv is provided by a nuclear stage. After staging, electric propulsion sets in. A circular orbit around Mars (26 Mars radii altitude) is entered, with 40 days staytime. Return occurs from that orbit to Earth, where impulsive chemical braking is applied, resulting in a direct aerodynamic entry with a speed of 15.85 km/sec.

Nuclear high-acceleration propulsion data: $I_{sp} = 850$ sec.

Electric propulsion data: constant thrust and specific impulse.

Realistic efficiency, as function of I_{sp}: $\alpha = 7$ kg/kW.

Chemical braking propulsion: $I_{sp} = 430$ sec.

Major results are:

(1) For a total mission duration of 400 days, we have:

For $\Delta v = 3.13$ km/sec (parabolic injection condition) initial mass in Earth orbit is 144%.

For $\Delta v = 3.74$ km/sec (minimum mass)[1] initial mass in Earth orbit is 100%.

For $\Delta v = 4.01$ km/sec (completely impulsive injection) initial mass in Earth orbit is 102%.

(2) For a total mission duration of 500 days or longer, use electric propulsion only.

For a total mission duration shorter than 500 days, mixed acceleration leads to minimum initial mass.

(3) Using high acceleration only, a minimum initial mass occurs for a mission duration of 470 days; let us call it 100%. Low acceleration alone

---

[1] An optimum condition is that during transition from high to low acceleration, the thrust direction should not change.

can do this mission for an initial mass of 64%, and mixed acceleration for 56%.

(4) Total electric power requirement for various mission durations are as follows:

Mission duration (days)	400	450	500	550
Power for all electric mission [MW(e)]	30	12	6	5
Power for mixed mission [MW(e)]	5	3.5	2.5	2

The advantage of the mixed mission is obvious.

Let us look now into one simple example, namely, motion in field- and resistance-free space:

	High thrust	Low thrust	Free flight
Time	0	t	T	τ
Path	0	s	S	σ
Speed	0	v	V	V

Does $t = 0$ always result in maximum payload?

2.9. The condition for an optimum low-acceleration trajectory has been shown to be ["ingenious solutions,"(1)]:

$$I = \int_0^T a^2 \, dt = \min,$$

where a is the acceleration and T the time of operation. Furthermore, from the performance point of view there may be

$$\int_0^T a \, dt = V = \text{given value.}$$

Show that $a = $ constant follows as criterion of optimization from the above two equations.

2.10. For electric propulsion systems, reliability problems appear to be of special significance because of the long operating times and long exposure times to the space environment. Therefore, the use of redundant power-plants may be desirable, as treated by Edelbaum (1962d). But some of the requirements thus introduced are difficult to satisfy—e.g., jettisoning of failed power plants, variable specific impulse, and power-to-weight ratio being the same for a single large and an equivalent cluster of smaller propulsive systems.

We will look briefly into a much simpler question. It is shown in the text that the payolad fraction ν increases monotonically with flight time.[1] Obviously, this is true only if the probability of mission success p is independent of the flight time. Make a plausible assumption for $p(t)$, estimate an analytic approximation for the optimum growth factor as shown in Fig. 2.33, and show how inclusion of this reliability factor leads to a "best" finite mission duration.

2.11. In Sec. 2.3,2,3 an expression for E/W has been derived for a spherical mirror. Introduce for the total weight $M = W + \alpha$, where the constant α stands for the boiler weight, etc. Compute the optimum rim angle φ_0.

2.12. What is the total energy release of a nuclear reactor after shutdown, compared to its energy release during operation? Estimate how much hydrogen is required for cooling of a heat-exchanger nuclear engine from shutdown until the reactor is really "cold."

2.13. Assume that an electrically propelled vehicle of acceleration a is used to launch from the surface of a spherical homogeneous celestial body of radius r. What is an upper limit for r?

2.14. Compute the payload capability for an advanced Saturn V launched probe which enters a circular orbit of 1 a.u. radius, 90° inclined to the ecliptic: Initial mass in circular Earth orbit, 200 km altitude: 250,000 lb (113.5 tons). Initial mass, delivered to parabolic energy: 95,000 lb (43.1 tons).

Case 1. Starting from Earth orbit, chemical propulsion: $I_{sp} = 450$ sec and $\varepsilon = 0.08$. Optimum staging (maximum payload).

Case 2. Starting from Earth orbit, nuclear propulsion: $I_{sp} = 850$ sec and $\varepsilon = 0.18$. Optimum staging (maximum payload).

Case 3. Starting from Earth orbit, electric propulsion: $\alpha = 19$ kg/kW (jet power) (Cluster of 5 SNAP 50 units, i.e., 1.375 MW electric) (for description of SNAP 50, see Chap. 3).

Case 4. Starting from escape, electric propulsion: $\alpha = 19$ kg/kW (jet power). Total power is 0.55 MW (Cluster of 2 SNAP 50).

---

[1] For this problem we shall neglect the difference between propulsive system operation duration and mission duration.

Assumed minimum payload requirements are given in the following tabulation:

	Weight (lb)			Weight (lb)
For nonelectric propulsion			For electric propulsion	
Payload	1,000		Payload	1,000
Power supply	3,000		Power conditioning[a]	500
			Extra shielding	200
Packaging	500		Packaging	400
Midcourse, etc.	500		Midcourse, etc.	400
Astrionics	500		Astrionics	500
Total	5,500		Total	3,000

[a] Main power supply is available.

See whether the vehicles can perform the mission.

2.15. Given are

(1) Saturn V (3-stage vehicle) payload capability as a function of hyperbolic excess speed. (For a typical choice, see Fig. 2.54.)

(2) The payload consists of an electrically propelled spacecraft using

   (a) Electric power supply of Case 4, Problem 2.14, viz., 0.55 MW jet power, 23,050-lb propulsion system mass.

   (b) Spacecraft structure: with full cesium load, 1900 lb (with no cesium, 950 lb less) (indicated on Fig. 2.54).

   (c) Payload: 3000 lb (requirement from Problem 2.14) (indicated on Fig. 2.51).

(3) Mission: Same as Problem 2.14. Compute the optimum speed of crossover from high to low acceleration leading to minimum powered flight time (i.e., minimum flight time from launch to arrival). The flight time of the high acceleration phase shall be neglected in comparison to the low acceleration phase. Since the latter is of the order of years, this is obviously justified.

2.16. Optimization for economy instead of performance might become important for low acceleration vehicles also. If, e.g., a low acceleration reusable orbit-to-orbit transportation system is considered, and if the

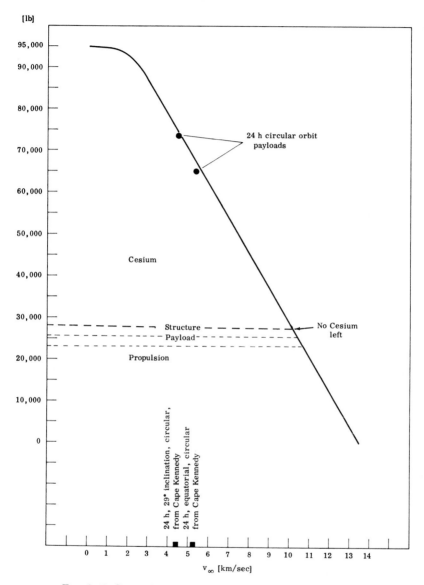

Fig. 2.54. Saturn V (3 stages) payload vs hyperbolic excess speed.

ground-to-orbit supply operation becomes the major cost item in this operation, then the ratio

$$\frac{\text{payload weight}}{\text{propellant weight}} = \frac{1}{P} \quad \text{instead of} \quad \frac{\text{payload weight}}{\text{launch weight}} = \frac{1}{G}$$

should be maximized. Use a procedure corresponding to that given in Sec. 2.3,6,2.

Major Symbols

A	Area	s	Path length
a	Acceleration	T	Temperature: half lifetime; time
C_p	Molar specific heat	t	Time
c	Exhaust velocity	U	Voltage
E	Energy	V	Volume; voltage
e	Energy; energy density	v	Velocity; voltage
F	Surface area; thrust; force	W	Weight
f	Thrust; thrust density	w	Weight
g	Gravitational acceleration	α	Specific weight
H	Enthalpy	γ	Gravitational constant
h	Altitude; moment	ε	Emissivity; absorptivity; eccentricity
I	Impulse; current		
j	Current density	η	Efficiency
L	Energy rate	k	Specific heat ratio
M	Molecular weight; mass	λ	Wavelength
m	Mass	ϱ	Density; reflectivity
P	Pressure	σ	Stefan-Boltzmann constant
p	Chamber pressure: permeance	τ	Time
R	Universal gas constant	φ	Flux

CHAPTER 3 EXTRATERRESTRIAL ENVIRONMENTS

3.1 Introduction

Space vehicle environment can differ from the standard laboratory environment in many ways; during transportation on the Earth's surface and during launch preparation, relatively hostile environments may be encountered. The same holds for the duration of powered flight through the atmosphere, for the duration of return to the Earth's surface, and for the following recovery period.

Inside the vehicle, environmental conditions can be very severe—for example, the chemical or cryogenic properties of the propellant, the presence of a nuclear source of radiation, the very high noise level resulting from the operation of the rocket engines (for chemical rocket engines, about 1% of the total jet[1] power appears as noise power), the steady or shock loading conditions, etc. Such environmental conditions play an important role in vehicle design, and no standard solutions are available. Specifications for military missiles differ from those for civilian space vehicles, and problems of sonic fatigue of materials are different in recoverable, multiusable vehicles as compared to one-shot vehicles.

If we neglect Earth and vehicle-created environments, we can say that all space vehicles have to move through space. In space they encounter extraterrestrial environments, and in many ways extraterrestrial environments can differ from the familiar environments here on Earth, as, for example:

---

[1] Typically, 0.5 $\pm$ 0.25% of the jet power appear as acoustic power, engine clusters being on the low noise side (from *Space/Aeronautics*, October 1965).

(1) The structure and behavior of a surrounding atmosphere can be both physically and chemically much different from the Earth atmosphere, e.g., Venus, Mars, Jupiter, Moon. An ionosphere can influence communication, among other things. Free space is the special case of practically no atmosphere. On other heavenly bodies the surface may be of an unfamiliar (both physically and chemically) nature.

(2) Gravitational acceleration can vary by a wide margin. Free space is again the special case where no gravitational loads act upon the structure of a vehicle in free flight. Fields other than the gravitational field—magnetic or electric—deserve attention.

(3) Both particle and wave radiation can differ from normal Earth conditions. On other heavenly bodies the surface could be radioactive. With no atmosphere, space radiation might reach the surface.

(4) Meteors and micrometeors rarely if ever reach the Earth ground, but can play an important role under other environmental conditions.

(5) Temperature—generally influenced by energy created within the vehicle, energy reaching the vehicle from the outside, and energy given by the vehicle to the outside—will depend upon the environment. Proper measures have to be taken to control temperature in the anticipated environment.

(6) On other celestial bodies, resources to be found and methods of finding and utilizing them can become of paramount importance to the economics of space flight and extraterrestrial settlements.

There are three different steps or phases which determine how the environment influences the technological development of space flight:

(1) First, one must know the environment to be able to design vehicles for it; so we instrument space probes, etc., to improve on the fund of existing knowledge.[1]

(2) After the environment is known, it is possible to shelter the payload from it. More desirable, sometimes the environment can be used to advantage (e.g., the absence of an oxidizing atmosphere allows the use of materials which cannot be used in the presence of such an atmosphere).

(3) Finally, in some cases it may be feasible to alter the environment, or to alter the payload such that the "new" environment is—as seen from the payload—a desirable one.

---

[1] The unmanned probe is a comparatively recent concept (Gatland et al., 1951; Braun and Ryan, 1953; Singer, 1953; Burgess, 1949, 1952).

After these introductory remarks, we shall describe some of the typical environmental differences and their effects. Completeness cannot be expected since this field is rapidly expanding. In many areas, little is known (e.g., environment on the surface of Venus), and individual judgement must be exercised as to what is typical and what is not. We will generally limit this discussion to space environment. For conditions on other celestial bodies, the astronomical literature should be consulted. For additional details see Legalley (1963).

3.2 Gas Density in Space

3.2,1 Earth Atmosphere (Rasool, 1963)

In the Appendix a chart showing pressure vs altitude for the Earth atmosphere can be found. Ingenious research was necessary to accumulate this information on the upper atmosphere since direct measurement of very low pressures or densities is very difficult, and since about only one decade has elapsed since the means have become available for carrying physical apparatus to such altitudes.

The composition of the Earth atmosphere at ground level is about 78% of N_2, 21% of O_2, and 1% of other gases. Up to about 70 km altitude this remains basically unchanged, with the exception of water vapor, which is present in the stratosphere in only small quantities. [In the Venusian atmosphere, it has been discovered that the water vapor above the cloud layer is even greater quantitatively than that in the Earth's stratosphere. The Mariner II experiment gave us the following results: The surface of Venus is dry, sandy, overcast, and hot (average 430°C). The atmospheric pressure is at least 12 atm. It is quite dark below the clouds. The cloud cover (condensed hydrocarbons similar to smog or possibly ice crystals) is 25–30 km thick, begins at about 70 km altitude, and has a temperature of about 90°C at its lower and − 50°C at its upper layer.]

Within the Earth atmosphere, untrained man can breathe up to 7 km altitude; with proper training, this can be increased to 9.5 km. At that altitude, the atmospheric pressure is 0.27 atm. Since within the human lungs there is a pressure of 0.053 atm CO_2 and 0.062 atm H_2O, we have a partial atmospheric pressure within the lungs of 0.155 atm, or a partial oxygen pressure of 0.033 atm, demanding 0.148 atm for the minimum required pressure of a pure oxygen atmosphere.

Pressure breathing should not be against a higher pressure than 0.06 atm, demanding an ambient pressure of 0.088 atm, which occurs at 16 km altitude. More elaborate breathing devices will suffice up to 19 km. At that altitude (pressure 0.059 atm), human blood begins to boil, therefore, full pressure suits are required.[1]

The Mars atmosphere as described in Chap. 5 (Vol. 1) has a surface density/pressure equivalent to the Earth atmosphere at about 31 km altitude. For more detail, see Section 5.2,1, Vol. 1.

It appears, then, that a full pressure suit will be required on the surface of Mars. Let us return to the discussion of the Earth atmosphere.

Because of solar ultraviolet radiation, ozone, O_3, is formed with a maximum concentration of 10 parts in 10^6 at about 30 km.[2] Some types of balloons cannot reach higher altitudes because their structural material is destroyed by the ozone. This simple example shows how materials or possibly designs (e.g., protective cover) must take into account the environment.

Above 80 km, formation of ions and dissociation of oxygen sets in. Diffusive separation of gases—prevented at lower altitudes by mixing processes—starts at about 70 km, and above 100 km the separation is quite pronounced. Above 150 km most of the oxygen is dissociated. Nitrogen dissociation starts at about 180 km, but molecules have been found up to 250 km. Above 250 km, only atomic nitrogen and oxygen are present. Again, the dissociated or ionized gases are harmful to certain materials.

Above 500 km, 10–100% of the particles are ionized. At 475 km, several million electrons per cubic centimeter, and about as many heavy ions (mostly O^+ between 250 and 950 km) have been found by satellites. This is surprising since, from radio observations, it was previously thought that the electron concentration has a maximum of about 3×10^5 particles/cm^3 in the F^2 layer, 300 km altitude. Furthermore, a structure of ionized layers in the atmosphere was expected which the measurements do not confirm at all. Fortunately, refined theoretical considerations had just shown that the ionized layer concept was erroneous, when first measurements became available.[3] Theory and experiments agree that the electron concentration is about constant throughout the whole ionosphere—from 100 km on to the exosphere. These electrons have mostly thermal energies. But some —about one out of 10^{10}—have energies up to 10^3 eV. These play an important part in inducing the aurorae.

The temperature at zero altitude is about 300°K. It drops to about 200°K above 10 km and starts to rise at about the ozone layer back to

---

[1] Full pressure protection is also required for pressures larger than 20–25 atm, for well-trained men. Because of heat of vaporization, boiling leads to freezing.

[2] Therefore, ozone may occur at the surface of Mars.

[3] For many details on environmental electricity, see Tilson (1964).

300°K, which is reached around 50 km. From there it drops again to 200°K around 75 km and starts rising again around 100 km. This low temperature explains why ice crystals—observed in the form of noctilucent clouds—can exist at this altitude. In airglow observation, among others, strong OH-emission from around 90 km have been observed, with the band structure of the emitting molecules indicating a temperature below 200°K. Why is so much water (or OH) up there? One theory is that hydrogen from space enters the atmosphere and reacts with oxygen.

The aforementioned temperature rise proceeds to about 1500°K at the beginning of the exosphere at an altitude of 530 km. (*Exosphere* is that region from which neutral atoms may escape unhindered by collisions.) Within the exosphere the temperature appears to be constant, at around 1500°K. In spite of this high temperature, heat transfer is mostly by radiation only because of the low gas density.

The mean free path of the molecules is only $\sim 10^{-7}$ m at zero altitude, but increases to 1 cm at 80 km, 10 cm at 100 km, and 100 m at 160 km. At 220 km the mean free path length is 1 km, increasing to 10 km at 300 km, and to 100 km at about 400 km altitude. From 300 km on, some molecules will follow ballistic paths, and from 550 km all of them will. This is the beginning of the exosphere. The exosphere consists of atomic[1] oxygen, atomic[1] nitrogen, and atomic[1] hydrogen. Initially we find mostly oxygen, but at 1300 km hydrogen starts to predominate. At an altitude of one Earth radius, the density may be ~ 1000 hydrogen atoms and a few protons and electrons per cubic centimeter. A band of helium around the Earth from 950 to 2600 km altitude was discovered by the satellites Echo I and Explorer VII. The thickness of the helium layer depends strongly upon temperature (day-night cycle) and solar activity (typical data are 200 km for quiet Sun and 2000 km for active Sun). At six Earth radii altitude, we find 10 H atoms and ~ 100 protons and electrons per cubic centimeter; this is about where free space begins.[2] Practical functional limits of the atmosphere are at vastly different altitudes; e.g., at about 9.5 km breathing becomes impossible for man; minimum altitude for a circular satellite might be about 150 km.

The mean molecular weight stays constant at 28.966 up to the beginning of dissociation of oxygen and diffusive separation. It drops to about 20 at 250 km, 16 at 500 km, and to about 1 above a few thousand kilometers. Because of these changes, scale heights[3] will vary widely.

---

[1] Or ionized.

[2] Density of atmosphere equals the density of interplanetary space at 5000 km altitude.

[3] A measure of the rate of density change.

This description shows that our atmosphere has a very complicated structure. There are still many unknown factors and oversimplifications. Obviously there will be variations, even when our description would accurately give mean values. The variations may be the result of latitude and longitude, solar or lunar tides, solar activity, day-night, time of the year, winds, etc. Table 3.1 gives some results from Sputnik satellite measurements.

TABLE 3.1

Sputnik Satellite Measurements

Altitude (km)	Density		Temperature (°K)
	Particles/cm³	gm/cm³	
225[a]	6.01×10^9	2.12×10^{-13}	936
430	1.7×10^8	4.51×10^{-15}	1500
500	8.24×10^7	2.21×10^{-15}	1950

[a] Density is greater at day than it is at night, and density is greater at polar latitudes than it is at the equatorial latitudes. These differences become pronounced above 200–300 km altitude.

The U.S. satellite Echo I (launched August, 1960) proved to be a valuable sensor for small forces, e.g., solar radiation pressure and atmospheric drag, besides its major function as a passive communications reflector. The atmospheric density at 1500 km altitude was found to be 1.1×10^{-18} gm/cm³, with an uncertainty of about a factor of two.

There is indication that in December the overall density of the upper atmosphere is about twice as great as in June. The ratio of maximum density at day (2 p.m.) to the minimum density at night (12 midnight), taken from different measurements, is given in Table 3.2.

Solar activity can lead to a density increase, perhaps up to a factor of three compared to a quiet Sun at 500 km altitude.

No density variation with latitude is observed. The scale height[1] H is given in Table 3.3, and the effects of solar activity on scale height are given in Table 3.4.

Because of such variations, none of the static atmospheric models describe reality; attempts are made to develop a dynamic model of the atmos-

[1] See Sec. 3.2,2.

phere, where properties are not only a function of location in space (longitude, latitude, altitude), but of time also.

TABLE 3.2

Altitude (km)	Ratio of densities[a]
180	1.4
200	1.7
270	2
350	2.5
600	6.6
700	8

[a] Ratio of maximum density at day (2 p.m.) to minimum density at night (12 midnight).

TABLE 3.3

Altitude (km)	Scale height (km)	
	Day	Night
200	40–45	40–45
600	90–100	55

TABLE 3.4

Altitude (km)	Scale height (km)	
	Maximum solar activity	Minimum solar activity
200	40	20
400	80	40
600	100	70
800	120	100

It goes without saying that the variations of the atmospheric properties
are of great importance regarding satellite lifetime computations; they do
not appear to be very significant for the direct reentry of space vehicles.

There are strong winds in addition to the rotation of the upper atmosphere. This rotation manifested itself in a small inclination change of the Earth satellite Sputnik 2, 3 (rocket carrier), as described in Sec. 4.4,2,5 of Vol. 1. Assuming a wind with a gas density ϱ blowing with a speed of $v = 200$ m/sec at an object with a ballistic factor (weight)/(drag coefficient $\times$ area) of 100 kg/m² for a time of $t = 100$ sec, the speed component induced by this wind is about

$$\varDelta v \approx \frac{\varrho}{\varrho_0} \frac{(\varrho_0/2)v^2}{(\text{weight/drag coeff.} \times \text{area})} g_0 t$$

$$= \frac{\varrho}{\varrho_0} \times 2.6 \times 10^4 \quad \text{m/sec} ,$$

or

$$\varDelta v < 2.6 \text{ m/sec} \qquad \text{for} \quad \varrho/\varrho_0 < 10^{-4} ,$$

which is true for altitudes above about 70 km. (On p. 550 of Vol. 1, a graph of atmospheric density vs altitude for Earth can be found.) Therefore, atmospheric motion above 70 km altitude will not appreciably change the flight path of a space vehicle returning to Earth.

3.2,2 Crude Atmospheric Models (Fig. 3.1)

The weight of the atmospheric element is, of course,

$$dw = s^2\gamma \; dr = g\varrho s^2 \; dr = g_0 \varrho \, \frac{R^2}{r^2} \, s^2 \; dr ,$$

where index 0 denotes zero altitude, γ is the gas specific weight, and ϱ is

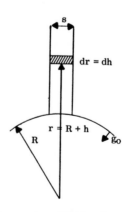

Fig. 3.1. Diagram to compute atmospheric model.

the gas density. From the gas law ($\mathscr{R}$ is the universal gas constant, M the molecular weight)

$$g_{0E}\varrho = \frac{p}{(\mathscr{R}/M)T} \ ,$$

where E denotes Earth; thus, for equilibrium,

$$dw = -\,s^2\,dp = \frac{p}{(g_{0E}/g_0)\,(\mathscr{R}/M)T}\,\frac{R^2}{r^2}\,s^2\,dr \ ,$$

or

$$\frac{g_{0E}}{g_0}\frac{\mathscr{R}}{M}\,T\,\frac{dp}{p} = -\,\frac{R^2}{r^2}\,dr \ .$$

Introducing the "scale height"

$$H = \frac{g_{0E}}{g_0}\frac{\mathscr{R}}{M}\,T = H_0\,\frac{T}{T_0}\frac{M_0}{M}$$

yields

$$H_0\,\frac{T}{T_0}\frac{M_0}{M}\frac{dp}{p} = -\,\frac{R^2}{r^2}\,dr \ .$$

Integration of this equation is possible only when T, M, as functions of altitude or pressure, are known. Let us describe two models.

(1) *Isothermal atmosphere.* With

$$\frac{T}{T_0}\frac{M_0}{M} = 1 \ ,$$

we get

$$\frac{p}{p_0} = \exp\left[-\frac{R}{H_0}\left(1 - \frac{R}{r}\right)\right] = \exp\left[-\frac{h}{H_0}\left(\frac{1}{1+h/R}\right)\right] \approx \exp\left(-\frac{h}{H_0}\right).$$

This is the familiar exponential law. With

$$\mathscr{R} = 820.57\,\frac{\text{m kg}}{°\text{K kmole}} \ , \qquad M_0 = 28.966, \qquad T_0 = 300, \qquad \frac{g_0}{g_{0E}} = 1 \ ,$$

it follows for Earth that $H_0 = 8498.6$ m, or, approximately, $H_0 = 8.5$ km. For a molecular weight of 16 and a temperature of about $1500°$K, which we may find at about 500 km altitude, we have

$$H = 8.5 \times \frac{1500}{300} \times \frac{29}{16} = 77 \quad \text{km} \ ,$$

which is not too different from the 119 km derived from Sputnik measurements for 500 km. (The main difference is the higher temperature.) At the
outer exosphere we should have

$$H = 8.5 \times \frac{1500}{300} \times \frac{29}{1} = 1230 \quad \text{km.}$$

But the whole derivation based on continuum physics breaks down here.

(2) *Polytropic atmosphere.* For isentropic processes it is valid that

$$\frac{T}{T_0} = \left(\frac{p}{p_0}\right)^{(k-1)/k},$$

with k being the ratio of specific heats; $k = c_p/c_v$; for normal temperatures,
approximately; $k = \frac{5}{3} = 1.67$ for monatomic gases, $k = \frac{7}{5} = 1.40$ for
biatomic gases; and $k = \frac{4}{3} = 1.33$ for most gases containing more than 2
atoms per molecule.

In the same order, for $\nu = (k - 1)/k$: $\nu = 0.4$ for monatomic gases,
$\nu = 0.29$ for biatomic gases, and $\nu = 0.25$ for most gases containing more
than 2 atoms per molecule.

Obviously, $\nu = 0$ would describe an isothermal process. Therefore, we
introduce a "polytropic exponent" ν and write, generally,

$$\frac{T}{T_0} = \left(\frac{p}{p_0}\right)^{\nu},$$

knowing that for air

$$0 \le \nu \le 0.3.$$

(Thus this model cannot describe any atmosphere where temperature rises
with diminishing pressure.)

Taking both ν and M/M_0 constant, the pressure vs altitude equation
can again be integrated. For $\nu = 0$, we get the isothermal result, and,
for $\nu \ne 0$,

$$\frac{p}{p_0} = \left\{ 1 - \nu \frac{R}{H_0} \left(1 - \frac{R}{r}\right) \right\}^{1/\nu}.$$

This has the interesting consequence of giving $p/p_0 = 0$ for

$$\nu \frac{R}{H_0} \left(1 - \frac{R}{r}\right) = 1 \quad \text{or} \quad \left(\frac{r}{R}\right)_{\text{max}} = \frac{1}{1 - H_0/\nu R}.$$

What about the parameter ν? From

$$\frac{T}{T_0} = \left(\frac{p}{p_0}\right)^{\nu},$$

we obtain

$$\frac{dT}{T} = \nu \frac{dp}{p},$$

or, approximately,

$$\nu \approx \frac{\Delta T/T}{\Delta p/p} \approx \frac{\Delta T}{T} \frac{H_0(T/T_0)\,(M_0/M)}{(R^2/r^2)\,\Delta r}.$$

For the lower atmosphere

$$\nu_0 \approx \frac{H_0 \,\Delta T/T}{\Delta r};$$

it is measured that

$$\frac{\Delta T}{\Delta r} \approx 5°\text{C/km},$$

thus,

$$\nu_0 \approx 0.14,$$

which appears to be reasonable. But for the maximum altitude ($p = 0$), there results

$$\left(\frac{r}{R}\right)_{\max} = \frac{1}{1 - (\Delta r/R)/(\Delta T/T)},$$

or numerically, with $\nu = 0.14$, only

$$\left(\frac{r}{R}\right)_{\max} = 1 + \frac{1}{105} \qquad \text{or} \qquad h_{\max} \approx 60 \text{ km}.$$

Thus, for the upper atmosphere, the isothermal model provides the much better description.

A note appears to be appropriate here on "geopotential altitude" h_p, as sometimes used in atmospheric work. By definition,

$$g_0 \, dh_p = g \, dh,$$

or

$$g_0 \int_R^{r_p} dr_p = g_0 \int_R^r \frac{R^2}{r^2} \, dr$$

$$h_p = \frac{h}{1 + h/R}.$$

3.2,3 Gas Density in Space

In the solar corona near the Sun the particles have energies corresponding to about 10^6°K. The temperature drop is approximately proportional to $(R_0/r)^{2/7}$ with distance r from the Sun which leads, near Earth, to about 220,000°K.[1] This gas—which is flowing outward from the Sun at perhaps 500 km/sec—consists of protons and electrons, but no hydrogen at such a high temperature. The density near Earth[2] is of the order of 100 protons and 100 electrons per cm³. The heat transfer resulting from this gas is very small. We will estimate it:

The mean thermal speed of a gas particle of molecular weight μ and temperature T (°K) is about $v = 156 \, (T/\mu)^{1/2}$ m/sec, or 73 km/sec for 2.2×10^5°K. With a density of 10^2 particles/cm³ and a speed of about 500 km/sec outward from the Sun, per second and square centimeter, not more than about 5×10^9 particles impact, delivering an energy of not more than 4×10^{-7} cal/cm² min or only about 2×10^{-7} of the energy flux resulting from solar radiation.

The planets move within the corona gas. But the speed of sound in this gas is so high (with a temperature of 2.5×10^5°K and a molecular weight of 1, about 55 km/sec) that even Mercury (orbital speed about 48 km/sec) moves subsonically. Furthermore,the free path length in this solar corona is comparable to planetary diameters, thus resulting in free molecular flow.

The electron density in the solar system will influence the speed of electromagnetic radiation passing through. Since this effect depends upon frequency, dispersion will result. With the low electron density, these effects are small. It has been estimated that for a frequency of 440×10^6 cps the speed would drop from its vacuum value by about 0.1 km/sec—this is comparable to the uncertainty in our knowledge of the vacuum speed of light, which is $299{,}792.5 \pm 0.1$ km/sec.

The "solar wind"—with a speed of about 500 km/sec (Mariner II: 300–900 km/sec) radially outward spiraling gas from the solar corona with perhaps up to 100 protons, 10 electrons and possibly 15 α particles per cubic centimeter—blows[3] the galactic gas out of the inner (within a few astrono-

---

[1] From Mariner II, the particles have a temperature of 1.9×10^5°K, radial speed of 460 km/sec, and a density of 2.5/cm³. Both density and radial speed may double during times of solar activity.

[2] Poorly known; estimates for electrons are between 10 and 50 per cm³. From experiments up to 1962 : 10–20 protons/cm³. Sporatic plasma bursts may have higher densities; Pioneer 6 measured 10 electrons per cm³ in the solar system near Earth.

[3] In interplanetary space, we find hardly more than, of the order of, 10^2 particles/cm³; generally, only 1 particle/cm³.

mical units) solar system. This galactic gas consists of about $\frac{1}{100}$ to 1 hydrogen atom[1] per cubic centimeter at a low temperature ($\sim 125°K$). It is only negligibly ionized. Due to uv-radiation from the solar corona, interplanetary gas is almost completely ionized.

During times of solar activity the solar wind may increase strongly[2]—up to 10^6 particles/cm^3, and up to 2000 km/sec. The ionized particles of the solar wind cannot penetrate the magnetic field of the Earth, but they deform it strongly at a high (several Earth radii) altitude. The closest approach of these particles may be about two Earth radii altitude. The particles of the solar wind appear to reach a maximum solar distance of between 40 and 100 a.u. (See Parker, 1964.)

In interstellar space, the density drops to less than 1 atom (perhaps 0.1) per cm^3 except in clouds, where a few atoms per cubic centimeter (perhaps 4) can be found. Intergalactic space appears to be really empty; 10^{10} cm^3 per neutral H atom are available.

The planets move with subsonic speed within the "solar wind," as shown. But the speed of the wind itself is hypersonic. Thus, a shock wave is created by interaction of the Earth magnetic field and the solar plasma. The shock front has the shape of an hyperboloid, its axis being approximately along the Sun-Earth line, and its closest distance to the Earth center being about 90,000 km. Inside the shock wave, there is a zone of magnetic turbulence about 20,000 to 30,000 km thick (Coleman, 1966).

This shock wave was discovered by the Earth satellite Explorer XVIII, or Interplanetary Monitoring Platform (IMP 1). Some data are given in Table 3.5.

TABLE 3.5

Some Data on Explorer XVIII

Launch date	November 26, 1963
Apocenter altitude	197,300 km
Pericenter altitude	193 km
Inclination	33.3 deg
Period	3 days 22.5 hours
Weight	138 lb

---

[1] H_1, H_2, very few partially ionized light elements and electrons; about 1% of the total mass is dust.

[2] Mariner II: solar wind: $5 \times 10^5°K$, 0.6–1.2 proton and electron per cubic centimeter counted; 3 particles/cm^2 sec at 750–2500 eV; during solar flare: 16 particles/cm^2 sec, up to 10–800 MeV. Flares travel in streams.

3.2,4 Design Considerations Specific to a Low Pressure Environment

Materials are affected in several ways by being put in a near-vacuum (Jaffe *et al.*, 1962).

(1) *Outgasing.* The gas layer adhering to the surface of materials is lost. There are indications that, at least with some materials, small surface deficiencies will, under load, lead to failure much sooner without the adhesive gas layer than it would with it (Notch failure).

(2) *Sublimation evaporation.* In some cases, the sublimation is just a kind of surface evaporation. A simplified theory treats this as evaporation of a material which is surrounded by an infinitely large receiver of the evaporated portions (see Fig. 3.2).

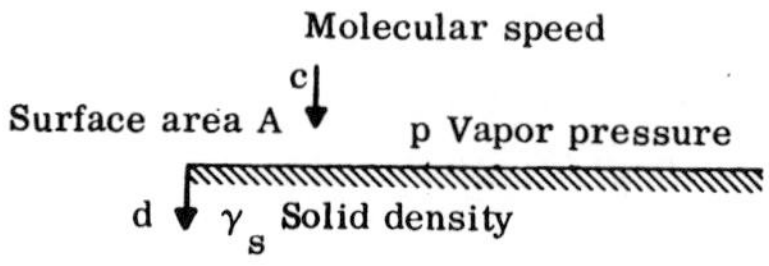

FIG. 3.2. Solid-vapor interface

From gas kinetics, we know that ($\dot{m}$ is the mass stream per second to the surface per unit area)

$$pA = 2\dot{m}c;$$

so

$$\dot{m} = A\,\frac{p}{2c} \quad \text{and} \quad c = \left(\frac{8\,\mathscr{R}g_0 T}{\pi\mu}\right)^{1/2},$$

where μ is the molecular weight and g_0 is the acceleration due to the Earth's gravity at zero altitude.

Equilibrium is obtained when $\dot{m}_{\text{leaving}} = \dot{m}_{\text{arriving}}$; that is,

$$(g_0\dot{m})_{\text{leaving}} = A\gamma_s\dot{d}$$

or

$$\dot{d} = \frac{g_0 p}{2\gamma_s (8Rg_0/\pi)^{1/2}(T/\mu)^{1/2}}.$$

This shows how the surface moves due to material evaporation.[1] A list of

---

[1] Knacke and Stranski (1956) introduced a corrective coefficient α to this equation. Often $\alpha \approx 1$, but in some cases α is appreciably less than 1 and may go down to $\alpha \approx 10^{-3}$.

vapor pressures at 450°K in millimeters of Hg (where 760 mm Hg ≈ 1 kg/cm²) is given in Table 3.6.

TABLE 3.6

VAPOR PRESSURES

Material	Vapor pressure (mm Hg)
Sulfur	1
Wax ($C_{24}H_{50}$)	7×10^{-1}
Ammonium chloride	1.3×10^{-2}
Cadmium	10^{-4}
Zinc	5×10^{-7}
Sodium hydroxide	10^{-7}
Magnesium	2×10^{-8}
Lithium	10^{-9}
Germanium, beryllium, aluminium oxide, silicon dioxide, magnesium oxide glass, sodium chloride	10^{-13}
Silver, iron, aluminum, silicon	10^{-14}

Inserting $\mu = 50$, $T = 450°K$, $\gamma_s = 5000 \text{ kg/m}^3$ and with the vapor pressure p in mm Hg we get:

$$\dot{d} \approx 10^4 p \quad \text{mm/day}.$$

Demanding only $\frac{1}{10}$ mm loss in 3 yr yields

$$\dot{d} < 10^{-4} \quad \text{mm/day}$$

or

$$p < 10^{-8}.$$

This rules out many materials.

The surface condition, treatment, and coating has a strong influence on outgasing, sublimation, and evaporation. For example, many inorganic surface coatings, such as oxides, have a lower vapor pressure than many metals. The vapor pressure of a metal from an alloy is in general smaller than that of the pure metal. Organic materials tend to have high vapor pressures. Therefore, special surface coatings may be developed to control outgasing, etc., for solid objects in space.

This evaporation or sublimation is especially critical for lubricants between moving parts which are open to space. Only a few solid lubricants, e.g., molybdenum disulfide MoS_2—which has only a 25% increase in coefficient of friction when switched from air to vacuum—show promise over extended time periods. Graphite would not work since it relies on contained water vapor for its lubrication effect.

Some plastic materials lose their plasticizer through sublimation. The rate of loss may be governed not by a "surface evaporation rate," but by the rate at which the plasticizer diffuses to the surface; and this latter rate can be much lower. In some cases, the resultant change in the properties of the material may be advantageous: e.g., a rubber-like structure may be made to harden in space.

(3) *Diffusion*. With no gas layer between them, solid materials can come into closer contact than under Earth environment. This can lead to a kind of cold welding process by diffusion of the materials into each other. In certain cases this must be prevented (e.g., roller bearings), in other cases it may be useful ("cold welding") and even be assisted by heating the materials (e.g., with solar radiation concentrators).

(4) *Electric arcing*. This is not much of a problem under reasonably high pressures (one atmosphere, as on Earth) or very low pressures (as in space). But at some intermediate, fairly low pressures, standard electrical equipment could not operate.

For reasons of temperature and other environmental control, it may be advantageous to place electric equipment in pressurized shells even if arcing would permit otherwise.

(5) *Pressure shells*. Pressure shells are advantageous or sometimes necessary to house some equipment (such as electrical devices) or materials (such as liquids), or, finally, man. The design should be failsafe or fail operational, i.e., still safe or operational after any component failure. In particular, a small hole or a few cracks should not lead to complete disintegration of the cabin. After an explosive decompression in space, an unprotected man has only about 15 sec[1] to provide himself with a more suitable environment. Therefore, the design should be such as to minimize the occurrence of explosive decompression.

---

[1] Major H. H. Reynolds, Air Force Aeromedical Research Laboratory at Holloman, said that chimpanzees have been exposed to space-equivalent vacuum for up to 150 sec. When pressure was restored, the animal eventually returned to normal, with no apparent injury. (See Reynolds, 1964.)

For a spherical cabin of radius R and internal pressure p, and a material of a strength (working stress) S and a safety factor of 2, the wall thickness necessary is $d = (p/S)R$, and the total weight is, with a density γ of the wall material,

$$W = 4\pi R^3 \frac{\gamma}{S} p \qquad \text{or} \qquad \frac{\text{weight}}{\text{volume}} = 3 \frac{p}{S/\gamma}.$$

For temperatures between 0 and 100°C the parameter S/γ can be, for both high quality aluminium and steel, between 8 and 16 km, which gives for a volume of 10^3 m³ and $p = 1$ kg/cm² a weight $W = 3.75$ to 1.88 tons. There are several possibilities for reducing this weight: materials with a higher S/γ figure could be used (for single crystals or whiskers very high values of S/γ—perhaps up to 200 km—have been observed). The pressure p could be lowered (there is some indication that man could live in a pure oxygen atmosphere of only $\frac{1}{5}$ kg/cm² pressure).

Because of internal pressure, wall thickness and material, and hence weight, may well be determined by considerations other than stress. Some of these considerations could be in-flight loads (e.g., design water impact speed of the 3-man Apollo command module is 7.6 m/sec), meteor hazards, or radiation protection. In this case, internal pressure p might have no influence upon total weight, or nearly so; then a "normal" atmosphere (pressure and composition) might be preferable because of (1) our familiarity with it, (2) the unchanged sound of voices, etc., and (3) in the case of cabin puncture, longer time until catastrophic low pressure levels occur.

Looking generally at structure designs of today, it appears that the standard methods of material processing, fabrication, and design lead to about double the weight compared to ideal processing, fabrication, and design with the same present materials. Better knowledge of the environment and materials could make possible the reduction of the safety factor.

All pressure vessels lose gas by several processes: (1) diffusion through the walls, (2) leaks through seals, etc., (3) through operation of air locks, and (4) through holes.[1] With the possible exception of air lock loss, the loss rate is proportional to internal pressure; this again is a reason for reducing this value as much as possible.

Let us now consider a pressure vessel of volume V filled with a gas of molecular weight μ, specific heat ratio k, temperature T, pressure p, and density ϱ having the equivalent of one hole of effective area a. The flow

---

[1] A typical leakage area of a pressure vehicle is about 5×10^{-9} m² of hole/m² of surface.

condition in the plane of the hole is approximately the same as it is in the throat of a rocket nozzle:

Pressure

$$p_a = p \left(\frac{2}{k+1} \right)^{k/(k-1)},$$

Density

$$\varrho_a = \varrho \left(\frac{2}{k+1} \right)^{1/(k-1)},$$

Temperature

$$T_a = T \left(\frac{2}{k+1} \right),$$

Speed

$$v_a = \left(g_0 \frac{2k}{k+1} \frac{\mathscr{R}}{\mu} T \right)^{1/2},$$

where $\mathscr{R}$ is the universal gas constant $= 820.57$ mkg/°K kmole, and $g_0 = 9.8$ m/sec².
Weight flow rate is

$$\dot{w} = g_0 a v_a \varrho_a = a p g_0 \frac{k\{[2/(k+1)]^{(k+1)/(k-1)}\}^{1/2}}{[g_0 k(\mathscr{R}/\mu)T]^{1/2}}.$$

Weight of gas in the container is

$$W = V g_0 \varrho_0 = V \frac{\mu p}{\mathscr{R}T}.$$

Now there are two limiting possibilities:

(1) Isothermal process, $T = \text{constant} = \text{initial gas temperature} = T_0$.
(2) Adiabatic process,

$$T = T_0 \left(\frac{p}{p_0} \right)^{(k-1)/k},$$

where p_0 is the initial pressure.
Thus,

$$W = V \frac{\mu p_0}{\mathscr{R}T_0} \frac{p}{p_0},$$

or

$$W = V \frac{\mu p_0}{\mathscr{R}T_0} \left(\frac{p}{p_0} \right)^{1/k},$$

or, in abbreviated form,

$$W = W_0 \left(\frac{p}{p_0} \right)^{1/k},$$

where $k = 1$ or c_p/c_v. Then

$$\dot{W} = \frac{W_0}{k} \left(\frac{p_0}{p} \right)^{(k-1)/k} \frac{\dot{p}}{p_0} .$$

On the other hand we also have

$$\dot{w} = a\alpha \frac{p/p_0}{(T/T_0)^{1/2}} = a\alpha \left(\frac{p}{p_0} \right)^{(k+1)/2k} ,$$

where

$$\alpha = p_0 g_0 \frac{k\{[2/(k+1)]^{(k+1)/(k-1)}\}^{1/2}}{[g_0 k (\mathscr{R}/\mu) T_0]^{1/2}}$$

and $\dot{W} = -\dot{w}$, or with $p/p_0 = x$, we have

$$\dot{x} = -\frac{k}{W_0} a\alpha x^{(3k-1)/2k} .$$

For $k \neq 1$, we have

$$\frac{p}{p_0} = \frac{1}{\{1 + [(k-1)/2W_0] a\alpha t\}^{2k/(k-1)}} ;$$

and for $k = 1$, we have

$$\frac{p}{p_0} = \exp[-(a\alpha/W_0)t] .$$

The numerical difference is quite small. Let $(a\alpha/W_0)t$ be 2; then with $k = 1.4$ we obtain

$$\frac{p}{p_0} = \frac{1}{(1.4)^6} = \frac{1}{7.52} \quad \text{and} \quad \frac{p}{p_0} = \exp(-2) = \frac{1}{7.4} .$$

Now we calculate the thrust F. Assume that a parallel jet leaves the hole, then impulsive thrust is

$$F_i = \frac{\dot{w}}{g_0} v_a = a p_0 k \left(\frac{2}{k+1} \right)^{k/(k-1)} \frac{p}{p_0} .$$

The exit pressure term of the thrust is

$$F_p = a p_a = a \frac{p}{p_0} p_0 \left(\frac{2}{k+1} \right)^{k/(k-1)} .$$

The total thrust is

$$F = (k + 1) \left(\frac{2}{k+1}\right)^{k/(k-1)} a p_0 \frac{p}{p_0}$$

or[1] for $k = 1.4$

$$F = 1.268 \, a p_0 \frac{p}{p_0} .$$

The functions pressure p vs time t are very similar; therefore, only the exponential law will be inserted:

$$F = 1.268 \, a p_0 \exp(a\alpha/W_0)t ,$$

or total impulse is

$$I = \int_0^\infty F \, dt .$$

Integrating and inserting

$$I = \frac{1}{\{[2/(k+1)]^{(k+1)/k-1}\}^{1/2}} \frac{p_0 V}{[g_0 k(\mathscr{R}/\mu)T_0]^{1/2}} ,$$

with $k = 1.4$, we have

$$I = \frac{5}{10^3} \, p_0 \left[\frac{kg}{m^2}\right] \times V \, [m^3] \, \frac{(\mu/30)^{1/2}}{(T_0/300)^{1/2}} \, [kg \ sec] .$$

Assuming that $p_0 = 10^4$, $V = 10^3$, $\mu = 30$, and $T_0 = 300$, then $I = 5 \times 10^4$ kg sec, which could give a speed of 125 m/sec to a container with an empty weight of 4×10^3 kg. (Indeed, a more accurate computation would have to take into account the container losses through the jettisoned gas:

$$empty \ weight \ = 4000 \ \ kg ,$$

$$full \ weight \ \ \ = 5300 \ \ kg$$

$$specific \ impulse = \frac{5 \times 10^4}{1.3 \times 10^3} = 38.4 \ \ sec$$

$$v_{id} = 38.4 \, g_0 \ln \frac{5.3}{4} = 106 \ \ m/sec .$$

Since the jet would hardly be a paralleled jet and because of friction losses, v_{id} would be reduced further—perhaps to between 40 and 80 m/sec.) This is

---

[1] Gas expansion through a hole is a nearly adiabatic process.

a rather high impulse. Of course, with a random hole, this speed cannot be expected; there would be a moment-inducing rotation and the impulse would act in various directions, so that there is partial cancellation. To get rid of an empty propellant tank, it might suffice to set it free and vent it.

Let us return to the cabin problem. The pressure drop is

$$\frac{p}{p_0} = \exp[-(a\alpha/W_0)t] \quad \text{or} \quad \frac{p}{p_0} = \exp(-t/t_c) ,$$

if a "characteristic time" t_c is introduced. Then

$$t_c = \frac{W_0}{a\alpha} = \frac{V}{a} \frac{1}{[kg_0(\mathscr{R}/\mu)T_0]^{1/2}} \frac{1/k}{\{[2/(k+1)]^{[(k+1)/(k-1)]}\}^{1/2}} ,$$

or, for constants as before (a in square meters),

$$t_c = \frac{3.36}{10^3} \frac{V}{a} \frac{(\mu/30)^{1/2}}{(T_0/300)^{1/2}} .$$

If the initial pressure p_0 is not very low, then a "safe" time is perhaps

$$\frac{t_c}{3} \approx \frac{V}{10^3 a} ,$$

or for a quite large hole of $a = 10^{-4}$ m², about $t_c/3 \approx 10$ V, or a minute for every 6 m³ of gas-filled volume. But if the original pressure were already close to minimum, no loss could be tolerated; the "safe" time is zero.

(6) *Scientific measurements.* It must be borne in mind that the previous effects may interfere or even invalidate scientific/environmental measurements in many ways:

(1) Arbitrary impulse and moment due to gas leak per hole.

(2) Environment change due to gas loss, evaporation, leaks, diffusion, etc.

(3) Environment change due to all types of rocket engine action.

(4) Voluntary or involuntary released materials may influence communication, surface structures, especially of optical or heat exhanging or other sensitive surfaces.

(5) Cold welding, lack of lubrication, material failure under load, arcing, etc., can interfere directly with the operation of the vehicle.

3.3 Gravitational Field within the Space Vehicle

When no forces other than gravitational act upon a vehicle, and the vehicle is free to follow these forces, it is in zero gravity state. There are some effects connected with this condition that deserve special attention:

(1) If a satellite is in a near circular orbit, the kinematic behavior of an object released from the satellite with relative speed is quite complicated and has already been treated in Chap. 4 of Vol. 1.

(2) The dynamic stability (dumbbell, tidal forces) of an object in a near circular orbit has already been described in Chap. 4 of Vol. 1.

(3) Liquids and their vapors or gases do not separate under zero gravity. This is important, e.g., to empty containers, or for the two-phase flow in a condenser or boiler. In a boiler a gas layer would be formed at the transfer surface, reducing further heat transfer and possibly causing wall overheating. To accomplish separation the container can be rotated or accelerated or the two-phase flow can be separated by leading it through a curved tube, through a tube of varying diameter, through a whirl chamber, or by adhesion of the liquid to the walls of small diameter tubes. In other cases, a diaphragm, piston or bladder can prevent the formation of a two-phase mixture, thus eliminating the need for liquid-gas separation. Pressurization to drive the piston could be produced by burning some chemical reactant, or perhaps simply by evaporating some of the liquid with the help of the Sun.

(4) Certain apparatus, like a pendulum, require gravity for their operation and are unsuited for space environment. In certain cases, a centrifugal force field generated by rotation of the vehicle or parts thereof can be substituted for a gravity field. This rotation can have other side-effects:

(a) Attitude stabilization of vehicle.

(b) Inducing precession.

(c) Influencing astronomical or other observations.

(d) Influencing communication, solar power supply, etc.

(e) Influencing exposure time of cryogenic fuels to the Sun.

(f) To make contact from the outside, either the rotation must be stopped, or at least a part (usually the hub) must be nonrotating, or nearly so; for certain experiments a gravity-free chamber should be provided.

(g) Interaction between rotation and magnetic field.

(h) Change of the moment of inertia by, e.g., pumping a liquid within a spacecraft will influence the angular speed, if it is not zero. Some limit (given by structure and design, experiments and apparatus, man, or other living beings) must not be surpassed.

To neutralize some of these effects, space vehicles counter-rotating around a common hub have been proposed.

(5) Short time (up to a few hours)[1] exposure to zero gravity affects men very little. The lack of gravity may induce a falling sensation, but with the visual inputs and training this appears to be rapidly overcome. Some cardiovascular system and blood changes have been observed, which in part appear to be due to weightlessness. Of course, long-time effects are not known, and there is evidence to assume that muscular atrophy might occur unless prevented by proper exercises and medical treatment. The same may be true regarding loss of calcium from the bones due to lack of or different distribution of stress. Orientation will be maintained if vision is available. Man orients himself on Earth with the assistance of his vestibular apparatus, which depends on gravity for proper functioning. Even if the gravitational field is reduced to 0.0005 of its Earth surface value, the vestibular apparatus will still function. If the gravitational field is reduced to zero, man must rely on his visual sense. It is believed that this will be only a minor problem.

According to some Soviet experiences, a "safe" period of weightlessness appears to be 24 h. After this period, irreversible physiological changes begin to occur in the human system, if no counter measures are taken. No significant effects were found in the manned space program of the United States.

Every-day life might be plagued with inconveniences, though. Therefore, very early it was proposed that an artificial gravity field be created by rotating the vehicle. (See Fig. 3.3.)

This has some secondary effects:

(a) *Gravity differential.* Centrifugal force $Z = \omega^2 r$, or

$$\frac{dZ}{Z} = \frac{dr}{r}.$$

Taking dr for the difference between head and feet of a standing man of the size of 1.80 m, we have $\Delta Z/Z = 1.80/r$. If for some reason $(\Delta Z/Z) < \frac{1}{100}$, then $r > 180$ m. (The Earth radius is so large compared to a man that head and feet are, on Earth, virtually in the same gravity field. It does not ap-

---

[1] From actual experience available in 1966, up to at least 14 days (Gemini 7). Titov's sickness, similar to sea sickness, was due to vestibular disturbances, which decreased after he had slept. At no time was he incapacitated, nor did any of the U.S. astronauts have a similar experience. Other effects were observed; none is believed to constitute a serious damage.

pear inconceivable that a large difference in the g level between head and feet would lead to disorientation, etc.) This might be impractically large for some designs (wheels). Oberth, for this reason, proposed to have two cabins

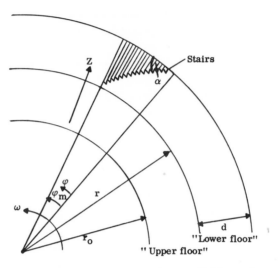

Fig. 3.3. Parameters for providing artificial gravity.

with a long cable between them rotate around their common center of gravity; this appears to be a fairly simple solution to get a large radius, but the internal dynamics of such a system will induce new problems.[1]

Sperry Gyroscope Company showed that these can be solved at least for cable length of 10–1000 m.

(b) *Staircase curvature.* Having a staircase with a constant slope demands that

$$\frac{dr}{r \, d\varphi} = \text{const} = \tan \alpha$$

or

$$r = r_0 \exp(\varphi \tan \alpha).$$

The angle φ_m is given by

$$\varphi_m = \frac{1}{\tan \alpha} \ln \left(1 + \frac{d}{r_0} \right).$$

[1] Tested in Sept. 1966 by Gemini II. The 2-man Gemini vehicle and an Agena stage were connected by a 30-m long dacron line; the system was set spinning (1 rev in about 500 sec).

To make the curvature slight, φ_m should be small, which means

    α large $\rightarrow$ steep staircase,

    d small $\rightarrow$ not very high floors,

    r_0 large $\rightarrow$ large radius.

Let us assume $\varphi_m < 6°$ and $\alpha = 30°$. Then $(d/r_0) < 0.0635$, or for $d = 2$ m we have $r_0 > 31.5$ m.

Again, the trend is toward a large station.

(c) *Coriolis acceleration.* Having a velocity component $\dot{r}$, and $\boldsymbol{\omega}$ being the angular speed of rotation, there is a Coriolis acceleration

$$\mathbf{a} = 2\,[\dot{\mathbf{r}}\,\boldsymbol{\omega}];$$

at the same time the "gravity" is

$$Z = r\omega^2\,,$$

or

$$\frac{a}{Z} = 2\,\frac{\dot{r}}{r\omega}\,.$$

This side force is not easily noticeable on Earth. To have it sufficiently small to prevent disturbing effects (such as visibly nonvertical motion of dropped objects, or—in man—leading to disorientation, even nausea) it may be advisable to demand

$$\frac{a}{Z} < 0.1\,,$$

or with $\dot{r} = 2$ m/sec as a "maximum speed" within the station $r\omega > 40$ m/sec. This is already a fairly high circumferential speed. Since Z can be written as $(r\omega)^2/r$, we have

$$Z > \frac{1600}{r}\,,$$

or, only for $r > 160$ m can $Z \approx 10$ m/sec^2 be realized. But there are structural reasons which favor a lower "gravity" Z, say, 2 m/sec^2; this leads to $r > 800$ m.

If the motion occurs with a speed Δv vertical upon $\boldsymbol{\omega}$ and $\dot{r}$, then there is an additional pseudogravitational acceleration (centrifugal plus Coriolis) of

$$\Delta Z = \frac{(v \pm \Delta v)^2}{r} - \frac{v^2}{r} = \frac{\Delta v^2}{r} \pm 2\omega\,\Delta v\,,$$

where the $\pm$ indicates whether $\varDelta \mathbf{v}$ is parallel or antiparallel to $[\omega \; \dot{\mathbf{r}}]$. For $\varDelta v = r \, \varDelta \omega$, we get

$$\frac{\varDelta Z}{Z} = 2 \, \frac{\varDelta \omega}{\omega} \left(\frac{\varDelta \omega}{2\omega} \pm 1 \right).$$

With (from the previous example) $r \, \varDelta \omega = 2$ m/sec and again $(\varDelta Z/Z) < 0.1$ we have

$$r\omega > 40 \quad \text{m/sec},$$

leading to the same conclusions as for the treated case of radial motion.

A simpler way than rotation to simulate partial gravity for man is to wear fiction-famous magnetic shoes. In tests it has been shown that this may work when the attractive force per foot is high enough (2 kg/foot is inadequate, 10 kg/foot should be adequate). Instead of magnetic shoes, other adhesive means (suction cups, but they do not work in vacuum; felt-like nylon hook-and-sling structures, but they may wear out) can be used.

As mentioned, proper exercises together with pre- and post-flight treatment may permit the use of zero-g vehicles. As a compromise, it may suffice to have a centrifuge on board, where every space traveler is exposed to some acceleration for a brief time in selected time intervals (say, 1 g for 1 h daily). For this centrifuge, a short radius of 2–3 m may be acceptable, because its occupant does not move.

(d) *Gyro forces.* Rotating the head around an axis which is not parallel to the axis of rotation produces a false tilting sensation by gyroscoping action on the semicircular canals (labyrinth, inner ear). This might lead to motion sickness if the angular speeds involved are not sufficiently low (rotation and tumbling rate should never exceed 1 rev/sec, and 4–6 rpm are the upper limits for the rotational rate of manned stations), which again demands a large space station.[1] In all these considerations, individual tolerances might be different, and training might render the effects harmless. Coriolis force acts not only on moving objects but also on moving parts of objects, e.g., body limbs, engine parts, etc., where they induce moments on the objects.

In a centrifuge test in November 1964, 5 men were exposed for 5 days to 6 rpm with a radius of gyration of 6.1 m without any adverse symptoms. Because of the presence of Earth gravity, it is not thought that such tests will result in safe design information.

---

[1] With 4 rpm we have $\omega = 0.42$ sec^{-1}, and $r\omega > 40$ leads to $r > 95.2$ m.

(6) *High accelerations.* During some phases, space vehicles can be subjected also to high accelerations. Important examples are:

(a) Handling before launch.

(b) Launch, especially near cutoff of stages.

(c) Launch malfunction and subsequent emergency escape operation.

(d) High spin rate.

(e) Collision, e.g., bumping from a previous stage, or during rendezvous maneuvers.

(f) Fast maneuvers, e.g., to avoid a collision.

(g) Landing on a celestial body, or atmospheric braking.

(h) Actual touchdown on a (solid or liquid) surface.

(i) After landing, before the vehicle is brought to a protected environment (e.g., swimming in water).

Structural tolerances in this respect depend upon design, materials, etc. More narrow tolerances may be set by some payloads or by life on board the vehicle.

Some limits for man are (see Fig. 3.37):

Leg-lifting gets difficult	$3\,g$
Arm-lifting gets difficult	$7\,g$
Supine, chest to back acceleration blackout occurs	15–$17\,g$
Immersed in water	$31\,g$ for 5 sec tested

Of course, these limits vary individually, and are dependent on the training of the individual. For short durations, higher accelerations can be tolerated than for long durations with the rate of change of acceleration also having some influence.

Task performance deterioration is first caused by loss of fine muscular coordination, then impairment of the blood flow to the eyes and brain. The immersion in water acts as a "super-contour-chair," preserving the fine muscular coordination. Water immersion by no means cancels the effects of acceleration. The acceleration forces act upon every molecule of the affected man, but the water balancing acts only upon his skin surface.

(7) *Weber-Fechner's law.* If S is the sensation as experienced by an observer, and c its cause as measured in physical units (say, energy per second and square centimeter), and c_0 is a standard value of the cause (often the minimum value which can just be felt by an observer), then, generally (Weber-Fechner's law),

$$S = A \log \frac{c}{c_0},$$

where A is an arbitrary scale factor. Thus, the standard value c_0 results in zero sensation, and lower values get negative sensations. In particular, $c = 0$ is connected with $S = -\infty$. Applied to gravity, this might indicate that something severe happens at zero. Fortunately, this is not the case. Workers in the field agree that Weber-Fechner's law is only a rule which fairly well describes conditions around the standard, but does not hold for extremes.

3.4 Fields in Space

3.4,1 Magnetic Fields

The Earth has a magnetic field that can be approximately described as the field of a dipole with a dipole moment (in 1922) of 8.06×10^{25} cgs units, sitting about 500 km from the Earth's center and being 11.5° inclined toward the rotational axis. Strength, orientation, and uniformity show slow "secular" variations; geographic irregularities are called "anomalies." The field is fairly constant over a period of some months, but "disturbances" cause changes for days, hours, or minutes. They appear to be caused by electric currents in and above the ionosphere and/or influx of solar particles. (Electric currents in the lower ionosphere and in the auroral zones have been observed by rocket flights, but their cause is not clear.)

Outside of Earth at a distance r (below the order of 10^4 km) with R being the Earth radius, the field strength is described by $0.5(R/r)^3$ Oe. The Earth magnetic field was observed by Pioneer V to a distance of $r = 110,000$ km, or $r/R \approx 17$. At this boundary, fluctuations having to do with solar activity were observed. Strong deviations compared to the dipole field occur at some earlier distance. For example, at 20,000 km, the field strength is only 40% of the dipole field; whereas at 50,000 km there is a field strength above the dipole field (Lunik III). This indicates that the Earth's magnetic field is a result of electric currents flowing within the planet Earth. At the same time, it is an indication of a ring current going around Earth in a westerly direction at 50,000–100,000 km altitude and 5×10^6 amp strength, carried by low energy protons and electrons. The existence of this current was suspected more than 50 years ago. (The existence of this ring current was not verified by Explorer XII on February 10, 1962; but at 6–7 Earth radii there was a turbulent magnetic field of an intensity of 60γ and of about 100 km thickness.)

The discrepancy of the Earth field compared to a dipole field is at least partly caused by interaction with solar and interplanetary gas clouds, and perhaps even MHD waves going through these gases. The main effect of the Earth's magnetic field on space flight appears to be the trapping of charged particles, leading to the van Allen radiation zones around Earth. There is some radioastronomical evidence of a similar radiation zone around the planet Jupiter, indicating that this giant planet also has a magnetic field[1] perhaps 100 times stronger than Earth. The planet Saturn appears to have an electron radiation belt too.

A secondary but important effect of the magnetic field of Earth is the electromagnetic and magnetic induction in moving objects, leading to a decrease in the spin rate of artificial Earth satellites as described in Chap. 4 of Vol. 1.

From Mariner II it was learned that the magnetic field of Venus is not larger than $\frac{1}{10}$ of that of Earth; this may be a further indication of the slow rotation of this planet. The slow retrograde rotation of Venus has recently been revealed.

Scientists expect our Moon to have a magnetic field of its own of only a surface strength between zero and 20γ.[2] Indeed, the Soviet impacting lunar probe Lunik II measured "no magnetic field strength above 60γ." Critical evaluation of the existing information appears to lead to the following conlusions:

(1) At the surface of the Moon, the magnetic field is smaller than $10^3\,\gamma$. (Luminescence of lunar surface caused by solar protons has been observed, and deflection of such protons to a night portion of the Moon has not; because of this, the magnetic field at the surface of the Moon is smaller than $10^3\,\gamma$.)

(2) Solar wind will influence this field strongly; on the dayside (where Lunik II impacted) of the Moon, the field strength may drop by a factor of 10 for every kilometer in altitude. Thus, in 2 km altitude the field strength would be smaller than 10γ, which could not be detected by Lunik II instruments. No lunar hard corpuscular radiation zone was registered.

Magnetic fields of the Sun and stars have been studied, but much exact knowledge is lacking. The Sun appears to have a magnetic field of a surface strength similar to the field strength at the Earth surface, but in sunspots field strength can be higher by a factor of 10^4. There is speculation that these solar spot fields are carried "frozen" in gas ejection streams through the solar system, moving with ion clouds of some 1000 km diameter and field strength around 10γ, which, by MHD effects, keeps the cloud together, thus preserving a high particle density. The solar vicinity is shielded by the

[1] From some estimates, polar field intensity is 7 ± 1 gauss, compared to 0.57 gauss at the surface of Earth.

[2] $10^5\,\gamma = 1$ gauss, and in vacuum 1 Oe $= 1$ gauss.

electrically conducting corona from the direct influence of the solar magnetic field. The strongest magnetic field so far discovered in space surrounds the neighboring star HD215441. It is ∼ 34,000 times stronger than that of Earth.

From $14\frac{1}{2}$ to $36\frac{1}{2}$ Earth radii distance, about 5γ have been measured. The interplanetary field—starting from 15–20 Earth radii outward—is relatively steady at 2–10γ; in solar storms, it may go up to between 25 and 50γ. With Pioneer V, an interplanetary magnetic field fluctuating in relation to solar activity was observed. The interplanetary field is tilted about 45° against the ecliptic.

3.4,2 Electric Fields

Much less is known about electric fields in space than about magnetic fields. The potential difference between the Earth surface and the ionosphere is about 290 kV, and no knowledge exists for space outside the ionosphere. Some speculations have it that the high energy particles of cosmic radiation get their energy from acceleration in interstellar electric fields. But no strong fields are likely because of the high electric conductivity created by protons.

The Sun appears to carry a large negative electric charge of about -3×10^{27} esu.

3.4,3 Gravitational Fields

Even in this area there are many problems in spite of our capability of describing these fields quite well. First, basic understanding is still lacking[1] —"what is gravity?" Is the general theory of relativity the answer? What about interaction between gravitational and other fields? There is some doubt whether Newton's law holds for intergalactic distances (Zwicky, 1959). What is the speed of gravitational propagation?

In a more practical way, artificial satellites have already contributed to the improvement of our knowledge about the higher harmonics of the Earth's gravitational field, which give information on Earth shape, internal structure, and perhaps on the Earth's origin (by comparing the actual shape and the equilibrium shape). For other heavenly bodies, even the knowledge in the basic term ("mass") usually needs improvement, and the higher terms are generally not known at all. Our knowledge of the Venusian mass was greatly improved by the Mariner II experiment. The artificial satellites of the Moon created in 1966 provided much relevant lunar information.

[1] For a survey on the present status, see Witten (1962).

3.5 Radiation in Space

3.5,1 Electromagnetic Radiation

Solar electromagnetic radiation has an energy density of 1.98–2 cal/cm² min $\approx$ 0.14 W/cm² near Earth. The energy is mainly in the visible range (wavelength 3600–7800 Å),[1] with the following approximate distribution: 1000–2700 Å, 5 W/m²; 2000–4000 Å, 100 W/m²; 2700–7900, 800 W/m²; above 7900 Å, 600 W/m²; and for soft X rays (which are no health hazard since they are easily stopped), only 10^{-3} W/m². Still, certain materials—especially organic ones—may be influenced by them. But it is mainly the (temperature dependent) evaporation which may harm certain materials, e.g., plastic, rubber, etc.

In the visible region, the solar radiation corresponds to that of a black body of 5700°K surface temperature. This radiation comes from the solar "photosphere." Ultraviolet (UV) radiation, around 2000 Å, originates higher up in the Sun, thus corresponding to a lower temperature of only 4500°K. But the radiation of only 5 Å wavelength, which originates in the chromosphere, corresponds to a black body temperature of about 4×10^6°K. In Sec. 3.2,3 the solar corona temperature of 10^6°K was mentioned.

In the short wavelength, most of the energy is concentrated in a few lines. Toward long wavelength, there is, in the radio frequency (from a few to a thousand megacycles) region, a weak galactic background with localized intense areas. The Sun emits a steady thermal radio noise, increasing by about 3 orders of magnitude for short bursts simultaneously with solar flares.

The energy density of starlight is hardly more than 10^{-9} W/cm².

Earth reflects about 36% of the incoming solar radiation (albedo of Earth $\approx$ 0.36), and the remaining 64% is radiated away as thermal radiation. Since the radiating surface is $4\pi R^2$ and the receiving surface only πR^2, one expects a mean Earth radiation energy of

$$\frac{0.64 \times 0.14}{4} = 0.0225 \quad \text{W/cm}^2 \,,$$

and a maximum of $0.64 \times 0.14 = 0.09$ W/cm², neglecting internal energy production.

Of course, the Earth radiation is in the infrared, with an energy peak at 11.3×10^4 Å, corresponding to a black body temperature of about 255°K.

Ultraviolet (1230–1350 Å) emissions of the night airglow and of stellar

---

[1] 1 Å = 10^{-8} cm.

sources have been measured; these measurements, though not yet fully understood, are of great scientific interest. The energy flux is not larger than approximately 2×10^{-9} W/cm² (night sky), and 10^{-12} W/cm² (stellar sources).

3.5,2 Particle Radiation

Particle radiation is also abundant in space:

(1) *Cosmic radiation.* Composition $\sim 83\%$ protons, $\sim 15\%$ α particles, $\sim 1.5\%$ nuclei of heavy elements up to about tin, $\sim$ perhaps 1% electrons, and γ radiation.

Energy. 10^8 to 3×10^{19} eV/particle[1]; usually around 10^{10} eV; intensity falls rapidly with increase in energy [roughly, intensity is proportional to $(\text{energy})^{-3}$].

Intensity. The motion of the particles is isotropic; about 2–4 particles (average 2.5) cross a square centimeter per second, corresponding to an energy transport of about 3×10^{10} eV/cm² sec, or about $5/10^9$ W/cm². This is comparable to the energy transport due to star light. (Close to Earth, the intensity drops to half of the free space value plus backscatter from the atmosphere. The intensity of cosmic primaries with an atomic weight over 6 is about 50% higher on the night side of Earth than on the day side, according to Explorer VII measurements.) As to the density, about 10^{10} cm³ contain one particle of this radiation.

Low Energy Primaries. On Earth, only high primary cosmic radiation and secondary radiation due to interaction with air are observable because the magnetic field and the atmosphere is a shield against low energy particles. Therefore, such low energy primary cosmic radiation may be present in space and may present a hazard to life in a space vehicle. The secondary radiation within the atmosphere reaches a maximum at about 19 km altitude.

Origin. During quiet Sun, about 10% of the particle radiation originates on the Sun, the source of the remainder is unknown (galactic). At the beginning of solar flares, the intensity of cosmic radiation appears to decrease, at least throughout the solar system (Forbush decrease). This may find application as a warning against solar flare activity.

Health Hazard. A man is exposed in free space to about 15–20 milliroentgen/day through cosmic radiation. To shield against the heavy energetic primaries, about 100 gm/cm² of shield weight appears to be necessary.

---

[1] Maximum observed value is of the order of 10^{20} eV ≈ 1.7 m kg; probably a proton.

Less shielding may worsen the situation because of the formation of secondary radiation.[1] But since a continuous radiation exposure up to 40 milliroentgen/day is not considered dangerous, no shielding may be required. The main danger appears to lie in a high energy particle hitting a sensitive area such as the retina of an eye. The heavy particles are, in spite of their low intensity, biologically more dangerous. Partial body shields, e.g., eye protection, to be worn during sleep, may be very useful in space. For sufficiently low radiation rates, self-healing effects become important. (More on this subject will be said later.)

(2) *Solar flares/solar streams.* These are little understood, and perhaps the most dangerous obstacles to manned space flight. Two types of solar emissions generate ionizing radiation:

(a) *Solar flares.* Energetic protons (near Earth, perhaps 10^{-6}–10^{-8} per cm³), emitted at times of solar flares may result in dosage rates up to 1000 roentgen/h in free space. Energy of the particles is high; frequently from a few hundred up to several thousand MeV. Shielding is difficult. Such outbursts follow no pattern; usually no warning time exists before the radiation arrives. (For Earth, the time difference between optical observation of a flare and arrival of the particles is, typically, 20 min.) The radiation may, at least in part, be directive (radially away from the Sun), thus requiring only one-sided "shadow shielding." The protons remain within the solar system for a few days.

Solar flares are classified in three groups. Type 3 is of the highest energy, containing protons of 5–50 MeV. Its duration is 5–10 sec, or it consists of a series of bursts over 1 to 2 min. Type 3 + contains particles of energies above 15 BeV, but such flares are rarer; therefore, the lower energy class 3 flares may turn out to be the main problem.

Over a total 3 + flare, 75 roentgen were received behind a wall of 1 gm/cm². The empirical data of the last 10 yr indicates that the radiation hazard for a solar flare event is of the order of 40 r when behind 10 gm/cm² of shielding.

Estimated shield weights are uncertain by a factor of 10 or so; a shield weight of 100 gm/cm² appears to be on the "high" side, and 30 gm/cm² or so may be a realistic value. On the other hand, Wallner *et al.* (1961) mention up to 165 gm/cm².

Relativistic flares are connected with a substantial flux of particles with energies in excess of 1 BeV; they seem to occur only once per 4.5 yr on the

---

[1] Intensity of Bremsstrahlung due to an electron is $(1836)^2$ as high as the intensity of Bremsstrahlung due to a proton of the same energy.

average, and none have been observed during sunspot maximum. Class 3 flares occur, on the average, once per month.

The peak of the solar flare activity appears to be about 1 to 2 yr after the peak in the number of sunspots[1]; this activity has minima in 1965 and 1967, and maxima in late 1968 and 1979. Thus, the most difficult times for manned space flights from this point of view appear to be 1969–1971 and 1980–1982. But we should add that the information is not conclusive, and the solar flare peak may well coincide with the sunspot maximum.

Possible improvements on flare shielding weights may result from:

(i) Further research may show that the dangers and shielding requirements have been ovestimated; or light weight, efficient shielding may be developed.

(ii) A capable "interplanetary-weather-forecasting office" might be established which, with the aid of space probes, solar observation, etc., enables us to predict hazardous "weather" in space (by observing the Forbush decrease of cosmic radiation intensity) sufficiently accurately and sufficiently into the future to allow "safe" interplanetary flights; possibly, at least, fast flights. There is, at present, a high probability of predicting a solar flare between 4 and 5 days ahead, and (with 70% probability) 35 days ahead according to the Space Information Division of North American Aircraft.

(iii) The development of solar or nuclear low acceleration vehicles or other advanced means of propulsion may permit the penalty of the heavy shielding as now envisioned, and still result in a reasonably efficient mission. With an efficient short time warning system the heavy shielding could be confined to a small "safety area" (coffins). Shield weight of the order of 100 gm/cm^2 seems to be on the safe side,[2] while shield weights below several grams per square centimeter are practically useless. (The shield against radiation from a nuclear reactor is in the same weight/area class, but need not be omnidirectional; therefore, the shield necessary here is at least 10 times as heavy as the nuclear shadow shield.)

An estimate of shield weight requirement against all environmental radiation effects during manned interplanetary space missions is given in Figs. 3.4 and 3.5.

---

[1] There may be no correlation between giant flare frequency and sunspot number.

[2] More recent information points out that $10–50 \text{ gm/cm}^2$ may suffice when local shielding, e.g., a head shield, and an eye shield during rest periods, is worn by the crew; much of this wall shield should be equipment or material which has to be carried along anyway, thus not constituting a weight penalty for the vehicle. See Kottler (1966) and Savin et al. (1967).

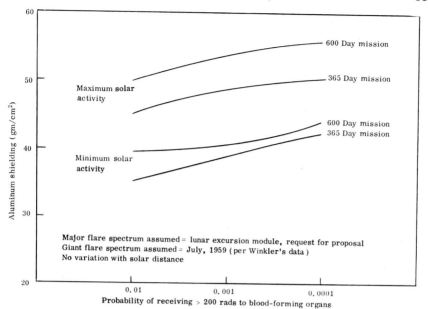

FIG. 3.4. Environmental radiation hazard: shield weight (Lockheed Aircraft Corporation).

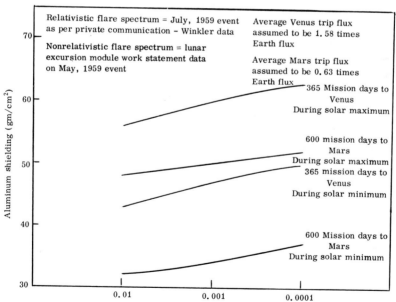

FIG. 3.5. Environmental radiation hazard: shield weight (Lockheed Aircraft Corporation).

Another estimate requires shielding, as shown in the following tabulation, for long duration space missions, holding a probability of 0.001 (0.01) that no more than 200 rads are delivered to the blood forming organs:

	Aluminum/polyethylene shield, laminated	Aluminum shield
Shield mass (gm/cm²)	15–20 (8.3–11)	24–32 (12.5–17)

Comparison of these data[1] with the data from Figs. 3.4 and 3.5 show the fairly large degree of uncertainty associated with radiation shielding weight estimates.

Some additional particle radiation data which may be of interest are given in Table 3.7.

So again, for long-duration mission shielding of 10–20 gm/cm² appears required.

However, the situation is different for relatively short-duration lunar missions. As an example,[2] Apollo astronauts will venture to the Moon with little more radiation protection than that provided by the hull of their space ship.

The men will have special protection only for their eyes. Neither the Lunar Excursion Module nor the Apollo spacecraft will carry special shielding.

Astronauts will be allowed yearly dose rates of 233 rads on the skin, 54 to blood-forming organs, 599 to the feet, ankles, and hands, and 27 to the eyes.

Maximum dosage per single radiation events: skin, 500; blood organs, 200; feet, ankles, hands, 700; eyes, 100.

The walls of the Apollo spaceship will provide most of the shielding. The honeycomb sandwich of aluminum will have a mass of 1.5 gm/cm².

The largest solar flare recorded up to May 1964 occurred in July 1959. If astronauts had been in free space within the Apollo sapacecraft at that time, they would have received a dose of 15 rads to the blood-forming organs, and 160 to the skin.

Conditions are different for Earth-orbital missions, because the environment there is markedly different from free space.

---

[1] A set of data obtained in April 1964 from the Research Projects Laboratory of NASA's G.C. Marshall Space Flight Center indicates still lower requirements: polyethylene 4–12.5; aluminum 9–10 gm/cm².

[2] *Missiles and Rockets*, November 17, 1962.

TABLE 3.7

PARTICLE RADIATION DATA

Average energy and dosage			
Date	Type	Average energy (MeV)	Integral dosage (rad)
2/23/56	Class 3 + flare	370	60
7/14/59	Class 3 + flare	46	30,000
4/1/60	Class 3 + flare	40	0.007
11/12/60	Class 3 + flare	50	1852 (97.6% due to protons of energy $30 < E < 80$ MeV)
Continually for 1 yr	Galactic cosmic radiation	4000	5
1 h passage	Trapped van Allen belt	144	6

Aluminum shielding against solar flare of 11/12/60								
Shield mass (gm/cm²)	0	2	4	6	8	10	18	44
Dosage (rad)	1852	5000	1000	200	100	70	10	1

Dangerous flares	3 +	Relativistic
Max proton energy	500 MeV	10^3 MeV
Proton energy > 30 MeV, total flux (protons/cm²)	5–150×10^7	100×10^7
Proton energy > 100 MeV	0.5–35×10^7	50×10^7
Proton energy > 30 MeV, flux (protons/cm² sec)	1–20×10^3	10×10^3
Proton energy > 100 MeV	0.1–3×10^3	5×10^3
Duration	A few days	

(b) *Solar streams.* The radiation dosage rate in free space can be even higher than for solar flares, but the lower energy of the particles makes shielding more feasible. Particle densities in the streams are high—perhaps 100 per cm³ in Earth vicinity. There is speculation that MHD interaction keeps "blobs" of the gas together thus preserving the original particle density (around 10^6/cm³) throughout the solar system.

The streams move radially away from the Sun, but the particles within the stream probably move in an isotropic manner, thus requiring all around shielding of sensitive payloads. As all streams are preceded by flares, some warning exists. But not all flares are followed by streams.

Streams and flares are not rare events. There appear to be an average number between $\frac{1}{5}$ to 5 serious solar bursts per year, of a duration of about 1 day each. Flare activity often follows sunspot activity.

It is interesting that satellite observations revealed an upper atmosphere density variation (25% in 200 km) in a period of 27 days, which is explained as an effect of solar flares. (Solar rotational period is about 27 days.)

(3) *van Allen radiation zones.* Van Allen announced the discovery (by instruments in the U.S. satellite Explorer I, and further explored by many space vehicles, even up to creating artificial "radiation belts" by nuclear explosions: Project Argus, Project Starfish) of a radiation zone around Earth, May 1, 1958. Since then, three "belts" of high intensity particle radiation have been discovered. The particles are ionized and trapped by the Earth's magnetic field. Whereas the outer belt appears to be fed by solar particle inputs (mainly electrons, which are accelerated after being caught by the Earth's magnetic field), the source for the inner belt appears to be mainly neutron albedo and decay; the neutrons being a result of interaction between cosmic radiation and the upper atmosphere. A third outer belt was discovered by Soviet scientists, resulting from interactions of solar wind and Earth's magnetic field.

Today we know that, instead of belts, a better description is given by zones of varying composition.

Wherever there is a magnetic field, incident solar particles, or cosmic radiation, with some atmosphere, we can expect similar radiation belts; there is indeed some radioastronomical information that Jupiter has strong (intensity 10^{14} times that near Earth) radiation zones located over the equatorial area at 350,000 km altitude with 150,000 km diameter. Saturn also appears to have a trapped radiation zone.

One of the Soviet lunar probes observed "either a belt or blanket of low energy ionized gases around the Moon." And solar radiation belts may explain some of the behavior of the corona.

On Mars not much of a magnetic field and hence, not much in the way of radiation zones, is expected.[1] According to Mariner II (December 1962) results, Venus has no radiation belts reaching more than 20,000 miles from Venus.

---

[1] This statement agrees with measurements from Mariner IV.

Inner belt. Maximum particle density is 1 per cm³ at 4000 km altitude. On the average, there are 10^{-6} protons/cm³ with energies up to 700 MeV, the most probable energy being a few MeV. There have been particles observed with positive charges larger than 15. Furthermore, on the average, 10^{-4} electrons/cm³ with energy below 1000 keV (most probable around 100 keV) have been found. The intensities rise strongly towards lower energies. The energy flux behind a shield of 1 mg/cm² at 2000 km altitude has been observed to be larger than 300 erg/cm² sec = 3×10^{-5} W/cm², more than 95% of which was carried by electrons.

The radiation intensity in the van Allen zone will reach the order of 10 roentgens per hour behind 1 gm/cm² shield (structure), in the heart of the inner belt. The main danger stems from γ radiation resulting from wall-electron interaction. The least concentration of hard particles is found in the polar areas, immediately after strong geomagnetic disturbances.

A manned or otherwise radiation-sensitive vehicle will require no shielding for altitudes below 600 km, and latitudes between $\pm$ 35°. Otherwise, the vehicle may touch the lower radiation belt. In the auroral zones the trapped radiation "leaks" to low altitudes. There are rare cases of intense solar particle radiation penetrating the atmosphere to low altitudes.

A tentative composition of the radiation in the inner van Allen belt is shown in Tables 3.8 and 3.9.

TABLE 3.8

ELECTRON FLUX FOR VARIOUS ENERGIES

Energy (keV)	Flux (per cm² sec)
> 20	6×10^9
> 40	10^9
> 600	2×10^7

High energy protons can be stopped by about 100 kg/m² of aluminum. At the lower fringe, 1% of the protons have energies > 700 MeV, 10% have energies > 300 MeV, and 100% have energies > 75 MeV.

The inner belt appears to be fairly stable—about 20% variation has been observed.

Within the belt, the radiation becomes softer with altitude following a distribution: maximum trapped momentum = constant/r^2. It should be remembered that shielding, against up to 70 MeV protons, is very simple —the normal structure will probably suffice. But the protons can produce

TABLE 3.9

Proton Flux for Various Energies

Energy (MeV)	Flux (per cm² sec)
> 40	2×10^4
> 75	1.4×10^3
> 100	10^3

secondary effects (e.g., γ radiation) which, even from 1-MeV protons, can be very penetrating. Because of this, choice of materials is important to suppress such secondary effects.

The radiation is not isotropic, allowing for shield weight savings of the order of 30% compared to all around shielding if a reliable attitude-control system permits the use of directional shielding.

The upper atmosphere (say, upward from 1000 km) determines the structure of the lower regions of the radiation zone. Thus it may become possible to determine data of the upper amtosphere (e.g., its density) by radiation measurements. It may even be that this is the only practical way to determine such data.

The lifetime of a proton in the inner belt may be typically 10^6 sec; with 10^{-7} particles/cm³, the "birth rate" is only $10^{-7}/10^6 = 10^{-13}$ protons/cm³ sec. Even so, with a proton speed of 10^{10} cm/sec, the flux is fairly high $10^{-7} \times 10^{10} = 10^3$ protons/cm² sec.

By increasing the "birth rate" (e.g., nuclear explosion, nuclear reactor operation, particle accelerator) or the "death rate" (e.g., a large, otherwise inert satellite, which absorbs the energy of impacting particles—for which the satellite needs thick walls—perhaps several centimeters lead equivalent—this is Professor F. Singer's "radiation sweeper") the radiation intensity can be influenced very drastically.

The NERV (Nuclear Emulsion Recovery Vehicle, NASA, September 1960) showed that the proton flux curve turns sharply upward in the inner van Allen zone at energies below 20 MeV.

The lower edge of the van Allen radiation zone is of special interest for many (manned) Earth orbital operations.[1] The radiation intensity is not extremely high, but one would still like to avoid penetrating into the belt. Some typical data concerning the altitude of this lower edge (except for near-polar areas) are:

Highest 1300 ± 25 km at $\sim 100°$ E longitude, $\sim 10°$ N latitude.

Average   800 km (over Earth)

Minimum 320 ± 25 km at $\sim 310°$ E longitude, $+ 18°$ S latitude.

Outer belt. Maximum particle density can be of the order of 10 per cm^3 at 16,000 km altitude; the average is 10^{-2} per cm^3. Very strong variations —up to a factor of 10^4—appear to occur. Most of the particles are electrons, 50% of which have energies below 100 keV, and only 1% exceed 500 keV up to 3×10^6 eV. The intensity may vary tenfold within a few hours for reasons possibly connected with solar disturbances. The belt moves north and south as much as 500 miles. The minimum altitude varies—in one particular measurement, 1600 km was the lower limit over the Soviet Union, and only 600 km over the United States.

The outer limit is at about 10 Earth radii altitude, and again depends on solar activity. Mariner IV measured last traces at an altitude of 26 Earth radii.

A tentative spectrum is given in Tables 3.10 and 3.11. Figures 3.6 and 3.7 give additional information.

TABLE 3.10

ELECTRONS

Energy (keV)	Flux (per cm^2 sec)
> 40	10^8
> 80	$10^6 - 10^7$
$> 20 \times 10^3$	10^5
$> 50 \times 10^3$	10^2

The unshielded exposure corresponds to several tens of roentgen per hour, which is almost completely absorbed by a shield of 40 kg/m^2 of lead. At high latitudes electrons from the outer belt "leak" to the atmosphere

---

[1] Gemini II reached a record altitude of 1367 km in Sept. 1966.

(1 erg/cm² sec), causing aurorae. This "leakage" might account for the unexpected temperature rise within the atmosphere with altitude and latitude.

TABLE 3.11

Protons

Energy (MeV)	Flux (per cm² sec)
Between 0.1 and 5	10^8
> 1	10^7
> 75	0.1

For a fast crossing, the van Allen radiation zones do not constitute a severe hazard; the total integrated dosage inside the space probe Pioneer IV

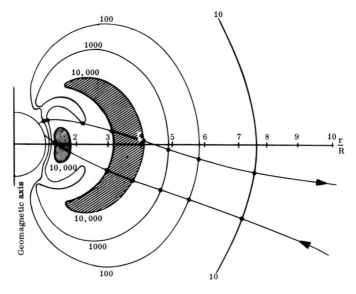

Fig. 3.6. Intensity structure of the trapped radiation around the Earth. *Note.* This diagram is a section through a figure of revolution around the geomagnetic axis. Contours of constant intensity are labeled with the numbers 10, 100, 1000, and 10,000, which are the true counting rates of an Anton type 302 Geiger tube carried by Explorer IV and Pioneer III. The linear scale of the diagram is relative to the radius of the Earth, 6371 km. The outbound and inbound legs of the trajectory of Pioneer III are shown by the slanting, undulating lines.

was below one roentgen.[1] But with a maximum of 10 roentgen/h (or in extreme cases 100 roentgen/h) and a stay time of 50 h, the fatal radiation dosage for man would be reached. Actual death may occur only ~1 month later. Thus, even in this most catastrophic case the man would be able to initiate landing on Earth and "tell the tale." (In one accident, a person was exposed

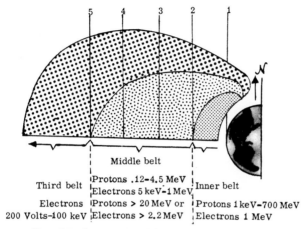

		Middle belt		
	Third belt	Protons .12–4.5 MeV	Inner belt	
		Electrons 5 keV–1 MeV		
	Electrons	Protons > 20 MeV or	Protons 1 keV–700 MeV	
	200 Volts–100 keV	Electrons > 2.2 MeV	Electrons 1 MeV	

Fig. 3.7. Composition of van Allen radiation belts.

to 7000 roentgens. He died about 2 days after the accident from cell damage leading to loss of body fluid and extreme shock.) These radiation belts are a strong point against return to Earth by a series of braking ellipses, if these lead to additional crossings of the van Allen zone. And it is obvious that the radiation zones will be much more of a hazard to manned low acceleration vehicles than to high acceleration ones. On the other hand, if shielding against solar streams/flares has to be carried anyway, then the same shielding might suffice against the van Allen radiation.[2]

The total number of particles in the Earth radiation zone is estimated to be of the order of 1 mole ($\approx 6 \times 10^{23}$).

Tentatively, the total radiation dosage received without special shielding, crossing the heart of the van Allen zones on an escape mission, may be as shown in Table 3.12.

---

[1] Possibly the total radiation intensity in space has been overestimated: The total radiation dose of only 3 roentgen penetrated the hull of Mariner II during its 109-day trip from Earth to Venus, behind less than 0.5 gm/cm² of shielding.

[2] One difference is that the streams/flares are short-duration phenomena, whereas the stay-time within the belts might be long.

TABLE 3.12

Radiation Dosage Crossing van Allen Zones

Acceration (g)	Radiation dosage (roentgens)
1	1
10^{-1}	5
10^{-2}	50
10^{-3}	500^a
10^{-4}	5000^a
10^{-5}	50000^a

^{a} Shielding of man is necessary.

(4) *Radiation from nuclear power sources.* These might be nuclear fission or fusion reactors or radioactive isotopes, the decay energy of which is utilized. As the latter will probably be small, and as little radiation is expected from a fusion reactor, there remain fission reactors for the main source of radiation.

In the previous chapter some remarks as to the shielding have been made. It might be added that already a few millimeters of a low atomic number material suffice to stop electrons of a few kiloelectron volts energy. But in doing this, Bremsstrahlung is produced, and high atomic number material is better suited to stop γ radiation. Thus a good shield should be laminated.

It was mentioned before that, by putting the reactor on a long boom away from the living quarters, shielding weight can be saved at the expense of boom construction weight, and an optimum exists. For a low weight boom, the optimum boom may be very large, and shielding weight small. To get a low weight boom it has been proposed to have only a cable between the payload section and the nuclear powerhouse. For high thrust nuclear rocket systems, the nozzle and hydrogen supply also has to be at the reactor, and the payload could be trailing. Some electric energy can be fed through the cable to the payload. A lunar landing becomes conceivable with such a system, putting the payload on the surface and the reactor-thrust system as far away as the cable length permits.

For low thrust systems, engines could be at both the reactor and the payload assuming that electric energy can be transported via the cable link.

The possibility of shielding against ionized particles by proper fields should not be dismissed, though on first sight it does not look promising. But considering recent developments in the fields of superconductors and cryogenics, effective active shielding against charged particles may be practical. A passive shield has to be added to stop or transform the non-charged radiation (Levy, 1961; Kash and Tooper, 1962).

According to Levy and Jones (1964), pure magnetic shielding is weightwise comparable to passive shielding showing some advantage for large shielded volume sizes (say, above 50 m³). For an electrostatic shield, the vehicle has to be kept at a potential of about 2×10^8 V, against infinity. Again, a magnetic field has to be added, in order to reduce the flow of electrons to the vehicle. Such shielding might be accomplished for a mass penalty an order of magnitude smaller than for the passive or the pure magnetic shield.

3.5,3 Effects of Radiation on Materials

Radiation can have many effects on materials, e.g., gas evolution, change in mechanical/electrical/optical properties, and even complete mechanical breakdown (liquids can become solid, or solids powdered). Let us look at some specific cases.

The van Allen radiation did not influence operation of transistors after exposure of the order of 10 days. Tubes can be expected to withstand radiation better than semiconductors. Materials within a nuclear reactor core become brittle. Over very long times, cosmic radiation should have similar effects.

Photographic materials, plastics, rubber, solid propellants, some liquids, lubricants, sealants, hydraulic fluids, gaskets, insulation can all be affected more or less. (For example, asbestos-filled phenolic has a very low radiation sensitivity, Mylar a little, and Teflon 10^4 times as much.) Ceramics may darken but show little other signs of sensitivity, but in extreme cases they may crumble. Unlike plastics, some glasses that have darkened will recover under certain light/heat conditions. Cesium is a glass additive that makes it more radiation resistant. Often about 10^6 roengten lead to noticeable effects in materials; some solid propellants, for instance, are damaged by a radiation dose of about 4×10^6 rad.[1]

---

[1] REP: roentgen equivalent physical. REM: roentgen equivalent man. RBE: relative biological effectiveness. RAD: radiation absorbed dose. One roentgen liberates 83 erg per gram of dry air. 1 REP = radiation dose which leads to 97 ergs liberated per gram of tissue. 1 RAD = radiation dose which leads to 100 ergs liberated per gram of absorbing material. Dose in REMs = RBE × dose in RADs.

For many substances one bond is broken by 25 eV absorbed radiation. The definition was 1 roentgen $= 83$ ergs/gm $\approx 50 \times 10^{12}$ eV $\approx 2 \times 10^{12}$ broken bonds. In 1 gm of a substance of a molecular weight of 30, there are 2×10^{22} molecules. Thus 10^6 roentgen breaks 2×10^{18} bonds, which influences one out of 10^4 particles; it is understandable that this is about the limit at which materials start to become notably affected. Obviously there can be much more sensitive cases—e.g., semiconductors, or forms of life.

It should be mentioned that the materials damage depends not only on radiation dosage and material, but also on kind of radiation, rate of application, load and temperature of the material, and other conditions. We differentiate between dose effects (resulting from total absorbed radiation), rate effects (resulting from absorption per unit of time), and transient effects (resulting from rapid changes in absorbed radiation).

3.5,4 Remarks Concerning Effects of Radiation on Man [1]

Some data concerning this question are given in Chap. 2 and in Figs. 3.4 and 3.5, and in the text accompanying these figures; therefore, we need add only a few additional remarks:

An acute, uniform whole body radiation exposure of 100 rads appears to result in an actuarial life shortening of about 1.5 yr. This is about 15–20% of the life shortening effect believed to follow from the habitual smoking of one pack of cigarettes per day. It can be shown conclusively that radiation doses in excess of 100 rads cause an increase in the incidence of leukemia and other malignant disease; this is also true for the formation of cataracts.

About 30 rads appear to double the natural incidence of mutations in man.[2]

RBE-values are usually based on continuous low dose exposure; for many high dose rate exposures the RBE may be much lower, e.g., less than one as compared to 5–10 for fast neutrons. This is shown in Table 3.13.

Equivalent Residual Dose (ERD) is a recent concept used in estimating what residual acute radiation injury persists for a period of weeks and months

[1] The requirements for radiation protection will be essentially alike in free space and on the lunar surface, and reduced on the surface of Mars, where the dosage is normally below 100 m rem/day, and during a large solar flare below 160 m rem/day. Against the meteoroid danger, the Mars' atmosphere renders sufficient protection.

[2] For more detail, see Vol. III/2, May 5, 1963, Proceedings of the Lunar and Planetary Colloquium, p. 117 ff.

after an exposure to radiation. ERD provides an estimate of damage remaining as a function of time elapsed since the exposure. If a second exposure occurs, ERD provides an estimate of the effects of the sum of the old and the new exposures. The effects considered are those of acute radiation illness alone, not other effects such as life shortening or genetic damage.

TABLE 3.13

RBE VALUES

	RBE values
Galactic cosmic radiation	5
Solar cosmic radiation (3 + flare)	1.5
van Allen, inner belt	1.5
van Allen, outer belt	1

The ERD at any time after onset of exposure can be calculated on the basis of the following assumptions:

(1) Ten per cent of the injury attributed to the dose is considered to be nonrepairable.

(2) The body repairs the remaining 90% at the rate of 2.5% per day.

(3) Recovery after a brief exposure (exposure time less than 4 days) begins 4 days after the start of the exposure.

(4) Recovery is continuous. If D_0 is dose during first 4 days (in roentgens), $\dot{D}$ is the constant daily dose after the fourth day, roentgens/day, t is the time in days, then

$$\text{ERD} = D_0[0.1 + 0.9(1 - 0.025)^{t-4}] + \dot{D} \int_4^t [0.1 + 0.9(1 - 0.025)^t]\, dt$$

[From NASA SP-3006, Bioastronautics Data Book, 1964.]

3.6 Temperature in Space

3.6,1 Introduction

The temperature of objects in space is determined by energy received from or given to the outside (radiation), and energy created (e.g., by exothermal reactions or friction of moving parts) or lost (e.g., to melt ice), or transported (e.g., conduction) or transients (temperature changes of materials) within the vehicle.

During some special phases, heat sources other than radiation can be important:

(1) Aerodynamic heating: launch, landing, or in the upper atmosphere.

(2) Main propulsive engine operation: near the engine, or radiation from the engine exhaust.

(3) Fire on board: it is hoped that this will present but little hazard, since flammable mixtures should rarely exist; when they do exist, diffusion should dissipate such mixtures rapidly.

(4) Man on board: 3000 kcal/day per man, or about 150 W per man.

(5) Exothermic reaction to generate internal power.

3.6,2 External Energy Inputs to the Vehicle

There are a number of sources of external energy input to the vehicle:

Solar radiation	1400 W/m², near Earth. (This shows about 3.5% seasonal variation due to the eccentricity of Earth's orbit.)
Solar wind	3×10^{-4}–30 W/m²; shielded by Earth magnetic field in Earth vicinity.

Solar streams/flares 1 W/m²; only during solar activity.

van Allen radiation 3×10^{-1} W/m² (only in Earth, etc., vicinity).

Meteors	3×10^{-5} W/m².
Cosmic radiation	10^{-5} W/m².
Starlight	10^{-5} W/m².

Radiation from Earth, close to Earth:

Albedo and thermal, mean sunlight side 475 W/m²

Thermal radiation, mean shadow side   225 W/m².

(Assuming for Earth a mean temperature T such that $0.64 \times (5.67/10^8) T^4 = 225$ W/m², we obtain $T = 281°K$, a reasonable value).

Radiation from Moon, close to Moon:

Mean sunlight side   685 W/m²

Mean shadow side   15 W/m².

Mean albedo 0.07; therefore, from the above figures we obtain

Mean night side temperature on Moon   130°K

Mean sunlight side temperature on Moon   325°K.

Aerodynamic heating in rarefied gases, maximum: for satellite speeds, and $g\varrho_0 = 1.3 \text{ kg/m}^3$, about $(\varrho/\varrho_0) \times 3.33 \times 10^{11} \text{ W/m}^2$, or below 100 W/m² for $(\varrho/\varrho_0) < 3 \times 10^{-10}$, which occurs for Earth at altitudes above 200 km.

The maximum radiation from a non self-energy producing and non energy concentrating object to a small vehicle in its vicinity close to the subsolar point can be equal to the solar constant—1400 W/m² near Earth.

If a space vehicle is sufficiently out of the atmosphere, and not in shadow, then the Sun will usually be the major source of external energy input. This changes in shadow, which is of special importance for Earth satellites and, of course, for satellites of other celestial bodies. On interplanetary flights no significant shadow time is encountered during transfer, but the varying distance vehicle to Sun, or the varying environment (near Earth, then free space, then near target) can make thermal control difficult.

The Earth throws a shadow cone into space which is shown, approximately, in Fig. 3.8.

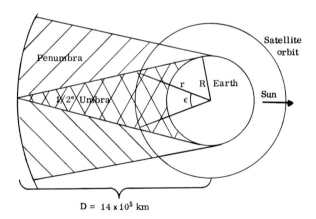

FIG. 3.8. Shadow regions of Earth caused by light from Sun. Beyond D, Earth appears to be smaller than the Sun; passages of "Earth before Sun" can occur beyond 14×10^5 km.

For a satellite close to Earth, the shadow time can obviously be between 0 and 50 per cent of a period, and there is, as shown before,[1] the possibility of having the satellite always in sunlight. Generally, the "shadow percentage" will vary during the life of a satellite, making thermal control more difficult. For a circular 24-h satellite (distance about 6.67 radii from Earth

[1] Section 4.4,2,4, Vol. 1.

center) the shadow time can be only between 0 and 4.8% per period (or not more than 1 h and 9 min per period).

Looking only at maximum shadow time, quite clearly the shadow time percentage of one period goes down with increasing altitude. How about absolute time in shadow? The maximum arc, which a circular orbit can spend within the umbra, is easily found (see Fig. 3.8):

$$\cos\left(90 - \frac{1}{4} - \frac{\varepsilon}{2}\right) = \frac{R}{r} \, ,$$

or

$$\sin\left(\frac{\varepsilon}{2} + \frac{1}{4}\right) = \frac{R}{r} \, ,$$

or in radians

$$\varepsilon = 2 \arcsin \frac{R}{r} - \frac{1}{110} \, .$$

On the other hand, the time to pass through an angle ε is, for a satellite in a circular orbit, equal to

$$\varDelta T = \varepsilon \left(\frac{R}{g_0}\right)^{1/2} \left(\frac{r}{R}\right)^{3/2} .$$

The resulting behavior is shown in Fig. 3.9; details are left to the reader.

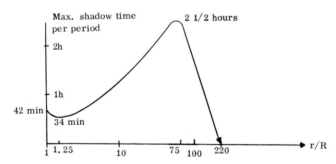

Fig. 3.9. Plot of maximum shadow time of Earth satellite.

(It should be remembered that these are maximum shadow times. For distant satellites such as our Moon, the shadow time per revolution is usually zero, and the maximum is very seldom realized.)

It can be quite difficult to have acceptable temperature within a satellite in sunlight as well as in shadow. The equilibrium temperatures are very different, and internal heat capacity plus the limited rate of energy exchange have to be balanced carefully so that a harmful temperature is not obtained. And it is not only extreme temperatures that are harmful, but thermal cycling and thermal stress have to be withstood by materials and design.

3.6,3 Internal Energy

Out of 100% received energy (solar, chemical, or nuclear), a powerplant may convert 30% to mechanical or electrical energy, and 70% to heat, which has to be radiated from the powerplant radiator. Of the remaining 30%, very little—say, 1%—may be radiated away in the form of radio waves, and 29% finally appears as heat also. This has to be radiated away from the payload, or taken up by some coolant (e.g., transforming ice to water). For long time operations, only radiating the heat away is attractive. The payload surface or a part thereof can be used as a radiator, or a special radiator can be provided. A liquid or gas forced convection system may be required to transport the energy from the instruments to the radiator, or one could rely on internal radiative, diffusive, and conductive heat exchange. Energy exchange by free convection does not work under zero gravity condition.

Internal heat is not only released by machines and apparatus, but, to a noticeable degree, by man, if present; 3000 kcal/day per man may be a usable figure.

Let us assume a thermodynamic engine with an efficiency η, compared to a Carnot engine, which runs between a high and low temperature T_1, T_2. The ratio of energy delivered from the engine to the energy given to the engine is

$$\frac{A}{Q_1} = \eta \left(1 - \frac{T_2}{T_1} \right),$$

or, for $\eta = 1$, the "waste heat" W is given by

$$\frac{W}{Q_1} = \frac{Q_1 - A}{Q_1} = \frac{T_2}{T_1},$$

or

$$\frac{W}{A} = \frac{T_2/T_1}{(1 - T_2/T_1)},$$

or

$$A = W \left(\frac{T_1}{T_2} - 1 \right).$$

This is the principle of a heat pump: to take energy W from a low temperature reservoir T_2 and to deliver $W + A$ at the high temperature reservoir T_1, energy A is required.

Again with an efficiency $\eta' < 1$, we have

$$A = \frac{W}{\eta'}\left(\frac{T_1}{T_2} - 1\right).$$

With $T_1/T_2 = 10$, $\eta' = \frac{1}{2}$, we get

$$A = 18W.$$

Now W may be the heat energy given off by the payload. If enough energy is available (e.g., if electric propulsion systems are used), by additionally spending $A = 18W$, we deliver $19W$ to a ten times hotter radiator. As radiation per square meter is proportional to T^4, the ratio

$$\frac{\text{area of the hot radiator}}{\text{area of the cold radiator}} = \frac{18}{10^4},$$

and perhaps the corresponding weight ratio is 10^{-2}. Thus the hot radiator is much lighter than the cold one, and this could conceivably result in a weight gain even when the additional weight of the heat pump, power generation for the $18W$, structure, etc., are taken into account. Furthermore, by controlling the engine delivering the energy A a convenient temperature regulating system can be envisioned. A detailed study will result in an optimum value for the temperature ratio T_1/T_2.

If part of the payload can be fairly warm then, for this part, T_2 may be high enough that $T_1 = T_2$ is the best choice (no heat pump). For the rest of the payload a lower temperature value T_2' may be required, and a heat pump may be utilized just for this low temperature section ("refrigerator system").

3.6,4 Radiation and Surfaces

Having a surface element df and radiative energy e falling upon it at an angle α to the normal of df, we obtain

$$f_1 \text{ is reflected:} \quad f_1 = re,$$
$$f_2 \text{ absorbed:} \quad f_2 = \varepsilon e,$$
$$f_3 \text{ transmitted:} \quad f_3 = te,$$
$$\overline{\phantom{f_3 \text{ transmitted:} \quad f_3 = te,}}$$
$$\text{Total} \quad r + \varepsilon + t = 1.$$

The thermal radiation from the element is, from Stephan-Boltzmann's law, $f_2' = \lambda \sigma T^4$, where the Stephan-Boltzmann constant is $\sigma = 5.67 \times 10^{-8}$ W/m^2 $^\circ$K^4, and the emissivity $\lambda \leq 1$ ($\lambda = 1$ is called a "black body"). Often, approximately,

$$\varepsilon = \varepsilon_0 \cos \alpha \,,$$

$$r = 1 - \varepsilon_0 \cos \alpha - t_0 \cos \alpha \,,$$

$$t = t_0 \cos \alpha \,.$$

A complication is that, for a given material, all the coefficients r, ε, t, and λ may depend upon the temperature T of the wall element df, and upon the frequency ν (or wavelength c/ν).[1] For a black body of temperature T, the energy distribution in its spectrum is described by Planck's law which states that the radiated energy within the frequency limits ν and $\nu + d\nu$ is

$$E \, d\nu = \frac{2\pi h \nu^3}{c^2} \frac{1}{\exp(h\nu/kT) - 1} d\nu \,,$$

where Planck's constant $h = 6.6237 \times 10^{-27}$ erg sec, and Boltzmann's constant $k = 1.38024 \times 10^{-16}$ erg/$^\circ$K.

Therefore, we should have written,

$$f_2' = \int_0^\infty \lambda(\nu, T) E \, d\nu \,.$$

Only if $d\lambda/d\nu = 0$ (gray body) do we get from this the indicated form

$$f_2' = \lambda(T)\sigma T^4 \,.$$

If $d\lambda/d\nu \neq 0$, some mean value $\lambda(\bar{\nu}, T) = \bar{\lambda}(T)$ can be chosen such that the form $f_2' = \bar{\lambda}\sigma T^4$ is maintained.

From the second law of thermodynamics it can be concluded that

$$\varepsilon(\nu, T) = \lambda(\nu, T) \,.$$

Furthermore, Wien's law has to be mentioned: From Planck's law we know that E has a maximum for a certain $\nu = \nu_{\max}$, or for a certain wavelength $\lambda = \lambda_{\max}$. Numerically we have

$$\frac{Tc}{\nu_{\max}} = 0.50990 \quad \text{cm} \, ^\circ\text{K} \,,$$

or

$$T\lambda_{\max} = 0.28975 \quad \text{cm} \, ^\circ\text{K} \,.$$

---

[1] c is the speed of light.

This opens the way to an interesting passive method of heat control for space vehicles. For the Sun, the surface temperature is about $T \approx 6000°K$, and thus $\lambda_{max} \approx 0.5 \times 10^{-4}$ cm (visible, yellow). For about 350°K we have $\lambda'_{max} = 8 \times 10^{-4}$ cm (infrared). The large difference between λ_{max} and λ'_{max} indicates that there may be materials having very different coefficients ε and λ for λ_{max} and λ'_{max}, e.g., absorbing well around λ_{max}, but reradiating poorly for λ'_{max}, leading to a hot surface element; or absorbing poorly around λ_{max} and reradiating well around λ'_{max}, leading to a cold surface element. Such materials do exist. Typical behavior is as sketched in Fig. 3.10. Some numerical examples are given in Table 3.14.

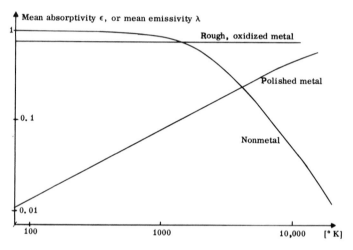

FIG. 3.10. Behavior of three materials as a function of temperature of surface, or of incoming radiation.

A basic difficulty is that ε and λ can change as a function of lifetime, materials aging, handling, method of preparation of the surface, radiation exposure, etc. More testing and accumulating of knowledge is necessary in this area.

As far as solar radiation goes, ε/λ determines the equilibrium temperature of a space vehicle. For planetary albedo radiation, the same ε/λ determines the temperature; but for planetary thermal radiation to a space vehicle, the absorptivity will be about equal to λ if planet and space vehicle have about the same temperature. To become independent of the varying planetary radiation, a small λ value is advantageous; this would lead to long durations before equilibrium is established with respect to the planetary radiation. Thus the vehicle would, in effect, average over the planetary radiation.

TABLE 3.14

NUMERICAL EXAMPLES

Material	Absorptivity ε to solar radiation	Emissivity λ at room temperature	Ratio ε/λ
Deposited copper oxide	0.95	0.10	9.5
Silver, optical reflector	0.07	0.01	7
Nickel, polished	0.4	0.06	6.7
Magnesium alloy	0.3	0.07	4.3
410 stainless steel, etched	0.38	0.19	2
410 stainless steel, bare	0.26	0.42	0.62
White paint (ZnO)	0.15	0.95	0.16

Internal energy production may force us to depart from a small λ value in order to keep the vehicle temperature low enough, because, with respect to internal energy production alone, the equilibrium temperature is determined as follows (see Fig. 3.11.):

$$\dot{e} = \frac{k}{d}\,(T_i - T_0) \qquad \text{and} \qquad \dot{e} = \lambda\sigma T_0{}^4 .$$

From these

$$T_i = \frac{d}{k}\,\dot{e} + \left(\frac{\dot{e}}{\lambda\sigma}\right)^{1/4} .$$

For thin walls (d small) of good thermal conductivity (k large),

$$T_i \approx \left(\frac{\dot{e}}{\lambda\sigma}\right)^{1/4} ,$$

or λ alone becomes the temperature governing material constant.

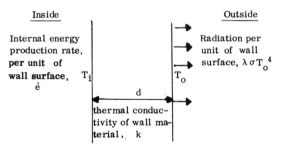

FIG. 3.11. Diagram of thermal conduction through a wall.

It might be mentioned that, for interstellar vehicles, we desire $\dot{e}$ small for a given T_i. This leads to large d, small k (thermal insulation), and small λ. With vacuum-type insulation k could be made a controllable variable by controlling a gas pressure within the insulating material.

Absorptivity to solar radiation should be small also, again in order to make the response slow in going from shadow to sunlight. But the required ratio ε/λ can force us to use a large ε value. As this discussion shows, there will be compromises necessary in the choice of λ and ε. This often leads to patterns of various materials on the surface of a space vehicle. In order to get an "average surface" without local hot—or cold—spots, the patterns should be narrow.

The thermal environment of a space vehicle varies for many reasons: satellites of a given type may be launched under different light–shadow conditions, or a space probe may, or may not, be close to another celestial body, or a space vehicle may change its distance from the Sun noticeably, or it might go from a light zone to a shadow zone.

To cope with this variable environment and keep the vehicle interior practically unaltered, the surface or surface pattern has to be changed.[1] In some cases this change can be done on the ground before launch, but usually this change will have to occur during flight: bimetallic strips or similar activators can operate light shields, shades, blinds, etc. In the future, materials may be developed that change their radiation characteristics as a function of temperature.

3.6,5 Temperature of Objects in Space

The balance of energy for an object in space can be written easily:

(1) Energy transfer by radiation to the vehicle in time dt is

$$\frac{dE}{dt} = \int_{\text{surface}} \varepsilon \mathbf{e} \, d\mathbf{f} ,$$

where ε is the absorptivity, $\mathbf{e}$ the incoming energy rate, and $d\mathbf{f}$ the surface element.

(2) Radiation from the vehicle is given by

$$\frac{dR}{dt} = \sigma \int_{\text{surface}} \lambda T^4 \, \mathbf{N} \, d\mathbf{f} ,$$

---

[1] One might change something else—e.g., radiation flow rate, of the thermal conduction path—in an active system.

where **N** is a unit vector which is vertical upon d**f**, σ the Stefan-Boltzmann constant, λ the emissivity, and T the temperature.

(3) Internally generated energy (positive, negative, or zero), with $d\tau$ as the volume element, is then

$$\frac{dG}{dt} = \int_{\text{volume}} \dot{g}\, d\tau \;.$$

(4) If a temperature change dT occurs within the volume $d\tau$, then an energy

$$\frac{dW}{dt} = \int_{\text{volume}} n\, \frac{dT}{dt}\, d\tau$$

is "soaked up" by the vehicle. The thermal capacity per unit volume of the mass $d\tau$ is given by $n = $ specific heat $\times$ specific weight.

(5) Heat conduction. Heat conductivity to the volume $d\tau$ is k; then the total heat conduction is

$$\frac{dC}{dt} = -\int_{\text{surface}} k\, \text{grad}\, T\, d\mathbf{f} = -\int_{\text{volume}} \text{div}(k\, \text{grad}\, T)\, d\tau$$

$$= -\int_{\text{volume}} c\varrho \dot{T}\, d\tau = -\frac{dW}{dt}\;,$$

excluding internal radiative heat exchange.

The balance is written as

$$\dot{E} + \dot{G} = \dot{R} + \dot{W}\;,$$

$$\int_{\text{surface}} \varepsilon\mathbf{e}\, d\mathbf{f} + \int_{\text{volume}} \dot{g}\, d\tau = \sigma \int_{\text{surface}} \lambda T^4 \mathbf{N} d\mathbf{f} + \int_{\text{volume}} n\dot{T}\, d\tau\;,$$

or

$$\int_{\text{volume}} d\tau\, (\varepsilon\, \text{div}\, \mathbf{e} + \dot{g} - n\dot{T} - \sigma\, \text{div}\, \lambda T^4 \mathbf{N}) = 0\;,$$

and

$$n\dot{T} = \text{div}\, k\, \text{grad}\, T\;.$$

From the integral we have

$$\text{div}\, \varepsilon\mathbf{e} + \dot{g} = n\dot{T} + \sigma\, \text{div}\, \lambda T^4 \mathbf{N}\;, \tag{3.1a}$$

and

$$n\dot{T} = \text{div}(k\, \text{grad}\, T) + \text{radiative exchange terms}. \tag{3.1b}$$

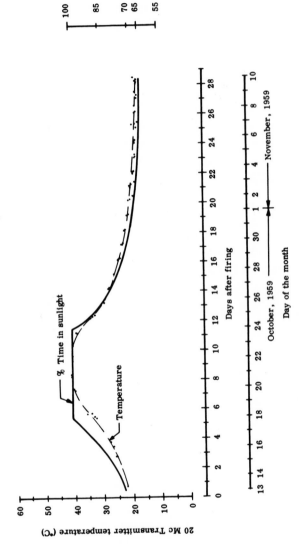

FIG. 3.12. Measured temperatures of transmitter of Explorer VIII.

This is a very complicated equation, or really, set of equations for all volume elements $d\tau$. From the integral form it can be seen that the balance is—because of the surface integral containing $\mathbf{e}$—attitude dependent. For spherical bodies, this attitude dependence vanishes. Figures 3.12 and 3.14 (from Heller, 1960) show results from actual experiments.

3.6,6 Simple Cases of Temperature Determination in Space

To show the fundamental behavior let us look at a sphere (radius r) with

$$\dot{g} = 0, \qquad \text{grad } T = 0, \qquad \dot{T} = 0,$$

which is under solar influence only, with the solar constant being e. (See Fig. 3.13.)

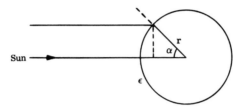

Sun

FIG. 3.13. Solar energy incidence upon a sphere.

Absorbed energy is given by (with $\varepsilon = $ constant)

$$\dot{E} = \varepsilon_n \int_0^{\pi/2} \cos \alpha \; (2\pi r \sin \alpha) \; (r \, d\alpha) \; (e \cos \alpha)$$

$$= \tfrac{2}{3}\varepsilon_n e \pi r^2 = \varepsilon e \pi r^2,$$

where we introduce $\varepsilon = \tfrac{2}{3}\varepsilon_n$. [We used $\varepsilon(\alpha) = \varepsilon_n \cos \alpha$.] The reradiation is simply

$$\dot{R} = 4\pi r^2 \lambda \sigma T^4 \,,$$

and for equilibrium[1]

$$T = \left(\frac{\varepsilon}{4\sigma\lambda} e \right)^{1/4}.$$

Measuring the distance d from the Sun in astronomical units, we can write $e = e' / d^2$, and

$$T = \left(\frac{\varepsilon}{4\sigma\lambda} e' \right)^{1/4} d^{-1/2} \,.$$

---

[1] Assuming that the only source of radiation is the Sun. It should be noted that the sink temperature is assumed to be (absolute) zero degrees.

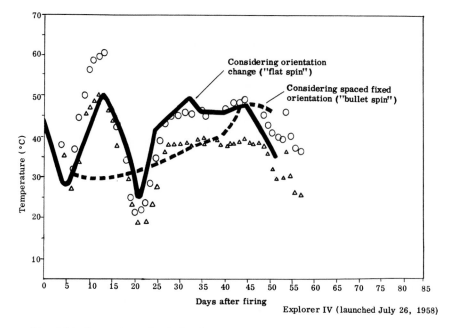

Fig. 3.14. Comparison of calculated temperatures with observed temperatures: $\bigcirc$, high frequency; $\triangle$, low frequency. The difference in frequency is probably due to frequency drift after calibration.

Numerically, $e' = 1400$ W/m², and $\sigma = 5.67 \times 10^{-8}$ W/m² °K⁴. Thus,

$$T = 280.3 \left(\frac{\varepsilon}{\lambda}\right)^{1/4} d^{-1/2} \text{ °K} .$$

Assume that we desire $T = 300$°K. Then for given values of d, the required values of ε/λ are as shown in Table 3.15. Thus passive temperature control appears to be achievable within the inner solar system. But further out than about halfway to Jupiter, other means (e.g., concentration of solar radiation or use of internal heat generation, or design for operation at lower temperature) have to be applied.

Let us now consider a spherical vehicle of radius r as before, again putting $\dot{g} = 0$, grad $T = 0$, $\dot{T} = 0$, but this time the vehicle shall be in a close satellite orbit around Earth or the Moon. The incoming radiation from the Sun is 1400 W/m² or zero (in shadow). The incoming radiation from the Earth and the Moon is shown in Table 3.16.

Therefore, the incoming radiation to a close Earth satellite is between 1960 W/m² and zero from sunlight, and between 200 and 400 W/m² from

TABLE 3.15

THE REQUIRED VALUES OF ε/λ FOR GIVEN VALUES OF d

Distance from Sun d (a.u.)	Planet	ε/λ
0.349	Mercury[a]	0.1600
0.723	Venus	0.6859
1.000	Earth	1.3122
1.524	Mars	3.0476
2.690	—[b]	9.5000

[a] For Mercury, $d = 0.387$ a.u.
[b] For Jupiter $d = 5.203$ a.u.

TABLE 3.16

INCOMING RADIATION FROM EARTH AND MOON

	Radiation (W/m²)		
	Maximum	Average	Minimum
From Earth			
Albedo radiation	560	250[a]	0
Thermal radiation	400	225	200
From Moon			
Albedo radiation	110	50[a]	0
Thermal radiation	1100	635[a], 15[b]	10

[a] Sunlight side.
[b] Shadow side,

Earth thermal radiation. If the satellite has sufficient heat capacity of its own, and the trajectory is chosen correctly, then long shadow times can be avoided, and the satellite averages over the extremes, without reaching equilibrium conditions corresponding to such extremes. For this desirable situation the mean satellite temperature $\bar{T}$ follows from

$$4\pi r^2 \lambda \sigma \bar{T}^4 = (\varepsilon_s \times 1400 + \varepsilon_s\,125 + \varepsilon_t\,225) \times \pi r^2,$$

where ε_s is the absorptivity to solar radiation and ε_t is the absorptivity to thermal radiation. With $\varepsilon_t \approx \lambda$,

$$\frac{\bar{T}}{10^2} = \left(67.2399 \, \frac{\varepsilon_s}{\lambda} + 9.9206\right)^{1/4} .$$

For $\bar{T} = 300°$K, $\varepsilon_s/\lambda = 1.0571$ is required, quite different from the value $\varepsilon/\lambda = 1.3122$ for free solar space. With $\varepsilon_s/\lambda = 1.3122$ we would get $\bar{T} = 314.8°$K—on the average temperature, the influence of Earth is not very pronounced.

For the close lunar satellite we would have, on the average,

$$\frac{\bar{T}}{100} = \left(62.8307 \, \frac{\varepsilon_s}{\lambda} + 14.3298\right)^{1/4} .$$

For $\bar{T} = 300°$K, the choice should be

$$\frac{\varepsilon_s}{\lambda} = 1.0611 .$$

Thus, it does not appear to be too difficult to have an acceptable temperature within a space vehicle near Earth, during transfer to the Moon, and near the Moon. But it should be pointed out again that we have considered a highly idealized picture.

The vehicle was assumed to be spherical with constant surface properties (locally and with time), constant temperature (again locally and with time), internal energy production was neglected, and only the average incoming radiation was considered. So it can be understood that for real cases—where the distance with respect to the Sun can vary considerably, and all the other simplifying assumptions may not be fulfilled, and the operating temperature range may be small, e.g., because of chemical batteries or organic life—temperature control can be quite involved. For nonspherical objects, the attitude becomes important. As an example, see Fig. 3.14.

Radiation from a planet to a satellite consists of two parts: albedo radiation and thermal radiation. For the albedo radiation we write for the average:

$$i_1 = I_\odot \alpha \, \frac{\pi R^2}{4\pi r^2} ,$$

where $I_\odot$ is the solar intensity at the planet, R the planet's radius, and r the distance to the planet. This is valid only for $r \gg R$.

For the thermal radiation,

$$i_2 = \varepsilon\sigma T^4 \frac{4\pi R^2}{4\pi r^2} = I_\odot(1-\alpha)\frac{\pi R^2}{4\pi r^2} \, .$$

The sum is $i = i_1 + i_2 = (I_\odot/4)(R/r)^2$; i.e., we get for $r = 2R$ that $i = I_\odot/16$, or i can be neglected against $I_\odot$. This is not true for $r \approx R$, where i can be about equal to $I_\odot$. (The absorptivity of the vehicle surface may be markedly different for i_1 and i_2; this was neglected in the above simple summation.) For an important practical case, see Finch *et al.* (1966).

3.6,7 Planetary Temperatures and Atmospheres

From the previous section we use the formula[1]

$$T = 280.3 \left(\frac{\varepsilon}{\lambda}\right)^{1/4} d^{-1/2} \quad °K \, .$$

Since the average Earth thermal radiation corresponds—as pointed out—to 281°K, we may use for celestial bodies, approximately,

$$T = \frac{281}{d^{1/2}} \quad °K \, .$$

This results in Table 3.17.

TABLE 3.17

PLANETARY TEMPERATURES

Planet	Temperature		Measured values (°C)		
	(°K)	(°C)	Subsolar point	Average	Night
Mercury	452	+ 179	~ 300	~ 200	~ 0
Venus	330	+ 57	− 38 above clouds, 16–27 within clouds, 400 ± 50 at ground (because of the greenhouse effect)		
Mars	228	− 45	+ 10	− 20	− 100
Earth	281	+ 8			

[1] Assuming no internal energy production.

The root mean square molecular speed of a gas of molecular weight μ, and temperature T, is given by $v_m = 155.3(T/\mu)^{1/2}$ m/sec. Escape speed at the surface of a celestial body (radius R, mass m, gravitational constant γ) can be written as

$$v_{esc} = \left(\frac{2\gamma m}{R}\right)^{1/2} \frac{m}{sec},$$

and Jeans[1] has shown that, for $v_m > \frac{2}{10} v_{esc}$, the atmosphere is lost to space fairly rapidly. Therefore, $v_m < \frac{2}{10} v_{esc}$ is necessary for the existence of a stable atmosphere. Thus it can be derived that, for the molecular weight of a possible permanent atmosphere,

$$\mu > \frac{170}{v_{esc}^2 \, d^{1/2}},$$

where μ is the molecular weight, d the distance from Sun (in astronomical units), and v_{esc} the escape speed at the surface, in km/sec. Lower molecular weight gases can be present only temporarily, or they have to be resupplied constantly. Of course, there is no guarantee that the lowest permissible molecular weights are actually present: they may never have been there, may have been lost by chemical processes, or may have been lost during times of higher temperatures.

The results shown in Table 3.18 follow from the above inequality. Typical molecular weights are:

$H_2 : 2$ $CH_4 : 16$ $NH_3 : 17$ $H_2O : 18$ $N_2 : 28$

$O_2 : 32$ $CO_2 : 44$ $Kr : 84$ $Xe : 131$ $Rn : 222$

3.6,8 Temperature of Objects on the Lunar Surface

The lunar surface is partly covered with a dust layer of a few centimeters thickness according to radioastronomical measurements. Slopes are, contrary to the general impression from lunar photographs, not steep. (They are seldom above $10°$; within an area of $30,000$ km^2 near the center of the visible lunar disk, only about 1% of the area has average gradients of $37°$. The mountain Piton is at least $34°$ steep, and the inner rim of

[1] The following tabulation is quoted from Jeans (1925):

v_m/v_{esc}	0.258	0.232	0.202
Atmosphere lifetime (yr)	10^3	10^6	10^9

TABLE 3.18

Satellite	Planet	v_{esc} (km/sec)	d (a.u.)	Minimum μ required
	Jupiter	61.0	5.2	0.020[b]
	Saturn	36.6	9.54	0.042[b]
	Neptune	23.7	30.1	0.056[b]
	Uranus	21.7	19.2	0.084[b]
	Pluto	12.9(?)	39.5	0.166(?)[b]
	Earth	11.3	1.00	1.36[b]
	Venus	10.3	0.723	1.88[b]
Triton	Neptune	2.7	30.1	4.3[b]
	Mars	5.1	1.524	5.2[b]
Titan	Saturn VI	3.0	9.54	5.4[b]
Ganymede	Jupiter III	2.9	5.20	9.2[c,d]
Callisto	Jupiter IV	2.5	5.20	11.8[c,d]
Io	Jupiter I	2.3	5.20	13.8[c,d]
Europa	Jupiter II	2.0	5.20	17.8[c,d]
	Mercury[a]	3.6	0.387	20.3[c,d]
Moon	Earth	2.4	1.00	29.5[c,d]
Rhea	Saturn V	0.6	9.54	140.3[c]
Dione	Saturn IV	0.49	9.54	210[c]
Thethys	Saturn III	0.37	9.54	471[c]

[a] On Mercury, a dark side temperature of 15.6°C has been measured. This high value points towards the existence of a heat-transferring atmosphere; it may also be explained partially by the observation (recently discovered by radio astronomy) that Mercury does not point the same side to the Sun always: its sidereal period is not 88 days, but only 58.5 ± 1 days. The length of a solar day then follows to be 175 ± 9 days, or about equal to two of its years.

[b] Have atmosphere.

[c] Do not have atmosphere.

[d] Trace atmosphere (?).

the crater Moesting has an inclination of 37°.) From radar reflections, the surface appears to be smooth at about 36 mm wavelength, rough at 8.6 mm, and rough (from optical scattering) at 10^{-4} cm. Some authors say it is rough at 10 cm wavelength. This behavior may be some indication of grain size.[1] In places, there might be a deep dust layer. But on the other hand, sand in high vacuum may behave more like a solid body. It is probable that electrostatic charges (due to incident radiation) have accumulated. The

[1] Height of irregularities, 40 ± 10 cm. Average distance between them 2.7 ± 0.8 m.

electron density caused by cosmic, solar γ, and particle radiation immediately above the lunar surface should be considerable. At least the sunlit surface must possess a strong electrostatic charge, the size of which should be a function of lunar phase (in Sun light, estimated to be $+$ 20 V). The electron layer might have a "thickness" of 100 m, with a base density of the order of 10^4 to 10^5 e^-/cm^3. The space charge might be reduced by positive dust due to meteor impacts. The radar echo might be reflected from the top of this electron layer, falsely indicating—by specular reflection—a smooth surface. This lunar ionosphere cannot be neglected regarding radio communication with, and between, objects on the lunar surface.

Contrary to popular belief, the lunar surface would not look very rugged to an observer located on the Moon because of the small slopes and smoothness around 1 cm. The horizon would be fairly close—only about 2.5 km away, whereas it is 4.6 km away on Earth. A 1700-m high mountain could barely be seen by a man about 80 km away (on Earth about 150 km). Thus standing in the middle of a walled plane or a large crater, the surrounding mountains cannot even be seen; the popular concept of comparing the interior of a crater to a hole is certainly wrong. On the other hand, there are some fairly small but deep craters, the bottoms of which are rarely ever seen by the Sun. (About 0.5% of the surface is never reached by solar radiation.)

The first explorers will find large local differences; faint local colors, differences in surface composition,[1] the "rays," the escaping gas, possible "moonquakes." The Moon is certainly no dead and dull world waiting to be explored. About surface radiactivity, nothing is known. The radiation environment may be similar to that in free space.[2]

During an eclipse, the surface temperature drops rapidly. But at about 10 m depth, there is not even a monthly temperature variation observed. (According to U.S.S.R. studies, the temperature rises with depth: at 15–20 m, the temperature is 25°C above the surface value, and at 50–70 km depth about 1000°C.) This shows an extremely low thermal conductivity of the surface material—further evidence of a dust layer.

Temperature measurements indicate local variations. The subsolar point temperature can be between 80 and 140°C, whereas at the limb 65°C has been measured, and[3] from $-$ 160 to $-$ 120°C at the dark side (typi-

---

[1] Kopal (1961) has stated "Water is likely to exist near the surface of the Moon and it is probable that ice is beneath the surface."

[2] Astronauts will be safe against solar flare effects at 1 to 1.5 m below the surface.

[3] Lowest temperature measured: $-$ 170°C.

cally, — 135°C, 6 hours after sunset, and — 160°C, 48 hours after sunset; but local spots have been found which cool much more slowly). Similar values are reached at the of end an eclipse. An approximate balance of radiation for the subsolar point is as sketched in Fig. 3.15.

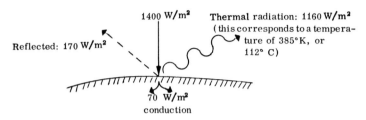

FIG. 3.15. Lunar radiation at the subsolar point.

Let us think for a moment about a photocell arrangement on the lunar surface. As is known, photocell efficiency is quite markedly dependent upon temperature—the system in Fig. 3.16 might find use.

The postulated coatings do not exist today, but developing them would allow the building of radiation coolers that face the Sun and are still effective. This could find application in space vehicles where it would eliminate

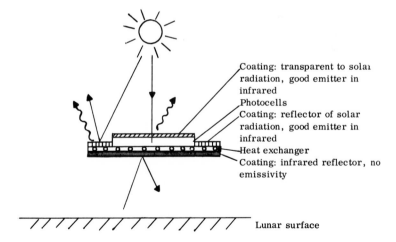

FIG. 3.16. Temperature control for photocells.

the need to orient radiation coolers away from the Sun. Similarly, of course, it might be used for radiation coolers of space suits. The attitude problem would not be completely eliminated, as the radiation cooler's surface must not "see" strong infrared emitters, since it would absorb this radiation rea-

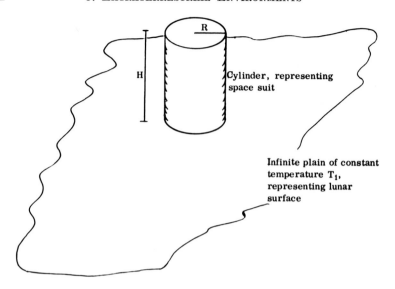

FIG. 3.17. Diagram to idealize man on the lunar surface.

dily. In practical cases, the design has to be optimized for maximum power/weight ratio.

What is the radiation a man in a space suit receives from the lunar surface? To simplify this problem we will idealize (see Fig. 3.17).

Radiative heat flow from surface element 1 to surface element 2 is shown in Fig. 3.18.

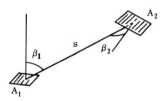

FIG. 3.18. Radiative heat between surface elements. $dQ/dA_2 = \lambda \sigma_n T_1{}^4 \cos \beta_1 (\cos \beta_2/s^2)dA_1$.

Let us pick a cylinder wall element and look for the radiation it receives from a lunar surface element. From Fig. 3.19,

$$\cos \beta_1 = \frac{h}{(h^2 + \varrho^2)^{1/2}},$$

$$\cos \beta_2 = \sin \beta_1 \cos \gamma.$$

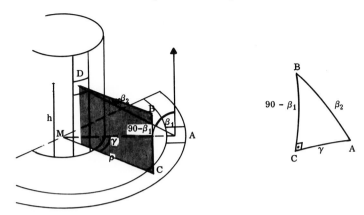

FIG. 3.19. Radiative heat flow received by a cylindrical wall element from a surface element.

Thus,

$$\left(\frac{dQ}{dA_2}\right)_{\text{from } dA} = \lambda \sigma_n \, T_1^{\,4} \cos \beta_1 \frac{\sin \beta_1 \cos \gamma}{s^2} \, dA \,,$$

or[1]

$$\left(\frac{dQ}{dA_2}\right)_{\text{total}} = 2\lambda \sigma_n T_1^{\,4} \int_{\varrho=0}^{\infty} \int_{\gamma=0}^{\pi/2} \frac{h}{(h^2 + \varrho^2)^{1/2}} \frac{\varrho}{(h^2 + \varrho^2)^{1/2}} \frac{\cos \gamma}{h^2 + \varrho^2} \varrho \, d\gamma \, d\varrho$$

$$= 2\lambda \sigma_n T_1^{\,4} \int_0^{\infty} \frac{x^2 \, dx}{(1 + x^2)^2} \,.$$

With $x = \tan \alpha$, $dx = d\alpha/\cos^2\alpha$, we get

$$\int_0^{\infty} \frac{x^2}{(1 + x^2)^2} \, dx = \int_0^{\pi/2} \sin^2\alpha \, d\alpha = \frac{1}{2} \int_0^{\pi/2} (\sin^2\alpha + \cos^2\alpha) \, d\alpha = \frac{\pi}{4} \,,$$

and, finally,

$$\left(\frac{dQ}{dA_2}\right)_{\text{total}} = \lambda \frac{\pi \sigma_n}{2} T_1^{\,4} \,.$$

If α is the angle between a "ray" of radiation and the vertical of the surface element, from which the radiation emanates, then it often can be assumed that $\sigma_\alpha = \sigma_n \cos \alpha$, where σ_n is the Stefan-Boltzmann constant for normal emittance direction.

[1] The correct lower limit of ϱ should be R, which we simplified by choosing 0 instead.

For the total radiation from the surface element

$$\sigma = \int_0^{\pi/2} \sigma_\alpha 2\pi \sin \alpha \, d\alpha = \pi\sigma_n \; ;$$

so

$$\left(\frac{dQ}{dA_2}\right)_{\text{total}} = \frac{1}{2} \lambda\sigma T_1{}^4 \, .$$

If ε_t is the absorptivity of A_2 with respect to thermal radiation, and ε_s with regard to solar albedo radiation, then the energy absorbed by dA_2 is

$$dE = \left[\frac{\varepsilon_t}{2} \times \text{thermal emission from the lunar surface per unit area} \right.$$

$$\left. + \frac{\varepsilon_s}{2} \times \text{albedo radiation from the lunar surface per unit area} \right] dA_2 \, .$$

If the Sun is about β deg overhead, then the heat input through the cylinder mantle by direct solar radiation is given by [from Fig. 3.13, interpreting the circle to be the cylinder cross section, it follows that for the angle γ between the solar ray and the normal to the surface element: $\cos \gamma = \cos \beta \cos \alpha$. Therefore, for the average absorptivity $\bar{\varepsilon}_s = (\pi/2)^{-1} \varepsilon_s \times \int_0^{\pi/2} \cos \gamma \, d\alpha = (2/\pi)\varepsilon_s \cos \beta$].

$$(2/\pi)\varepsilon_s \times 1400 \times 2RH \cos^2\beta \quad \text{W}.$$

Neglecting heat conduction through the base, and radiation to the top end of the cylinder, we get, for the total radiation input in sunlight, about

$$E = \varepsilon_t \times 318 \times 2\pi RH + \varepsilon_s \times 25 \times 2\pi RH + \varepsilon_s \times 892 \times 2RH \cos^2 \beta$$

$$\approx 2000 \, (\varepsilon_t + \tfrac{1}{2}\varepsilon_s)RH \quad \text{W}, \qquad \text{for} \quad \beta = 45°.$$

A man gives off about 150 W.[1] Thus, the surface temperature T of the cylinder follows (with an emissivity equal to $\varepsilon_t \neq 0$) from

$$2\pi\sigma T^4 = 2000 \left(1 + \frac{\varepsilon_s}{2\varepsilon_t} \right) + \frac{150}{\varepsilon_t RH} \, .$$

For $\varepsilon_s/\varepsilon_t \approx 0.31$, with the final term being 200, we have

$$2\pi\sigma T^4 \approx 2510, \qquad T = 290°\text{K or } 17°\text{C},$$

[1] During stress up to 1100 W, as shown during extravehicular activities of the Gemini 9 flight.

and for $\varepsilon_s/\varepsilon_l = 2.2$, with the final term being 300, we have

$$2\pi\sigma T^4 = 4500, \qquad T = 335°\text{K} \text{ or } 62°\text{C}.$$

Obviously, a sizeable portion of the radiation stems from the lunar surface. Therefore, a "shadow roof" against the Sun will not be very useful —it could even do harm in hindering reradiation. It appears better to have a cylinder surface such that solar light is not absorbed ($\varepsilon_s = 0$) and at the same time ε_l is sufficiently large. This would work in sunlight, but not at the night side. Therefore, a more complicated system might be as follows:

For the suit, $\varepsilon_s = \varepsilon_l = 0$—perhaps even slightly controllable. This would make the suit independent of the environmental heat input. The internally generated heat should be radiated away through a radiator that is pointed towards the sky. By controlling effective heat exchange area, heat exchanger flow rate, etc., it should be possible to develop a universal lunar suit. (Effective heat exchanger radiator area to radiate 250 W at 290°K is a circle with only 45 cm radius.)

3.6,9 Storage of Liquids in Space

Obviously this is an important problem with regard to orbital technique, lunar and interplanetary flights, maneuverable satellites, etc.; in many of these cases liquids (propellants or hydrogen for nuclear rockets) have to be stored in space for considerable periods of time.

The term "storable liquid" is well defined on Earth: we call a liquid storable when its vapor pressure at ambient temperature is below atmospheric pressure. In space this loses its meaning, since there is no atmospheric pressure. In a closed tank containing both liquid and gas, a pressure equal to the vapor pressure at the tank temperature will develop unless a pressure vent valve keeps a lower pressure and vents gas to the outside. To have a liquid, the tank temperature should be below the critical temperature of the liquid. Section 3.3 of this chapter outlined how difficulties of separating two-phase flows can be overcome. Care must be taken to transfer little heat to the liquid during pumping—it may be that transfer of liquids between various containers should be avoided, at least for LH_2.[1] For the receiving container, prechilling—usually by sacrificing some amount of the cryogenic liquid—may be required. Attention has to be given to the avoidance of thermal stress damages.

The storage of liquid hydrogen will pose the largest practical difficulties,

---

[1] Liquid hydrogen.

which can be seen from the following tabulation which gives the vapor pressure at different temperatures:

Vapor pressure (atm)	Temperature (°K)
0.08	14[a]
1.1	20.4
1.3	21
10	28

[a] Melting point.

Therefore, let us look mainly at liquid hydrogen. The specific heat is about 2 kcal/kg °K, the heat of fusion is about 13.5 kcal/kg, and the heat of evaporation is about 107 kcal/kg. The density of liquid hydrogen is only 70 kg/m³.

To store hydrogen in space, three possibilities exist:

(1) To supercool the hydrogen and reduce the heat input by insulation such that sufficiently long storage time results before the operating pressure and temperature are reached. Further heat input could be compensated by vaporization of liquid hydrogen, and venting the gaseous hydrogen so that the pressure remains constant. This would mean that a mass loss occurs. During the heating-up period, some mass loss can occur as a result of changes in liquid density.

This method uses a nonequilibrium condition. It cannot be extended indefinitely, since the supercooling should probably not go so far that the hydrogen solidifies (14°K) because of problems of uniform "thawing".[1] The low temperature hydrogen vapor pressure is very low. Therefore, pressurization of the tank will be necessary to withstand the loads. This can be done by a helium pressurization system (helium does not solidify at any temperature, if the pressure is below 25 atm). To use the full heat capacity of the hydrogen, it should be kept in motion, thereby giving a constant temperature distribution within the liquid.

Superconductivity is a phenomenon appearing at low temperatures. The highest temperature at which it has been observed is 18°K, for Nb₃Sn.

---

[1] On the other hand, the solid hydrogen could carry a load, and withstand meteor impacts; the above objection does permit slush.

Thus, the temperature of solid hydrogen is below, and the temperature of liquid hydrogen above this value.

Superconductivity could become important for space vehicle astrionic systems, computers, possibly even for propulsion systems, shielding, power supply systems, etc.

An estimate of the influence of heat insulation can be made using Fig. 3.20.

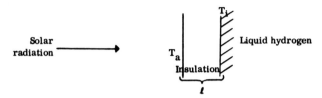

FIG. 3.20. Diagram to determine insulation.

The value of T_A can be estimated by assuming that no heat flow occurs to the inside. Then the small heat flow $\dot{q}$ to the inside follows from

$$\frac{k(T_A - T_i)}{l} = \dot{q},$$

where k is the thermal conductivity. For a modern vacuum-type insulation material,

$$k = 10^{-5} \quad \text{kcal cm/cm}^2 \text{ h } °\text{C.}$$

(In atmosphere, k is 2×10^3 times larger. For styrofoam at $2/100$ gm/cm^3, k is 4×10^4 times larger.) The weight of this material is about 0.1 gm/cm^3. Thus, with $T_a - T_i = 300°$, $l = 10$ cm:

$$\dot{q} = 3 \quad \text{kcal/m}^2 \text{ h.}$$

An irradiated surface[1] of 1 m^2 might belong to 10 m^3 = 700 kg of LH$_2$, allowing for 7000 kcal total heat flow, or about 2300 h = 90 days storage time. As mentioned before, this low heat capacity must not be used otherwise, e.g., during transfer from one container to another, or during aerodynamic heating phases, etc.

Allowing 5% liquid hydrogen loss, or 35 kg loss, we get another $107 \times 35 = 3745$ kcal allowable heat flow, or 1250 h $\approx$ 50 days of storage time. Starting out with solid hydrogen, another 130 days can be gained.

---

[1] An attitude control system is required to keep one end of the tank pointed at the Sun.

A practical difficulty is that with good insulation the heat flow through the tankage mounting must be carefully watched.

(2) Reduce with radiation shields the heat flow reaching the tank such that under equilibrium condition liquid hydrogen is maintained (or at least such that, again, the heat-up time of the supercooled fluid is sufficiently long).

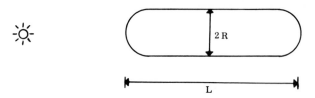

FIG. 3.21. Orientation of hydrogen tank relative to the Sun.

Volume of tankage is (see Fig. 3.21)

$$V = \pi R^3 \left(\frac{L}{R} - \frac{2}{3} \right).$$

Total surface area is

$$A = 2\pi RL.$$

With attitude control as indicated, the cross-sectional area exposed to sunlight is

$$A_s = \pi R^2 \quad \text{and} \quad \frac{A_s}{A} = \frac{R}{2L}.$$

With no attitude control system, the angle between tank axis and direction to the Sun—here zero—has to be included in the analysis, and less favorable results follow. Of course, for $L = 2R$ the problem becomes attitude independent. Radiation heat shields are shown in Fig. 3.22.

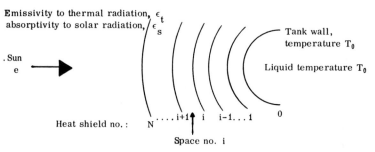

FIG. 3.22. Radiation heat shields.

What is the radiative heat transfer between two narrow spaced shields? These are shown in Fig. 3.23. The heat flow from left to right (Fig. 3.23) is

$$\frac{\dot{Q}_1}{\sigma} = \varepsilon_l T_l{}^4 + (1 - \varepsilon_r)(1 - \varepsilon_l)\varepsilon_l T_l{}^4 + \{(1 - \varepsilon_r)(1 - \varepsilon_l)\}^2 \varepsilon_l T_l{}^4 + \cdots$$
$$+ (1 - \varepsilon_l)\varepsilon_r T_r{}^4 + (1 - \varepsilon_r)(1 - \varepsilon_l)^2 \varepsilon_r T_r{}^4 + \cdots$$
$$= \{\varepsilon_l T_l{}^4 + (1 - \varepsilon_l)\varepsilon_r T_r{}^4\}\{1 + (1 - \varepsilon_r)(1 - \varepsilon_l)$$
$$+ [(1 - \varepsilon_r)(1 - \varepsilon_l)]^2 + \cdots\}$$
$$= \{\varepsilon_l T_l{}^4 + (1 - \varepsilon_l)\varepsilon_r T_r{}^4\} \frac{1}{\varepsilon_r + \varepsilon_l - \varepsilon_r \varepsilon_l} .$$

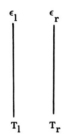

$$T_l \qquad T_r$$

FIG. 3.23. Diagram of two heat shields.

From the right to the left, in Fig. 3.23, flows

$$\frac{\dot{Q}_2}{\sigma} = \{\varepsilon_r T_r{}^4 + (1 - \varepsilon_r)\varepsilon_l T_l{}^4\} \frac{1}{\varepsilon_r + \varepsilon_l - \varepsilon_r \varepsilon_l} .$$

The net flow from left to right is

$$\frac{\dot{Q}}{\sigma} = \frac{\dot{Q}_1}{\sigma} - \frac{\dot{Q}_2}{\sigma} = \frac{\varepsilon_l \varepsilon_r}{\varepsilon_l + \varepsilon_r - \varepsilon_l \varepsilon_r}(T_l{}^4 - T_r{}^4) .$$

Let us write

$$\frac{\varepsilon_{l(i+1)}\,\varepsilon_{r(i)}}{\varepsilon_{l(i+1)} + \varepsilon_{r(i)} - \varepsilon_{l(i+1)}\,\varepsilon_{r(i)}} = \varepsilon_i' .$$

Then the heat flow over space No. i is (A_s is the cross section and σ the Stefan-Boltzmann constant)

$$\dot{Q}_i = \sigma \varepsilon_i'(T_{i+1}^4 - T_i{}^4)A_s ,$$

and likewise for the space $i - 1$:

$$\dot{Q}_{i-1} = \sigma \varepsilon'_{i-1}(T_i^4 - T_{i-1}^4) A_s .$$

For steady state, the heat flow passing through the total heat shield is

$$\frac{\dot{Q}_{net}}{A_s \sigma} = \varepsilon_0'(T_1^4 - T_0^4) = \varepsilon_1'(T_2^4 - T_1^4) = \cdots = \varepsilon'_{N-1}(T_N^4 - T_{N-1}^4) .$$

Furthermore, the overall heat flow can be written as

$$\frac{\dot{Q}_{net}}{A_s \sigma} = \varepsilon_t \left[\frac{(\varepsilon_s/\varepsilon_t)e}{\sigma} - T_N^4 \right] .$$

The total tankage can reradiate, $\dot{Q}_r = A \bar{\varepsilon}_t \sigma T_0^4$.

From

$$\varepsilon'_{N-1}(T_N^4 - T_{N-1}^4) = \varepsilon_t \left[\frac{(\varepsilon_s/\varepsilon_t)e}{\sigma} - T_N^4 \right] ,$$

we obtain

$$T_{N-1}^4 = T_N^4 - \frac{\varepsilon_t}{\varepsilon'_{N-1}} \left[\frac{(\varepsilon_s/\varepsilon_t)e}{\sigma} - T_N^4 \right] ,$$

and from

$$\varepsilon'_{N-2}(T_{N-1}^4 - T_{N-2}) = \varepsilon_t \left[\frac{(\varepsilon_s/\varepsilon_t)e}{\sigma} - T_N^4 \right] ,$$

we have

$$T_{N-2}^4 = T_N^4 - \left(\frac{\varepsilon_t}{\varepsilon'_{N-1}} + \frac{\varepsilon_t}{\varepsilon'_{N-2}} \right) \left[\frac{(\varepsilon_s/\varepsilon_t)e}{\sigma} - T_N^4 \right] ,$$

etc., until

$$T_0^4 = T_N^4 - \left(\frac{\varepsilon_t}{\varepsilon'_{N-1}} + \frac{\varepsilon_t}{\varepsilon'_{N-2}} + \cdots + \frac{\varepsilon_t}{\varepsilon'_0} \right) \left[\frac{(\varepsilon_s/\varepsilon_t)e}{\sigma} - T_N^4 \right] .$$

Assume T_0 is known, then

$$T_N^4 = \frac{T_0^4 + [(\varepsilon_t/\varepsilon'_{N-1}) + (\varepsilon_t/\varepsilon'_{N-2}) + \cdots + (\varepsilon_t/\varepsilon'_0)] (\varepsilon_s/\varepsilon_t)(e/\sigma)}{1 + (\varepsilon_t/\varepsilon'_{N-1}) + (\varepsilon_t/\varepsilon'_{N-2}) + \cdots + (\varepsilon_t/\varepsilon_0')} ,$$

and

$$\frac{\dot{Q}_{net}}{A_s \sigma} = \frac{\varepsilon_s(e/\sigma) - \varepsilon_t T_0^4}{1 + (\varepsilon_t/\varepsilon'_{N-1}) + (\varepsilon_t/\varepsilon'_{N-2}) + \cdots + (\varepsilon_t/\varepsilon_0')} ,$$

or, finally,

$$\frac{\dot{Q}_{net}}{A_s} = \frac{\varepsilon_s e - \varepsilon_t \sigma T_0{}^4}{1 + \varepsilon_t [(1/\varepsilon_0') + (1/\varepsilon_1') + \cdots + (1/\varepsilon'_{N-1})]} .$$

If $\varepsilon_0' = \varepsilon_1' = \varepsilon_2' \dots = \varepsilon_{N-1} = \varepsilon'$, then simply

$$\frac{\dot{Q}_{net}}{A_s} = \frac{\varepsilon_s e - \varepsilon_t \sigma T_0{}^4}{1 + N(\varepsilon_t/\varepsilon')} < \frac{\varepsilon_s e}{1 + N(\varepsilon_t/\varepsilon')} .$$

Thus, the heat flow $\dot{Q}_{net}$ to the tank can be found. The heat flow $\dot{Q}_{net}$ is partly reradiated, partly utilized to heat the tank or to boil liquid off. Let the total specific heat of the tank be C, then

$$\dot{Q}_{net} = A\bar{\varepsilon}_t \sigma T_0{}^4 + C\dot{T} ,$$

(or, for boil-off, write $\dot{w} H_v$ instead of $C\dot{T}$, where T_v is the boiling temperature, H_v the heat of vaporization per kilogram of liquid, and $\dot{w}$ the vaporization rate $\approx$ loss rate in kilograms per second; correspondingly for melting a solidified material).

From $\dot{T}$, a new value T_0 follows, etc. Analytically, we write

$$\frac{A_s \varepsilon_s e - A_s \varepsilon_t T^4}{1 + N(\varepsilon_t/\varepsilon')} = A\bar{\varepsilon}_t \sigma T^4 + C\dot{T} .$$

Rearranging and assuming $\bar{\varepsilon}_t = \varepsilon_t$, we get

$$\int_0^\tau dt = \tau = \frac{C[1 + N(\varepsilon_t/\varepsilon')]}{A_s \varepsilon_s e} \left\{ \frac{(\varepsilon_s/\varepsilon_t)(e/\sigma)}{[1 + (A/A_s)][1 + N(\varepsilon_t/\varepsilon')]} \right\}^{1/4} \int_{x_0}^{x_f} \frac{dx}{1 - x^4} ,$$

$$(3.2)$$

where

$$x = \left\{ \frac{\varepsilon_t}{\varepsilon_s} \frac{\sigma}{e} \left[1 + \frac{A}{A_s} \left(1 + N \frac{\varepsilon_t}{\varepsilon'} \right) \right] \right\}^{1/4} T ,$$

and index 0 designates the beginning, index f the final (begin of boiling) phase of the heating process, and τ its duration. So

$$\tau > \frac{C(T_f - T_0)}{A_s \varepsilon_s e} \left(1 + N \frac{\varepsilon_t}{\varepsilon'} \right) .$$

To have an infinite storage time, we need only $x_f \geq 1$ (because the integral diverges then), or

$$\sigma T_f{}^4 \geq \frac{(\varepsilon_s/\varepsilon_t)e}{1 + (A/A_s)[1 + N(\varepsilon_t/\varepsilon')]} ,$$

or, since N is practically the only adjustable variable:

$$N \geq \left[\left(\frac{\varepsilon_s e}{\varepsilon_l \sigma T_f^4} - 1 \right) \frac{A_s}{A} - 1 \right] \frac{\varepsilon'}{\varepsilon_l} .$$

With the following constants $\varepsilon_s = 0.15$, $\varepsilon_t = 0.95$, $e = 1400 \text{ W/m}^2$, $\sigma = 5.67/10^8 \text{ W/m}^2 (^\circ\text{K})^4$, T_f is in degrees Kelvin, $A_s/A = \frac{1}{40}$,

$$\varepsilon' = \frac{\varepsilon_l \varepsilon_r}{\varepsilon_l + \varepsilon_r - \varepsilon_l \varepsilon_r} ;$$

because of the symmetry, there is no point in having $\varepsilon_1 \neq \varepsilon_r$; thus $\varepsilon_1 = \varepsilon_r = \varepsilon$:

$$\varepsilon' = \frac{\varepsilon}{2 - \varepsilon} ;$$

ε' should be small to keep N small:

$$\varepsilon = 0.1, \qquad \varepsilon' \approx 0.05.$$

Then, to indefinitely keep the fluid from boiling,

$$N_{\min} = 512.9 \left(\frac{10}{T_f} \right)^4 - 0.054 .$$

$T_f = 20^\circ\text{K}$ (H$_2$, 1 atm): $N_{\min} = 32$
$T_f = 28^\circ\text{K}$ (H$_2$, 10 atm): $N_{\min} = 9$
$T_f = 47^\circ\text{K}$ $N_{\min} = 1$
(LOX: $\sim 90^\circ\text{K}$)
$T_f = 99^\circ\text{K}$ $N_{\min} = 0$

Thus, it can be seen that only the storage of liquid hydrogen appears to be difficult in space. LOX[1] should be simple, and the so-called "storable liquids" present no difficulties whatsoever.[2] This again will be different on the Moon or on the planets, where heat transfer other than solar radiation becomes important.

Looking at the storage method of allowing the hydrogen to heat slowly, the storage time with N radiation shields was

$$\tau > \frac{C(T_f - T_0)}{A_s \varepsilon_s e} \left(1 + N \frac{\varepsilon_t}{\varepsilon'} \right) .$$

[1] Liquid oxygen.
[2] There may be danger of freezing.

For $N = 0$ and thermal insulation we estimated 90 days (or 140 days with 5% loss, or 270 days with melting and 5% loss) of storage time: with N shields, $\tau > 29(N + 1)$ days approximately, or two to three shields are about equal to the insulation scheme. Thus, the combination of heat shields, favorable tankage shape, attitude control, and supercooling of the liquid promises to solve the problem of storage of liquids in space.

Near celestial bodies, the radiation from these bodies will further complicate the situation. This is important for orbital refuelling, where, for energy reasons, the orbit should be as low as the atmosphere permits, or for waiting times during interlanetary flights which are spent in satellite orbits. In the latter case, perhaps noncryogenic propellants have to be taken, at least for the return leg. In interplanetary flight, the solar constant is dependent upon distance from the Sun. An optimization tradeoff between attitude control, increased heat protection weight, and favorable tankage (from both mass and heating considerations) shape occurs. Obviously, much detail work remains to be done.

(3) A third method to maintain liquids in space is to keep their temperature controlled by either a heating or a refrigeration system. The energy of this system could be derived from the Sun, a nuclear source, or any other suitable power source. Such a system might appear to be less attractive when the reliability and weight are considered, but it could be very versatile and operate not only in space, but on the Moon and planets as well. It could operate regardless of solar distance, and storage time becomes unlimited. Furthermore, other systems (gyroscope, computer, maser, etc.) can benefit very much or become possible only when they can be kept at very low temperatures. Therefore, an efficient refrigeration system might become of universal utility in space operations.

3.7 Meteors and Cosmic Dust

3.7,1 Terminology

Meteor. Astronomical body that results in a luminescent appearance within the atmosphere (bright ones: fireballs; exploding ones: bolides; faint ones: shooting stars).

Meteorite. Meteor or part thereof that reaches the surface of the planet.

Meteoritics. Science which treats meteorites; a meteorist is a specialist in this field.

Meteoroid. An object in space which could become a meteor.

Micrometeor. Very small meteor, the cross section/mass ratio of which is so large that it is braked in the upper atmosphere without appreciable heating.

Meteor dust. Dust resulting from meteors.

Comet. The nucleus of a comet is probably a group of small particles, frozen together by an ice of ammonia, methane, and possibly carbon dioxide, cyanogen. These "lumps" may have a diameter of about 1 km and several may form a "nucleus." They move in elliptic or near-parabolic, some perhaps in hyperbolic, orbits around the Sun. Near the Sun, evaporation of the ice solar wind, and solar radiation pressure upon the vapor give rise to the "tail," containing, besides dust, neutral and ionized gases. There may be 10^5 or more comets belonging to the solar system. Masses are much below 10^{-6} Earth mass. All orbital inclinations occur, but there is a tendency to crowd towards direct orbits and low inclinations against the ecliptic.

3.7,2 Physical Characteristics

(1) Meteroids can originate from comets (90% of them do), from breakup of asteroids (possibly by collision; less than 10%), or they may come from interstellar space. Since less than 1% of the observed meteors have hyperbolic speed, and since no hyperbolic speeds have been observed with certainty, we may safely neglect the interstellar ones.

(2) Observations show that ordinary meteoric bodies are very fragile. Whipple concludes that the density is only of the order of 0.05 gm/cm³. The evidence is strong, though not conclusive. Since there are stone meteors and iron meteors of a solid structure density of 3.5 and 7.8 gm/cm³, respectively, the low density of 0.05 gm/cm³ can only result from a very porous structure. If this porous structure is broken up into smaller and smaller fragments, then finally the full densities of 3.5 or 7.8 gm/cm³ will be reached. But at present it is not known what the "grain size" in the porous structure is.[1] (Indications are that 99% of the meteoroids show the low density, and only 1% show the high density of 3.5 or 7.8 gm/cm³.)

(3) The ratio of stone to iron meteorites is about 10 : 1.

(4) Due to the photoeffect or due to impacting electrons, meteoroids will have an electric charge below 100 V; both polarities may occur.

(5) By observation of a meteor, a "visual magnitude" M is established. Theory has given the result that a meteor of visual magnitude zero has

---

[1] Besides the very small meteoroids, those resulting from asteroid breakup might have high density (3.5 or 7.8 gm/cm³). Possibly, all meteorites come from asteroidal meteoroids, or some are lunar (or a similar body) surface objects which result from meteoroid impacts on the surface.

25 gm mass, and the mass decreases by a factor of 2.512 per magnitude step. This is only true for a speed of 28 km/sec, entering Earth's atmosphere. A size can be ascribed to the mass by assuming a density and spherical shape. (Micrometeors may have $M \geq 20$.)

(6) Visual observations reach only to about the fifth magnitude. Radar and telescopic observations reach further—to a magnitude of about 10. Within these observations it has been found that about the same mass per magnitude step and day hits Earth (54 tons/day, Earth, magnitude; some estimates are much lower). In extrapolating the visual observation to higher magnitudes it is assumed that this feature is maintained.

This leads to a number N of meteors of mass m grams striking Earth per day, given by

$$N = \frac{5.4 \times 10^7}{m} \, .$$

If the visual magnitude is M, then

$$m = \frac{25}{2.512^M} \quad \text{gm} \, ,$$

or, finally,

$$N = 2.16 \times 10^{0.4M+6} \, ,$$

i.e., number of meteors of magnitude M per day and Earth.

(7) Meteoroids move either in groups, usually along cometary orbits (streams), or they may be single (sporadic). The groups can result in "meteor showers" when Earth crosses the path of such a group at the right time. Sporadic meteoroids are rare.

There is a concentration of meteoroids moving around the Sun in direct motion near (not more than $\pm 15°$ off) the plane of the ecliptic:

$$\frac{\text{number of meteoroids in direct motion}}{\text{number of meteorides in retrograde motion}} \approx 50 \, .$$

Assume near Earth an average speed, with respect to the Sun, of 40 km/sec. This may result in an average speed, with respect to Earth, of about 20 km/sec, or a speed entering Earth's atmosphere of about

$$(20^2 + 11.3^2)^{1/2} \approx 22 \quad \text{km/sec.}$$

This is indeed close to some observations.

The minimum speed of meteoroids near Earth should be about 12 km/sec (Earth escape speed), and the maximum below 73 km/sec. (Meteoroid in parabolic orbit with respect to Sun, hitting Earth head-on; indeed, hyperbolic orbits have not been observed. Their number is below 1%, if such meteoroids are present at all.)

In free interplanetary space both vehicle and meteors move in similar orbits, and the vehicle has negligible mass to attract meteors. Earth, on the other hand, attracts meteors, thus increasing their number and speed, but otherwise Earth itself is a kind of shield against half of the meteors for a sufficiently close Earth satellite. Thus, coarsely, the meteor danger may be about the same near Earth and in interplanetary space, except for micrometeors and meteor dust, where the Earth environment is worse (Whipple, 1962).

(8) Asteroids perhaps can be regarded as the upper size limit of meteoroids. The largest of them is Ceres with about 730 km diameter.

For the small sizes, radiation pressure from the Sun becomes important. All meteoroids of a diameter between 10^{-4} and 10^{-6} cm will be repelled out of the solar system; still smaller ones (gas molecules) can be expelled, if the gas absorbs one or a few frequencies within the solar spectrum. Larger ones experience the Poynting-Robertson effect: the meteoroid is heated by solar radiation and emits this energy in the form of thermal radiation. Due to the Doppler effect, this thermal radiation is of somewhat higher frequency and therefore, energy, in the direction of motion, resulting in a braking effect which makes the meteoroid spiral in towards the Sun. It has been estimated that meteoroids with a diameter below 0.1 cm and an orbit close to the asteroid belt will be swept into the Sun in about 60×10^6 yr.

(9) The "Zodiacal light" is an extension of the solar corona, extending in a lenticular layer from the Sun to well beyond the Earth orbit. It contains particle sizes around at least 2×10^{-3} cm diameter, i.e., this is a kind of dust. Polarization measurements preclude the zodiacal light being caused by electrons. Such small particles, together with energetic radiation and nonpenetrating meteoroids, will lead, for space vehicles, to surface degradation, such as sputtering, abrasion of coatings, etc.

(10) As a result of meteoroid/atmosphere interaction, the Earth is surrounded[1] by a cloud of meteoric dust extending many thousand kilometers

---

[1] There is a "dust cloud" around Earth reaching from 100 to 100,000 km altitude. Its density is 4×10^{-19} gm/cm³ at 1000 km altitude (maximum density); larger than atmospheric density > 3000 km altitude; 2.6×10^{-20} gm/cm³ at 6000 km altitude. Therefore, in free space there are 10^3–10^4 times less micrometeoroids than near Earth (Mariner II). Mariner II did not detect such a dust cloud around Venus; it approached Venus to within about 30,000 km.

out. This might be the principle source of the "Gegenschein" (Counterglow). There are also other explanations: accumulation of dust in the outer libration point of the Earth-Sun system, or Earth has a kind of cometary tail, or a special light-scattering effect in interplanetary matter, or a combination of these sources. This dust could be, because of the photoelectric effect, a source of electrons which must be assumed to be present at about 1000 per cm³ to explain the observed low frequency electromagnetic "whistlers." (Electromagnetic noise from thunderstorms is propagated thousands of kilometers into space along the Earth's magnetic field lines, and is observed returning to Earth at the opposite hemisphere.)

(11) Near the equilateral libration points of the Earth-Moon system, there appear to be dust clouds.

(12) The total mass hitting the Earth per day can be estimated to be about 2000 tons. (From about $M = -5$ to $M = 31$ there are 37 steps, and $37 \times 54 \approx 2000$.) This figure may differ considerably from the true value and is at best a statistical mean value. Per square centimeter and second this gives 4.5×10^{-15} gm/cm² sec, leading to about 1 gm/cm² in about 6×10^6 yr.

With its orbital speed being about 30 km/sec, Earth sweeps, per square centimeter cross-sectional area, a volume of 3×10^6 cm³/sec. Thus, the space density of meteoroid material may be estimated to be

$$\frac{4.5}{10^{15} \times 3 \times 10^6} = \frac{1.5}{10^{21}} \; \frac{gm}{cm^3} \; .$$

In free space, away from the ecliptic, the density is much lower—about 10^{-22} gm/cm³ may be an average figure. Of the order of 100 hydrogen atoms have the same weight: interplanetary gas and meteoroids appear to have a similar space density.

(13) A summary is given in Table 3.19.

(14) Some of the satellite experiments have resulted in meteoroid impact information (Martin, 1960; Dalton, 1962).

It is quite surprising how good the satellite information agrees with astronomical predictions (Fig. 3.24). Perhaps the frequency of hits should be multiplied by 2. As this results in more conservative values, we will do so (dashed curve).

It should be pointed out again that all the meteoroid information is rather tentative, whether it results from astronomical observation, physical experiments or theory, or satellite experiments. Judging from Mariner II data, we may have overestimated the danger by a factor of 10^3 to 10^4, for the small particles. Rapid progress can be expected because of special, large satellites, and because of recovery of penetration samples from space.

TABLE 3.19

Visual magnitude[a]	Mass (gm) energy[b] (4.5 × 10^{12} erg)	Radius[d] (cm)	Number per square meter[c] and day
− 5	2.5 × 10^3	23	0.42 × 10^{-10}
0	25	4.9	0.42 × 10^{-8e}
+ 5	0.25	1.1	0.42 × 10^{-6}
10	2.5 × 10^{-3}	0.23	0.42 × 10^{-4}
15	2.5 × 10^{-5}	4.9 × 10^{-2}	0.42 × 10^{-2}
20	2.5 × 10^{-7}	1.1 × 10^{-2}	0.42
25	2.5 × 10^{-9}	1.6 × 10^{-3}	42.2
30	2.5 × 10^{-11}	1.6 × 10^{-4}	4.22 × 10^3
31	10^{-11}	1 × 10^{-4}	1.06 × 10^4

[a] Visual magnitude M includes all values between $M - 0.5$ and $M + 0.5$.

[b] Speed: Assume all particles to have a speed of 30 km/sec.

[c] Number: This is the number per square meter of Earth surface. As mentioned, this may be taken tentatively per square meter surface area of a vehicle in space, too.

[d] Assuming spherical shape and density to be 0.05 gm/cm^3. (For the small ones, density is actually higher so that solar light pressure does not remove them from the solar system.)

[e] Other investigations quote 0.5 gm, density 2, 0.4 cm, radius. This shows the uncertainty of these data. [According to Whipple (1963), there is $\varrho = 0.44$ gm/cm^3, and the mass of a zero visual magnitude body is 1 gm only. Impact rates per square meter and day are 3.5×10^{-10} for 1 gm bodies, and 8.6 for 10^{-8} gm bodies.]

3.7,3 Meteroid Penetration

3.7,3,1 Probability of Hits

Let N be the average number of hits per square meter per day, and A be the surface (in square meters) of the space vehicle under consideration. Assuming a Poisson distribution, the probability to have exactly k hits in T days is

$$P_k = \frac{(NAT)^k}{k!} \exp(- NAT).$$

The probability of zero hits then is $P_0 = \exp(- NAT)$, and the probability of one or more hits (or nonzero hits) is $P = 1 - \exp(- NAT) \approx NAT$ for $NAT < 0.1$.

For $A = 50$ m², $T = 10^3$ days, we get $P = 1 - \exp(- N \times 10^5)$, when N is taken directly from the Table 3.19 (a corrective factor 2 is included in the 10^5).

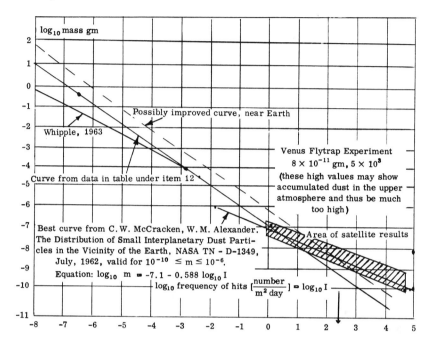

FIG. 3.24. Meteoroid impact curves.

3.7,3,2 PENETRATION AS CONSEQUENCE OF A HIT

The effect of penetration of a wall because of very high speed impacts is not well understood. A number of very approximate formulas have been developed:

Grimminger (1948) gave the following relation:

$$\frac{T}{d} = \frac{4}{3\sigma} \ln \frac{v}{1.524} + \varrho_m \frac{(1524)^2}{3c} ,$$

where[1] T is the penetration, d the meteor diameter,

$$\sigma = \frac{\text{density of material}}{\text{density of meteorite material}} ,$$

[1] The number 1524 has the dimension of meters per second.

v is the speed of the meteoroid[1] in kilometers per second, ϱ_m the meteoroid density, and c a constant for the wall material which can obtained as follows:

Dural/copper	10.3×10^7 kg/m²	$(g_0\varrho_{\text{dural}}$	2.79 gm/cm³)
Aluminum	5.2×10^7 kg/m²	$(g_0\varrho_{\text{aluminum}}$	2.70 gm/cm³)
Stainless steel	21.7×10^7 kg/m³	$(g_0\varrho_{\text{steel}}$	7.87 gm/cm³)
Chrome steel	61.8×10^7 kg/m²	$(g_0\varrho_{\text{chrome}}$	7.87 gm/cm³).

With $v = 30$ km/sec, and $g_0\varrho = 0.05$ gm/cm³ we get, approximately,

Dural	$T/d = 0.5$
Aluminum	$T/d = 0.9$
Stainless steel	$T/d = 0.2$
Chrome steel	$T/d = 0.1$.

Quite a different result is obtained by Langton (1954): If v is in kilometers per second, $g\varrho_m$ in grams per cubic centimeter, then, for an aluminum wall,

$$\left(\frac{T}{d}\right)^3 = \frac{(v^2 - 2.3)g\varrho_m}{54}.$$

With $g\varrho_m = 0.05$, $v = 30$, there results

$$\frac{T}{d} = 0.95.$$

Such a formula is quite easy to understand. For the crater volume (half sphere), we have

$$V = \frac{1}{2}\frac{4\pi}{3}T^3.$$

This value V is proportional to the energy of the impacting meteoroid (according to experiments, the data correlate much better with energy than they do with impulse):

$$E = \frac{1}{2}\varrho\frac{\pi}{6}d^3v^2 = \frac{m}{2}v^2.$$

---

[1] *Meteoroid Speed.* Within solar system, relative to Earth 0–73 km/sec. At Earth surface 11.2–73.9 km/sec. Relative to satellite 3.5–82 km/sec. Mean $\sim$ 40 km/sec.

In solar system. Meteor (reference to Sun) $\sim < 50$ km/sec. Space ship $\sim < 50$ km/sec. Relative speed 0–100 km/sec. Mean 50 km/sec.

But, generally, we have nearly parallel motion between meteoroids and space vehicles. Therefore, a usable estimate may again be 40 km/sec.

With a factor of proportionality, α, we have

$$\left(\frac{T}{d}\right)^3 = \frac{\alpha}{8}\,\varrho v^2 \quad \text{or} \quad \frac{T^3}{m} = \frac{3}{4\pi}\alpha v^2\,.$$

From Eichelberger *et al.* (1962), we find that $\alpha = 0.2$ for a lead wall, $\alpha = 0.1$ for an aluminum wall, and $\alpha = 0.06$ for a steel wall, if we measure T in centimeters, m in grams, and v in kilometers per second.

In these units for the lead wall: $T = [0.1(m/2)v^2]^{1/3}$, or with $v = 30$ km/sec, $T \approx 3.55m^{1/3}$ for a lead wall, $T \approx 2.80m^{1/3}$ for an aluminum wall, and $T \approx 1.96m^{1/3}$ for a steel wall. These are, at present, probably the best data available. For completeness, some others shall be quoted:

Whipple (1957) states that, for an aluminum wall,

$$\frac{T}{d} \approx 2.3.$$

Bjork (1958) states that $T/d \approx 0.15$ against steel and $T/d \approx 0.27$ against an aluminum shield. (Bjork's original results are different; but they are modified here to take the low meteoroid density into account.) More information is given by Gehring *et al.* (1965) and by Posever *et al.* (1965).

Whatever data are used it may be advisable to utilize them with a safety factor of three.

Beard (1961) concludes that "meteoritic puncture is less likely than is generally thought." The meteoroid satellite Explorer 16 had a useful lifetime of about 220 days, and a total test surface of 2.6 m². More than 15,000 hits were recorded by microphone sensor, and the number of penetrations were measured (Table 3.20).

Assuming that we had 2 m² of 0.001 in. = 0.0025 cm walls and 50 penetrations, we get $50/(2 \times 220) = 0.114$ penetrations per day and square meter; the meteoroids to go with that frequency have a mass of 10^{-6} gm (Fig. 3.24), and—from Table 3.19 a diameter of about 4×10^{-2} cm. Thus, we get $T/d \approx 0.06$, about a factor of four lower than expected.

Early data (mid-January 1966) from the large Pegasus Earth orbiting satellites (3 satellites; ~ 214 m² exposed area each,[1] launched February 16, May 25, and July 30, 1965) are shown in Table 3.21. Assuming that 0.048 mm aluminum are equivalent to about 0.0025 cm steel, the figures of Table 3.21 agree quite well with data from Explorer 16.

---

[1] On Pegasus *A*, only 8.3 m² sensor area were still operating in mid 1965. It takes meteoroids above 10^{-6} gm mass to penetrate the thickest sensor wall.

TABLE 3.20

Penetration of Explorer 16

Wall type	Thickness (in.)	Number of penetrations
Beryllium-copper	0.001	44
	0.002	11
	0.005	0
Copper	0.002	1
	0.003	1
Stainless steel	0.001	6
	0.006	0
Total		63

On the other hand Dalton (1963) warns: "Present information about meteoroid puncture is so poor that there is only a 50% chance that the mean puncture rate is between lower and upper predictions which are separated by almost 6 orders of magnitude." Also, see Shaffer (1964).

TABLE 3.21

Pegasus Data (January 1966)

Wall type (mm)	Area (m²)	Number of penetrations[b]
0.048[a]	8.3	0.171
0.213[a]	17.7	0.0158
0.417[a]	188	0.00402

[a] Aluminum equivalent.

[b] Per square meter per day.

3.7,4 Protection against Meteoroid Penetration

There appear to be at least three possible ways to protect vital parts of a space vehicle from meteoroids. These three ways can be used alone or combined:

(1) *Thick walls.* As can be seen, impacts are likely only for smaller meteoroids. Thus, walls 50% thicker than the penetration T should give sufficient protection.

(2) *Wall healing*. Either self-sealing features, repair en route, or similar means can be envisioned. For repair, leak detectors are essential, but quite difficult due to the smallness of the expected leaks. There appear to be quite a number of possible leak detection methods, e.g.:

(a) Pressure monitoring (does not work in presence of a boiling liquid).

(b) Continuous observation of a mass which diminishes in case of leaks (difficult).

(c) Temperature determination of liquids that will drop in case of boil off (difficult).

(d) Determination of flow due to a leak (difficult).

(e) Monitoring of outer environment to detect escaping matter, e.g., spectroscopically, or arcing in electric equipment.

(f) Observation of escaping matter by adding fluorescent, radioactive or colored additives.

(g) Treating the vehicle surface so that escaping matter leads to color changes.

(3) *Meteor bumpers*. Whipple proposed in 1947 to protect the main walls by a "meteor bumper"—this is another wall, a few centimeters before the main wall. Upon impact with the bumper, the meteoroid will vaporize or disintegrate to dust, and thus be rendered nearly harmless. The main wall then can withstand the impact.

Assume a 1 mm thick meteor bumper of chrome steel, weighing in total perhaps 10 kg/m². It is thought that this will protect against meteoroids with a penetration up to about $T = 0.2$ cm, or $d = 2$ cm.[1] From Table 3.19 we see that a diameter $d = 2$ cm belongs to about a magnitude of $+ 5M$, having $N = 0.42 \times 10^{-6}$. For $A = 50$ m² and $T = 10^3$ days we get the probability of nonzero hits to be

$$P = 1 - \exp(- 0.042) \approx 4.12\%.$$

Therefore, this fairly light shield (relatively speaking) gives a high probability (95.9%) of complete protection. A further improvement would be a load bearing bumper that would not fail due to single holes.

Further laminating, development of special materials, fillers between the laminations, use of additional self-sealing, utilization of radiation protection materials, proper design (where applicable, both temperature and meteoroid shields protecting tankage should be jettisoned just prior to

---

[1] Taking $T/d = 0.1$.

utilization of the liquid contents of the tank, if the time duration of this utilization is sufficiently short to risk operation, without such shields; or, for clustered containers, empty outer tankage is maintained to protect inner filled tankage required later; again, just prior to burn, the empty tankage is staged; etc.), and better understanding of the fundamentals involved will no doubt serve to further reduce the meteoroid penetration danger. Though we have to design for meteoroids, they do not appear to be a very great hazard, even to manned interplanetary flight.[1] On the other hand, present knowledge is quite incomplete:

Meteoroid environment, predictions of impact rate are

$$\frac{\text{maximum predicted}}{\text{minimum predicted}} \approx 250.$$

For a given meteoroid, the penetration depth predictions are

$$\frac{\text{maximum predicted}}{\text{minimum predicted}} \approx 10 \ .$$

Thus, for the mass of a meteoroid protection system, we have

$$\frac{\text{most pessimistic prediction}}{\text{most optimistic prediction}} \approx 2500 \ .$$

More data and facts are required for firm designs.

3.7,5 Spalling

When a meteoroid hits a plate, it makes a hemispherical crater on the surface and initiates a strong shock which travels through the material. The reflection at the inner surface may cause a piece of the material to be ejected inward at high velocity: spalling. The thickness of the piece spalled off may be from 10 to 50% of the plate thickness, and its diameter may be several times the plate thickness. Spalling appears to occur up to a plate thickness of 2 to 3 times the penetration thickness.

---

[1] Eichelberger *et al.* (1962) doubt the utility of a meteorite bumper. Experimental evidence, on the other hand, is in its favor, and multiple sheets are better than two sheets, at constant total sheet thickness. The single sheets should be 0.6–0.9 mm thick, the distance between sheets should be about 2.5 cm (a slight improvement results from going to 5 cm), and a substantial improvement results from filling the space between the sheets with light-weight filling material, e.g., polyurethane (2.4 gm/cm³). See, also, Maiden and McMillan (1964).

3.7,6 Erosion and Sputtering

A small meteoroid hitting a surface may remove some surface material —let us assume that it removes the material belonging to a 90° cone of height T having a volume $V' = \frac{1}{3}\pi T^3$. If there are N such meteoroids per day per square meter, they remove a volume $V = \frac{1}{3}\pi T^3 N$ cm³/m² day, or an "average removed depth" is

$$a = \frac{V}{10^4} = \frac{\pi}{3}\left(\frac{T}{d}\right)^3 d^3 \frac{N}{10^4} \quad \frac{\mathrm{cm}}{\mathrm{day}}\ .$$

The mass of a meteoroid with density 0.05 gm/cm³ can be written $m = 0.05(\pi/6)d^3$, giving

$$a = 2\left(\frac{T}{d}\right)^3 \frac{m}{0.05} \frac{N}{10^4}\ .$$

In this equation, mN is just the meteoroid mass flux, which is about 4×10^{-6} gm/m² day.

So, finally,

$$a = \frac{1.6}{10^8}\left(\frac{T}{d}\right)^3 \quad \frac{\mathrm{cm}}{\mathrm{day}}\ .$$

We know that $T/d < 1$. It appears safe, therefore, to estimate

$$a < 10^{-8}\quad \mathrm{cm/day}.$$

Singer in 1956 estimated a maximum surface erosion rate of 0.054 cm/day; this is certainly much too high. For example, the solar cells on the little Vanguard I[1] satellite (3.25 lb)—which were protected by fused silica covering 1.588 mm thick—were operating up to December 1964, when last transmissions were detected. That is a lifetime of nearly 7 yr (March 1958–December 1964), indicating that there is at least $a < 6.4 \times 10^{-5}$ cm/day.

The most critical effect of surface erosion can be expected against optical surfaces. If the erosion depth is $\lambda/(2\pi)$, where λ is the wavelength, the optical surface will be degraded. For $\lambda = 5 \times 10^{-5}$ cm there follows a time of unprotected operation of about 2.18 yr, with $a = 10^{-8}$ cm/day.

Sputtering is the surface removal due to incident high-energy particle radiation. The flux of incoming particle radiation may vary between 10 (free space, cosmic radiation) and 10^{12} (inside solar streams) particles per square centimeter and second. Assuming that between 1 and 10 surface

---

[1] Launched March 17, 1958.

atoms are removed per arriving particle, the mass removal is about 10^5–10^{18} atoms/day. For aluminum, this corresponds to a weight of 5×10^{-18} to 5×10^{-5} gm/cm² day, or depths of 2×10^{-18} to 2×10^{-5} cm/day.

Considering the upper limit only, we have to take into account that solar streams are present only for a fraction of the time, and that we probably used high estimates. Thus, even the upper limit may lead to an estimate for the average sputtering rate below 10^{-8} cm/day,[1] or sputtering and micro-meteorite erosion rate may be of the same order of magnitude.

Surface sublimation in the high vacuum of space and photoeffect or photon sputtering due to electromagnetic radiation are other possible effects of surface mass loss. The latter is probably not a large effect with regard to mass removal, and the former is strongly material dependent, as discussed earlier in this chapter.

If we take a value of 2×10^{-8} cm/day for a total surface loss rate,[2] the useful lifetime of an unprotected optical surface is reduced to about 1 yr.

The existence of meteoroids themselves indicates that the total surface erosion rate cannot be too high. Assuming a surface loss of 1 cm in 10^6 yr (this would make the Poyinting-Robertson effect unimportant, as the meteoroid was eroded away before its orbit had changed markedly) we obtain a rate[3] of 0.3×10^{-8} cm/day, giving a useful lifetime for unprotected optical surfaces of about 7 yr.

Coatings can reduce sputtering and possibly erosion. Optical surfaces could be covered when they are not in use, and even during use shade-like tubes could give protection against radiation and meteorids arriving at an oblique angle.

The Ehricke spheres which were discussed in the previous chapter (to

---

[1] Whipple (1960) mentions a particle radiation sputtering rate of 10^{-9} cm/day. The report is recommended reading.

[2] According to Wehner *et al.* (1963), total surface loss rate is about $0.85 (1 \pm 0.5) \times 10^{-10}$ cm/day, of which about 27% is due to sputtering.

[3] As described for Vanguard I, the observed total surface loss rate is smaller than 6.4×10^{-5} cm/day. Discoverer 26 (Earth satellite, 230 km perigee, 810 km apogee, July 1961 launched) measured an erosion rate of a gold surface of $(0.2 \pm 0.1) \times 10^{-8}$ cm/day, from which was derived that

$$\frac{\text{number of gold atoms ejected}}{\text{incident upper atmospheric molecule}} < 5 \times 10^{-6} .$$

Whipple computed an erosion rate for iron meteoroids to be less than 4.1×10^{-10} cm/day, stony meteoroids to be less than 4.7×10^{-9} cm/day, and fluffy meteoroids to be $\sim 1.1 \times 10^{-7}$ cm/day. These rates are mostly due to micrometeoroid action (Whipple, 1962).

serve as a solar mirror, or as visibility "tracers" in space) will be punctured in only a short time. Therefore, they should either be stable without internal pressurization or have such a low internal pressure that the gas loss through the holes becomes acceptable. At a wall thickness of only $2/10^3$ cm, they would be eroded away in several years. Thus, their useful lifetime appears to be of the order of one year, and because of large size and low weight it does not appear possible to protect them adequately; if the meteoroid and radiation environment and effects are as described, then Ehricke spheres (and solar sails) will be of limited value only, having greatly reduced general applicability.[1] Final conclusions can be drawn only after more information on the environment and its effects become available.

Sputtering due to the impact of the gases from the upper atmosphere can be important for Earth satellites.

Solar plasma hitting a surface will lead to embedded hydrogen in a surface layer about 1000 Å thick. It will take years in space before the maximum possible concentrations are reached.

3.8 Generation of Nonpropulsive Energy (Snyder, 1960)

3.8,1 Introduction (*Industrial Research*, 1961)

Space vehicles usually require nonpropulsive or auxiliary—usually electric, pneumatic, or hydraulic—energy for various purposes, such as storage or liquefaction of cryogenics, feed of propellants to engines, operation of internal equipment, guidance and control devices, communication apparatus, etc. There are only some passive types (visibility, or tracer bodies, or radio reflectors) which do not need any such power. Even there, the trend appears to be to include a small radio beacon to ease finding and tracking.

As a rule of thumb, 1 W of electric power for every 1 to 4 lb net payload should be available. The early minimum-type satellites used on the order of one watt of electric power, whereas 100 W is representative for the more advanced unmanned space research vehicles. Several kilowatts are necessary when the Atlas-Centaur and Titan II and III vehicles are used to launch heavy satellites and other vehicles. A Saturn-boosted spacecraft may need 10–100 kW to keep operating. Manned space vehicles

---

[1] The Echo I satellite (launched August 12, 1960) is an Ehricke sphere type satellite used for passive communication experiments. It depends upon internal pressurization to keep its shape. Though punctured and having no longer a smooth surface, it was still visible and spherical in mid-1967. (Wall thickness 1.37×10^{-3} cm, erosion rate below 0.54×10^{-6} cm/day.)

—either large Earth satellites, or a Mars expedition—might use about 100 kW of electric power. Typical data are given below.

Power used for manned Earth satellites:

Mercury (minimum, 1 man vehicle)	approximately 0.55 kW
Gemini (2 man vehicle)	approximately 0.55 kW (max 2 kW)
Larger satellites, small crews ($\approx$ 3 men)	approximately 1 kW per man
Larger satellites, larger crews (10 or more)	approximately 0.3 kW per man
Apollo lunar vehicle (3 men)	approximately 1 kW (max 4 kW)

For a manned interplanetary vehicle having a crew ot six, we might have:

Crew/nearly closed ecologic system	11 kW
Communication	1 kW
Scientific equipment	1 kW
Internal sensors/automatic checkout	1 kW
Crew comfort/power tools	2 kW
Astrionics/computer	1 kW
Cryogenic liquifaction (for liquid H_2)	20 kW
Reserve for peak loads	3 kW
Sum	40 kW

The desired operational lifetime can be as short as a few minutes in the case of sounding altitude probes, up to several or many years for permanent satellites or interplanetary flights.

A survey of electric power systems is contained in Fig. 3.25. This chart indicates a very large number of possibilities, which become even larger when differences in technical realization are considered; e.g., open or closed cycle, different working fluid, single- or two-phase flow, turbine or reciprocating engine, electromagnetic or electrostatic generator, type of batteries, type of fuel cell, etc. Clearly, we can look into only a limited number of basic schemes here.

3.8,2 Batteries

Batteries have an impressive reliability record when utilized within their specifications (temperature, power drain, etc.). Furthermore, they are quite good for low power and short to medium operational times. They will find further applications as emergency power supplies and as standby devices to take up peak loads. Some typical characteristics—which can depend strongly upon operating conditions—are given in Table 3.22.

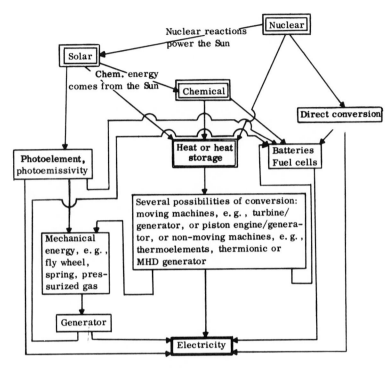

FIG. 3.25. Diagram of power sources.

In charging or discharging, "gassing" can be such a problem that the battery will need to be hermetically sealed.

TABLE 3.22

Type	Voltage/cell	W h/lb	Cycle life	Charge drop (%)
Lead-acid	2.0	12	A few hundred	20 per month
Nickel-cadmium	1.2	20	Several thousand	30 per year
Zinc-silver	1.5	60	A few hundred	30 per year
Primary battery		50 (20–100)		

3.8,3 Fuel Cells

In a fuel cell, a chemical reaction (e.g., between H_2 and O_2) is utilized to generate electric energy directly. In connection with another—perhaps nuclear—energy source, the product of the reaction (e.g., H_2O) can be split again, thus resulting in a regenerative fuel cell. Alternatively, the water may be used for other (e.g., drinking) purposes.

About 100–1000 W h/lb can be hoped for, but there is still a large amount of research and development necessary. As an example, some data on the Gemini fuel cell, as it was actually flown in space: peak power 2 kW, voltage ~ 27 V, water production ~ 0.4 liter per kWh, weight 150 lb $+ 0.11$ lb H_2 per kWh $+ 0.9$ lb O_2 per kWh.[1] Operating fuel cells under zero-g conditions can pose a problem, for some designs. Biochemical fuel cells may find application.

3.8,4 Chemical Engines

Solid or liquid energy carriers (e.g., solid propellants, gasoline $+$ LOX, or H_2O_2, etc.) can be utilized to drive a prime mover (turbine, piston engine). Either an "open cycle" (the reaction products drive the prime mover directly) or a closed cycle (the reactor heats an energy carrier, which flows in a closed cycle, within which it drives the prime mover) can be utilized. The closed cycle has the fundamental disadvantage of being Carnot-limited and requiring a radiator; whereas the open cycle can operate in space with very high pressure ratios and, therefore, good Carnot efficiency. Venting directly to space eliminates any need of a radiator. The primary disadvantage is, of course, the loss of mass.

The prime mover is coupled to an electric generator. About 1 lb/kWh can be reached for long duration applications (a few days). For a few hours, 10 lb/kWh appears possible. For low power (around 10 W), these weights can go up by a factor of 100 or so.

Thermionic convertors in connection with hot walls (e.g., wrapped around operating rocket nozzles) can provide electric energy during the time the wall is hot. Approximately 150 W/lb or better can be expected. This principle shows promise of generating high power (10^3 electric MW) for short times (a few minutes) at high (40%) efficiency.

3.8,5 Physical Engines

This title has been chosen for lack of a better one. We thought of stored pressure systems, springs, flywheels, etc. Flywheels are quite useful for certain cases of energy storage, viz., to equalize energy drain somewhat. About 10 W h/lb can be stored. Springs are, at 0.1 W h/lb, very inefficient, and stored pressure systems are usually heavy. But they might find appli-

---

[1] In 1967, the value of 1.1 kWh/lb including reactants was realized, at 2.5 kW power level.

cation for emergency hydraulic or pneumatic systems, and they are widely used for fluid feed systems.

A special case is the reentry vehicle: energy could be transferred from the aerodynamically heated wall to a cooling fluid, from which a part is recovered to produce internally required energy. Obviously, since no "heat sink" can be provided, the system should be open loop, e.g.,

$$\text{coolant liquid} \rightarrow \text{hot vapor by wall cooling} \rightarrow \text{turbine} \rightarrow \text{vented as} \\ \text{cold vapor.}$$

In venting through a nozzle, some propulsion or attitude control might be obtained.

3.8,6 Solar Engines

A large number of possibilities for solar engines exists; a very simple one is to focus solar energy to weld or solder for construction or repair. Complicated ones[1] have been described in the previous chapter to generate energy for electric propulsion systems. For shadow times, energy has to be stored. This can be done either in secondary chemical batteries, or simply as internal energy by heating up or melting (this is preferable, since it leads to operation at constant temperature) some mass; lithium hydride appears to be favorable, with a heat of fusion of about 460 W h/lb at 675°C. This could lead, with thermoelements, to a system storing about 30–50 W h/lb, thus being about equal to chemical batteries without having some of their difficulties, such as gas loss or the limited number of life cycles.

Solar power systems can be photocells ($\eta \approx 10\%$), thermoelements (low temperature, $\eta \approx 10\%$), thermionic engines[2] (high temperature up to 1800°C, $\eta \approx 20\%$), or rotating power plants (above 100 kW turbine, below 100 kW reciprocating, e.g., Stirling cycle with single-phase flow; piston engines are more flexible with regard to energy output variations than turbines) with rotating electric generators ($\eta \approx 30\%$). All can or must be coupled with solar concentrators (mirrors, lenses, Fresnel lenses), radiators, and temperature control devices (e.g., cooling devices for photocells). The solar engines convert an energy flow, which is available anyhow. In contrast, as an example, chemical batteries store their energy content.

---

[1] Photochemical energy converters (solar to electric) are still in the early development stage (Pitts *et al.*, 1961).

[2] Low-temperature thermionic converters exist; they operate at 1200°C, with an efficiency of about 15%. Ford Instrument Company has developed an ac low temperature (1250°C) thermionic cell; presently, the best efficiency is at 400 cps, but the unit has been operated up to 1700 cps.

Nuclear power supplies are somewhat in between since they store their energy, but the stored amount can be so great that it can be regarded as unlimited. Therefore, both solar and nuclear auxiliary power units (APU's) are to be used for long-time operations.

Solar cells have been used often in space vehicles, and can be said to be well developed. Surface protection (e.g., fused silica covering) against abrasive meteoric action may be necessary, and high energy radiation can damage the cells.[1] (To have 25% decrease in output at the maximum intensity of the inner van Allen radiation belt may take only a few months; for less extreme orbits, many years of operational lifetime can be expected.) Some slight drop in output could result from sand blasting the protective covers.

Efficiency is quite dependent upon temperature, as was mentioned in the section on temperature control on the Moon (e.g., $\eta = 8\%$ at 30°C, and 4% at 150°C). Thus the remarks made concerning solar cell power supplies on the Moon are also valid in space. What power/weight ratios can be expected? Rather optimistic upper limits are given in Table 3.23.

TABLE 3.23

Solar Cells (W/lb)

Year	Mercury	Venus	Earth	Mars
1980	150	100	60	30
1970	40	30	20	10
1960	20	15	10	5

Since 10 kg/kW or about 50 W/lb is sufficient to supply an electric propulsion system with energy, it can be seen that in a few years solar cells may become attractive even for electric propulsion systems, replacing the complicated solar power systems described in the previous chapter. A single cell may deliver 0.4 V; at the very good value of[2] 14% efficiency, we get

[1] Explorer XII satellite, launched August 15, 1961 into a highly elliptic orbit (293 to 77,000 km, period $\approx$ 26.5 h), carried four banks of solar cells; one bank was unprotected, and the others had 3, 20, and 60×10^{-3} in. of glass protective coating. The output of the unprotected bank decreased 50% during the first 10 orbits, and then to 29% in 112 days. The 3 mil protected bank showed 6 per cent degradation, the others none. During the experiment (112 days) the damage was done by protons in the 150 keV to 4.5 MeV range.

[2] According to *Missiles and Rockets*, November 7, 1960, p. 19, 15% are available.

200 W/m². To give 12 W/lb or 26 W/kg, the photocell weight must be about 7.6 kg/m². Indeed, the mere photocells now weigh 1.4 kg/m², which can be reduced possibly to 0.9 kg/m². To this weight, the weight of protective covering, structure, wiring, etc., has to be added.[1]

Cost is $ 300–5000 per watt delivered, not including development. Presently in the research state are thin film solar cells,[2] which show promise of cost reduction to $ 100–10 per watt, and—in spite of lower efficiency— of significant weight decreases for a given power. The data of watts per pound given in Table 3.23 refer to solar cells that are oriented toward the Sun (within about 5°) without taking requirements for attitude control into account. If the power output is to be independent of attitude, weight may go up by a factor of four or so for the same output. But attitude control system weight might be saved and reliability gained. Typical for the 1962 state of the art is the RANGER photovoltaic power supply system whose total output near Earth is 180 W, 97 W/m², and 4.75 W/lb. It may be possible to replace photocells by photoemissive units, which will work in vacuum only. Low weight and cost could result at the expense of low efficiency. (It appears feasible to obtain 3% efficiency, a total power up to a few kilowatts, 50–150 W/lb, and 25 W/m².) Such "electron farms" have been proposed for power generation on the lunar surface. (See *Astronautics*, February 1961, p. 34.) Thermionic solar systems (10 W/lb, 30 W/m²) and thermoelectric ones (25 W/lb, 7 W/m²) appear to be possible.

Sunflower I is a solar power unit of the type described in the previous chapter, but of smaller size. It is presently pursued for state of the art advancement, and flyable hardware will not be developed unless a firm mission requirement can be established. The system could have been available in 1965.

A parabolic mirror of about 69 m² area is utilized, intercepting, near Earth, about 97 kW of solar energy, and passing this on to a cavity boiler. Three kW appear as electric output (ac, 2000 cps), even at about 50% shadow-time, for which a lithium hydride energy storage system is provided. For zero shadow-time, approximately 6 electric kW output could be expected with a larger turboalternator. (Typical energy balance: 97 kW fall upon the mirror, of which 85 kW are given on to a cavity boiler, from which 5 are reradiated, 15 are conduction and other losses, 30 are given to the lithium hydride, and 35 are given to the working fluid; 3 of those 35 are

---

[1] Boeing developed (in Fall 1966) for NASA a system delivering 12.5 kW, for 20 W/lb, with 116 m² area.

[2] *Technology Week*, August 8, 1966 reports that thin film flexible cells (cadmium sulfide, $\eta = 8\%$) delivering 100 W/lb have been tested.

transformed to electric energy, 32 are reradiated as heat from a radiator of 8.92 m² area and 316°C temperature.)

Total weight of the system[1] is about 400 kg. Of course, the attitude control requirements of such mirror-boiler systems are quite stringent (about 1°).

There is quite a number of possible working fluids. In practical cases, not only the thermodynamic behavior but chemical activity (demanding perhaps coating of the parts coming in contact with the liquid), availability, experience, etc., must be taken into account. Some data are given in Table 3.24.

TABLE 3.24

	Melting point (°C)	Heat of vaporization (cal/kg)	Maximum proposed temperature (°C)	Corresponding working pressure (atm)
Helium			800	70
Hydrogen			800	70
Water	0	1000	650	70
Mercury	− 39	4.9	750	80
Rubidium	38	11	1200	25
Sodium	97	49.5	1250	14
Sulfur	115	16.7	700	70

Much can be learned from a plot of vapor pressure versus temperature as shown in Fig. 3.26.

The single-phase flow engine (gas cycle) appears to be competitive with the two-phase flow engine (vapor cycle) only for a small ratio of minimum temperature to maximum temperature. In space flight this ratio cannot be too small, to keep the radiator light; vapor cycles generally appear to be superior.[2] Sunflower I utilizes a mercury Rankine turbine cycle, with

---

[1] According to Welsh et al. (1959) a 3 kW output Stirling engine solar satellite power system is described, having a total weight of only 190 kg. Whereas such a large weight reduction appears to be unrealistic, a smaller gain may result due to the Stirling engine.

[2] Multiloop possibilities have been mentioned in Chap. 2. The superiority of the vapor cycle mentioned above may not prove to be decisive. The Brayton cycle may find application (see Grey and Williams, 1963). If its specific weight is to be equal to that of a Rankine cycle, the gas temperature at turbine inlet has to be higher by 400 ± 150 °C. Major reasons for this are the nonisothermal heat addition and rejection, and the necessity of a compressor.

the upper temperature at the melting point of the lithium hydride (675°C) and a pressure of 17 atm. The lower values are 320°C and 0.5 atm. Lifetime in space shall be one year or longer—the rotating machinery of Sunflower and SNAP 2 are very similar.

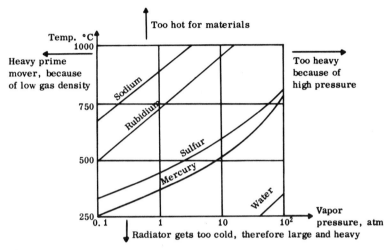

FIG. 3.26. Plot of vapor pressure versus temperature for various materials.

Sundstrand Corporation is prime contractor for the Air Force to develop the ASTEC system, a more advanced solar power supply system than Sunflower I, which would have

Lifetime in space	1 yr or more
Availability	After 1966
Mirror area	148 m²; intercepted solar energy: 166 kW (near Earth)
Condenser/radiator area	4.65 m² (at 346°C)
Working fluid, at the same time lubricant	Rubidium; alternate choice is water
Maximum temperature	960°C
Minimum temperature	360°C
Weight	550 kg

Sophisticated cavity boiler

Closed Rankine turbine cycle (turbine: 24,000 rpm)

Turbine, generator, pump are on one shaft

Thermal energy storage for shadow time periods with closing cavity

Electric output   15 kW.

Thermionic systems operate at quite high temperatures, demanding a mirror of high quality; it may be more practical to cluster a group of smaller, high quality mirrors than to develop a single, large reflector of the same quality.

A new thought on radiator design has been described by Weatherston and Smith (1960) and is shown in Fig. 3.27.

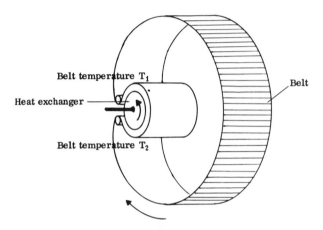

Fig. 3.27. A possible radiator design using a moving belt.

At the heat exchanger the heat is given to a belt which is in contact with the heat exchanger surface. (It appears from some test data that a sufficiently high heat transfer rate cannot be obtained in vacuum.) The heat exchanger is rotating, the belt moving. The belt loses energy by radiation. Therefore, when it reaches the exchanger again it has a temperature T_2, less than the temperature $T_1 \approx$ heat exchanger surface temperature, with which it leaves the heat exchanger.

Minimum belt weight occurs for about $T_2/T_1 = 0.69$, but the total optimum is at a larger T_2/T_1 value. A total optimization is quite difficult because of the many parameters (e.g., band heat capacity per unit surface, speed of rotation, belt/heat exchanger-surface ratio, T_1) which are involved. Actual design is more complicated, and can probably withstand only low acceleration in resistance-free space. On the other hand, this device appears to be less sensitive to meteoroids than a conventional design.[1] It appears

---

[1] Even in conventional radiators, high meteor safety can be achieved by proper design; e.g., the fluid-carrying tubes are protected by a meteor bumper, and only meteor-insensitive radiator fins connected to the tubes are unprotected.

possible that a so-designed radiator weighs only one-fourth of a conventional tubular design, which it replaces.

Another novel concept for space radiators is based upon the heat pipe which is a simple heat transfer device almost ideally suited for high temperature radiator applications. It operates by a process of two-phase convection. The heat pipe consists of a metal tube hermetically sealed, containing a metal heat transfer agent which typically might be one of the alkali metals. A layer of porous, refractory metal covers the inside wall of the heat pipe. This metal must be nonreactive with the heat transfer agent. Heat is transferred to the heat pipe at one end by vaporizing the heat transfer agent. This vapor then fills the length of the tube and condenses on the tube walls, which are a few degrees cooler than the location of heat input. The condensed heat transfer agent is transported back to the heat input point by capillary action through the porous metal liner. It may be seen that this simple device possesses several advantages:

(1) Nearly isothermal operation.

(2) Simplicity—no moving parts or mechanical power input.

(3) Will operate well in a zero gravity environment.

(4) May be fabricated into a radiator with a very large number of individual elements (heat pipes), where the heat pipes have a role comparable to cooling fins in a conventional heat exchanger. Damage or puncture of any one element will cause loss of heat transfer surface of only that one element, and the radiator will therefore possess a high order redundancy.

3.8,7 Nuclear Engines

Another novel concept showing also the feature of relatively great meteoroid insensitivity is described by Weatherston (1963). For electric power outputs of the order of megawatts, it promises to reduce the radiator weight to 20–25% of a conventional tube-type design. The radiation amplifier avoids a major difficulty of the belt radiator, viz., the drum-belt heat transfer problem.

The energy source in a nuclear power supply can be either a reactor or a radioisotope.

Very low output batteries (milli- or microwatt) utilize a radioisotope collecting, say, electrons on one plate of a condenser thus creating a potential difference. The current can be no larger than the electron flow (microamperes at kilovolts). Another possibility is to transform the energy output of the radioisotope by phosphorescence into light, and convert this, with photocells, into electric energy (microamperes at volts).

The Atomic Energy Commission has, in answer to NASA and other requirements, an extensive SNAP (Systems for Nuclear Auxiliary Power) program under way. Odd numbers in connection with SNAP designate radioisotope, and even numbers reactor power supplies.

In the radioisotope SNAP devices, a radioisotope (often an α emitter, because of the relative ease of shielding) is used as a heat source, and thermocouples[1] convert the heat to electric output. As the decay process proceeds, power output goes down. By dumping a variable amount of energy before or after it has been converted to electricity, constant power output can be enforced for some time.

The radioisotope can have either high energy output and short lifetime, or long lifetime and low output: Geiger-Nuttall's relation.

In the radioisotope power supplies, radioactive material is present from the beginning, whereas in a nuclear reactor it only accumulates during operation, to a larger extent. Therefore, a radioisotope device could present a larger launch hazard. But the active material can be encapsuled so thoroughly that virtually nothing can release it; in very extensive, hard, and thorough tests no radioactivity was released from SNAP 3.

SNAP 3 was a feasibility proof model developed by the Martin Company Nuclear Division and has the following characteristics:

Diameter	12 cm
Height	14 cm
Weight	1.8 kg
Source	0.38 gm of polonium 210
Initial thermal output	60 W
Initial electric output	3.3 W to optimum load (1.7 ohm)
Number of thermocouples	27
Total output over 2 half-lives ($\approx$ 276 days)	10 kWh
Maximum voltage	5 V
1.7 ohm load-voltage	2.5 V
Hot junction temperature	496°C
Cold juction temperature	107°C
Dosage rate 1 m away	$\sim$ 3 mr/h.

About 75 kg of zinc-silver batteries can store 10 kWh; this shows what progress even quite simple nuclear devices imply. By further development,

---

[1] Thermionic converters are used too, e.g., in SNAP 13. Power levels of radioisotope generators are usually below 1 kW, because of the high cost of radioisotopes. Such systems cost $ 3000–5000 per electric watt.

SNAP 3 can reach a power output of 5 W with perhaps 1.3 kg of weight.

SNAP 1 is larger than SNAP 3. It utilizes the more readily available cerium 144 (γ emitter, 290 days half-life) for fuel, is nearly 1 m long, has about 1½ m diameter and weighs ~ 80 kg, producing a constant 125 W for 60 days. SNAP 1A was under development as a ground demonstration unit (80 kg weight, delivering 125 W at 28 V for about 1 yr, and containing 277 thermocouples). The development of the SNAP 1 system has been discontinued.

SNAP 2 is a reactor-based system, as shown in Fig. 3.28.

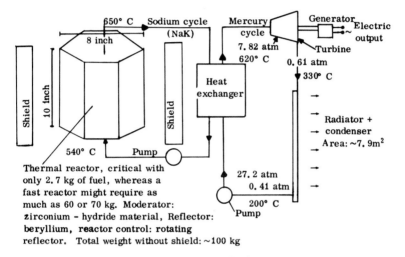

FIG. 3.28. Schematic diagram of SNAP 2 power unit.

The two pumps, generator, and turbine have one common shaft, rotating at 40,000 rpm, lubricated by hermetically sealed mercury bearings. (To use hydrodynamic or hydrostatic bearings operating with a working fluid which is completely sealed appears now to be "standard" for the long lifetime, no service space powerplants.) SNAP 2 has the following characteristics:

Availability	After 1968
Reactor output	50 kW thermal
Electric output	3 kW (2000 cps, 110 V)
System weight[1]	670 kg
Design lifetime	1 yr with a shield for component protection.

[1] From Welsh *et al.* (1959), a Stirling engine promises to reduce this weight by typically 20%.

SNAP 8 could be ready for operational use in 1973. It is a mercury cycle reactor-turbine-radiator (area 139 m², temperature 287°C) system, with the turbine powering the generator. Design lifetime of such a system will be 10,000 h, and net electric output 35 kW (3 phase, 1000 cps, 75 V). The weight of such a system (with shadow shielding for component protection) is about 2700 kg. The reactor thermal output is 0.45 MW; its mass including control drums and reflector is 245 kg; the reactor is a scale-up version of the SNAP 2 reactor.

It is remarkable that SNAP 8 is a five-loop system; the reactor is cooled by Na K (outlet temperature 710°C). The Na K transfers the heat in a boiler (at 576°C) to mercury, which is expanded through a turbine and condensed in a second heat exchanger, which is cooled by a second Na K loop. This second Na K loop radiates to space. Besides these three main loops, there are two other loops using organic fluids for power generating equipment cooling and bearing lubrication.

SNAP 10A takes a derated SNAP 2 reactor. The thermoelectric elements are powered by this reactor, and a finned radiator (6.1 m², 324°C) together with the Na K cooling loop which is driven by an electromagnetic pump make this a completely static system. Its characteristics are:

Electric output	500 W (28 V, dc)
Reactor output, thermal	30 kW
System weight (with a typical shadow shield for component protection)	450 kg
Hot junction temperature	500°C
Cold junction temperature	340°C.

The first reactor-unit flown in space (1965) was a SNAP 10A:

Electric output	585–630 W, at 28–31 V
System weight	
Reactor	250 lb
Shield	225 lb (Shadow)
Instruments	75 lb (Diagnostic)
Conversion	420 lb (Power conversion, etc.)
Shield	50 lb (Special spot shields, for operational system)
Sum	1020 lb.

The Soviet system Romashka is comparable: total weight 500 lb, power

500 W at 5.7 V. Silicon-germanium thermoelectric elements with hot side temperature of 1770°C and reactor of enriched U^{235}.

Trends in electric power plants are shown in Fig. 3.29.

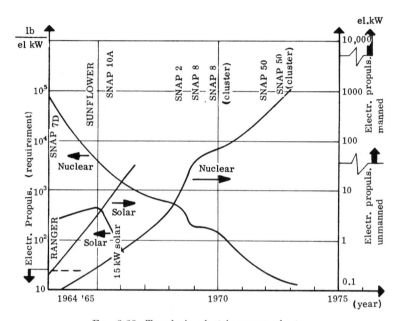

Fɪɢ. 3.29. Trends in electric power plants.

The SNAP 50/SPUR[1] system is in the conceptual design state. Figure 3.30 contains some important data. SNAP 50 will be an advanced about 300 kW electric output, reactor/turboelectric system having a weight[2] of about 20 lb electric kW unshielded, and 30 shielded. The thermal power of the reactor is approximately 2 MW. An even more advanced system (SNAP 70) might use a thermionic generator, having a total weight of only 5 lb/kW at 1 MW total electric output. These systems can be available after 1980 for operational usage.

There are many other systems which are available (e.g., SNAP 7D, a 60-W isotope thermoelectric system of 10 yr lifetime and 2100 kg weight) or planned (e.g., SNAP 4, of several MW output, for terrestrial or under-water usage, or the STAR series of power plants). We will mention only

---

[1] SPUR = Space Power Unit Reactor.

[2] For the value of α_0, as introduced in Section 2.3,6,2, is expected about 40 lb/kW jet power.

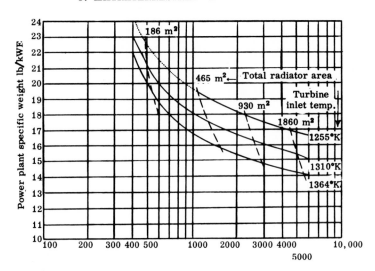

FIG. 3.30. Calculated weights for high temperature Rankine cycle turbogenerator systems. Net power plant output is in kWE (power conditioning equipment included). *Power plant parameters*: shielding leaks 10^{13} nvt and 10^7 rad γ in 10,000 h (nvt stands for: n is the particle (neutron) density, v the particle speed, t the time. Therefore, nvt means: total particle flux through 1 cm² during the time t measured) just behind the shield; reactor is a fast spectrum; UO_2 fueled; Cb alloy clad; 15 MW yr ft³ maximum burnup design. For the radiator: materials are berylium and columbium; coolant is Na K; primary radiator temperature is 949°K (inlet), $\Delta T = 83.4$°C; secondary radiator temperature is 589°K at 0.5 MW, and 699°K at 5 MW; excess primary radiator capacity is 10% at 0.5 MW and 25% at 1 and 5 MW. Nonpuncture probability is 0.90 in 10,000 h based upon near Earth meteoroid population data.

one more system, investigated for usage on the lunar surface (Armstrong *et al.*, 1960) whose characteristics are:

Electric output	1 MW
Thermal output	56 MW
Weight	9800 kg (no shielding; lunar surface material is used for shielding)
Size	Cylindrical, 4.85 m length, 2.14 m diameter
Lifetime	2 yr
Fast reactor	492 kg critical mass
	35.6% enrichment
	73% void volume
System	Turboelectric
Working fluid	Mercury.

The status of SNAP systems in early 1964 is given in Tables 3.25–3.27.

TABLE 3.25

RADIO ISOTOPE POWER GENERATORS[a]

Unit designation	Use	Power (eW)	Weight (lbs)	Isotope	Unit's design life	Status
	Space Applications					
SNAP 1	Air Force satellite	500		Ce^{144}	6 months	Program canceled
SNAP 1A	Air Force satellite	125	175	Ce^{144}	1 yr	Program canceled
SNAP 3	Demonstration device	2.5	4	Po^{210}	90 days	Program completed
Undesignated (modified SNAP 3)	Navy navigational satellites	2.7	4.6	Pu^{238}	5 yr	First space use of nuclear systems; 2 in space, June and November, 1961, first in operation, second failed after 8 months
SNAP 9A	DOD satellites	25	27	Pu^{238}	5 yr mission	2 in space September and December, 1963, both in operation
SNAP 11	Moon probe (surveyor)	~20	~40	Cm^{242}	90 day mission	Being tested[b]; thermoelectric; 900 W thermal
SNAP 13	Thermionic development demonstration device	12	4	Cm^{242}	90 day mission	Fabrication of fueled unit
SNAP 17	Communication satellite	25	28	Sr^{90}	5 yr	Just initiated
SNAP 19 SNAP 25 SNAP 27	IMP, Nimbus[c]	30 75	18 25	Pu^{238} Pu^{238}	5 yr	Design study stage
Undesignated	Lightweight demonstration device	6-10	3	Pu^{238}/Sr^{90}	> 1 yr	Being tested[b]

[a] Source: SNAP—An Evaluation, January 1964, USAEC, TID-20079. SNAP—A Report by the Commission, 1964, USAEC.

[b] Electrically heated generator.

[c] Advanced 9A.

TABLE 3.26

RADIO ISOTOPE POWER GENERATORS[a]

Unit designation	Use	Power (eW)	Weight (lbs)	Isotope	Unit's design life	Status
	Terrestrial Applications					
Undesignated	Axel Heiberg weather station	5	1680	Sr^{90}	2 yr minimum	Operating since August, 1961
SNAP 7	AEC concept design	10				Protype
SNAP 7A	Navigational buoy	10	1870	Sr^{90}	10 yr	Operating since January, 1964
SNAP 7B	Fixed navigational light	60	4600	Sr^{90}	10 yr	Operating since November, 1963
SNAP 7C	Weather station	10	1870	Sr^{90}	10 yr	Operating since February, 1962
SNAP 7D	Floating weather station	60	4600	Sr^{90}	10 yr	Operating since January, 1964
SNAP 7E	Ocean-bottom beacon	6.5	6000	Sr^{90}	10 yr	Demonstration; ocean beacon
SNAP 7F	AEC	60				
SNAP 15A/B	Nuclear weapons	0.001	1	Pu^{238}	4 yr	Being tested[b]
SNAP 21	Ocean bottom	10	500	Sr^{90}	5 yr	Just initiated
SNAP 23	(Advanced 7B)	60	1000			
Undesignated	Undersea seismograph	5	500	Cs^{137}	> 1 yr	Terminated
Undesignated	Demonstration device	5		Mixed fission products	> 1 yr	Being tested[b]

[a] Source: SNAP—An Evaluation, January 1964, USAEC, TID-20079. SNAP—A Report by the Commission, 1964, USAEC.

[b] Electrically heated generator.

TABLE 3.27

NUCLEAR REACTOR GENERATORS

Designation Reactor projects	Use	Power (kWe)	Weight[a] (pounds)	Design life	Current status
SNAP 10A	Thermoelectric system	0.5	1000	1 yr	January 22, 1965; full power. Successfully orbited: April 3, 1965. First space reactor. Expected lifetime: over 90 days; but device stopped operating after 43 days
SNAP 2	Rankine cycle demonstration system	3	1470	1 yr	Reoriented toward component improvement; flight unit canceled
SNAP 8	Communication satellites or space station	35	6000 (est.)	10,000 h	Power test of experimental reactor performed; flight unit canceled
SNAP 50	Electric propulsion and auxiliary power	300	6000 (est.)	10,000 h	Development of components and technology continuing

[a] Includes weight of a radiation shield to reduce cumulative dose over a year's operation to levels that will not damage sensitive instrumentation.

The characteristics of isotopic heat sources are given in Table 3.28.

The quoted operational times can be realized with adequate funding and interest in the particular SNAP devices. At present, there is no system other than SNAP 50 under development which can be utilized to power a useful electrically propelled deep space probe. Thus, we can hardly expect to see such tests before 1975. And 10 MW systems, as required for manned electric interplanetary vehicles,[1] will apparently become available only long after 1975.

There are other interesting possibilities, e.g., "staged" operation of APU's as shown in Fig. 3.31; or a regenerative fuel cell can be coupled to an isotope heat source, as described extensively by DelDuca *et al.* (1959) and shown schematically in Fig. 3.32. With a cesium 144 heat source,

[1] Mixed high-low acceleration vehicles require less power.

TABLE 3.28
CHARACTERISTICS OF ISOTOPIC HEAT SOURCES

	Strontium 90	Cesium 137	Promethium 147	Plutonium 238	Curium 244	Curium 242	Polonium 210	Cerium 144	Cobalt 60
Type of decay	Beta	Beta-gamma	Beta	Alpha	Alpha	Alpha	Alpha	Beta-gamma	Beta-gamma
Half-life (yr)	28	30	2.7	89	18	0.45	0.38	0.78	5.3
Specific power of isotope (thermal watts/gram)	0.90	0.42	0.33	0.56	2.8	120	141	25.6	17.4
Estimated isotopic purity (%)	50	35	95	80	98	90	95	18	10
Typical fuel form	SrO	Glass	Pm_2O_3	PuO_2	Cm_2O_3	Cm_2O_3	Metal	CeO_2	Metal
Active isotope in compound (%)	42	16	82	71	89	82	95	15	10
Specific power of compound (thermal watts/gram)	0.38	0.067	0.27	0.39	2.49	98	134	3.8	1.7
Density of compound (gm/cc)	3.7	3.2	6.6	8.9	10.6	11.75	9.3	6.4	8.9
Power density of compound (thermal watts/cc)	1.40	0.21	1.8	3.5	26.4	1150	1210	24.5	15.5
Shielding requirement	Heavy	Heavy	Minor	Minor	Moderate	Minor	Minor	Heavy	Heavy
Emission requiring shielding	Bremstrahlung	Gamma			Neutron			Gamma	Gamma
Annual availability, 1964–1966 (eW/year, efficiency 5%)	1000–1600	250–850	6	After 1968: available	900				
Cost ($/eW, efficiency, 5%)	3000–4500	3500	40000	6000	2000				

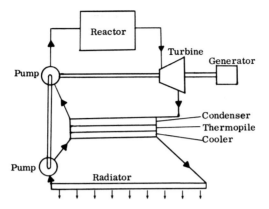

FIG. 3.31. Operating auxiliary power units in stages.

the total weight has been estimated to be 115 kg. Evidently other heat sources (solar, nuclear reactor) could replace the nuclear one in this application.

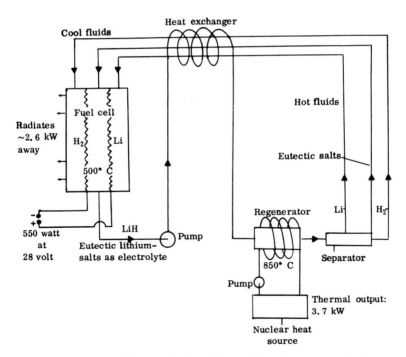

FIG. 3.32. Schematic diagram showing the coupling of an isotope heat source to a regenerative fuel cell.

Figure 3.33 adapted from Howard and McJones (1959) shows the area of application for various systems. It should be remembered that the boundaries are ill-defined, may shift with time or when new developments come

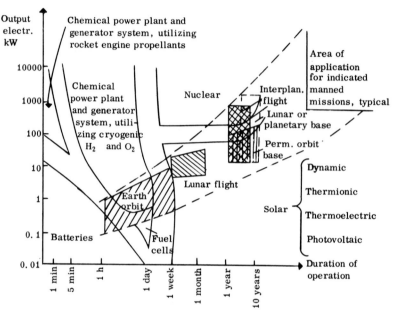

FIG. 3.33. Application of various power systems as a function of power output and time.

along, or may be neglected when other reasons (availability, development status, reliability, etc.) dominate.

3.9 Man in Space

3.9,1 Introduction

In some instances, remarks have already been made as to man's performance in a space environment. On the other hand, whole books are available on this very subject, at least one of them with the same title as this section (Gantz, 1959; Benson and Strughold, 1960).

Very logically, the first question appears to be why have man in space at all. Arguments for and against can be written down, weighed, and discussed. In the meantime development goes on and man ventures out into space. The astronautical scientist would be incredibly shortsighted if he had not started to direct his thinking and planning to take into account Project Mercury, Project Gemini, and Project Apollo[1]; incredibly shortsighted indeed will be the only verdict for those who neglect man's desire to explore for himself. Clarke (1961) writes, "The justification of man in space must depend not upon the deficiencies of his machines, but upon the positive advantages that he personally will gain from going there. There is no point in exploring—still less colonizing—a hostile and dangerous environment unless it opens up new opportunities for experience and spiritual enrichment." Without any further justification, let us glance over some of the problems of man in space.

Man cannot be changed easily or quickly to suit a strange environment. Therefore, he has to be protected from this strange environment, living in a "capsule" containing his familiar environment or something reasonably close to it. On the long term view—e.g., planetary colonization—altering man is not out of the question (see Stapledon, 1948). In some cases, adapting man to the environment may be possible with the help of other gadgets smaller than full pressure chambers. See, e.g., *Astronautics*, September 1960 "Cyborgs[2] and Space" or "Can Man be Modified," ARS preprint 2601, 1962.

3.9,2 Basic Requirements (Konecci, 1959)

Assume a pressure shell is in space, temperature controlled and sufficiently radiation and meteoroid protected. As described before, it may be simpler to live without gravity than to simulate it by rotation. In the first case, some means of exercise must be provided—this might be nothing more than a spring, a rubber band, a friction brake, or an energy generator to work against.

How much volume is required to live? Per man, about 1 m³ can suffice

---

[1] Project Mercury: Manned Earth satellite, 4000 lb (one man, ATLAS booster; first unmanned capsule test in ballistic flight on Redstone booster: December 19, 1960; manned ballistic flight: May 5, 1961; first manned orbital flight: February 20, 1962; 5 h in orbit; fourth and last orbital flight: May 15, 1963; 34 h in orbit).

Project Gemini 7000 lb, two-man Earth satellite; launch vehicle is TITAN II. The first orbital flight took place on March 23, 1965 (3 revolutions, 5 h mission). The second flight lasted for 98 h (62 revolutions, June 3–June 7, 1965), and brought the first U.S. extravehicular activity in free space (20 min). The first true rendezvous flight (Gemini, Agena target) was completed in March, 1966.

Project Apollo: 11,000 lb, three-man space vehicle, for Earth orbital and lunar missions; in lunar flights, two men would land on the lunar surface, using lunar orbital technique. The launch vehicle will be the SATURN V, whereas SATURN I B suffices for orbital flights. Orbital flights are scheduled to begin in 1967, lunar missions before 1970. (From "Manned Space Flight-1963," NASA.)

[2] Cybernetic organism.

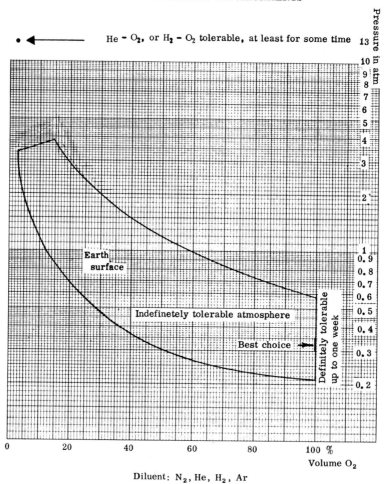

Fig. 3.34. Comfort zone for breathing atmosphere.

for low activity (e.g., radiation shelter with, for manned interplanetary missions, typically 10–30 gm/cm² of shielding); 2 m³ may be adequate space for a time duration up to a week; on long-duration submarine missions, 14 m³ have proved to be sufficient; such a "living module" may have a wall mass of about 2–3 gm/cm².

What breathing atmosphere should be supplied? A graph from the "Space Handbook"[1] helps to answer this question (Fig. 3.34).

Nitrogen as a diluent presents the problem of "divers sickness" (Caisson

[1] See Bibliography.

disease) in case of pressure drops. This problem can be avoided by going to other diluent gases. On the other hand, real long-time experience of the possible effects of diluents other than nitrogen are lacking.

Low pressures[1] are favorable to save structure weight and gas losses, but pressures well above the minimum provide relatively long "safe" times in cases of puncture. Thus, a pure oxygen atmosphere of 0.3 atm pressure appears to fit the bill perfectly—but will fire hazards increase? And are we positively sure there are no adverse health effects over periods of time? *Missiles and Rockets* of October 1, 1962, reports that "Previous studies used volunteers breathing pure oxygen for two to three weeks while performing various tasks in a space simulator. Early results have indicated slight changes in subjects' blood and some loss of peripheral and night vision."[2] Furthermore, there appears to be a larger meteoroid hazard utilizing pure O_2. (See *Missiles and Rockets*, November 20, 1961, p. 42.) According to these findings, double-wall type construction is mandatory.

Amplification of our speech by our resonators (mouth, etc.) depends upon wavelength λ, while our receivers (ears) register frequency ν. When, because of the altered atmosphere, the speed of sound c changes (e.g., becomes higher), then, because $\nu = c/\lambda$, the received frequency ν is also higher; a speaker appears to have a "high pitch." This shift in voice pattern will normally be no more than a nuisance, or even less. But could it impair communication in an emergency, just when it is needed most?

As stated low pressure atmosphere has advantages; a pure oxygen atmosphere of about 0.2 atm is the lower limit. If, on the other hand, the atmosphere is used for heat transport and cooling purposes, a low density gas requires a high mass invested in the blower energy source, for a given heat flow. Parker and Ekberg (1963) point out that, from such considerations, the optimum pressure is 0.45 atm, of which 0.21 atm is O_2 and 0.24 atm N_2.

Much further research is necessary before we know what man's ideal space vehicle atmosphere is like.

There are gases other than O_2 and the diluent (if any). Humidity (H_2O) has to be controlled, at least for long-duration missions, and CO_2 definitely has to be controlled. For long durations, not more than perhaps 15 gm/m³ should be present. (Green plants prefer 40 gm/m³. In submarines, an upper limit of 59 gm/m³ is used). In normal sea level air, there is only ~ 0.6 gm/m³ of CO_2. But obviously it would be much simpler to keep the CO_2

---

[1] High pressure limit: Skin-diving depth record is more than 300 m, i.e., the pressure is larger than 31 atm.

[2] At a pressure of 0.34 atm, 100% oxygen can be tolerated for 14 days, but symptoms similar to those of oxygen toxicity were encountered.

level below, say, 10 gm/m³ than to keep it below 0.5 gm/m³; this is a typical example to show that overly cautious specifications can hurt a program as much as overly relaxed ones. And evidently there is not enough knowledge to give meaningful specifications on the allowable CO_2 tolerances. All toxic gases have to be closely controlled, e.g., it is known that carbon monoxide is produced at a rate of about 10^{-2} gm/man day. Ammonia may accumulate. Materials may produce contaminations. Trace contaminations resulting from man being under stress may differ from that when man is under normal conditions.[1] Most of the present experience of man, contained within an artificial atmosphere, stems from submarines. But there is the basic difference that the "real" atmosphere is always so comfortably close, and even long times of confinement may not appear so long when compared to interplanetary missions.

Some results indicate that the type of and concentration of ions in the atmosphere has some influence upon the well-being of human occupants. Negative ions seem to relieve hay fever and arthritis, and raise the spirits while positive ions do the opposite.

Under zero gravity free circulation does not develop. A sleeping man could suffocate in his own exhaled air, quite similar to a candle flame going out after utilizing the oxygen in its near vicinity. The latter experiments have been made under zero-g condition. Forced air circulation is the obvious answer—will space crews have permanent colds and headaches due to draft? Maybe a "wind-pulse" after a predetermined time of quiet gives a more habitable environment. Habitability includes items such as light and lighting conditions. In space, very strong contrasts can be expected between light and shadow—similarly on the Moon, where there is no atmosphere. Perhaps a kind of visor must be worn that adjusts automatically and much faster than the human eye to lighting conditions in order to avoid damage to the eye. Such a visor could conceivable turn opaque under the influence of a harmful dosage of radiation, providing some limited degree of protection in this respect. Odor, smoke, fumes and control of them, color, noise, vibrations, etc., are other items under habitability. Their effects become more important the longer the missions lasts—they can be neglected for a few hours, but not for several months.

What is the ideal work-rest period? On Earth, we have roughly 8 hours work, 8 h off duty, and 8 h sleep. For 24 h service, 3 full crews have to be

---

[1] This is of great importance for closed ecologic systems. Drugs may be developed to control such contaminations at the place of their origin. In modern submarines, about 300 contaminants are removed from the atmosphere.

carried. In some tests, a 4 h duty, 4 h off cycle has been successful, necessitating only two crews.

Sleep deprivation leads to impairment of performance; not gradually, as sleep loss progresses, but rather irregular, with intermittent lapses (drowsiness) of dramatic changes (hallucinations), increasing in frequency and depth. After 100 h of no sleep, a 24 h rest period restores a person to normal performance. Contrary to this a British scientist, Cunningham (1960) reports, that if selected and trained space travellers are kept purposefully occupied, it may be possible for them to stay awake for a few weeks without ill effects.

A standard man of 25 yr of age weighs 65 kg and has 1.8 m² surface. For normal activity, his food should represent an energy of 3000 kcal/day. We write down a possible diet per day[1] (see also Fig. 3.35):

Protein	90 gm
Carbohydrate	600 gm
Fat	100 gm
Salts	10 gm
Total	800 gm
H_2O	2600 gm
O_2	900 gm
Total	4300 gm
5% packaging	200 gm

Hence the total load would be 4.5 kg per day and per man.[2]

Several methods exist to store the oxygen for breathing; commonly proposed is the storage of liquid oxygen, from which the breathing oxygen is evaporated. For several reasons, noncryogenic systems are preferable. An example is the H_2O_2 system, utilizing

$$1.5875 \text{ kg } H_2O + 1.9125 \text{ kg } H_2O_2 = 3.5 \text{ kg of } 54.6\% \text{ } H_2O_2 \text{ solution}$$

$$\rightarrow 2.6 \text{ kg } H_2O + 0.9 \text{ kg } O_2 + 1.538 \text{ kW h of thermal energy.}$$

How do you keep food over long periods of time in space? The packaging should be light or of secondary use (e.g., edible), the food possibly dehydrated (if, namely, water is recycled), but it should lose neither nutritional value nor taste. Canning, freezing, pickling, γ- or β-irradiation, and freeze

---

[1] For 30 kcal/kg body weight, one needs: 2 kg water, 0.75 kg O_2.

[2] Drinking water requirement is quite dependent upon the temperature.

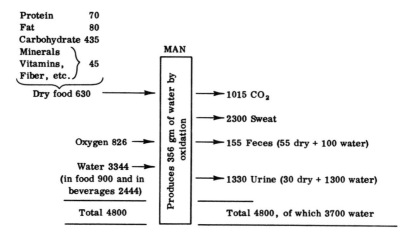

Fig. 3.35. Food balance per man and day. All values are in grams. Energy value is ∼ 2300 kcal. The surplus O_2 (223 gm) or H_2O(356 gm) produced results from the dry food. For the manned lunar project Apollo, 2800 kcal per man day will be provided in the Apollo capsule (command module), and 3200 kcal in the lunar landing vehicle (lunar excursion vehicle). The daily diet consists of ∼ 90 gm protein, ∼ 270 gm fat and ∼ 380 gm carbohydrate, within the capsule.

drying are all developed to at least some degree. Perhaps the space environment itself is favorable for food preservation.

3.9,3 Preserving the Artificial Environment

Man uses oxygen, water, and food, and gives back to the atmosphere water vapor and carbon dioxide (which must be removed), produces urine and feces, and grows hair, nails, etc.

The diluent gas is not consumed, but a reserve has to be carried to replace losses (by leakage or diffusion).[1]

A very large number of systems is possible:

(1) CO_2/H_2O vapor/odors are removed, e.g., by Li_2O (∼ 1 kg/day and man), or calcium oxide. Nothing shall be recovered. The mass of the food, etc., is not altered by its use, only its chemical, etc., nature is, of course, changing; e.g., the water output is about 10% higher than the water input due to metabolic water, coming from oxidation of H_2. Therefore, the life support items could form a shield of constant mass around the crew cabin, where packages of food are replaced by packages of "used food."

---

[1] The gas leakage can be estimated from the data in Sec. 3.2,4, part 5; typical data are: Mercury spacecraft, one man, leakage rate of 0.1 lb/h, and Apollo cabin, three men, leakage rate of 0.25 lb/h.

A total of 6 kg per day per man indicates for a 5-man 1000-day Mars expedition, 30 tons of the life support items alone; this is a convincing argument for trying to recover some of the life support items for reuse.[1]

(2) Water recovery, for wash purposes only; there is no difficulty in recovering at least the water from the atmosphere.

(3) Water recovery for drinking. The recovery of water from urine for drinking purposes has been solved, at least in the laboratory. (A device, investigated by Ionics, Inc., for usage by a seven-man crew in space has a weight of 30 lb, requires a continuous power of 50 W, and processes about 200 kg of water per 24 h. The requirement for water resupply is only 1.2 kg/month.)

(4) Recover water from urine, and water and the calcium oxide from the calcium carbonate or bicarbonate by heating and venting the CO_2 to space. But there may be better systems; Oberth proposed freezing CO_2 and H_2O out of the air by taking advantage of the relative ease of creating low temperatures.

In a few days, the heavier weight per day of calcium oxide compared to Li_2O is compensated for by its reusability.

(5) The completely closed ecologic system: One thinks of fast growing plants, taking CO_2, and possibly reworked human excrements with the possible addition of a few trace elements, salts, etc., producing oxygen again and new food. To resynthesize food from human waste products appears to be much more difficult than the plant cycle. There are practical ways other than via plants to gain O_2 from CO_2, e.g., via physical-chemical systems (e.g., hydrogen reduction and electrolysis).

(6) An interesting possibility is an open system in which the excrements, etc., are put to some use other than food, e.g., it might be possible to produce a reentry coolant, or a medium-performance rocket propellant from them, or, at least, use them for radiation protection. (Always taking into account that solar or nuclear energy is available; even in the case of nuclear propulsion being available, a chemical propellant can be interesting, e.g., when the main ship is of the low-acceleration type carrying chemically powered landing boats.)

(7) The more closed a system is, the more weight in food, water, and oxygen can be saved but more apparatus and energy[2] are required. Togeth-

---

[1] Project Mercury, one-man-day Earth satellite, had 280 lb for life support, environmental control, and power supply (silver zinc batteries).

[2] Typical data: for an open system, $\frac{3}{4}$ kW per man, and for a closed system $\frac{7}{4}$ kW per man.

er with this go reliability problems of many types: Will the plants become sick, or degenerate, or will a slowly accumulating poison or a solar
burst or a short-time mechanical failure of some subsystem upset the deli-
cate balance of the closed system such that it fails? What are "fail safe"
operating conditions? It is by no means certain that completely closed,
very small ecologic systems can be operated safely over a few years. Much
research is necessary in this field. Some weight data are given in Fig. 3.36.
For additional life-cycle system possibilities, see Gafford (1963).

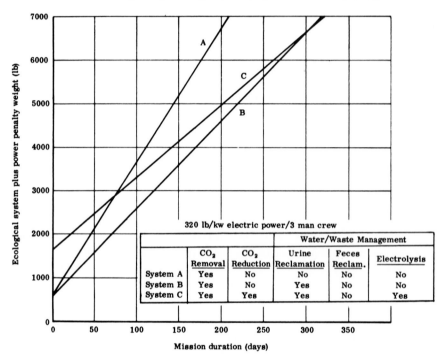

FIG. 3.36. Ecological system weight. From NAA, Inc.; Contract NAS2–1408. Manned
Mars landing and return mission study, September 25, 1963.

Hydroponic farming does not seem to be a good way to provide for green
plants in a space ship, since weight is high and plant growth slow. But it
might be well suited for lunar conditions, where many basic plant nutrients
can be produced, possibly from sand and rocks. "Insect farms" should not
be discarded lightly because of the high reproduction rate and relatively
simple environmental demands.

For space vehicles, algae of the chlorella species look quite promising
(Bowman, 1953). About 50–70% of their dry weight is protein, and they have

a good fat/vitamin content. They must be kept in a solution containing all nutrients, minerals, bacteria, etc., in a controllable manner. The algae concentration can be easily 1 gm dry weight (or 10 gm wet weight) per liter. The fluid in the tank must be kept in constant agitation. Illumination (by Sun, lamps, or other means) should be such as to avoid mutual shading, and temperature should be closely controlled (25°C for chlorella). Under good conditions, 2.3 kg wet algae (or 230 liter solution) produce about 900 gm oxygen per day. Thus, per man, about 230 liters of algae culture appear necessary for oxygen regeneration. These 2.3 kg wet algae produce about 550 gm dry substance per day, which is not quite enough to feed a man even one day. This indicates that a closed system needs a special "breed" of algae—but there are about 40,000 different types of them. So some type or an appropriate mixture should fit the bill.

In passing it might be noted that much further work is necessary to make algae really edible. Taste and variety of food will be no unimportant matter on a long journey in space.

In connection with algae or other suitable plants, bacteria or lower or perhaps even higher animals could improve some of the drawbacks (taste, monotony), but probably at the price of higher complexity[1] (Tischer, 1959).

3.9,4 Crew Selection (Gerathewohl, 1959)

There is much information available as to the endurance of humans under a single stress: temperature, acceleration, or others. Data of the effects of combined stresses are more rare, and the true stress of space flight is hard to simulate.

These endurance limits are important as possible design limits; for many manned vehicles, it may not be required to design the vehicle for more than the pilot can endure, e.g., a "crash limit" may be around 50 g's for $\frac{1}{3}$ sec, with the change rate being smaller than 500 g's/sec. In practice, it may not be possible to design a vehicle to this specification. Man is not necessarily the "weakest link" in the system.

But performance degradation is observable long before dangerous stress levels are reached. Man's role on board is decision making (e.g., reprogramming), supervising, and repairing; the environment should be as comfortable as possible to assist in these functions, and not waste human energy battling the environment. The popular concept of supermen fighting for survival in a space vehicle is hopefully very wrong, since the pur-

---

[1] Possibly, 25 liters of suspension of hydrogen-eating bacteria and 1 kW of power will suffice per man, to close the ecologic system (Mattson, 1966).

pose of astronautics is not to transport test pilots, but scientists and other customers through space and to other celestial objects.

Some crew selection criteria are: health, IQ, and knowledge; performance under short, high stress, performance under long, medium stress, mental stability, skill, motivation and eagerness, and age (since much radiation damage is expected to be genetic, astronauts may be selected from an age group which has completed families; a more radical solution is to set up a semen bank for departing astronauts).

The problems in crew holding should be mentioned only in passing: Crew holding either during the long training period to acquire the manifold skills and knowledge, or during the time immediately preceding launch, involves many factors which must not be neglected; e.g., complete isolation would reduce certain health hazards, but increases other stresses. Returning space travelers might have to go through a quarantine to make sure that no harmful life-forms or sublife-forms are brought to Earth. But, what is a safe and acceptable duration?

To show that last point in proper perspective: The epidemic of plague known as the Black Death began in 1348 in the ports of Italy. Apparently brought in by merchant ships from Black Sea ports, it gradually spread through Italy and then swept through Spain, France, England, Germany, and Scandinavia. At least a quarter of the European population was wiped out from 1348 through 1350, and in the next 50 yr the total mortality rose to more than a third of the population. It took until about 1560 to regain the population level of 1348, about 84 million people. (From *Scientific American*, February 1964.)

3.9,5 Man-Machine Systems (Thompson, 1959; Starkey, 1959)

In practical cases, the active role of man must be carefully analyzed, and then man must be given all the tools to fulfill this role effectively; proper displays, actuators, warning lights, control lights, buzzers, contour chair, etc. There is much experience and information available in the field of "human engineering." Properly applied, it can assist greatly in avoiding pilot errors by foolproof design and by helping the pilot to concentrate on what is important. Here is an area where, without increase in weight, complexity, or cost, results can be improved. It should be fully utilized.

3.9,6 Emergency

During launch, high acceleration, noise, vibrations, fire, and explosion, nonstart of engine or stage, and failure of separation may be the most dangerous difficulties to be encountered. The mission may be aborted—then a "crew safety system" should lead to crew rescue. The powered trajectory should be chosen so that, at any time, the mission can be aborted without running into excessive acceleration or heating. (See Fig. 3.37.)

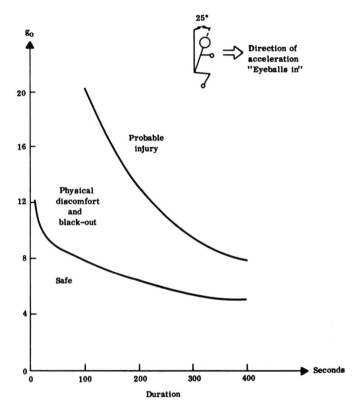

FIG. 3.37. Human acceleration tolerance. From Manned Interplanetary Mission Study, Loockheed MSC, March 1963 (NAS8–5024).

In case of landing, returning from a mission, or an aborted mission, actual recovery after landing may be difficult and take some time. Adequate survival provisions for nearly all climates, land and water, etc., must be carried along by the crew.

What are the possible failures in space? They can come from the propulsion unit during times of propulsion, from other vehicle subsystems (life support system, or oxygen regeneration plant failure, APU[1] system failure, etc.), from environment-vehicle interaction (meteoroids, radiation), or

---

[1] Auxiliary power unit.

from accidents (fire; there are additives which make the treated material release a fire extinguisher if burning).

Some possible safety features are a small heavily protected chamber ("coffin" or "shelter"), or fast Earth return (practical from Earth satellites only), sending several vehicles on space expeditions with the capability of transfer between vehicles, to have adequate repair means, fire fighting means, mutual assistance, etc., on board, plus perhaps a part of the crew constantly in space suits on alarm duty. Can drugs help and how? Could they heal, or prevent radiation damage? Generally, staying with a damaged space vehicle will be better than leaving it in some completely inadequate "lifeboat." Lifeboats of space would need performance comparable to the main space vehicle itself—this is hardly feasible, with the possible exception of Earth landing boats for Earth satellites.

Space suit questions are not yet all solved either; anthropomorphic or non-anthropomorphic, how to keep leakage rate and weight down and mobility high (low pressure differential helps), how to ventilate, what about body waste and temperature control,[1] what is a good visor construction, how to move around by application of a small thrust without spinning, is radiation and meteoroid protection required (in free space, on the lunar surface); how long, under emergency conditions, should a man be able to wear the suit, how to achieve proper limb movement, communication, light weight design. A full pressure suit to be worn within a spacecraft may weigh 10 kg; a lunar suit perhaps 40 kg.

3.9,7 Final Remarks

What can be man's role in space? In a rendezvous operation or in a lunar landing? How about visibility in space? What can a pilot do when the launch vehicle misbehaves?

How can we sterilize a vehicle and a payload? This is important in order not to contaminate the target. Since microorganisms may survive the journey through space, even an impact on the Moon, carelessness might destroy or cover up whatever traces of lunar life exist.[2] See Clarke (1963).

---

[1] Actual experience during the first U.S. manned satellite flights show that the human thermal output under stress is about two to three times as high as the expected normal value. Extravehicular activities in free space in reasonably well-designed and fairly conventional space suits do not appear to pose fundamental problems, as shown for 10 min by A. Leonov (Soviet Union, March 18, 1965) and for 20 min by E. H. White II (United States, June 3, 1965), and for several hours during the flight of Gemini 12 (November 1966).

[2] One kg of mammal intestine contains 10^{12} microorganisms! Strict environmental cleanliness may be harmful to humans through effects upon the intestinal microflora.

The least radiation-sensitive microorganisms known to date on Earth are a number of viruses which have mean lethal doses of the order of 10^6 roentgen.[1]

Other microorganisms (Bacillus subtilis, variety niger) have been exposed to high vacuum (10^{-8} mm Hg) for 35 days, and survived. But it appears that nothing could survive the ultrahigh vacuum (around 10^{-14} mm Hg) in space.

Thermal sterilization is believed to have damaged vital equipment in unmanned space vehicles, contributing to the failure of the mission.[2]

Chemical sterilization is effective, if the agent can contact the micro-life.[3]

In case of some higher life, it might be harmed by Earth bacteria and vice versa. Who knows how the astronauts exploring an alien world may react to some microorganisms living there? And what if such microorganisms are brought back to Earth?

Organic molecules can show right-left asymmetry, but only one of these two possibilities is employed in Earth life. If on some other celestial body life is found which employs the other mirror image molecule type, such life would have, for Earth life, not only no nutritive value, but might—if eaten—prove harmful or fatal.

Antibodies make us immune to some diseases. The artificial environment may remove the disease, leading to decay of the antibodies: upon return to Earth the disease strikes. This possibility exists, but is unlikely to occur. It is cited here only as an example of things which might happen unexpectedly.

Biomagnetic effects may be present, but it is not likely that they are important to manned space flight. See Barnothy (1964).

Some workers in the field think that the most severe problems in space flight will be to keep a relatively small group of people, not only alive, but at high efficiency during a space expedition of several years duration. Some even believe that this surpasses our technology so far that we will be forced to use very "fast" interplanetary transfers of much less than 1 yr duration. To do this economically, the gaseous-core nuclear reactor high-acceleration propulsion system appears to be the simplest solution.[4] In this manner, systems considerations could exclude possibilities which look, taken per se, very promising, such as, e.g., low-acceleration propulsion

[1] Some bacteria live and multiply within nuclear reactors.
[2] Bacteria survive in hot springs at 76°C, at Yellowstone Park.
[3] Microbiological life has been found in jet fuel.
[4] Or propulsion by nuclear pulses.

systems. But obviously it is much too early to decide any such questions. The author, being so much closer to the vehicle field, is rather inclined to believe that the life sciences will provide us with a system allowing long duration manned space flight even at the price of moderately high payload weights, thus keeping the "conventional" nuclear propulsion systems in the game.

Throughout this whole chapter, more questions than answers have been formulated. Space flight has just begun—it will take a considerable amount of diligent work before we know all the answers posed by "extraterrestrial environment and what to do about it." But already, it is obvious that the concept of empty space with little or no activity within it is far from the truth. And step by step we will learn to survive in this alien and hostile space environment—in a similar way to that in which we learned step by step to survive and explore beneath the sea.

Problems

3.1. Draw a curve $p(h)$ for the atmospheres of Moon, Earth, Mars, and Venus. Assume $H = $ constant. For the Earth, compare with the curve in the Appendix.

3.2. Find extreme temperature variations for spherical Earth-lunar satellites [see considerations after Eq. (3.1)].

3.3. For a satellite in a circular orbit, what is the maximum, mean, minimum shadow time?

3.4. Investigate Eq. (3.2) for evaporation of liquid or melting of solidified propellant. What extensions of space storage time can be obtained for hydrogen?

3.5. What is the spin decay rate of spinning Earth satellites in circular orbits as a function of radial distance from the center of the Earth?

3.6. *Atmospheric model.* We had in the text

$$\frac{dp}{p} = -\frac{dh}{H}.$$

For larger altitudes we can assume that $H = H_0 + A(h - h_0) = B + Ah$, where A and B are constants. (For Earth, we have, for $h > 185$ km, $B = 21.6$ km and $A = 0.127$.) Derive and discuss the atmospheric model which results.

3.7. Assume that, in a manned space vehicle, a contaminant builds up in the cabin atmosphere. We are given

(a) the net production rate (equals gross production rate minus removal rate by filtering, etc.) k in kg/day, being a constant;

(b) the overall removal rate of atmospheric gas, r in liter/day, being a constant;

(c) the total gas value, V, in liters, being a constant.

Compute the contaminant concentration c in kg/liter, assuming that initially $c = 0$.

3.8. *Optimization of thermal insulation thickness d.* Assume the following data to be given constants: k the thermal conductivity of insulation material, ΔT the temperature difference across insulation material, ϱ the density of insulation material, A_1 the heat input area, q_1 the energy per unit mass of propellant required to heat fluid to boiling point, W the mass of propellant, q_2 the heat of evaporation of propellant, r the radiation from tank, per unit time, h the heat leakage to tank, per unit time, t_1 the time to reach boiling point, t_2 the mission duration ($t_2 > t_1$), and A_2 the insulation area.

Compute the optimum insulation thickness, assuming:

(a) a vented tank design;

(b) all the evaporated material is reliquefied.

3.9. *Meteoroid impulse transfer.* A meteoroid hits a thick wall; mass is ejected in the direction from which the meteoroid came. Estimate the total impulse transfer. Show that this can be significantly larger than the original impulse of the meteoroid.

3.10. Assume a given solar constant a (energy per m² and day, at 1 a.u. from Sun) and the cross section S (m²) of a vehicle. The trajectory is an interplanetary elliptic orbit as shown in Fig. 3.38. Which amount of solar energy has been received by the vehicle, moving from φ_0 to φ_1?

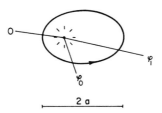

Fig. 3.38. Vehicle trajectory.

Major Symbols

A	Area, energy	E	Energy
a	Area; acceleration	F	Thrust
c	Molecular speed; speed of light	g	Gravitational acceleration
D	Radiation dose	H	Scale height
d	Distance	h	Altitude
I	Impulse	t	Time
k	Ratio of specific heats	V	Volume
M	Molecular weight; mass; visual magnitude	v	Velocity
		W	Weight; energy
m	Mass	w	Weight
P	Probability	Z	Centrifugal force
p	Pressure	γ	Density; gravitational constant
Q	Heat	ε	Absorptivity
q	Heat	η	Efficiency
R	Radius; radiation	λ	Emissivity; wavelength
r	Radius	μ	Molecular weight
T	Temperature; thickness	ϱ	Density
		τ	Time

Solutions to Problems

Chapter 1

1.1. Here $r = 4 \times 10^{14}$ km, or about 40 light years.

1.3. Since

$$\frac{x^2}{a^2} + \frac{y^2}{b^2} = 1 \rightarrow \frac{x\,dx}{a^2} + \frac{y\,dy}{b^2} = 0,$$

$$\tan \alpha = \frac{dy}{dx} = -\frac{b^2}{a^2}\frac{x}{y},$$

$$\tan(180 - \alpha) = \frac{b^2}{a^2}\frac{x}{y} = \tan \beta,$$

$$\tan(90 - \beta) = \cot \beta = \tan L = \frac{a^2}{b^2}\frac{y}{x} = \frac{1}{1 - \varepsilon^2}\frac{y}{x},$$

we have

$$\tan \varphi = \frac{y}{x} \quad \text{and} \quad \tan L = \frac{\tan \varphi}{1 - \varepsilon^2}.$$

Hence for Earth, $\tan L = 1.006768170 \tan \varphi$.

In precision orbit description, such effects cannot be neglected.

1.4. Since $R_1/d = \sin \alpha$, we have (see Fig. S.1)

$$h = d - R_2 = \frac{R_1}{\sin \alpha} - R_2,$$

$$\Delta h = \frac{R_1}{\sin^2\alpha} \cos \alpha \mid \Delta \alpha \mid + \frac{\mid \Delta R_1 \mid}{\sin \alpha} + \mid \Delta R_2 \mid.$$

The expected error in h then is

$$\left(\frac{\Delta h}{R}\right)^2 = \left(\frac{\Delta R}{R}\right)^2 \left(A^2\frac{1 - \sin^2\alpha}{\sin^4\alpha} + 1 + \frac{1}{\sin^2\alpha}\right),$$

485

where $A = R\,\Delta\alpha/\Delta R$, $\Delta R_1{}^2 = \Delta R_2{}^2$, and $R_1 = R_2 = R$. Again

$$\left(\frac{h}{R}\right)^2 = \left(\frac{1}{\sin\alpha} - 1\right)^2$$

$$\left(\frac{\Delta h}{h}\right)^2 = \left(\frac{\Delta R}{R}\right)^2 \frac{A^2 + (1 - A^2)\sin^2\alpha + \sin^4\alpha}{\sin^2\alpha - 2\sin^3\alpha + \sin^4\alpha}.$$

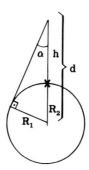

FIG. S.1. Horizon scanning geometry.

We look for the value of $\sin\alpha$, which results in the minimum error $\Delta h/h$ for a given value of A,

$$\left(\frac{\partial}{\partial\sin\alpha}\right)\left(\frac{\Delta h}{h}\right)^2 = 0 \rightarrow A^2 - 3A^2\sin\alpha + 2A^2\sin^2\alpha$$
$$- (1 - A^2)\sin^3\alpha - A^2\sin^4\alpha + \sin^5\alpha = 0,$$

or

$$A^2 = \frac{1 - \sin^2\alpha}{1 - 3\sin\alpha + 2\sin^2\alpha + \sin^3\alpha - \sin^4\alpha}\sin^3\alpha\,.$$

From Table S.1, the pair $A = 1.22$ and $\sin\alpha = 0.5$ leads to

$$\left(\frac{\Delta h}{h}\right)_{\min} \approx 5\,\frac{\Delta R}{R}\,.$$

If $\Delta R/R = 0.1\%$, then we have

$$\left(\frac{\Delta h}{h}\right)_{\min} \approx 0.5\%\,.$$

The range of applicability of the horizon scanner may be given by

$$\left|\frac{\Delta h}{h}\right| \leq 0.1\,.$$

TABLE S.1

RELATION BETWEEN A AND SIN α

A	sin α
∞	0.62
1.22	0.50
0.35	0.33
0	0.00

The solutions of the equation (keeping $A = 1.22$, $\Delta R/R = \frac{1}{1000}$, and substituting x for sin α)

$$\left(\frac{1}{1000}\right)^2 \frac{1.5 - 0.5\,x^2 + x^4}{x^2(1-x)^2} = \left(\frac{1}{10}\right)^2$$

are simple for

$$x \ll 1: \qquad x \approx 0.012 = \sin \alpha; \qquad \text{or} \qquad \left(\frac{h}{R}\right)_{\text{max}} \approx 80,$$

and for

$$x \approx 1: \qquad x \approx 0.986 = \sin \alpha; \qquad \text{or} \qquad \left(\frac{h}{R}\right)_{\text{min}} \approx 0.014.$$

This shows that a horizon scanner can have a large range of applicability, if 10% error is permitted, with the maximum accuracy of better than 1% occurring around $h/R = 1$.

1.5. (a) Here $\Delta v_a = 2\,|\,v_1\,|\sin(\alpha/2)$. (b) Here $\Delta v_b = 2(2^{1/2} - 1)\,|\,v_1\,|$. So

$$\frac{\Delta v_b}{\Delta v_a} = \frac{2^{1/2} - 1}{\sin(\alpha/2)} \qquad \text{and} \qquad \frac{\Delta v_b}{\Delta v_a} \le 1 \qquad \text{for} \quad \alpha \ge 48.8°.$$

1.6. From Eq. (4.19) of Vol. 1, we have

$$v_{\text{min}}^2 = \frac{\gamma m}{a} \frac{1 - \varepsilon}{1 + \varepsilon};$$

here $a(1 + \varepsilon) = 1$ $\gamma m = 1$ (see Fig. S.2). Then

$$v_{\text{min}}^2 = 1 - \varepsilon = \frac{\varrho}{a} = \varrho(1 + \varepsilon).$$

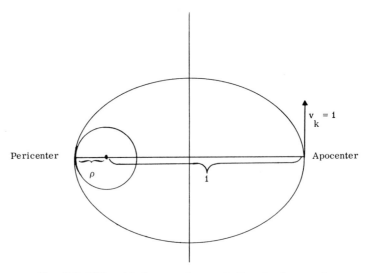

FIG. S.2. Ellipse/circle geometry; v_k is the circular speed.

From Eq. (1.27) we have

$$\varrho = \frac{1 - \varepsilon}{1 + \varepsilon} = \frac{r_{\min}}{r_{\min}} = \frac{v_{\min}^2}{2 - v_{\min}^2} \quad \text{or} \quad v_{\min}^2 = \frac{2\varrho}{1 + \varrho};$$

differentiating, we obtain

$$\frac{\partial \varrho}{\varrho} = 2(1 + \varrho)\frac{\partial v_{\min}}{v_{\min}},$$

$$v_{\min} = \left(\frac{2\varrho}{1 + \varrho}\right)^{1/2} v_k .$$

So

$$\frac{\partial r_{\min}}{r_{\min}} = 2^{1/2}\left(1 + \frac{r_{\min}}{r_{\max}}\right)\left(1 + \frac{r_{\max}}{r_{\min}}\right)^{1/2}\frac{\partial v_{\min}}{v_k} .$$

If $r_{\min} = 6500$ km, $r_{\max}/r_{\min} = 7$, then $v_k = 3000$ m/sec.

For $\partial v_{\min} = 1$ m/sec, we have $\partial r_{\min} = 9.9$ km. What effects do the pericenter kicks have on the change in apocenter altitude? The ∂r value is $r_{\max}/r_{\min}$ times as large as given by the above equation. Hence

$$\frac{\partial r_{\max}}{r_{\min}} = 2^{1/2}\left(1 + \frac{r_{\max}}{r_{\min}}\right)\left(1 + \frac{r_{\max}}{r_{\min}}\right)^{1/2}\frac{\partial v_{\max}}{v_k} .$$

1.7. From Table S.2 we see that the smaller vehicle appears to be of advantage if the cost per vehicle is proportional to lift-off weight.

TABLE S.2

COMPARISON COST BETWEEN SMALL AND LARGE VEHICLES

Vehicle type 1 (large)	Vehicle type 2 (small)
(a) $\dfrac{100}{10} = 10$	$\dfrac{100}{1} = 100$
(b) $\dfrac{100}{10 \cdot 0.8} = 12.5$, practically 13	$\dfrac{100}{1 \cdot 0.8} = 125$
(c) $n = 19.045$, because $[0.8n - 3 \,(0.8 \times 0.2 \cdot n)^{1/2}] \, 10 = 100$ is solved by $n = 19.045$. Practically, $n = 20$	Correspondingly, $n = 142.925$ or, practically, $n = 143$

But many other considerations enter; for example:

(1) The larger vehicle can be more economical just because it is larger. (For example, its guidance and control weight is a smaller percentage of its gross payload.)

(2) The larger vehicle can have a higher reliability, because it allows for more redundancy, and less marginal design.

(3) The larger vehicle can have a smaller reliability, because it is usually the newer (less proven) vehicle, and its firing rate (hence rate of accumulation of experience) is smaller.

(4) Additional considerations (e.g., handling and logistics, noise, payload capability, availability, time schedule, development cost, mission flexibility) can speak decisively for or against the larger vehicle.

(5) The larger vehicle is more economical if cost per launching is approximately independent of vehicle size.

(6) The orbital operation costs money. The larger vehicle will be cheaper in this respect.

(7) Some payloads may be incapable of further breakdown and may require (either because of mass or because of volume) the larger vehicle.

(8) The smaller vehicle may run into impractically high firing rates or the larger one into impractically low firing rates.

1.8. Here

$$\sigma^2 = \frac{1}{n-1} \sum_1^n \delta_i^2 \,,$$

because, if $n = 1$, then no rational determination of σ is possible.

The standard deviation for $\bar{x}$ is given by

$$\sigma_{\bar{x}} = \frac{\sigma}{n^{1/2}} \,.$$

The probability that a measurement shows a deviation from the true value larger than $g\sigma$ (where g is a positive number) is given by

$$P = 1 - \int_{-g}^{+g} \frac{1}{(2\pi)^{1/2}} \exp(-x^2/2) \, dx.$$

The expected number of such measurements is Pn, and a rational criterion to reject measurements is to reject those which have a deviation $\delta_i > g\sigma$, where g follows from

$$n - n \int_{-g}^{+g} \frac{1}{(2\pi)^{1/2}} \exp(-x^2/2) \, dx = 0.5.$$

For $g > 1.5$, we have

$$\frac{1}{(2\pi)^{1/2}} \int_0^g \exp(-x^2/2) \, dx \approx \frac{1}{2} \left[1 - \frac{\exp(-g^2/2)}{g} \left(\frac{2}{\pi}\right)^{1/2} \left(1 - \frac{1}{g^2}\right) \right];$$

so

$$\frac{\exp(-g^2/2)}{g} \left(1 - \frac{1}{g^2}\right) = \left(\frac{\pi}{8}\right)^{1/2} \frac{1}{n} \,,$$

or

$$n \approx \left(\frac{\pi}{8}\right)^{1/2} \frac{g \exp(g^2/2)}{1 - 1/g^2} \,.$$

From this, $n = n(g)$ can be plotted and the desired function $g = g(n)$ can be read from the graph.

1.9. Since $WA + GP = S = \min$ and $AP = \text{constant} = c$, with the Lagrangian multiplier λ, we have

$$W + \lambda P = 0, \qquad G + \lambda A = 0.$$

So for the optimum system,

$$A^2 = \frac{Gc}{W}, \qquad P^2 = \frac{Wc}{G}, \qquad \text{and} \qquad S_{min} = 2(cGW)^{1/2}.$$

1.10. The probability that in a thermal group of molecules a specific particle has a speed which is between c and $c + dc$ is given by

$$P_c = \frac{4c^2 \exp(-mc^2/2kT)}{\pi^{1/2}(2kT/m)^{3/2}} \, dc \, .$$

This equation yields the following terms:

The most probable speed $\qquad\qquad\qquad c_m = \left(\dfrac{2kT}{m}\right)^{1/2}.$

The average speed $\qquad\qquad\qquad\quad \bar{c} = \left(\dfrac{8kT}{\pi m}\right)^{1/2}.$

The average of the square of the speed $\overline{c^2} = \dfrac{3kT}{m}\,.$

The average energy $\qquad\qquad\qquad\quad \bar{E} = \tfrac{1}{2}\,m\overline{c^2} = \tfrac{3}{2}\,kT.$

If we ask for the probability P_E that a particle has an energy between E and $E + dE$, then, from the above equation, we have

$$P_E = \frac{2}{\pi^{1/2}} f^{1/2} \exp(-f) \, df, \qquad \text{where} \quad f = \frac{E}{kT} = \frac{(3/2)E}{\bar{E}}\,.$$

We now say that whenever the noise E is larger than the signal S, then an erroneous transmission occurs.

The signal-to-noise ratio is given by $R = S/\bar{E}$; the probability that $E \geq R\bar{E}$ of $f \geq (3/2)R$ is given by

$$P = \frac{2}{\pi^{1/2}} \int_{\frac{3}{2}R}^{\infty} f^{1/2} \exp(-f) \, df \, .$$

With the simple transformation $f = x^2/2$, we obtain

$$P = \left(\frac{2}{\pi}\right)^{1/2} \int_{(3R)^{1/2}}^{\infty} x^2 \exp(-x^2/2) \, dx \, .$$

Let us call $\varphi(x) = [1/(2\pi)^{1/2}] \exp(-x^2/2)$; then

$$\varphi'(x) = -x\,\varphi(x) \qquad \text{and} \qquad \varphi''(x) = (x^2 - 1)\,\varphi(x).$$

Thus,

$$P = 2 \int_{(3R)^{1/2}}^{\infty} [(x^2 - 1)\varphi + \varphi] \, dx = 1 + 2(3R)^{1/2} \varphi[(3R)^{1/2}] - 2 \int_{0}^{(3R)^{1/2}} \varphi \, dx.$$

The numerical results are given in Table S.3.

TABLE S.3

NUMERICAL RESULTS

R	P
0	1
$\frac{1}{2}$	0.801
$\frac{4}{3}$	0.262
3	0.029
∞	0

The graph (Fig. S.3) shows the probability of transmission error (P), as a function of signal-to-noise ratio (R).

1.11. (1) *Passive redundancy.* Probability that both elements do not fail is given by

$$R_P = 1 - (1 - R_E)(1 - R_E)$$
$$= 1 - (1 - \exp[-T/T_0])^2$$
$$= (2 - \exp[-T/T_0]) \exp(-T/T_0),$$

or for $T/T_0 \ll 1$,

$$R_P = \left(1 + \frac{T}{T_0}\right)\left(1 - \frac{T}{T_0}\right) = 1 - \left(\frac{T}{T_0}\right)^2,$$

and for $T/T_0 \gg 1$, $R_P = 2 \exp(-T/T_0)$.

(2) *Active redundancy.* This is given by

$$R_A = R_E(T) + r \int_0^T \frac{d}{dt}[1 - R_E(t)] \, dt \, R_E(T - t)$$
$$= \left(1 + r \frac{T}{T_0}\right) \exp(-T/T_0),$$

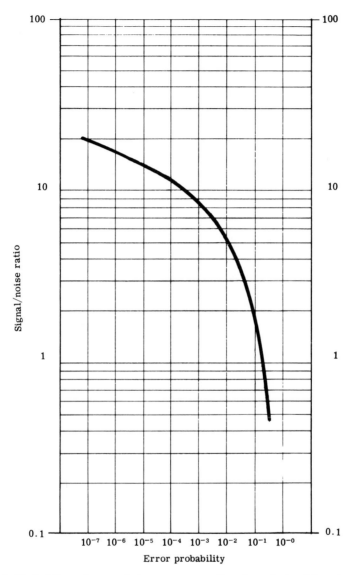

FIG. S.3. Probability of transmission error as a function of signal-to-noise ratio.

or for $T/T_0 \ll 1$,

$$R_A = 1 - (1 - r) \frac{T}{T_0} - r \left(\frac{T}{T_0} \right)^2,$$

and for $rT/T_0 \gg 1$, $R_A = r(T/T_0) \exp(- T/T_0)$.

(3) Minimum requirement for r so that $R_A = R_P$ (or for $r > r_{min}$, $R_A > R_P$) are given by

$$r_{min} = \frac{1 - \exp(- T/T_0)}{T/T_0},$$

or for $T/T_0 \ll 1$, $r_{min} = 1 - (T/2T_0)$, and for $T/T_0 \gg 1$, $r_{min} = T_0/T$.

Comment. The example is very simple; thus, general conclusions cannot be drawn. This is so because

(1) In passive redundancy, the elements are—if no failure has occurred— so little stressed that the lifetime of the dual system may be much longer than T_0. This improves the case of passive redundancy.

(2) The value r might degrade with time: this lowers R_A.

A simple general introduction is found in Pierce (1964).

1.12. From geometric considerations, simply

$$C_1 = 50\% + \tfrac{1}{2} C, \qquad C_2 = 50\% + \tfrac{1}{2} C.$$

1.13. The results are as follows:

(1) For 100 tests, 10 failures (both components),

$$R = 1 - \frac{10}{100} = 0.9 ;$$

$$\sigma^2 = 100 \times 0.9 \times 0.1 = 9, \qquad \text{hence} \quad \sigma = 3 ;$$

$$\sigma_R = \left(\frac{100}{99}\right)^{1/2} \times \frac{3}{100} = 0.0302.$$

(2) For 100 tests, 5 failures, the results for component 1 are

$$r_1 = 1 - \frac{5}{100} = 0.95 ;$$

$$\sigma^2 = 100 \times 0.95 \times 0.05 = 4.75, \qquad \text{hence} \quad \sigma = 2.18 ,$$

$$\sigma_1 = \left(\frac{100}{99}\right)^{1/2} \times \frac{2.18}{100} = 0.0219.$$

The results are the same for component 2; thus,

$$R = r_1 r_2 = 0.903,$$

$$\sigma_R{}^2 = (r_1 \sigma_2)^2 + (r_2 \sigma_1)^2 = 2 \times 0.95^2 \times 0.0219^2,$$

$$\sigma_R = 0.0294.$$

Thus case (2) results in more favorable data than case (1); on the other hand, the total amount of testing and instrumentation is larger.

(3) For 100 tests, 10 failures, the results for component 1 are the same as for case (1).

For 100 tests, 0 failures, the results for component 2 are obtained by considering Eq. (1.21). For $k = 0$, we have

$$\frac{n}{n + g^2} \leq \alpha \leq 1.$$

For $g = 1$, $n = 100$,

$$0.99 \leq \alpha \leq 1.$$

Best estimate of reliability is given by

$$r_2 = \tfrac{1}{2}(0.99 + 1) = 0.995,$$
$$\sigma^2 = 100 \times 0.995 \times \tfrac{5}{1000} = 0.4975,$$
$$\sigma = 0.705,$$
$$\sigma_2 = 0.0071.$$

So it follows that $R = 0.9 \times 0.995 = 0.896$, and

$$\sigma_R{}^2 = (0.9 \times 0.0071)^2 + (0.995 \times 0.0302)^2,$$
$$\sigma_R = 0.0308.$$

This is the worst case, since component (1) above is as bad as the system of case (1), and component (2) might fail; therefore, component 2 makes the case potentially worse.

Appendix to solution 1.13. A very interesting case is as follows, comparing two test series:

(1) For 100 tests of the two-component system, zero failures, let the reliability of the system be R, and an approximation as established by the tests is R_0. The same holds for σ_R and σ_{R0}. Then $R_0 = 0.995$ and $\sigma_{R0} = 0.0071$.

We know that $R = r_1 r_2$ and $\sigma = (r_1{}^2 \sigma_2{}^2 + r_2{}^2 \sigma_1{}^2)^{1/2}$; these relationships will hold—approximately—for the approximations. Since the system tests reveal nothing on how the failures are distributed between the two components, we have as limiting cases

$$r_{10} = 1, \quad \sigma_{10} = 0 \quad \text{and} \quad r_{20} = 0.995, \quad \sigma_{20} = 0.0071$$

or

$$r_{10} = 0.995, \quad \sigma_{10} = 0.0071 \quad \text{and} \quad r_{20} = 1, \quad \sigma_{20} = 0,$$

or, finally, as "pessimistic limits,"

$$r_{10} = r_{20} = R_0 = 0.995 \quad \text{and} \quad \sigma_{10} = \sigma_{20} = \sigma_{R0} = 0.0071.$$

(2) For 100 tests of each of the components, zero failures, we have

$$r_{10} = r_{20} = 0.995, \quad \sigma_{10} = \sigma_{20} = 0.0071,$$

which agrees with the last line of preceding case (1). If we compute from this the prediction of the system reliability, we have

$$R_0 = 0.99 \quad \text{and} \quad \sigma_{R0} = 0.010.$$

Compare this with *the same measurements leading to different numbers* in the beginning of case (1).

The explanation has to do with the fact that what we compute from the experiments are approximations only. If, e.g., regardless of number of tests *never* a failure occurs, then

$$r_1 = 1, \quad r_2 = 1, \quad \sigma_1 = 0, \quad \sigma_2 = 0,$$

and

$$R = 1, \quad \sigma_R = 0,$$

whether we compute R, σ_R from r_i, σ_i or whether we compute R, σ_R directly from the experiments. No disagreement exists.

With a finite—e.g., 100—number of tests and no failure, we assume, e.g., that we have just been lucky and one failure might have occured. This leads to potentially one failure per hundred tests, for the system. Or, if we tested the components, one potential failure per 100 tests on each of the components. If we now synthesize the system from the components, we will have to expect about two bad systems within the 100 systems, again in apparent contrast to the interpretation of the system tests. The contrast diminishes if we interpret the potential failures as "no more than" one failure in 100 component tests, leading to no more than 2 failures in the 100 system tests (as predicted), which does not contradict the sharper formulation of "no more than one failure" resulting from the system tests.

1.14. We have $\varLambda = (g_0 R)^{1/2} (R/r)^{3/2} (d/R)$, where R is the radius of the central body, r is the orbital radius, and g_0 is the gravitational acceleration on the surface of the central body. For Earth, if $r = R + h$ and $h/R < 0.2$, we have, approximately, $\varLambda(\text{cm/sec}) \approx [1 - (3h/2R)]0.124\ d(m)$.

This problem may have practical utility considering docking and assembly of masses in space, i.e., for the terminal rendezvous phase.

Chapter 2

2.1. For $c = 0$, the fundamental equation is

$$\frac{(\alpha/1.05 - 2)\eta}{ab} = \varLambda = \frac{y}{y-1}\left[(1 - \eta)y^4 u + \eta y^3 u + 1\right].$$

Clearly, with respect to u the minimum of $\varLambda$ occurs for $u = 0$, which means $\tau = \infty$. This cannot be realized. The best, then, is to choose τ as large as possible and optimize for y only. This has been done for the case of the energy supply from a nuclear reactor.

Inserting the constants $a \approx 0.0242$, $b \approx 7.1$, $c = \gamma/b \approx 0.561/7.1 = 0.079$, $y = T_1/T_2 > 1$, $\tau = (1/bu)^{1/4} = T_1[^\circ\text{K}]/1400 \le 1$, $\tau_{\max} = 1$, $(bu)_{\min} = 1$, $u_{\min} = 1/b$ (where η is the efficiency and α is the specific weight in kilograms per kilowatt) in

$$u - c = \left[4c\frac{y-1}{y^4} + \frac{1}{(2y^4)^2}\right]^{1/2} - \frac{1}{2y^4},$$

we have

$$c_{\min} = \left(\frac{1}{b} + 2\frac{y - 1.25}{y^4}\right) - \left[\left(\frac{1}{b} + 2\frac{y - 1.25}{y^4}\right)^2 - \frac{1}{b}\left(\frac{1}{b} + \frac{1}{y^4}\right)\right]^{1/2}.$$

Numerically, $c_{\min}$ is around 0.042.

If c is smaller, then the case has to be treated as if $c = 0$, i.e., choose $\tau = 1$ and optimize for y only. In other words, if c is improved below $c_{\min}$ optimization with respect to τ is no longer possible, because τ_{opt} becomes too large.

2.2. (1) Reach final speed as fast as possible, coast with final speed to target. Ideal could be a "kick." Optimization then simply means to have the maximum speed as high as possible. If a kick is utilized, then $S = v_{\max} T$.

(2) Here

$$c^2 = \frac{2\,Pm_e}{m_T} = \frac{2\,P}{x}\,,$$

where $x = m_T/m_e$,

$$1 + x = \frac{m_e + m_T}{m_e} = \frac{m_0}{m_e} = \text{mass ratio},$$

and the maximum speed

$$v_{\max} = (2P)^{1/2}\,\frac{\ln(1+x)}{x^{1/2}}\,,$$

$$\frac{\partial v_{\max}}{\partial x} = 0 \rightarrow \ln(1+x) = \frac{2\,x}{1+x}\,;$$

the only real root is $x_{\mathrm{opt}} = 3.922$. Inserting the results,

$$v_{\max\,\mathrm{opt}} = 1.14 P^{1/2}, \qquad c_{\mathrm{opt}} = 0.713 P^{1/2}.$$

Initial acceleration is interesting:

$$a_0 = \frac{\dot{m}c}{m_e(1+x)} = \frac{2\eta\dot{E}}{m_e[(2P/x)(1+x)]^{1/2}} = \frac{(2x)^{1/2}}{1+x}\,\frac{L}{P^{1/2}}\,,$$

and inserting x_{opt} we have

$$a_{0\,\mathrm{opt}} = 0.557\,\frac{L}{P^{1/2}}\,;$$

obviously P shall be high for performance reasons; only when L is also high does a high acceleration (kick) become possible.

(3) Here

$$v_{\max} = -\int_{m_0}^{m_e} \frac{c}{m}\,dm\,;$$

the condition is

$$\int_{m_0}^{m_e} \frac{c^2}{2}\,dm = -Pm_e\,.$$

Determine $c = c(m)$ such that $v_{\max}$ is as large as possible. With λ a constant, Euler-Lagrange's equation has to be formed from

$$F(c, c', m) = \frac{c}{m} - \lambda\frac{c^2}{2}\,.$$

Because of the absence of c', Euler-Lagrange's differential equation becomes a simple equation: $c = 1/\lambda m$; putting this in the condition, we have

$$\frac{x}{1+x} = \lambda^2\, 2Pm_e{}^2 \qquad \text{or} \qquad c_{\text{opt}} = (2P)^{1/2} \left(\frac{1+x}{x}\right)^{1/2} \frac{m_e}{m}.$$

This is (with $LT = P$) exactly the same as it was in the corresponding case for constant L. So again constant acceleration is the optimum:

$$v_{\text{max opt}} = (2P)^{1/2} \left(\frac{x}{1+x}\right)^{1/2}$$

Again, the optimum shifts to $x \to \infty$. For $x = 3.922$ we obtain $v_{\text{max opt}} = 1.26P^{1/2}$ and, for $x \to \infty$, $v_{\text{max opt}} = 1.41P^{1/2}$, increases of 10.5% and 23.6%, respectively, over the best that can be done with constant exhaust speed. To get $v_{\text{max}} = 1.14\dot{P}^{1/2}$, only $x = 1.86$ instead of $x = 3.922$ is required: this can be transformed in a payload increase of more than 100%, for constant launch weight.

2.3. From Fig. S.4, we have $\varepsilon = \theta - \beta_{\text{opt}}$, hence

$$\tan \varepsilon = \tan(\theta - \beta_{\text{opt}}) = \frac{\tan\theta - \tan\beta_{\text{opt}}}{1 + \tan\theta \tan\beta_{\text{opt}}} = \frac{\tan\theta - \frac{1}{2}\tan\theta}{1 + \frac{1}{2}\tan^2\theta}$$

$$= \frac{\tan\theta}{2 + \tan^2\theta} = \frac{\tan\theta}{1 + 1/\cos^2\theta} = \frac{\sin\theta\cos\theta}{2 - \sin^2\theta}.$$

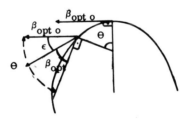

FIG. S.4. Thrust vector diagram. Here $\tan\beta_{\text{opt}} = \frac{1}{2}\tan\theta$.

Because of the identities

$$\sin 2\theta = 2\sin\theta\cos\theta \qquad \text{and} \qquad \cos 2\theta = 1 - 2\sin^2\theta,$$

we have

$$\tan\varepsilon = \frac{\sin 2\theta}{3 + \cos 2\theta},$$

$$\frac{d\varepsilon}{d(2\theta)} \cong (3 + \cos x)\cos x + \sin^2 x = 0.$$

Hence
$$3 \cos x + 1 = 0 \qquad \text{and} \qquad \cos x = \cos 2\theta = -\tfrac{1}{3}.$$

Thus $2\theta = 109.45°$ and $250.55°$, and $\varepsilon_{\max} = 19.5°$ and $-19.5°$. The maximum deviation of the space-fixed $\beta_{\text{opt}\,0}$ direction from the optimal direction is only $19.5°$.

2.4. For chemical rockets $P = -P'\dot{m}$, where P' is a constant. Then

$$P' = +\frac{c^2}{2}, \qquad \text{and} \qquad a = \frac{\dot{m}c}{m} = (2P')^{1/2}\frac{\dot{m}}{m} = (2P')^{1/2}\frac{d}{dt}\ln m,$$

or

$$\ln M_0 - \ln M_e = \frac{1}{(2P')^{1/2}} \int_0^T a\, dt,$$

or

$$\ln \frac{1}{M_e} = \ln \frac{1}{M_0} + \frac{1}{(2P')^{1/2}} \int_0^T a\, dt = \ln \frac{1}{M_0} + \frac{1}{(2P')^{1/2}} v_{\text{req}}\,.$$

For $P = \text{constant}$ (instead of $P' = \text{const}$) it was shown that

$$\frac{1}{M_e} = \frac{1}{M_0} + \frac{1}{2P} \int_0^T a^2\, dt = \frac{1}{M_0} + \frac{1}{2P} \gamma\,.$$

This shows that generally γ must be minimized when P is fixed, and v_{req} must be minimized when P is proportional to $\dot{m}$.

2.5. Here

$$v = \bar{a}T = \int_0^T \frac{F\, dt}{M - [(M-m)/T]t} = \frac{FT}{M}\frac{M}{M-m} \int_0^{(M-m)/M} \frac{dx}{1-x}$$

$$= \frac{FT}{M}\frac{M}{M-m} \ln \frac{M}{m}\,;$$

so

$$\bar{a} = \frac{F}{M}\frac{\ln(M/m)}{1 - m/M} \approx \frac{F}{M} \ln \frac{M}{m}\,, \qquad \text{for large } \frac{M}{m}\,.$$

Putting $M/m = 1 + x$, we have, for sufficiently small $x < 1$,

$$\bar{a} = \frac{F}{M}\frac{1+x}{x} \ln(1+x) \approx \frac{F}{M}\frac{1+x}{x}\left(x - \frac{1}{2}x^2\right)$$

$$\approx \frac{F}{M}\left(\frac{M}{m}\right)^{1/2} \approx \frac{F}{M}\left(\frac{1 + M/m}{2}\right).$$

(Indeed, $\bar{a}$ is less than this value. Again $v = c \ln(M/m)$; from comparison with the above equation we obtain

$$c = \frac{F}{(M-m)/T} = \frac{F}{\dot{m}} \qquad \text{or} \qquad F = \dot{m}c \,,$$

a well-known result.)

2.6. Since $\Delta v/U = y$, $c/U = x$, we have

$$y = x \ln\left(1 + \frac{1}{x^2}\right),$$

$$\frac{dy}{dx} = 0 \rightarrow \ln\left(1 + \frac{1}{x^2}\right) = \frac{2}{1+x^2} \,;$$

approximately,

$$\frac{1}{x^2} = \frac{2}{1+x^2}$$

or

$$x = x_{\text{opt}} = \frac{c_{\text{opt}}}{U} \approx 1, \qquad \text{giving} \quad y_{\text{opt}} \approx 0.693.$$

A numerical[1] solution gives $x_{\text{opt}} \approx 0.506$ and $y_{\text{opt}} \approx 0.81$.

The graph gives for this case $c_{\text{opt}}/U \approx 0.47$. Taking $\tau = 3$ yr $= 94.68 \times 10^6$ sec and $\alpha = 2.5$ kg/kW yields $U = 278$ km/sec. So $c_{\text{opt}} \approx 131$ km/sec. and, from the graph, $\Delta v/U = 0.8$; thus $\Delta v = 222$ km/sec. The same problem was treated in Chap. 2, resulting in $c \approx 136$ km/sec, $v_{\text{max}} = 217$ km/sec. The agreement is well within the accuracy of numerical approximation and graph reading.

2.7. Here

$$I = \frac{m_b c}{m_0 g} = \frac{m_b}{m_p + m_b(1+\beta) + \alpha L} \frac{c}{g} \,.$$

Electric energy rate is given by

$$L_e = \frac{m_b}{2t} c^2 = \eta L \,;$$

$$m_0 = m_b \frac{\exp(v/c)}{\exp(v/c) - 1} \,.$$

---

[1] For $\alpha \neq 0$, approximately $0.5 + 0.5\, \alpha^{1/2}$.

From these equations, we obtain

$$\frac{1}{gI} = \frac{\alpha}{2\eta t}c + \frac{1}{c}\left(1 + \beta + \frac{m_p}{m_0}\frac{\exp(v/c)}{\exp(v/c) - 1}\right).$$

Series development for $v/c \leq 0.5$ gives

$$\frac{1}{gI} \approx \frac{\alpha}{2\eta t}c + \frac{1}{c}\left(1 + \beta + \frac{m_p}{m_0}\right) + \frac{m_p}{m_0}\frac{1}{v},$$

$$v \approx \frac{Ft}{(m_0 + m_f)/2} \approx \frac{Ig}{1 - \frac{1}{2}(v/c)} \approx \frac{Ig}{1 - \frac{1}{2}(Ig/c)}.$$

So

$$\frac{1 - m/_pm_0}{gI} \approx \frac{\alpha}{2\eta t}c + \frac{1}{c}\left(1 + \beta + \frac{m_p}{2m_0}\right).$$

For given t, m_p, m_0, g, α, η, β, a maximum of I occurs for

$$c^2 = c_{\text{opt}}^2 = \frac{2(1 + \beta + m_p/2m_0)\eta t}{\alpha}.$$

There is the relationship $I = F\,t/m_0\,g = m_b\,c/m_0\,g$. So the computation has maximized $m_b c$ or the thrust F. Some further results are

$$(m_b c)_{\text{opt}} = (m_0 - m_p)\left[\frac{\eta t}{2(1 + \beta + m_p/2m_0)\alpha}\right]^{1/2},$$

$$F_{\text{opt}} \quad = \frac{(m_b c)_{\text{opt}}}{t}.$$

$$(m_b)_{\text{opt}} \quad = \frac{m_0}{2}\frac{1 - m_p/m_0}{1 + \beta + m_p/2m_0},$$

$$(v)_{\text{opt}} = -\left[\frac{2(1 + \beta + m_p/2m_0)\eta t}{\alpha}\right]^{1/2}\ln\left[1 - \frac{1}{2}\frac{1 - m_p/m_0}{1 + \beta + m_p/2m_0}\right]$$

$$\approx \left(1 - \frac{m_p}{m_0}\right)\left[\frac{\eta t}{2\alpha(1 + \beta + m_p/2m_0)}\right]^{1/2}.$$

The problem was to maximize v. Because of

$$\exp(-v/c) \approx 1 - \frac{v}{c} = 1 - \frac{m_b}{m_0} \quad \text{or} \quad v \approx \frac{c\,m_b}{m_0},$$

the problem is solved approximately.

We have

$$\frac{v}{c} = \frac{m_b}{m_0} = \frac{1}{2} \frac{1 - m_p/m_0}{1 + \beta + m_p/2m_0} < \frac{1}{2},$$

or approximately $m_p/m_0 > 0.3$—the approximations made are only valid for sufficiently large payload ratios. For the initial acceleration it follows that $a_0 \sim 1/(\alpha t)^{1/2}$; on the other hand, $v \sim (t/\alpha)^{1/2}$ or $t \sim v^2\alpha$, so $a_0 \sim 1/v\alpha$ or for a given v simply, $a_0 \sim 1/\alpha$. In the text it is shown that for $\alpha \approx 1 \text{ kg/kW}$ there is at best $a_0 \approx 10^{-3}g$. An increase to $a_0 \approx 1g$ can be expected only for $\alpha \approx 1 \text{ kg/MW}$.

The problem treated here is complimentary to the one treated in the text, where for given t, g, v, m_0, α, β, η the value of m_p is maximized.

2.8. *For the time between 0 and t.* For constant high acceleration $a(10 \text{ m/sec}^2)$ and low exhaust speed $c(5000 \text{ m/sec})$, $s = (a/2)t^2$, $v = at$, $at = c \ln(M_0/M_e)$, $M_e/M_0 = \exp(-at/c)$,

Propellant used $\qquad \dfrac{M_p}{M_0} = 1 - \exp(-at/c)$;

Thrust $\qquad\qquad F \quad = aM_0$;

Engine mass $\qquad\quad m \quad = \dfrac{M_0}{50} \dfrac{a}{g_0}$.

Initial mass for low acceleration phase, with structure of $\frac{1}{20}(M_p/M_0)$, is

$$\frac{M_e{}'}{M_0} = \left(1.05 \exp(-at/c) - \frac{a}{50g_0} - 0.05\right).$$

For the time between t and T. For constant low acceleration $b(10^{-3} \text{ m/sec}^2)$ and high exhaust speed $w(10^5 \text{ m/sec})$

Thrust $\quad f = M_e{}'b = \dot{m}w$,

Energy $\quad E = \dfrac{\dot{m}}{2} w^2 = \dfrac{M_e{}'b}{2} w$,

the engine mass is given by the specific weight α in kg sec/m kg—let it be 0.1, corresponding to 10 kg/kW.

Then the payload is given by

$$\frac{M_p}{M_e{}'} = \left(1.05 \exp[-b(T-t)/w] - \frac{\alpha w}{2} \frac{b}{g_0} - 0.05\right).$$

Finally,

$$y = \frac{M_p}{M_0} = \left(1.05 \exp[-at/c] - \frac{a}{50g_0} - 0.05\right)$$

$$\times \left(1.05 \exp[-b(T-t)/w] - \frac{aw}{2}\frac{b}{g_0} - 0.05\right)$$

$$\approx 0.63 \exp(-at/c) \exp(-bT/w).$$

Approximately,

$$\frac{S}{T} = at + \frac{b}{2}T = \text{average speed over } S,$$

and

$$\tau - T = \frac{\sigma - at\,T - (b/2)T^2}{at + bT} = \frac{\text{residual path length}}{\text{cutoff speed}} = \begin{array}{l}\text{residual available}\\ \text{time.}\end{array}$$

From this

$$t = \frac{\sigma + (b/2)T^2 - b\tau T}{a\tau}$$

or

$$\frac{y}{0.63} = Z^{-1} = \exp\{[-\sigma + (b/2)T^2 - b\tau T]/c\tau\} \exp(-bT/w),$$

$$\ln Z = \frac{\sigma}{c\tau} + \frac{bT^2}{2c\tau} - \frac{bT}{c} + \frac{bT}{w},$$

$$\frac{\partial \ln Z}{\partial T} = \frac{bT}{c\tau} - \frac{b}{c} + \frac{b}{w} = 0,$$

or

$$\left(\frac{T}{\tau}\right)_{\text{opt}} = 1 - \frac{c}{w},$$

$$\left(\frac{t}{\tau}\right)_{\text{opt}} = \frac{\sigma}{a\tau^2} + \frac{b}{2a}\left(1 - \frac{c}{w}\right)^2 - \frac{b}{a}\left(1 - \frac{c}{w}\right)$$

$$= \frac{\sigma}{a\tau^2} - \frac{1}{2}\frac{b}{a}\left[1 - \left(\frac{c}{w}\right)^2\right],$$

$$t_{\text{opt}} = \frac{\sigma}{a\tau} - \frac{1}{2}\frac{b\tau}{a}\left[1 - \left(\frac{c}{w}\right)^2\right].$$

So

$$\left(\frac{M_p}{M_0}\right)_{\text{opt}} \approx \frac{0.63}{\exp(\sigma/c\tau - b\tau/2c)}.$$

Numerically,

$$\sigma = 100 \times 10^9 \text{ m},$$

$$\tau = \frac{2}{3} \times 10^7 \text{ sec},$$

$$\frac{c}{w} = \frac{5000}{100{,}000} = \frac{1}{20},$$

$$\left(\frac{T}{\tau}\right)_{\text{opt}} = \left(1 - \frac{1}{20}\right) = \frac{19}{20} \approx 1,$$

$$t = \frac{3 \times 100 \times 10^9}{2 \times \; 10 \times 10^7} - \frac{1 \times 2 \times 10^{-3}}{2 \times 3 \times 10} \times 10^7 = 1200 \text{ sec},$$

$$\frac{M_p}{M_0} = y_{\text{max}} \approx 0.06.$$

The important result is $t \neq 0$. This follows because $(b/2)\tau^2 < \sigma$. If we choose $\alpha = 10 \text{ kg/kW}$, $\tau = \frac{2}{9}$ yr $= \frac{2}{3} \times 10^7$ sec, $v = 30 \text{ km/sec}$, then follows, for the characteristic figure as introduced in Chap. 2, $A = 0.65$, and the pure low-acceleration vehicle has no payload capability at all (Fig. 2.33).

Likewise, for a pure high thrust vehicle and $v = 15 \text{ km/sec}$, only a small payload capability results (3% for two stages with $\varepsilon = 0.05$).

The—somewhat surprising— answer is that $t = 0$ does not necessarily result in the maximum payload.

2.9. Introducing a Lagrangian multiplier λ we get

$$\frac{d}{dt} I + \lambda \frac{d}{dt} V = 0,$$

or executing the differentiations, observing that the upper limit T is not a constant but must be adjusted to fulfill the performance equation,

$$\int_0^T (2a + \lambda)\dot{a} \, dt + a_T(a_T + \lambda) = 0.$$

Putting $\lambda = -a_T$, it follows that $\dot{a} = 0$ or $a = \text{constant} = a_0$. Then $V = a_0 T$, and $I_{\text{min}} = a_0 V = V^2/T$.

2.10. Let p be the probability of mission success, t the time, F the mean time to failure, F_m (where $m = 1, 2, 3, \cdots$) the mean time to failure in a more general case, t_m the minimum time to perform the mission, v_{id} the payload fraction for $p = 1$, v the payload fraction, G_{id} the growth factor for $p = 1$, and G the growth factor.

Define

$$v = \frac{1}{G}, \qquad \tau = \frac{t}{t_m}, \qquad f = \frac{F}{t_m}, \qquad x = \tau^{1/2}, \qquad y = \frac{1}{0.95} v.$$

Also let the number of operating systems be n, initial number of operating systems be n_0, α be constant, and m (where $m > 1$) be the constant in Weibull's distribution. Probability of mission success as a function of mission duration is called $p(t)$. This must fulfill the following conditions:

$$p(0) = 1, \qquad p(\infty) = 0, \qquad \frac{dp}{dt} < 0.$$

Probability of failure is $1 - p$, and the probability that the failure occurs during the time interval dt is given by $(- dp/dt)\, dt$, and

$$- \int_0^\infty \frac{dp}{dt}\, dt = 1.$$

The integral relationship is fulfilled automatically.

Le us assume that only random failures occur. This means that the number of failures $(- dn)$ occurring during the time dt is proportional to the number of operating systems n, but not dependent upon when the time interval dt occurs.

Mathematically,

$$\frac{(- dn)}{dt} = \alpha n,$$

where α is a constant. Integrated, $n = n_0 \exp(- \alpha t)$, and the probability that one particular system is alive at the time t is given by $p(t) = n/n_0 = \exp(- \alpha t)$.

The average lifetime is given by

$$F = \frac{1}{n_0} \int_0^\infty t\, |\, dn\, | = - \frac{1}{n_0} \int_0^\infty t \frac{dn}{dt}\, dt$$

$$= - \frac{1}{n_0} \left[t\, n \, \Big|_0^\infty - \int_0^\infty n\, dt \right] = \int_0^\infty \frac{n}{n_0}\, dt,$$

if $[t(n/n_0)]$ is zero for both $t = 0$ and $t = \infty$. For $p = \exp(- \alpha t)$ we have $F = 1/\alpha$, or $p = \exp(- t/F)$.

A more general remark appears to be in place: if we choose $p = \exp[f(t/F)]$, where f stands for a yet undefined function, then we have for the ratio of

$$\frac{\text{number of operating systems}}{\text{number of systems at time zero}} = \frac{n}{n_0} = \exp(-f),$$

and

$$\frac{\text{number of failures during time } dt}{n_0} = \frac{-dn}{n_0} = f'\frac{n}{n_0}, \quad \text{or} \quad \frac{-dn}{n} = f'.$$

The case of $f' = $ constant describes the case of random failures as discussed. If wearout failures are considered instead, then we expect f to be zero initially, and to increase in time. Therefore, we might write, more generally,

$$\frac{-dn}{n} = \frac{m}{F}\left(\frac{t}{F}\right)^{m-1},$$

where $m \geq 1$, or $p = \exp[-(t/F)^m]$.

The case $m = 1$ corresponds to the random failure characteristic, and $m = 2, 3$, etc. (Weibull's distribution) corresponds to increasingly dominant wearout failure characteristics.

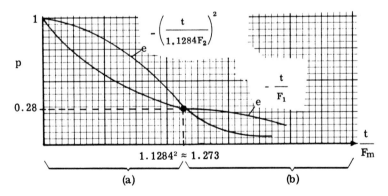

FIG. S.5. Probability of failure. For $F_1 = F_2$, (a) better survival chance for wearout failures, (b) better survival chance for random failures.

This is shown in Fig. S.5. The mean time to failure is here

$$F_m = F \int_0^\infty \exp(-x^m)\, dx,$$

which gives, for example, $F_1 = F$, and $F_2 = (\pi^{1/2}/2)F \approx 0.8862F$, or $F \approx 1.1284F_2$. So F is no longer the mean lifetime for $m \neq 1$.

As an approximation for the growth factor putting $p = 1$ we found in the text that

$$G_{\mathrm{id}} \approx \frac{1}{0.98} \frac{1 + A^{1/2}}{1 - A^{1/2}}.$$

From this and inspecting Fig. 2.33 we can write, valid for all A values,

$$\frac{1}{G_{\mathrm{id}}} = \nu_{\mathrm{id}} \approx 0.95 \frac{0.8 - A^{1/2}}{0.8 + A^{1/2}},$$

usually within better than 10%. We write

$$\nu_{\mathrm{id}} = 0.95 \frac{1 - (1.25^2 A)^{1/2}}{1 + (1.25^2 A)^{1/2}}.$$

Since $A \sim 1/t$, this can be written defining the minimum time to perform the mission by $t_m = 1.25^2 At$:

$$\nu_{\mathrm{id}} = 0.95 \frac{1 - (t_m/t)^{1/2}}{1 + (t_m/t)^{1/2}} \qquad \text{or} \qquad \nu_{\mathrm{id}} = 0.95 \frac{\tau^{1/2} - 1}{\tau^{1/2} + 1}.$$

This results in $(\nu_{\mathrm{id}})_{\max}$ for $\tau \to \infty$, the well-known result. Including the reliability factor (for random failures) comes

$$\nu = \nu_{\mathrm{id}}\, p(t) = 0.95 \frac{\tau^{1/2} - 1}{\tau^{1/2} + 1} \exp(-\tau/f).$$

With $x = \tau^{1/2}$ and $\nu/0.95 = y$ follows

$$y = \frac{x - 1}{x + 1} \exp(-x^2/f).$$

Differentiating as usual, we obtain for the relationship between F and t which gives the best growth factor: $f = (x^2 - 1)x$, or for finite f we have $(x^2)_{\mathrm{opt}} \sim t_{\mathrm{opt}} \neq \infty$.

In Table S.4, G is the optimum value of the most probable optimum growth factor for a given F/t_m value, optimized by selecting the best corresponding mission duration t/t_m. It is seen that, of course, $G > G_{\mathrm{id}}$, and—more important— the best mission duration t/t_m is finite unless F is infinitely large. But $F = \infty$ is the—unrealistic—case of $p = 1$ as treated in the main chapter. The reader should repeat this investigation using Weibull's distribution with $m = 2$.

TABLE S.4

SUMMARY OF RESULTS

Mean time to failure (given) F/t_m	Best corresponding mission duration t/t_m	Optimum growth factor for $F = \infty$ G_{id}	Most probable optimum growth factor G
0	1	∞	∞
1.875	2.25	5.26	17.5
6	4	3.16	6.16
13.125	6.25	2.46	4.10
24	9	2.11	3.07
60	16	1.76	2.29
120	25	1.58	1.95
∞	∞	1.05	1.05

It is remarkable that by introducing redundancy without any additional refinements the survival chance is increased, but the growth factor G_{id} is decreased: this points out that an optimum degree of redundancy will exist for a given $(F/t_m)_{\text{without redundancy}}$ value. A maximum F/t_m value can be obtained by using up all payload for redundancy, but as this leads to zero payload, we obtain $G = \infty$. This limiting case is, therefore, undesirable.

In the main text an example case is considered for a mission duration of 1.5 yr and $A = 0.044$, or 0.22, or 0.44. This leads—in the same order—to $t_m = 0.103$, or 0.516, or 1.03 yr; thus, $t/t_m = 14.55$, or 2.92, or 1.46. If we assume these are the optimum time durations from the reliability point of view, then $F/t_m = 52$, or 3.5, or 1.2, or $F = 5.4$, or 1.8, or 1.2 yr, quite reasonable time periods. The growth factors in the example are $1/0.66 = 1.52$, $1/0.25 = 4$, and $1/0.08 = 12.5$. The inverse reliability would be $p^{-1} = \exp(t/F) = 1.32$, or 2.31, or 3.49, resulting in a most probable growth factor of 2, or 9.25, or 43.6. It is seen that now the third case becomes unattractive, and only the first case remains very good. The remedy for the less attractive cases would be to improve F and increase t correspondingly. If, e.g., for the worst case $t_m = 1.03$ yr, but $F = 6.2$ yr, then $F/t_m = 6$, and we should use $t/t_m = 4$ or $t = 4.12$ yr. This then results in a most probable optimum growth factor of 6.16, or a relative payload weight increase by a factor $43.6/6.16 = 7.1$. Of course, in a practical case the increase from $F = 1.2$ to 6.2 yr is not easy to obtain, and the mission duration increase from 1.5 to 4.12 yr is an operational disadvantage. If we keep the 1.5 yr mission duration with the improved value of $F = 6.2$ yr, then the most probable optimum growth factor is about 16. So, in a practical situation we may be forced to use t/t_m values smaller than the optimum, and skill is required to obtain an "optimum overall system."

2.11. Here

$$\frac{E}{M} = \frac{(e/2w)(1 + \sin \varphi_0)}{1 + \alpha/[w\, 2\pi R^2(1 - \sin \varphi_0)]} = \frac{e}{2w} \frac{1 + \sin \varphi_0}{1 + \beta/(1 - \sin \varphi_0)}$$

$$= \frac{e}{2w} \frac{1 - \sin^2\varphi_0}{1 + \beta - \sin \varphi_0}.$$

Now (E/M) becomes a maximum for

$$\sin \varphi_0 = 1 + \beta - (\beta^2 + 2\beta)^{1/2},$$

that is,

$$\left(\frac{E}{M}\right)_{\max} = \frac{e}{w}\, [1 + \beta - (\beta^2 + 2\beta)^{1/2}].$$

Assume, for example, that $\beta = 0.25$; then we have $\sin \varphi_0 = 0.5$, or $\varphi_0 = 30°$. This is much more realistic than the $\varphi_0 = 90°$, which is obtained for $\beta = 0$.

2.12. In the text it is given that

$$\frac{\Delta P}{P} = \frac{5.9}{10^3} \left[\frac{1}{(T - T_0)^{0.2}} - \frac{1}{T^{0.2}} \right].$$

By integration between T_0 and ∞, we obtain

$$\int_{T_0}^{\infty} \frac{\Delta P}{PT_0}\, dt = \frac{7.4}{10^3 T_0^{0.2}}.$$

If $T_0 = 0.5/24$, then the above expression becomes 0.016, or—assuming that the main propulsion hydrogen flow is proportional to PT_0, and the aftercooling hydrogen flow because of the lower temperature proportional to $2 \int_{T_0}^{\infty} \Delta P\, dt$—we obtain a hydrogen aftercooling requirement of 3.2%, of which about half must be considered to constitute a loss (because of the lower temperature, i.e., lower specific impulse).

Aftercooling can be accomplished by reducing the flow rate as the power goes down; but this will lead, finally, to laminar flow in the cooling channels, with usually catastrophic reduction of heat transfer. Therefore, another possibility is to leave the flow rate constant, cool the reactor below its operating temperature, shut off the flow. When the reactor has again reached its operating temperature, full cooling flow is established again, etc. ("pulsed cooling mode"). The average acceleration during the cooldown period is low, leading to increased gravity losses and slow maneuvering; the average specific impulse during the pulsed cooldown period may be about 75% of its normal operational value.

If a heat sink is on board (e.g. reliquefaction unit, or closed-loop electric power production) a closed-loop cooling system becomes possible, in principle.

2.13. If M and R are the mass and radius of Earth, respectively, and ϱ_E is the density of Earth, then

$$g = \gamma \frac{M}{R^2},$$

$$M = \frac{4\pi}{3} \varrho_E R^3,$$

$$g = \gamma \frac{4\pi}{3} \varrho_E R.$$

For the celestial body, in order to launch we must have

$$a > \gamma \frac{4\pi}{3} \varrho r \quad \text{or} \quad \frac{a}{g} > \frac{\varrho r}{\varrho_E R} \quad \text{or} \quad \frac{r}{R} < \frac{\varrho_E}{\varrho} \frac{a}{g}.$$

With $a/g = 3 \times 10^{-4}$ (ion propulsion), $\varrho_E/\varrho = 2$, $R = 6500$ km, we obtain $r < 3.9$ km (asteroids). With $a/g = \frac{1}{2} \times 10^{-2}$ (arc jet) follows $r < 65$ km (Mars moons).

2.14. *Impulsive case.* Circular speed, 200 km Earth satellite orbit, is 7788 m/sec. Parabolic speed, 200 km altitude, Earth, is 11,014 m/sec. To impulsively enter the 90° inclined heliocentric orbit,

$$v_\infty = 2^{1/2} \times \text{Earth orbital speed} = 2^{1/2} \times 29.76 = 42.09 \quad \text{km/sec}:$$

$\Delta v_{\text{id}} = (42.09^2 + 11.014^2)^{1/2} - 7.788 = 35.72$	
Gravity loss	0.60
Steering, etc.	1.00
1.8% Reserve	0.68
Total Δv requirement	38.00 km/sec

Low acceleration case. Escape from satellite orbitis $\Delta v_1 \approx 7.8$ km/sec. Using 8 km/sec, we have included very generous reserves. To establish the inclined heliocentric orbit, from Eq. (1.33) we have

$$\Delta \gamma = \frac{2}{\pi} \frac{\Delta v}{v_{\text{circ}}} .$$

Here $\Delta \gamma = \pi/2$, or

$$\Delta v_2 = \left(\frac{\pi}{2} \right)^2 v_{\text{circ}} = 73.48 \quad \text{km/sec}$$

$$\text{Steering losses} \quad = \quad 1.00$$

$$2\% \ \text{Reserve} \quad = \quad \underline{1.52}$$

$$\Delta v_2 \qquad\qquad = 76.00 \quad \text{km/sec}$$

$$\Delta v_3 = \Delta v_1 + \Delta v_2 = 84.00 \quad \text{km/sec}$$

Case 1

$$\lambda_{\text{opt}} \qquad = 0.3292 \qquad [\text{Eq. (2.14), Vol. 1}]$$

$$\varepsilon \qquad = 0.08$$

$$\frac{1}{r} \qquad = \overline{0.4092}$$

$$r \qquad = 2.4438$$

$$I_{\text{sp}} g \ln r = 3.94 \quad \text{km/sec}$$

$$\frac{38}{3.94} \quad = 9.6 \quad \text{stages for maximum payload.}$$

This is very impractical. Let us nevertheless assume 9 stages:

$$\Delta v(\text{stage}) \quad = \frac{38}{9} = 4.222 \quad \text{km/sec,}$$

$$r \qquad = 2.605,$$

$$\frac{1}{r} \qquad = 0.38387,$$

$$\lambda \qquad = 0.30387,$$

$$\lambda^9 \qquad = \frac{22.1}{10^6} ,$$

Payload: $250{,}000 \times \dfrac{22.1}{10^6} \approx 5.5$ lb .

Obviously, this vehicle cannot perform this mission.

Case 2

$$\lambda_{\text{opt}} = 0.2832$$
$$\varepsilon = 0.1800$$
$$\overline{0.4632}$$
$$r = 2.1589,$$
$$\Delta v = 6.41 \quad \text{km/sec},$$
$$5.92 \quad \text{stages}.$$

Let us use 5 stages.

$$\frac{38}{5} = 7.2 \quad \text{km/sec per stage}$$
$$r = 2.372$$
$$\frac{1}{r} = 0.4216$$
$$-\varepsilon = 0.1800$$
$$\lambda = \overline{0.2416}$$
$$\lambda^5 = \frac{823.16}{10^6}$$

Payload: $250{,}000 \times \dfrac{823.16}{10^6} = 206$ lb.

Again, the vehicle cannot perform the mission.

Case 3

$$\Delta v = 84$$
$$M_0 = 250{,}000 \ (113.5 \ \text{t})$$
$$\text{jet power} = 1.375 \ \text{MW}$$
$$\alpha = 19 \ \text{kg/kW}$$
$$\begin{array}{l}\text{propulsion system}\\ + \text{ power plant}\end{array} = 26{,}125 \ (57{,}600 \ \text{lb}) \ \text{kg}$$
$$100 \ \frac{M_p}{M_0} = 23.02\% .$$

Case 4

$$\Delta v = 76$$

$$M_0 = 95{,}000 \ (43.1 \text{ t})$$

$$\text{jet power} = 0.55 \text{ MW}$$

$$\alpha = 19 \text{ kg/kW}$$

$$\begin{array}{c} \text{propulsion system} \\ + \text{ power plant} \end{array} = 10.450 \ (23{,}050 \text{ lb}) \text{ kg}$$

$$100 \frac{M_p}{M_0} = 24.25\%.$$

Read from Fig. 2.33 the corresponding A values and the corresponding $100(M_L/M_0)$ values for cases 3 and 4. You will find two solutions in each case, which Stuhlinger calls very descriptively "racing car" and "truck."

Compute the propulsive duration τ, which in this case equals the total transfer flight time. Results are shown in Table S.5.

TABLE S.5

LOW ACCELERATION MISSIONS

	Case 3		Case 4	
	Truck	Racing car	Truck	Racing car
A	0.12	0.565	0.16	0.503
$100(M_L/M_0)$	42	2.5	34.5	5.05
τ (yr)	18.2	3.87	11.2	3.56
M_L (lb)	105,000	6250	32,750	4800
2% structure (lb)	5,00	5000	1900	1900
Cesium (lb)	82,400	181,150	37,300	65,250
Jet speed (km/sec)	210	65.1	152.5	65.5

In both instances, the "racing car" can perform the mission adequately. Case 4 is probably the better choice, because it takes so much less power, and it arrives on station a little faster. Any single one of the two SNAP 50's will suffice amply to power the payload—therefore, some redundancy is available.

This example is so important because it shows that there are missions which cannot be performed any other foreseeable way but by electric propulsion.

The assumed value of 19 kg/kW jet power corresponds to about 13 kg of power supply system per kilowatt electric power, a value within reach for the SNAP 50 system.

2.15. (1) The maximum cesium mass is given by total Saturn payload minus (propulsion mass + payload mass + structure mass). Is there any advantage to carrying less cesium than the maximum, for a given hyperbolic excess speed?

Answer. No, because if less cesium is carried, the Saturn V could propel the vehicle to a higher hyperbolic excess speed, thus giving a more favorable initial condition to the electric vehicle without introducing any penalty.

(2) The hyperbolic excess speed shall be converted into inclination angle α: from problem 2.14, we take the "useful speed" to be equal to $(35/38)v_\infty$. Then we have

$$\sin \frac{\alpha}{2} = \frac{1}{2} \frac{(35/38)v_\infty}{29.76} \qquad \text{or} \qquad \alpha^\circ \approx 1.778 v_\infty \quad \text{km/sec.}$$

This relation is plotted in Fig. S.6.

(3) The electric propulsion has to provide the inclination $90 - \alpha$. The speed requirement (see problem 2.14) is

$$v_e = 76 \frac{90 - \alpha}{90}.$$

This is also plotted in Fig. S.6.

(4) Table S.6 is easily constructed.

TABLE S.6

PARAMETRIC DATA FOR GIVEN v_∞

v_∞ (km/sec)	0	2	4	6	8	9
v_e (km/sec)	76	72.97	69.97	66.99	63.98	62.45
$90 - \alpha$ (deg)	90	86.47	82.9	79.36	75.80	74
M_0 (lb)	95,000	92,480	77,700	61,300	44,800	36,800
m (lb)	28,950	28,900	28,500	28,300	28,200	28,050
M_c (lb)	66,050	63,580	49,200	33,000	16,600	8,750
r	3.282	3.200	2.726	2.166	1.589	1.312
$\ln r$	1.1895	1.1615	1.001	0.7725	0.4622	0.2715
c (km/sec)	63.89	62.82	69.9	86.72	138.42	230.02
τ (yr)	3.44	3.19	3.06	3.16	4.05	5.90

In Table S.6, M_0 is the initial mass of electric vehicle (Fig. 2.51), m the final mass of electric vehicle (Fig. 2.51), $M_c = M_0 - m$ is the cesium mass, $r = M_0/m$ is the mass ratio, $c = v_e/\ln r$ is the electric exhaust

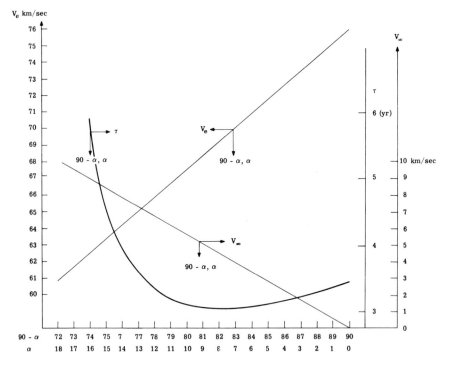

FIG. S.6. The relation between α, v_e, and v_∞.

speed, and τ is the flight time. Since the jet energy is the same as in problem 2.14, and since jet energy $(\dot{m}/2)c^2$, thus, $\dot{m} \sim 1/c^2$, we have with values from problem 2.14:

$$\tau = 3.56 \frac{M_c}{65{,}250}\left(\frac{c}{65.5}\right)^2$$

$$= 0.1272 \frac{M_c}{10^5}\left(\frac{c}{10}\right)^2.$$

The relation τ vs α has again been plotted.

(5) We read for the optimum solution: $\alpha = 8°$, $90 - \alpha = 82°$, $v_\infty = 4.5$ km/sec, $\tau = 3.05$ yr, $v_e = 69.2$ km/sec, $M_0 = 73{,}500$ lb, $m = 28{,}450$ lb, $M_c = 45{,}050$ lb, $r = 2.583$, $\ln r = 0.95$, $c = 72.9$ km/sec.

Compared to the case of problem 2.14, the flight duration is reduced by 14.3% and the payload by 37.5%.

2.16. Here (for symbols see Chap. 2) $M_0/M_e = \exp(x)$, or from this $M_c/M_0 = 1 - \exp(-x)$, and

$$0.98\ G = \frac{\exp(x)}{1 - (A/x^2)\ (e^x - 1)}.$$

From these two equations we obtain, with $G(M_c/M_0) = P$,

$$0.98\ P = \frac{e^x - 1}{1 - (A/x^2)(e^x - 1)}.$$

In this equation, x shall be chosen so that P becomes a minimum. By differentiation, we obtain, with $x_{\text{opt}}/2 = z$,

$$z^3 = A\ (\sinh z)^2.$$

By series development for small z ($z < 1$):

$$1 + \frac{z^2}{3} = \frac{z}{A},$$

from which

$$\left(\frac{v}{c}\right)_{\text{opt}} \approx \frac{3}{A}\left[1 - \left(1 - \frac{4A^2}{3}\right)^{1/2}\right] \qquad \text{for} \quad A < 0.6,$$

or

$$\left(\frac{v}{c}\right)_{\text{opt}} \approx 2A\left(1 + \frac{A^2}{3}\right) \approx 2A \qquad \text{for} \quad A < 0.5.$$

For the growth factor optimization, we had

$$\left(\frac{v}{c}\right)_{\text{opt}\ G} = \frac{A}{2} + A^{1/2} \qquad \text{for} \quad A < 0.3.$$

So, finally,

$$\left(\frac{c_P}{c_G}\right)_{\text{opt}} \approx 0.25 + \frac{0.5}{A^{1/2}} > 1 \qquad \text{for} \quad A < 0.3.$$

This was to be expected: the optimization of P leads to higher jet speeds than the optimization of G.

Chapter 3

3.3. Intersection of satellite orbital sphere and Earth shadow cone is shown in Fig. S.7 (compare Fig. 3.9—draw it more precisely).

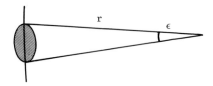

Fig. S.7. Intersection of satellite orbital sphere and Earth shadow cone; indicated area $= 4\pi r^2 \sin^2(\varepsilon/4)$.

Maximum fraction of shadow time[1] $= \dfrac{\varepsilon}{2\pi}$;

Average fraction of shadow time $= \sin^2(\varepsilon/4)$;

Average shadow time per period $= 2\pi \left(\sin^2 \dfrac{\varepsilon}{4}\right) \left(\dfrac{R}{g_0}\right)^{1/2} \left(\dfrac{r}{R}\right)^{3/2}$;

Minimum shadow time per period $= 0$.

3.5. We know that $H \sim 1/r^3$ and, from Eq. (4.73) of Vol. 1, $T \sim 1/H^2$. Thus, $T \sim r^6$; this is a very steep increase of T. For a low satellite, we had $T \sim 1$ day, typically. For a 24-h satellite we get, under the same conditions, $T \approx 233$ yr.

3.6. From

$$\frac{dp}{p} = -\frac{dh}{B + Ah},$$

we have

$$\frac{p}{p_0} = \frac{\varrho}{\varrho_0} = \left(1 + \frac{A}{B} h\right)^{-1/A}$$

3.7. Here

$$\dot{V} = k - rc; \qquad c = \frac{k}{r}(1 - \exp[-(r/V)t]) .$$

3.8. (a) *Vented tank.*

(1) Time to reach boiling condition is given by

$$\frac{k\Delta T A_1}{\delta} t_1 + ht_1 - rt_1 = q_1 W.$$

---

[1] Fraction of period, for a circular orbit.

(2) Boiloff mass w is given by

$$\left(\frac{K\Delta T A_1}{\delta} + h - r\right)(t_2 - t_1) = wq_2 .$$

(3) Insulation mass is $\varrho\delta A_2$.

(4) Loss because of empty tankage due to boiloff is εw.

Total penalty P is given by

$$P = (1 + \varepsilon)\frac{k\Delta T A_1 t_2}{q_2\delta} + \varrho A_2\delta + (1 + \varepsilon)\frac{h - r}{q_2}t_2 - (1 + \varepsilon)\frac{q_1}{q_2} W ,$$

$$\frac{\partial P}{\partial \delta} = 0 \rightarrow \delta_{opt} = \left(\frac{(1 + \varepsilon)k\Delta T A_1 t_2}{\varrho\, q_2 A_2}\right)^{1/2}$$

Data for k and ϱ for polyurethane and Linde S4 superinsulation are given in the following tabulation:

	k (kcal/h m°K)	P (kg/m³)
Polyurethane	0.01	32
Linde S4 superinsulation	3.7×10^{-5}	75

(b) *Reliquefaction.* If all the evaporated propellant is reliquefied, the mass of the liquefaction plant plus power supply may be

$$\alpha\,\frac{k\,\Delta T\,A_1}{\delta} ,$$

where α is in kg sec/kcal (typically $\alpha = 10^4$). The insulation mass equals $\varrho A_2\delta$; the sum is

$$P = \frac{k\,\Delta T\,A_1\alpha}{\delta} + \varrho A_2\delta, \quad \text{and} \quad \delta_{opt} = \left(\frac{k\,\Delta T\,A_1\alpha}{\varrho A_2}\right)^{1/2}$$

It is seen that for interplanetary missions ($t_2 = 10^7$ sec, $q_2 = 100$ kcal/kg), the liquefaction plant leads to the lighter system; the weights are about equal for shorter missions ($t_2 = 10^6$ sec), and the vented storage is superior for Earth satellite missions of below 10 days duration.

3.9. From Section 3.7,3,2, we have $V = \alpha(m/2)v^2$, or with ϱ being the density of the wall material, the dislocated wall mass is $M = \alpha\varrho(m/2)v^2$. A fraction β of $(M + m)$ is ejected, with a speed c:

$$\beta\,\frac{M + m}{2}\,c^2 = \gamma\,\frac{m}{2}\,v^2\,.$$

Inserting for M, we obtain

$$c = \left[\frac{2(\gamma/\beta)v^2}{2 + \alpha\varrho v^2}\right]^{1/2}\,.$$

The impulse can be estimated from

$$I' = \frac{2^{1/2}}{2}\,\beta(M + m)c\,.$$

Substituting values we obtain

$$I' = \tfrac{1}{4}\,[\gamma\beta(2 + \alpha\varrho v^2)]^{1/2}mv\,.$$

The total impulse transferred to the wall is

$$I = \left\{\frac{1}{4}\,[\beta\gamma(2 + \alpha\varrho v^2)]^{1/2} + 1\right\}mv\,.$$

With $\gamma = \beta = \tfrac{1}{2}$, $\alpha = 0.1$, $\varrho = 6\ \text{gm/cm}^3$, $v = 30\ \text{km/sec}$, it follows that $I = 3.9mv$.

3.10. For the received solar radiation we have

$$R = \alpha S \int_{T_0}^{T_1} \frac{dt}{r^2}$$

$$= \alpha S \int_{\varphi_0}^{\varphi_1} \frac{d\varphi}{r^2}\,\frac{dt}{d\varphi}$$

$$= \alpha S \int_{\varphi_0}^{\varphi_1} \frac{d\varphi}{r^2\dot\varphi}\,.$$

From Kepler's second law, using Eq. 4.31 of Vol. 1,

$$r^2\dot\varphi = \text{constant} = [\gamma Ma(1 - \varepsilon^2)]^{1/2}\,.$$

For $a = 1$, and $\varepsilon = 0$ (Earth),

$$r^2\dot{\varphi} = \text{constant} = (\gamma M)^{1/2} = \frac{360}{365}\frac{\text{deg}}{\text{day}}.$$

So

$$R = \alpha S\,\frac{365}{[a(1 - \varepsilon^2)]^{1/2}}\,\frac{\varphi_1 - \varphi_0}{360}.$$

If τ is the flight time from φ_0 to φ_1 in days, then we have the following useful comparison numbers:

Total received energy, during τ:	R
Average received energy per day:	R/τ
Average solar constant, during τ:	$R/S\tau$
Equivalent number of days in Earth orbit, to receive the same energy R:	$R/\alpha S$
Average solar constant during τ per average solar constant near Earth:	$R/\alpha S\tau$

For Hohmann missions,

$$\varphi_1 - \varphi_0 = 180 \qquad \text{and} \qquad \tau = (1/2)365a^{3/2};$$

hence

$$R/\alpha S\tau = a^{-2}(1 - \varepsilon^2)^{-1/2}.$$

Appendix

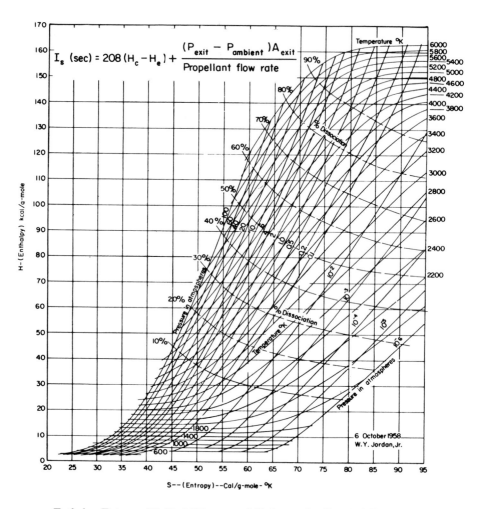

$$I_s \text{ (sec)} = 208 \left(H_c - H_e \right) + \frac{\left(P_{exit} - P_{ambient} \right) A_{exit}}{\text{Propellant flow rate}}$$

Enthalpy-Entropy (Mollier) Diagram of Hydrogen in Chemical Equilibrium.

References

Allan, R. R. (1963). Perturbations of a geostationary satellite by the longitude-dependent terms in the Earth's gravitational field. *Planetary Space Sci.* **77**, 1325.

Anthony, M. L., and Sasaki, F. T. (1965). Rendezvous problem for nearly circular orbits. *AIAA Journal* September.

Armstrong, R. H., *et al.* (1960). A lunar powerplant. Argonne Natl. Lab., December.

ARS Journal (1959). Guidance Issue, December.

Barker, C. L., and Straly, W. H. (1959). Rendezvous by the chasing technique. ABMA-DSP-TM-15.

Barnothy, M. F., ed. (1964). "Biological Effects of Magnetic Fields." Plenum Press, New York.

Beard, D. B. (1961). Meteoritic impact. *ARS Journal* January.

Benney, D. J. (1958). *Jet Propulsion* March.

Benson, O. O., Jr., and Strughold, H., eds. (1960). "Physics and Medicine of the Atmosphere and Space." Wiley, New York, 1960.

Bjork, R. L. (1958). Effects of a meteoroid impact on steel and aluminum in space. Rand Corporation paper 1662, December 16.

Bowman, N. J. (1953). The food and atmosphere control problem on space vessels. *BIS Journal* **12**.

Breakwell, J. V., Gillespie, R. W., and Ross, S. (1959). Researches in interplanetary transfer. ARS Preprint 954.

Brice, J. W. (1963). A method for determining orbital launch windows. Vought Astronautics report, June.

Buchheim, R. W. (1956). Lunar instrument carrier-attitude stabilization. Rand Corp. Res. Memo RM-1730, June 5.

Burgess, E. (1949). The establishment and use of artificial satellites. *Aeronautics* (G. Britain), September.

Burgess, E. (1952). The Martian probe. *Aeronautics* (G. Britain), November.

Burns, R. E. (1959). The optimization of interplanetary trajectories. ABMA-DSP-TN-20.

Bussard, R. W., and DeLauer, R. D. (1958). "Nuclear Rocket Propulsion." McGraw-Hill, New York.

Camac, M. (1958). Reduction of flight time and propellent requirements of satellites with electric propulsion by the use of stored electrical energy. ARS Preprint 721.

Camac, M. (1960). Plasma propulsion devices. *Advan. Space Sci.* **2**.

Chandra, S. (1960). Optimum frequency selection for interplanetary communication. *BIS Journal* **17** (10).

Clarke, A. C. (1948). Electronics and space flight. *BIS Journal* **7** (2).

Clarke, A. C. (1953). Jupiter five. *In* "Research for Tomorrow." Ballantine Books, New York.

Clarke, A. C. (1961). Space flight and the spirit of man. *Astronautics* October.

Clarke, A. C. (1963). Before Eden. *In* "Tales of Ten Worlds." Harcourt, Brace, and World, New York.

Coleman, Jr., P. J. (1966). Interaction of the solar wind with the planets. *AIAA Journal* January.

Cooper, R. S. (1961). Applications for low-power nuclear rockets. *Astronautics* August.

Copeland, J. (1959). Interplanetary trajectories under low thrust radial acceleration. *ARS Journal* April.

Croft, R. M. (1965). Utilization of an orbital launch facility for planetary missions. NASA - TMX - 53311.

Cunningham, C. (1960). *BIS Journal* **17** (9), 311–313.

Dalton, C. C. (1962). Meteoroid hazard to space vehicles in orbit near the Earth. NASA TM X-789.

Dalton, C. C. (1963). Estimation of tolerance limits for meteoroid hazard to space vehicles 100–500 km above the surface of the Earth. NASA TN D1996, August.

DelDuca, M. G., Fuscoe, J. M., and Johnston, T. A. (1959). Regenerative fuel cells as auxiliary power supplies for space vehicles. ARS Preprint 1039.

Demetriades, S. T. (1962). Plasma propulsion *Astronautics* **7** (3) and (4).

Dugan, Jr., J. F. (1960). Analysis of trajectory parameters for probe and round-trip missions to Mars. NASA TN-D-281, June.

Eckert, E. R. G. (1950). "Introduction to the Transfer of Heat and Mass." McGraw-Hill, New York.

Edelbaum, T. N. (1961a). Propulsion requirements for controllable satellites. *ARS Journal* August.

Edelbaum, T. N. (1961b). The use of high and low thrust propulsion in combination for space missions. United Aircraft Corp. Res. Labs., Rept. R-1753-3, August.

Edelbaum, T. N. (1962a). Multi-engine reliability for electric propulsion systems. ARS Preprint 2388.

Edelbaum, T. N. (1962b). Optimum low thrust transfer between circular and elliptic orbits. United Aircraft Corp. Rept. A-110058-1, January.

Edelbaum, T. N. (1962c). The use of high and low-thrust propulsion in combination for space missions. *J. Astronaut. Sci.* Summer.

Edelbaum, T. N., and Oickle, C. (1959). Propulsion requirements for controllable satellites. United Aircraft Corp. Rept. R-1383-3. (See also Edelbaum, 1961a.)

Eggleston, J. M. (1960). Optimum time to rendezvous. *ARS Journal* November.

Ehricke, K. A. (1956a). The solar-powered space ship. ARS Preprint 310.

Ehricke, K. A. (1956b). On the application of solar power in space flight. *Proc. VII Intern. Astron. Congr., Rome.*

Ehricke, K. A. (1958). Error analysis of single and two-force field spacecraft orbits. *Franklin Inst. Monograph.* No. 6, December.

Ehricke, K. A. (1959). Interplanetary operations. *In* "Space Technology." Wiley, New York.

Ehricke, K. A. (1962). "Space Flight," Vol. 2. Van Nostrand, Princeton, New Jersey.

Ehricke, K, A., (1966). Solar transportation. NAA/Autonetics publication No. X6–661/3061.

Eichelberger, R. J., *et al.* (1962). Effects of meteoroid impacts on space vehicles. *ARS Journal* **32** (10), October.

Esnauld-Pelterie, R. (1928). Astronautik und Relativitaets-Theorie. *Die Rakete* August.

Faulders, C. R. (1961). Minimum time steering programs for orbital transfer with low thrust rockets. *Astronaut. Acta* **VII** (1), 35.

Fimple, W. R. (1960). A general three dimensional trajectory analysis of planetary escape by solar sail. United Aircraft Corp. Res. Labs., Rept. R-1737-1, November.

Fimple, W. R. (1963). An improved theory of high and low thrust propulsion in combination. *J. Astronaut. Sci.* Winter.

Fimple, W. R., and Edelbaum, T. N. (1965). Applications of SNAP 50 class powerplants. *J. Spacecraft and Rockets* Sept.–Oct.

Finch, H. L., Noland, M. C., Brown, R. G., and Chimenti, E. T. (1966). Thermal analysis of the Apollo. *17th Intern. Astronaut. Congr., Madrid, Spain.*

Fowler, T.K., and Post, R.F. (1966). Progress towards fusion power. *Sci. Am.* December.

Fox, R. H. (1960). An accurate expression for gas-pressure drop. *J. Appl. Mech.* December.

Fox, R. H. (1961). Powered trajectory studies for low thrust space vehicles. *ARS Journal* **31** (1), January.

Gafford, R. D. (1963). Fully regenerative life support systems for Mars missions. *Advan. Astronaut. Sci.* **15**.

Gantz, K. F., ed. (1959). "Man in Space." Duell, Sloan and Pearce, New York.

Gatland, K. W., Kunesch, A. M., and Dixon, A. E. (1951). Minimum satellite vehicles. *Proc. 11th Intern. Astron. Congr., London.*

Gehring, J. W., *et al.* (1965). Experimental studies concerning the meteoroid hazard. *J. Spacecraft and Rockets* Sept.–Oct.

Gerathewohl, S. J. (1959). Psychological problems of selection, holding, and care of space fliers. U.S. Army Medical Services, R & D Command, CSCRD-16-4.

Gignoux, D. (1966). Electrostatic generators in space power systems. *J. Spacecraft and Rockets* December.

Goldsmith, M. (1959). Augmentation of nuclear rocket specific impulse through mechanical-electrical means. *ARS Journal* August.

Grey, J., and Williams, P. M. (1963). Analyses of gas-cycle and hybrid nuclear-electric space power systems. *Proc. XIV Astron. Congr., Paris, France* Fall.

Grimminger, G. (1948). Probability that a meteorite will hit or penetrate a body situated in the vicinity of the earth, *J. Appl. Phys.* **19**, 947.

Gudzent, D. (1960). Motion of the angular momentum vector of Explorer IV. NASA, G. C. Marshall Space Flight Center, Aero-2.

Gunkel, R. J., and Shutte, R. H. (1960). Trajectories for direct vehicle transfer from Moon to Earth. *Proc. XI Intern. Astron. Congr., Stockholm.*

Haeussermann, W. (1962). Recent advances in attitude control of space vehicles. *ARS Journal* February.

Heller, G. (1959). The plasma jet as an electric propulsion system for space application. ARS Preprint 1004.

Herrick, S., Baker, R. M. L., and Hilton, C. G. (1957). Gravitational and related constants for accurate space navigation. ARS Preprint 497.

Himmel, S. C., Dugan, Jr., J. F., Luidens, R. W., and Weber, R. J. (1961). Nuclear rocket missions to Mars. Lewis Research Center, Aerospace Eng., July.

Hornby, H. (1961). Least fuel, least energy, and salvo rendezvous. IRE/ARS, 15th Annual Spring. Tech. Conf., Cincinnati, Ohio, April 12, 13.

Howard, H. J., and McJones, R. W. (1959). Available power systems for space vehicles. ARS Preprint 1032.

Hunter, M. W. (1960). Advantages of high-thrust space vehicles. *Astronautics* February.

Industrial Research (1961). Special issue on "energy conversion," October.

Irving, J. H. (1959). Low thrust flight: variable exhaust velocity in gravitational fields. *In* "Space Technology" (H. S. Seifert, ed.). Wiley, New York.

Jaffe, L. D., *et al.* (1962). Behavior of materials in space environment. *ARS Journal* **32** (3), March.

Jeans, J. (1925). "The Dynamical Theory of Gases," p. 346. Dover S136, New York.

John, R. R., *et al.* (1963). Arcjet engine performance: experiment and theory. *AIAA Journal* **1** (11), 2517.

Johnson, P. G., and Rom, F. E. (1962). Perigee propulsion for orbital launch of nuclear rockets. NASA TR R140.

Jordan, Jr., W. Y. (1958). Theoretical performance and thermodynamic working charts for the nuclear hydrogen rocket. ABMA-DSP-TN-6.

Kash, S. W., and Tooper, R. F. (1962). Active shielding for manned spacecraft. *Astronautics* September.

Knacke, D., and Stranski, I. N. (1956). The mechanism of evaporation. *Progr. Metal Phys.* **6**, 181.

Konecci, E. B. (1959). Manned space cabin systems. *Advan. Space Sci.* **1**.

Kopal, Z. (1961). *Discovery* **22** (4), April.

Kottler, C. F. (1966). Radiation shielding considerations for interplanetary spacecraft. *J. Astronaut. Sci.* July, Aug.

Krause, H. G. L. (1956). *Astronaut. Acta* **II** (1).

Krause, H. G. L. (1962). Astrorelativity. MSFC, MTP-P & VE-F-62-4, May 22.

Kuebler, M. E. (1959). Spin reductions of a satellite by extension of masses on strings. ABMA, unnumbered report.

Langton, N. H. (1954). Thermal dissipation of meteorites by bumper screens. *Proc. VI Astron. Congr., Innsbruck.*

Tilson, S. (1964). Environmental electricity. *Intern. Sci. and Tech.* January.

Tischer, R. G. (1959). Nutrition in space flight. *Advan. Space Sci.* 1.

Tross, C. (1960). Astronomical constants and their importance in lunar trajectory determination. *ARS Journal* October.

Tsien, H. S. (1953). Take-off from satellite orbit. *ARS Journal* July-August.

Tumm, G. W. (1966). Vergleichende Analyse von Gaskern-Reaktoren für Antriebe von Raumfahrzeugen. Ph.D. Diss., T.U. Berlin.

Unger, J. H. W. (1958). On the mid-course navigation for manned interplanetary space flight. ABMA, DSP-TR-2-58.

Unger, J. H. W. (1959). Radio links for space flight. ABMA-DSP-TN 4–59.

von Braun, W. (1952). "Das Marsprojekt." Umschau Verlag, Germany.

von Braun, W., and Ryan, C. (1953). Baby space station. *Collier's* June.

Vertregt, M. (1958). Interplanetary orbits. *BIS Journal* **16** (6).

Wallner, L. E., *et al.* (1961). Radiation shielding for manned space flight. NASA TN D-681, July.

Weatherston, R. C. (1963). The radiation amplifier. *Astronaut. and Aerospace Eng.* October.

Weatherston, R. C., and Smith, W. E. (1960). *ARS Journal* March.

Wehner, G. K., Kenknight, C., and Rosenberg, D. L. (1963). Sputtering rates under solar-wind bombardment. *Planetary and Space Sci.* **11** (8), 885–895.

Welsh, H. W., Poste, E. A., and Wright, R. B. (1959). The advanced Stirling engine for space power. Allison Res. Dept. Rept. EDR 1456, July.

Whipple, F. L. (1957). The meteoritic risk to space vehicles. ARS Preprint 499.

Whipple, F. L. (1960). "Solid Particles in the Solar System," pp. 28ff., in House Rept. No. 2226, U.S. Government Printing Office, Panel on Science and Technology (2nd meeting).

Whipple, F. L. (1962). Dust and meteorites. *Astronautics* August.

Whipple, F. L. (1963). On meteoroids and penetration. *J. Astronaut. Sci.* Fall.

Witten, L., ed. (1962). "Gravitation." Wiley, New York.

Wood, O. L., and Fox, H. L. (1963). Fluid computers. *Intern. Sci. and Tech.* November.

Zola, C. L., and MacKay, J. S. (1963). Methods for computing round trip trajectories for low thrust vehicles. NASA Lewis Research Center, NASA TM X-50122, July.

Zwicky, F. (1959). Is Newton's law of gravitation really universal? *Astronautics* January.

INDEX

Date Due